# Calculus Volume 3

## Part 1: Chapters 1–4

SENIOR CONTRIBUTING AUTHORS

**EDWIN "JED" HERMAN, UNIVERSITY OF WISCONSIN-STEVENS POINT**
**GILBERT STRANG, MASSACHUSETTS INSTITUTE OF TECHNOLOGY**

ISBN: 978-1-50669-805-2

**OpenStax**

Rice University

6100 Main Street MS-375

Houston, Texas 77005

To learn more about OpenStax, visit https://openstax.org.

Individual print copies and bulk orders can be purchased through our website.

| | |
|---|---|
| **HARDCOVER BOOK ISBN-13** | 978-1-938168-07-9 |
| **PAPERBACK BOOK ISBN-13** | 978-1-947172-83-8 |
| **B&W PAPERBACK BOOK ISBN-13** | 978-1-50669-805-2 |
| **DIGITAL VERSION ISBN-13** | 978-1-947172-16-6 |
| **Revision Number** | C3-2016-003(03/18)-MJ |
| **Original Publication Year** | 2016 |

Printed by

**XanEdu**

4750 Venture Drive, Suite 400

Ann Arbor, MI 48108

800-562-2147

www.xanedu.com

## OpenStax

OpenStax provides free, peer-reviewed, openly licensed textbooks for introductory college and Advanced Placement® courses and low-cost, personalized courseware that helps students learn. A nonprofit ed tech initiative based at Rice University, we're committed to helping students access the tools they need to complete their courses and meet their educational goals.

## Rice University

OpenStax, OpenStax CNX, and OpenStax Tutor are initiatives of Rice University. As a leading research university with a distinctive commitment to undergraduate education, Rice University aspires to path-breaking research, unsurpassed teaching, and contributions to the betterment of our world. It seeks to fulfill this mission by cultivating a diverse community of learning and discovery that produces leaders across the spectrum of human endeavor.

## Foundation Support

OpenStax is grateful for the tremendous support of our sponsors. Without their strong engagement, the goal of free access to high-quality textbooks would remain just a dream.

Laura and John Arnold Foundation (LJAF) actively seeks opportunities to invest in organizations and thought leaders that have a sincere interest in implementing fundamental changes that not only yield immediate gains, but also repair broken systems for future generations. LJAF currently focuses its strategic investments on education, criminal justice, research integrity, and public accountability.

The William and Flora Hewlett Foundation has been making grants since 1967 to help solve social and environmental problems at home and around the world. The Foundation concentrates its resources on activities in education, the environment, global development and population, performing arts, and philanthropy, and makes grants to support disadvantaged communities in the San Francisco Bay Area.

Calvin K. Kazanjian was the founder and president of Peter Paul (Almond Joy), Inc. He firmly believed that the more people understood about basic economics the happier and more prosperous they would be. Accordingly, he established the Calvin K. Kazanjian Economics Foundation Inc, in 1949 as a philanthropic, nonpolitical educational organization to support efforts that enhanced economic understanding.

Guided by the belief that every life has equal value, the Bill & Melinda Gates Foundation works to help all people lead healthy, productive lives. In developing countries, it focuses on improving people's health with vaccines and other life-saving tools and giving them the chance to lift themselves out of hunger and extreme poverty. In the United States, it seeks to significantly improve education so that all young people have the opportunity to reach their full potential. Based in Seattle, Washington, the foundation is led by CEO Jeff Raikes and Co-chair William H. Gates Sr., under the direction of Bill and Melinda Gates and Warren Buffett.

The Maxfield Foundation supports projects with potential for high impact in science, education, sustainability, and other areas of social importance.

Our mission at The Michelson 20MM Foundation is to grow access and success by eliminating unnecessary hurdles to affordability. We support the creation, sharing, and proliferation of more effective, more affordable educational content by leveraging disruptive technologies, open educational resources, and new models for collaboration between for-profit, nonprofit, and public entities.

The Bill and Stephanie Sick Fund supports innovative projects in the areas of Education, Art, Science and Engineering.

# Table of Contents

# PREFACE

Welcome to *Calculus Volume 3*, an OpenStax resource. This textbook was written to increase student access to high-quality learning materials, maintaining highest standards of academic rigor at little to no cost.

## About OpenStax

OpenStax is a nonprofit based at Rice University, and it's our mission to improve student access to education. Our first openly licensed college textbook was published in 2012, and our library has since scaled to over 25 books for college and AP® courses used by hundreds of thousands of students. OpenStax Tutor, our low-cost personalized learning tool, is being used in college courses throughout the country. Through our partnerships with philanthropic foundations and our alliance with other educational resource organizations, OpenStax is breaking down the most common barriers to learning and empowering students and instructors to succeed.

## About OpenStax's resources

### Customization

*Calculus Volume 3* is licensed under a Creative Commons Attribution 4.0 International (CC BY) license, which means that you can distribute, remix, and build upon the content, as long as you provide attribution to OpenStax and its content contributors.

Because our books are openly licensed, you are free to use the entire book or pick and choose the sections that are most relevant to the needs of your course. Feel free to remix the content by assigning your students certain chapters and sections in your syllabus, in the order that you prefer. You can even provide a direct link in your syllabus to the sections in the web view of your book.

Instructors also have the option of creating a customized version of their OpenStax book. The custom version can be made available to students in low-cost print or digital form through their campus bookstore. Visit your book page on OpenStax.org for more information.

### Errata

All OpenStax textbooks undergo a rigorous review process. However, like any professional-grade textbook, errors sometimes occur. Since our books are web based, we can make updates periodically when deemed pedagogically necessary. If you have a correction to suggest, submit it through the link on your book page on OpenStax.org. Subject matter experts review all errata suggestions. OpenStax is committed to remaining transparent about all updates, so you will also find a list of past errata changes on your book page on OpenStax.org.

### Format

You can access this textbook for free in web view or PDF through OpenStax.org, and for a low cost in print.

## About *Calculus Volume 3*

*Calculus* is designed for the typical two- or three-semester general calculus course, incorporating innovative features to enhance student learning. The book guides students through the core concepts of calculus and helps them understand how those concepts apply to their lives and the world around them. Due to the comprehensive nature of the material, we are offering the book in three volumes for flexibility and efficiency. Volume 3 covers parametric equations and polar coordinates, vectors, functions of several variables, multiple integration, and second-order differential equations.

### Coverage and scope

Our *Calculus Volume 3* textbook adheres to the scope and sequence of most general calculus courses nationwide. We have worked to make calculus interesting and accessible to students while maintaining the mathematical rigor inherent in the subject. With this objective in mind, the content of the three volumes of *Calculus* have been developed and arranged to provide a logical progression from fundamental to more advanced concepts, building upon what students have already learned and emphasizing connections between topics and between theory and applications. The goal of each section is to enable students not just to recognize concepts, but work with them in ways that will be useful in later courses and future careers. The organization and pedagogical features were developed and vetted with feedback from mathematics educators dedicated to the project.

**Volume 1**

## Pedagogical foundation

Throughout *Calculus Volume 3* you will find examples and exercises that present classical ideas and techniques as well as modern applications and methods. Derivations and explanations are based on years of classroom experience on the part of long-time calculus professors, striving for a balance of clarity and rigor that has proven successful with their students. Motivational applications cover important topics in probability, biology, ecology, business, and economics, as well as areas of physics, chemistry, engineering, and computer science. **Student Projects** in each chapter give students opportunities to explore interesting sidelights in pure and applied mathematics, from navigating a banked turn to adapting a moon landing vehicle for a new mission to Mars. **Chapter Opening Applications** pose problems that are solved later in the chapter, using the ideas covered in that chapter. Problems include the average distance of Halley's Comment from the Sun, and the vector field of a hurricane. **Definitions, Rules,** and **Theorems** are highlighted throughout the text, including over 60 **Proofs** of theorems.

## Assessments that reinforce key concepts

In-chapter **Examples** walk students through problems by posing a question, stepping out a solution, and then asking students to practice the skill with a "Checkpoint" question. The book also includes assessments at the end of each chapter so students can apply what they've learned through practice problems. Many exercises are marked with a **[T]** to indicate they are suitable for solution by technology, including calculators or Computer Algebra Systems (CAS). Answers for selected exercises are available in the **Answer Key** at the back of the book. The book also includes assessments at the end of each chapter so students can apply what they've learned through practice problems.

## Early or late transcendentals

The three volumes of *Calculus* are designed to accommodate both Early and Late Transcendental approaches to calculus. Exponential and logarithmic functions are introduced informally in Chapter 1 of Volume 1 and presented in more rigorous terms in Chapter 6 in Volume 1 and Chapter 2 in Volume 2. Differentiation and integration of these functions is covered in Chapters 3–5 in Volume 1 and Chapter 1 in Volume 2 for instructors who want to include them with other types of functions. These discussions, however, are in separate sections that can be skipped for instructors who prefer to wait until the integral definitions are given before teaching the calculus derivations of exponentials and logarithms.

## Comprehensive art program

Our art program is designed to enhance students' understanding of concepts through clear and effective illustrations, diagrams, and photographs.

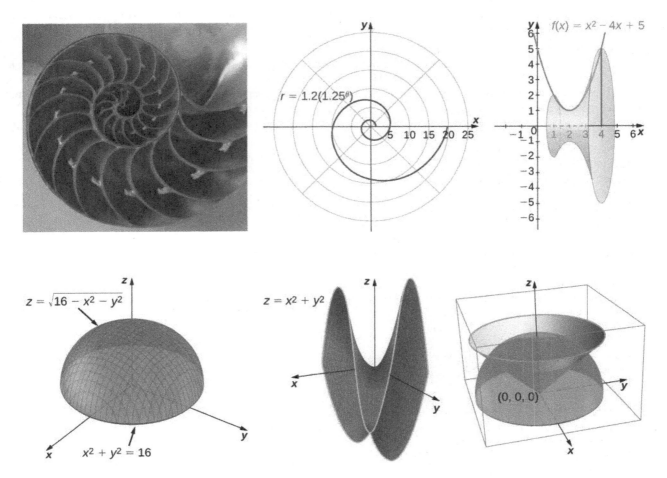

# Additional resources

### Student and instructor resources

We've compiled additional resources for both students and instructors, including Getting Started Guides, an instructor solution manual, and PowerPoint slides. Instructor resources require a verified instructor account, which you can apply for when you log in or create your account on OpenStax.org. Take advantage of these resources to supplement your OpenStax book.

### Community Hubs

OpenStax partners with the Institute for the Study of Knowledge Management in Education (ISKME) to offer Community Hubs on OER Commons – a platform for instructors to share community-created resources that support OpenStax books, free of charge. Through our Community Hubs, instructors can upload their own materials or download resources to use in their own courses, including additional ancillaries, teaching material, multimedia, and relevant course content. We encourage instructors to join the hubs for the subjects most relevant to your teaching and research as an opportunity both to enrich your courses and to engage with other faculty.

To reach the Community Hubs, visit **www.oercommons.org/hubs/OpenStax**.

### Partner resources

OpenStax Partners are our allies in the mission to make high-quality learning materials affordable and accessible to students and instructors everywhere. Their tools integrate seamlessly with our OpenStax titles at a low cost. To access the partner resources for your text, visit your book page on OpenStax.org.

## About the authors
### Senior contributing authors

**Gilbert Strang, Massachusetts Institute of Technology**

Dr. Strang received his PhD from UCLA in 1959 and has been teaching mathematics at MIT ever since. His Calculus online textbook is one of eleven that he has published and is the basis from which our final product has been derived and updated for today's student. Strang is a decorated mathematician and past Rhodes Scholar at Oxford University.

**Edwin "Jed" Herman, University of Wisconsin-Stevens Point**

Dr. Herman earned a BS in Mathematics from Harvey Mudd College in 1985, an MA in Mathematics from UCLA in 1987, and a PhD in Mathematics from the University of Oregon in 1997. He is currently a Professor at the University of Wisconsin-Stevens Point. He has more than 20 years of experience teaching college mathematics, is a student research mentor, is experienced in course development/design, and is also an avid board game designer and player.

### Contributing authors

Catherine Abbott, Keuka College
Nicoleta Virginia Bila, Fayetteville State University
Sheri J. Boyd, Rollins College
Joyati Debnath, Winona State University
Valeree Falduto, Palm Beach State College
Joseph Lakey, New Mexico State University
Julie Levandosky, Framingham State University
David McCune, William Jewell College
Michelle Merriweather, Bronxville High School
Kirsten R. Messer, Colorado State University - Pueblo
Alfred K. Mulzet, Florida State College at Jacksonville
William Radulovich (retired), Florida State College at Jacksonville
Erica M. Rutter, Arizona State University
David Smith, University of the Virgin Islands
Elaine A. Terry, Saint Joseph's University
David Torain, Hampton University

### Reviewers

Marwan A. Abu-Sawwa, Florida State College at Jacksonville
Kenneth J. Bernard, Virginia State University
John Beyers, University of Maryland
Charles Buehrle, Franklin & Marshall College
Matthew Cathey, Wofford College
Michael Cohen, Hofstra University
William DeSalazar, Broward County School System
Murray Eisenberg, University of Massachusetts Amherst
Kristyanna Erickson, Cecil College
Tiernan Fogarty, Oregon Institute of Technology
David French, Tidewater Community College
Marilyn Gloyer, Virginia Commonwealth University
Shawna Haider, Salt Lake Community College
Lance Hemlow, Raritan Valley Community College
Jerry Jared, The Blue Ridge School
Peter Jipsen, Chapman University
David Johnson, Lehigh University
M.R. Khadivi, Jackson State University
Robert J. Krueger, Concordia University
Tor A. Kwembe, Jackson State University
Jean-Marie Magnier, Springfield Technical Community College
Cheryl Chute Miller, SUNY Potsdam
Bagisa Mukherjee, Penn State University, Worthington Scranton Campus
Kasso Okoudjou, University of Maryland College Park
Peter Olszewski, Penn State Erie, The Behrend College
Steven Purtee, Valencia College
Alice Ramos, Bethel College

Doug Shaw, University of Northern Iowa
Hussain Elalaoui-Talibi, Tuskegee University
Jeffrey Taub, Maine Maritime Academy
William Thistleton, SUNY Polytechnic Institute
A. David Trubatch, Montclair State University
Carmen Wright, Jackson State University
Zhenbu Zhang, Jackson State University

# 1 | PARAMETRIC EQUATIONS AND POLAR COORDINATES

**Figure 1.1** The chambered nautilus is a marine animal that lives in the tropical Pacific Ocean. Scientists think they have existed mostly unchanged for about 500 million years.(credit: modification of work by Jitze Couperus, Flickr)

## Chapter Outline

# Introduction

The chambered nautilus is a fascinating creature. This animal feeds on hermit crabs, fish, and other crustaceans. It has a hard outer shell with many chambers connected in a spiral fashion, and it can retract into its shell to avoid predators. When part of the shell is cut away, a perfect spiral is revealed, with chambers inside that are somewhat similar to growth rings in a tree.

The mathematical function that describes a spiral can be expressed using rectangular (or Cartesian) coordinates. However, if we change our coordinate system to something that works a bit better with circular patterns, the function becomes much simpler to describe. The polar coordinate system is well suited for describing curves of this type. How can we use this coordinate system to describe spirals and other radial figures? (See Example 1.14.)

In this chapter we also study parametric equations, which give us a convenient way to describe curves, or to study the position of a particle or object in two dimensions as a function of time. We will use parametric equations and polar coordinates for describing many topics later in this text.

# 1.1 | Parametric Equations

## Learning Objectives

1.1.1 Plot a curve described by parametric equations.
1.1.2 Convert the parametric equations of a curve into the form $y = f(x)$.

1.1.3 Recognize the parametric equations of basic curves, such as a line and a circle.

1.1.4 Recognize the parametric equations of a cycloid.

In this section we examine parametric equations and their graphs. In the two-dimensional coordinate system, parametric equations are useful for describing curves that are not necessarily functions. The parameter is an independent variable that both $x$ and $y$ depend on, and as the parameter increases, the values of $x$ and $y$ trace out a path along a plane curve. For example, if the parameter is $t$ (a common choice), then $t$ might represent time. Then $x$ and $y$ are defined as functions of time, and $(x(t), y(t))$ can describe the position in the plane of a given object as it moves along a curved path.

## Parametric Equations and Their Graphs

Consider the orbit of Earth around the Sun. Our year lasts approximately 365.25 days, but for this discussion we will use 365 days. On January 1 of each year, the physical location of Earth with respect to the Sun is nearly the same, except for leap years, when the lag introduced by the extra $\frac{1}{4}$ day of orbiting time is built into the calendar. We call January 1 "day 1"

of the year. Then, for example, day 31 is January 31, day 59 is February 28, and so on.

The number of the day in a year can be considered a variable that determines Earth's position in its orbit. As Earth revolves around the Sun, its physical location changes relative to the Sun. After one full year, we are back where we started, and a new year begins. According to Kepler's laws of planetary motion, the shape of the orbit is elliptical, with the Sun at one focus of the ellipse. We study this idea in more detail in Conic Sections.

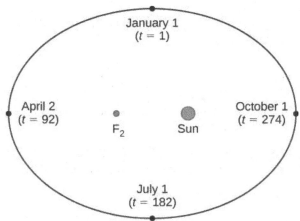

**Figure 1.2** Earth's orbit around the Sun in one year.

**Figure 1.2** depicts Earth's orbit around the Sun during one year. The point labeled $F_2$ is one of the foci of the ellipse; the other focus is occupied by the Sun. If we superimpose coordinate axes over this graph, then we can assign ordered pairs to each point on the ellipse (**Figure 1.3**). Then each $x$ value on the graph is a value of position as a function of time, and each $y$ value is also a value of position as a function of time. Therefore, each point on the graph corresponds to a value of Earth's position as a function of time.

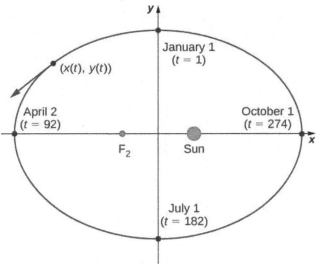

**Figure 1.3** Coordinate axes superimposed on the orbit of Earth.

We can determine the functions for $x(t)$ and $y(t)$, thereby parameterizing the orbit of Earth around the Sun. The variable $t$ is called an independent parameter and, in this context, represents time relative to the beginning of each year.

A curve in the $(x, y)$ plane can be represented parametrically. The equations that are used to define the curve are called **parametric equations**.

---

**Definition**

If $x$ and $y$ are continuous functions of $t$ on an interval $I$, then the equations

$$x = x(t) \text{ and } y = y(t)$$

are called parametric equations and $t$ is called the **parameter**. The set of points $(x, y)$ obtained as $t$ varies over the interval $I$ is called the graph of the parametric equations. The graph of parametric equations is called a **parametric curve** or *plane curve,* and is denoted by $C$.

Notice in this definition that $x$ and $y$ are used in two ways. The first is as functions of the independent variable $t$. As $t$ varies over the interval $I$, the functions $x(t)$ and $y(t)$ generate a set of ordered pairs $(x, y)$. This set of ordered pairs generates the graph of the parametric equations. In this second usage, to designate the ordered pairs, $x$ and $y$ are variables. It is important to distinguish the variables $x$ and $y$ from the functions $x(t)$ and $y(t)$.

## Example 1.1

### Graphing a Parametrically Defined Curve

Sketch the curves described by the following parametric equations:

a. $x(t) = t - 1,$   $y(t) = 2t + 4,$   $-3 \le t \le 2$

b. $x(t) = t^2 - 3,$   $y(t) = 2t + 1,$   $-2 \le t \le 3$

c. $x(t) = 4 \cos t,$   $y(t) = 4 \sin t,$   $0 \le t \le 2\pi$

### Solution

a. To create a graph of this curve, first set up a table of values. Since the independent variable in both $x(t)$ and $y(t)$ is $t$, let $t$ appear in the first column. Then $x(t)$ and $y(t)$ will appear in the second and third columns of the table.

| $t$ | $x(t)$ | $y(t)$ |
|-----|--------|--------|
| −3  | −4     | −2     |
| −2  | −3     | 0      |
| −1  | −2     | 2      |
| 0   | −1     | 4      |
| 1   | 0      | 6      |
| 2   | 1      | 8      |

The second and third columns in this table provide a set of points to be plotted. The graph of these points appears in **Figure 1.4**. The arrows on the graph indicate the **orientation** of the graph, that is, the direction that a point moves on the graph as $t$ varies from −3 to 2.

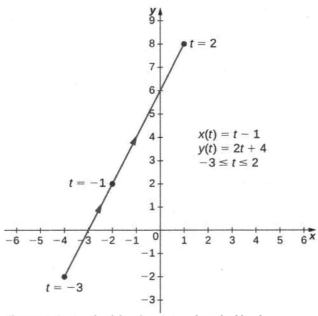

**Figure 1.4** Graph of the plane curve described by the parametric equations in part a.

b.  To create a graph of this curve, again set up a table of values.

| t | x(t) | y(t) |
|---|---|---|
| −2 | 1 | −3 |
| −1 | −2 | −1 |
| 0 | −3 | 1 |
| 1 | −2 | 3 |
| 2 | 1 | 5 |
| 3 | 6 | 7 |

The second and third columns in this table give a set of points to be plotted (**Figure 1.5**). The first point on the graph (corresponding to $t = -2$) has coordinates $(1, -3)$, and the last point (corresponding to $t = 3$) has coordinates $(6, 7)$. As $t$ progresses from −2 to 3, the point on the curve travels along a parabola. The direction the point moves is again called the orientation and is indicated on the graph.

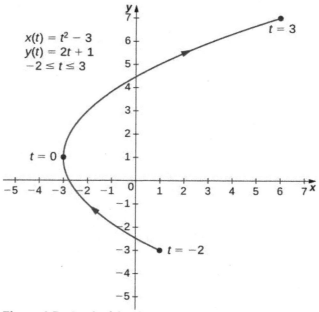

$$x(t) = t^2 - 3$$
$$y(t) = 2t + 1$$
$$-2 \leq t \leq 3$$

**Figure 1.5** Graph of the plane curve described by the parametric equations in part b.

c.  In this case, use multiples of $\pi/6$ for $t$ and create another table of values:

| $t$ | $x(t)$ | $y(t)$ | | $t$ | $x(t)$ | $y(t)$ |
|---|---|---|---|---|---|---|
| 0 | 4 | 0 | | $\dfrac{7\pi}{6}$ | $-2\sqrt{3} \approx -3.5$ | 2 |
| $\dfrac{\pi}{6}$ | $2\sqrt{3} \approx 3.5$ | 2 | | $\dfrac{4\pi}{3}$ | $-2$ | $-2\sqrt{3} \approx -3.5$ |
| $\dfrac{\pi}{3}$ | 2 | $2\sqrt{3} \approx 3.5$ | | $\dfrac{3\pi}{2}$ | 0 | $-4$ |
| $\dfrac{\pi}{2}$ | 0 | 4 | | $\dfrac{5\pi}{3}$ | 2 | $-2\sqrt{3} \approx -3.5$ |
| $\dfrac{2\pi}{3}$ | $-2$ | $2\sqrt{3} \approx 3.5$ | | $\dfrac{11\pi}{6}$ | $2\sqrt{3} \approx 3.5$ | 2 |
| $\dfrac{5\pi}{6}$ | $-2\sqrt{3} \approx -3.5$ | 2 | | $2\pi$ | 4 | 0 |
| $\pi$ | $-4$ | 0 | | | | |

The graph of this plane curve appears in the following graph.

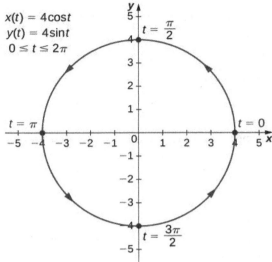

**Figure 1.6** Graph of the plane curve described by the parametric equations in part c.

This is the graph of a circle with radius 4 centered at the origin, with a counterclockwise orientation. The starting point and ending points of the curve both have coordinates $(4, 0)$.

 **1.1** Sketch the curve described by the parametric equations

$$x(t) = 3t + 2, \quad y(t) = t^2 - 1, \quad -3 \le t \le 2.$$

## Eliminating the Parameter

To better understand the graph of a curve represented parametrically, it is useful to rewrite the two equations as a single equation relating the variables $x$ and $y$. Then we can apply any previous knowledge of equations of curves in the plane to identify the curve. For example, the equations describing the plane curve in **Example 1.1b.** are

$$x(t) = t^2 - 3, \quad y(t) = 2t + 1, \quad -2 \le t \le 3.$$

Solving the second equation for $t$ gives

$$t = \frac{y - 1}{2}.$$

This can be substituted into the first equation:

$$x = \left(\frac{y-1}{2}\right)^2 - 3 = \frac{y^2 - 2y + 1}{4} - 3 = \frac{y^2 - 2y - 11}{4}.$$

This equation describes $x$ as a function of $y$. These steps give an example of *eliminating the parameter*. The graph of this function is a parabola opening to the right. Recall that the plane curve started at $(1, -3)$ and ended at $(6, 7)$. These terminations were due to the restriction on the parameter $t$.

## Example 1.2

### Eliminating the Parameter

Eliminate the parameter for each of the plane curves described by the following parametric equations and describe the resulting graph.

    a.  $x(t) = \sqrt{2t + 4}, \quad y(t) = 2t + 1, \quad -2 \le t \le 6$

    b.  $x(t) = 4\cos t, \quad y(t) = 3\sin t, \quad 0 \le t \le 2\pi$

### Solution

    a.  To eliminate the parameter, we can solve either of the equations for $t$. For example, solving the first equation for $t$ gives

$$\begin{aligned} x &= \sqrt{2t + 4} \\ x^2 &= 2t + 4 \\ x^2 - 4 &= 2t \\ t &= \frac{x^2 - 4}{2}. \end{aligned}$$

Note that when we square both sides it is important to observe that $x \ge 0$. Substituting $t = \frac{x^2 - 4}{2}$ this into $y(t)$ yields

$$\begin{aligned} y(t) &= 2t + 1 \\ y &= 2\left(\frac{x^2 - 4}{2}\right) + 1 \\ y &= x^2 - 4 + 1 \\ y &= x^2 - 3. \end{aligned}$$

This is the equation of a parabola opening upward. There is, however, a domain restriction because of the limits on the parameter $t$. When $t = -2$, $x = \sqrt{2(-2) + 4} = 0$, and when $t = 6$, $x = \sqrt{2(6) + 4} = 4$. The graph of this plane curve follows.

**Figure 1.7** Graph of the plane curve described by the parametric equations in part a.

b.  Sometimes it is necessary to be a bit creative in eliminating the parameter. The parametric equations for this example are

$$x(t) = 4 \cos t \text{ and } y(t) = 3 \sin t.$$

Solving either equation for $t$ directly is not advisable because sine and cosine are not one-to-one functions. However, dividing the first equation by 4 and the second equation by 3 (and suppressing the $t$) gives us

$$\cos t = \frac{x}{4} \text{ and } \sin t = \frac{y}{3}.$$

Now use the Pythagorean identity $\cos^2 t + \sin^2 t = 1$ and replace the expressions for $\sin t$ and $\cos t$ with the equivalent expressions in terms of $x$ and $y$. This gives

$$\left(\frac{x}{4}\right)^2 + \left(\frac{y}{3}\right)^2 = 1$$
$$\frac{x^2}{16} + \frac{y^2}{9} = 1.$$

This is the equation of a horizontal ellipse centered at the origin, with semimajor axis 4 and semiminor axis 3 as shown in the following graph.

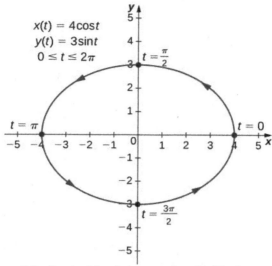

$$x(t) = 4\cos t$$
$$y(t) = 3\sin t$$
$$0 \le t \le 2\pi$$

**Figure 1.8** Graph of the plane curve described by the parametric equations in part b.

As $t$ progresses from $0$ to $2\pi$, a point on the curve traverses the ellipse once, in a counterclockwise direction. Recall from the section opener that the orbit of Earth around the Sun is also elliptical. This is a perfect example of using parameterized curves to model a real-world phenomenon.

 **1.2** Eliminate the parameter for the plane curve defined by the following parametric equations and describe the resulting graph.

$$x(t) = 2 + \frac{3}{t}, \quad y(t) = t - 1, \quad 2 \le t \le 6$$

So far we have seen the method of eliminating the parameter, assuming we know a set of parametric equations that describe a plane curve. What if we would like to start with the equation of a curve and determine a pair of parametric equations for that curve? This is certainly possible, and in fact it is possible to do so in many different ways for a given curve. The process is known as **parameterization of a curve**.

## Example 1.3

### Parameterizing a Curve

Find two different pairs of parametric equations to represent the graph of $y = 2x^2 - 3$.

### Solution

First, it is always possible to parameterize a curve by defining $x(t) = t$, then replacing $x$ with $t$ in the equation for $y(t)$. This gives the parameterization

$$x(t) = t, \quad y(t) = 2t^2 - 3.$$

Since there is no restriction on the domain in the original graph, there is no restriction on the values of $t$.

We have complete freedom in the choice for the second parameterization. For example, we can choose $x(t) = 3t - 2$. The only thing we need to check is that there are no restrictions imposed on $x$; that is, the range of $x(t)$ is all real numbers. This is the case for $x(t) = 3t - 2$. Now since $y = 2x^2 - 3$, we can substitute $x(t) = 3t - 2$ for $x$. This gives

$$\begin{aligned} y(t) &= 2(3t - 2)^2 - 2 \\ &= 2\left(9t^2 - 12t + 4\right) - 2 \\ &= 18t^2 - 24t + 8 - 2 \\ &= 18t^2 - 24t + 6. \end{aligned}$$

Therefore, a second parameterization of the curve can be written as

$$x(t) = 3t - 2 \text{ and } y(t) = 18t^2 - 24t + 6.$$

 **1.3** Find two different sets of parametric equations to represent the graph of $y = x^2 + 2x$.

## Cycloids and Other Parametric Curves

Imagine going on a bicycle ride through the country. The tires stay in contact with the road and rotate in a predictable pattern. Now suppose a very determined ant is tired after a long day and wants to get home. So he hangs onto the side of the tire and gets a free ride. The path that this ant travels down a straight road is called a **cycloid** (Figure 1.9). A cycloid generated by a circle (or bicycle wheel) of radius $a$ is given by the parametric equations

$$x(t) = a(t - \sin t), \quad y(t) = a(1 - \cos t).$$

To see why this is true, consider the path that the center of the wheel takes. The center moves along the $x$-axis at a constant height equal to the radius of the wheel. If the radius is $a$, then the coordinates of the center can be given by the equations

$$x(t) = at, \quad y(t) = a$$

for any value of $t$. Next, consider the ant, which rotates around the center along a circular path. If the bicycle is moving from left to right then the wheels are rotating in a clockwise direction. A possible parameterization of the circular motion of the ant (relative to the center of the wheel) is given by

$$x(t) = -a \sin t, \quad y(t) = -a \cos t.$$

(The negative sign is needed to reverse the orientation of the curve. If the negative sign were not there, we would have to imagine the wheel rotating counterclockwise.) Adding these equations together gives the equations for the cycloid.

$$x(t) = a(t - \sin t), \quad y(t) = a(1 - \cos t).$$

Figure 1.9 A wheel traveling along a road without slipping; the point on the edge of the wheel traces out a cycloid.

Now suppose that the bicycle wheel doesn't travel along a straight road but instead moves along the inside of a larger wheel, as in Figure 1.10. In this graph, the green circle is traveling around the blue circle in a counterclockwise direction. A point on the edge of the green circle traces out the red graph, which is called a hypocycloid.

**Figure 1.10** Graph of the hypocycloid described by the parametric equations shown.

The general parametric equations for a hypocycloid are

$$x(t) = (a - b) \cos t + b \cos\left(\frac{a-b}{b}\right) t$$

$$y(t) = (a - b) \sin t - b \sin\left(\frac{a-b}{b}\right) t.$$

These equations are a bit more complicated, but the derivation is somewhat similar to the equations for the cycloid. In this case we assume the radius of the larger circle is $a$ and the radius of the smaller circle is $b$. Then the center of the wheel travels along a circle of radius $a - b$. This fact explains the first term in each equation above. The period of the second trigonometric function in both $x(t)$ and $y(t)$ is equal to $\frac{2\pi b}{a-b}$.

The ratio $\frac{a}{b}$ is related to the number of **cusps** on the graph (cusps are the corners or pointed ends of the graph), as illustrated in Figure 1.11. This ratio can lead to some very interesting graphs, depending on whether or not the ratio is rational. Figure 1.10 corresponds to $a = 4$ and $b = 1$. The result is a hypocycloid with four cusps. Figure 1.11 shows some other possibilities. The last two hypocycloids have irrational values for $\frac{a}{b}$. In these cases the hypocycloids have an infinite number of cusps, so they never return to their starting point. These are examples of what are known as *space-filling curves*.

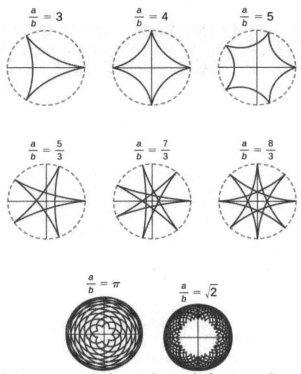

**Figure 1.11** Graph of various hypocycloids corresponding to different values of *a/b*.

# Student PROJECT

## The Witch of Agnesi

Many plane curves in mathematics are named after the people who first investigated them, like the folium of Descartes or the spiral of Archimedes. However, perhaps the strangest name for a curve is the witch of Agnesi. Why a witch?

Maria Gaetana Agnesi (1718–1799) was one of the few recognized women mathematicians of eighteenth-century Italy. She wrote a popular book on analytic geometry, published in 1748, which included an interesting curve that had been studied by Fermat in 1630. The mathematician Guido Grandi showed in 1703 how to construct this curve, which he later called the "versoria," a Latin term for a rope used in sailing. Agnesi used the Italian term for this rope, "versiera," but in Latin, this same word means a "female goblin." When Agnesi's book was translated into English in 1801, the translator used the term "witch" for the curve, instead of rope. The name "witch of Agnesi" has stuck ever since.

The witch of Agnesi is a curve defined as follows: Start with a circle of radius $a$ so that the points $(0, 0)$ and $(0, 2a)$ are points on the circle (Figure 1.12). Let $O$ denote the origin. Choose any other point $A$ on the circle, and draw the secant line $OA$. Let $B$ denote the point at which the line $OA$ intersects the horizontal line through $(0, 2a)$. The vertical line through $B$ intersects the horizontal line through $A$ at the point $P$. As the point $A$ varies, the path that the point $P$ travels is the witch of Agnesi curve for the given circle.

Witch of Agnesi curves have applications in physics, including modeling water waves and distributions of spectral lines. In probability theory, the curve describes the probability density function of the Cauchy distribution. In this project you will parameterize these curves.

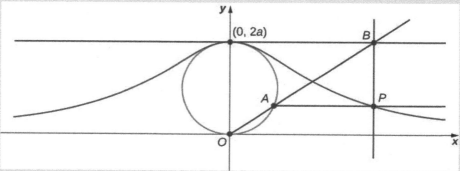

**Figure 1.12**  As the point $A$ moves around the circle, the point $P$ traces out the witch of Agnesi curve for the given circle.

1.  On the figure, label the following points, lengths, and angle:

    a.  $C$ is the point on the $x$-axis with the same $x$-coordinate as $A$.

    b.  $x$ is the $x$-coordinate of $P$, and $y$ is the $y$-coordinate of $P$.

    c.  $E$ is the point $(0, a)$.

    d.  $F$ is the point on the line segment $OA$ such that the line segment $EF$ is perpendicular to the line segment $OA$.

    e.  $b$ is the distance from $O$ to $F$.

    f.  $c$ is the distance from $F$ to $A$.

    g.  $d$ is the distance from $O$ to $B$.

    h.  $\theta$ is the measure of angle $\angle COA$.

    The goal of this project is to parameterize the witch using $\theta$ as a parameter. To do this, write equations for $x$ and $y$ in terms of only $\theta$.

2. Show that $d = \dfrac{2a}{\sin\theta}$.

3. Note that $x = d\cos\theta$. Show that $x = 2a\cot\theta$. When you do this, you will have parameterized the x-coordinate of the curve with respect to $\theta$. If you can get a similar equation for y, you will have parameterized the curve.

4. In terms of $\theta$, what is the angle $\angle EOA$?

5. Show that $b + c = 2a\cos\!\left(\dfrac{\pi}{2} - \theta\right)$.

6. Show that $y = 2a\cos\!\left(\dfrac{\pi}{2} - \theta\right)\sin\theta$.

7. Show that $y = 2a\sin^2\theta$. You have now parameterized the y-coordinate of the curve with respect to $\theta$.

8. Conclude that a parameterization of the given witch curve is

$$x = 2a\cot\theta,\ y = 2a\sin^2\theta,\ -\infty < \theta < \infty.$$

9. Use your parameterization to show that the given witch curve is the graph of the function $f(x) = \dfrac{8a^3}{x^2 + 4a^2}$.

# Student PROJECT

## Travels with My Ant: The Curtate and Prolate Cycloids

Earlier in this section, we looked at the parametric equations for a cycloid, which is the path a point on the edge of a wheel traces as the wheel rolls along a straight path. In this project we look at two different variations of the cycloid, called the curtate and prolate cycloids.

First, let's revisit the derivation of the parametric equations for a cycloid. Recall that we considered a tenacious ant trying to get home by hanging onto the edge of a bicycle tire. We have assumed the ant climbed onto the tire at the very edge, where the tire touches the ground. As the wheel rolls, the ant moves with the edge of the tire (Figure 1.13).

As we have discussed, we have a lot of flexibility when parameterizing a curve. In this case we let our parameter $t$ represent the angle the tire has rotated through. Looking at Figure 1.13, we see that after the tire has rotated through an angle of $t$, the position of the center of the wheel, $C = (x_C, y_C)$, is given by

$$x_C = at \text{ and } y_C = a.$$

Furthermore, letting $A = (x_A, y_A)$ denote the position of the ant, we note that

$$x_C - x_A = a \sin t \text{ and } y_C - y_A = a \cos t.$$

Then

$$x_A = x_C - a \sin t = at - a \sin t = a(t - \sin t)$$
$$y_A = y_C - a \cos t = a - a \cos t = a(1 - \cos t).$$

**Figure 1.13** (a) The ant clings to the edge of the bicycle tire as the tire rolls along the ground. (b) Using geometry to determine the position of the ant after the tire has rotated through an angle of $t$.

Note that these are the same parametric representations we had before, but we have now assigned a physical meaning to the parametric variable $t$.

After a while the ant is getting dizzy from going round and round on the edge of the tire. So he climbs up one of the spokes toward the center of the wheel. By climbing toward the center of the wheel, the ant has changed his path of motion. The new path has less up-and-down motion and is called a curtate cycloid (Figure 1.14). As shown in the figure, we let $b$ denote the distance along the spoke from the center of the wheel to the ant. As before, we let $t$ represent the angle the tire has rotated through. Additionally, we let $C = (x_C, y_C)$ represent the position of the center of the wheel and $A = (x_A, y_A)$ represent the position of the ant.

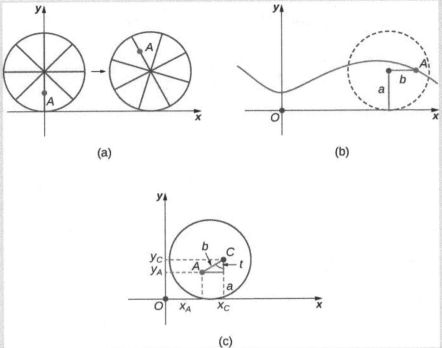

**Figure 1.14** (a) The ant climbs up one of the spokes toward the center of the wheel. (b) The ant's path of motion after he climbs closer to the center of the wheel. This is called a curtate cycloid. (c) The new setup, now that the ant has moved closer to the center of the wheel.

1. What is the position of the center of the wheel after the tire has rotated through an angle of $t$?

2. Use geometry to find expressions for $x_C - x_A$ and for $y_C - y_A$.

3. On the basis of your answers to parts 1 and 2, what are the parametric equations representing the curtate cycloid?

   Once the ant's head clears, he realizes that the bicyclist has made a turn, and is now traveling away from his home. So he drops off the bicycle tire and looks around. Fortunately, there is a set of train tracks nearby, headed back in the right direction. So the ant heads over to the train tracks to wait. After a while, a train goes by, heading in the right direction, and he manages to jump up and just catch the edge of the train wheel (without getting squished!).

   The ant is still worried about getting dizzy, but the train wheel is slippery and has no spokes to climb, so he decides to just hang on to the edge of the wheel and hope for the best. Now, train wheels have a flange to keep the wheel running on the tracks. So, in this case, since the ant is hanging on to the very edge of the flange, the distance from the center of the wheel to the ant is actually greater than the radius of the wheel (Figure 1.15). The setup here is essentially the same as when the ant climbed up the spoke on the bicycle wheel. We let $b$ denote the distance from the center of the wheel to the ant, and we let $t$ represent the angle the tire has rotated through. Additionally, we let $C = (x_C, y_C)$ represent the position of the center of the wheel and

   $A = (x_A, y_A)$ represent the position of the ant (Figure 1.15).

When the distance from the center of the wheel to the ant is greater than the radius of the wheel, his path of motion is called a prolate cycloid. A graph of a prolate cycloid is shown in the figure.

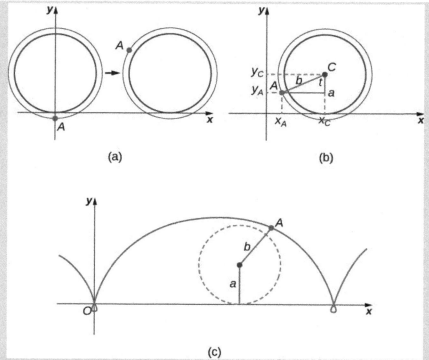

**Figure 1.15** (a) The ant is hanging onto the flange of the train wheel. (b) The new setup, now that the ant has jumped onto the train wheel. (c) The ant travels along a prolate cycloid.

4. Using the same approach you used in parts 1– 3, find the parametric equations for the path of motion of the ant.

5. What do you notice about your answer to part 3 and your answer to part 4?
   Notice that the ant is actually traveling backward at times (the "loops" in the graph), even though the train continues to move forward. He is probably going to be *really* dizzy by the time he gets home!

# 1.1 EXERCISES

For the following exercises, sketch the curves below by eliminating the parameter $t$. Give the orientation of the curve.

1. $x = t^2 + 2t, \quad y = t + 1$

2. $x = \cos(t), y = \sin(t), (0, 2\pi]$

3. $x = 2t + 4, y = t - 1$

4. $x = 3 - t, y = 2t - 3, 1.5 \le t \le 3$

For the following exercises, eliminate the parameter and sketch the graphs.

5. $x = 2t^2, \quad y = t^4 + 1$

For the following exercises, use technology (CAS or calculator) to sketch the parametric equations.

6. **[T]** $x = t^2 + t, \quad y = t^2 - 1$

7. **[T]** $x = e^{-t}, \quad y = e^{2t} - 1$

8. **[T]** $x = 3 \cos t, \quad y = 4 \sin t$

9. **[T]** $x = \sec t, \quad y = \cos t$

For the following exercises, sketch the parametric equations by eliminating the parameter. Indicate any asymptotes of the graph.

10. $x = e^t, \quad y = e^{2t} + 1$

11. $x = 6 \sin(2\theta), y = 4 \cos(2\theta)$

12. $x = \cos \theta, \quad y = 2 \sin(2\theta)$

13. $x = 3 - 2 \cos \theta, \quad y = -5 + 3 \sin \theta$

14. $x = 4 + 2 \cos \theta, \quad y = -1 + \sin \theta$

15. $x = \sec t, \quad y = \tan t$

16. $x = \ln(2t), \quad y = t^2$

17. $x = e^t, \quad y = e^{2t}$

18. $x = e^{-2t}, \quad y = e^{3t}$

19. $x = t^3, \quad y = 3 \ln t$

20. $x = 4 \sec \theta, \quad y = 3 \tan \theta$

For the following exercises, convert the parametric equations of a curve into rectangular form. No sketch is necessary. State the domain of the rectangular form.

21. $x = t^2 - 1, \quad y = \frac{t}{2}$

22. $x = \frac{1}{\sqrt{t+1}}, \quad y = \frac{t}{1+t}, t > -1$

23. $x = 4 \cos \theta, y = 3 \sin \theta, t \in (0, 2\pi]$

24. $x = \cosh t, \quad y = \sinh t$

25. $x = 2t - 3, \quad y = 6t - 7$

26. $x = t^2, \quad y = t^3$

27. $x = 1 + \cos t, \quad y = 3 - \sin t$

28. $x = \sqrt{t}, \quad y = 2t + 4$

29. $x = \sec t, \quad y = \tan t, \pi \le t < \frac{3\pi}{2}$

30. $x = 2 \cosh t, \quad y = 4 \sinh t$

31. $x = \cos(2t), \quad y = \sin t$

32. $x = 4t + 3, y = 16t^2 - 9$

33. $x = t^2, \quad y = 2 \ln t, t \ge 1$

34. $x = t^3, \quad y = 3 \ln t, t \ge 1$

35. $x = t^n, \quad y = n \ln t, t \ge 1, \quad$ where $n$ is a natural number

36. $\begin{aligned} x &= \ln(5t) \\ y &= \ln(t^2) \end{aligned}$ where $1 \le t \le e$

37. $\begin{aligned} x &= 2 \sin(8t) \\ y &= 2 \cos(8t) \end{aligned}$

38. $\begin{aligned} x &= \tan t \\ y &= \sec^2 t - 1 \end{aligned}$

For the following exercises, the pairs of parametric equations represent lines, parabolas, circles, ellipses, or hyperbolas. Name the type of basic curve that each pair of equations represents.

39. $x = 3t + 4$
$y = 5t - 2$

40. $x - 4 = 5t$
$y + 2 = t$

41. $x = 2t + 1$
$y = t^2 - 3$

42. $x = 3 \cos t$
$y = 3 \sin t$

43. $x = 2 \cos(3t)$
$y = 2 \sin(3t)$

44. $x = \cosh t$
$y = \sinh t$

45. $x = 3 \cos t$
$y = 4 \sin t$

46. $x = 2 \cos(3t)$
$y = 5 \sin(3t)$

47. $x = 3 \cosh(4t)$
$y = 4 \sinh(4t)$

48. $x = 2 \cosh t$
$y = 2 \sinh t$

49. Show that $\begin{aligned} x &= h + r \cos \theta \\ y &= k + r \sin \theta \end{aligned}$ represents the equation of

a circle.

50. Use the equations in the preceding problem to find a set of parametric equations for a circle whose radius is 5 and whose center is $(-2, 3)$.

For the following exercises, use a graphing utility to graph the curve represented by the parametric equations and identify the curve from its equation.

51. **[T]** $x = \theta + \sin \theta$
$y = 1 - \cos \theta$

52. **[T]** $x = 2t - 2 \sin t$
$y = 2 - 2 \cos t$

53. **[T]** $x = t - 0.5 \sin t$
$y = 1 - 1.5 \cos t$

54. An airplane traveling horizontally at 100 m/s over flat ground at an elevation of 4000 meters must drop an emergency package on a target on the ground. The trajectory of the package is given by $x = 100t$, $y = -4.9t^2 + 4000$, $t \geq 0$ where the origin is the point on the ground directly beneath the plane at the moment of release. How many horizontal meters before the target should the package be released in order to hit the target?

55. The trajectory of a bullet is given by $x = v_0 (\cos \alpha) t \, y = v_0 (\sin \alpha) t - \frac{1}{2} g t^2$ where $v_0 = 500$ m/s, $g = 9.8 = 9.8$ m/s$^2$, and $\alpha = 30$ degrees. When will the bullet hit the ground? How far from the gun will the bullet hit the ground?

56. **[T]** Use technology to sketch the curve represented by $x = \sin(4t)$, $y = \sin(3t)$, $0 \leq t \leq 2\pi$.

57. **[T]** Use technology to sketch $x = 2 \tan(t)$, $y = 3 \sec(t)$, $-\pi < t < \pi$.

58. Sketch the curve known as an *epitrochoid*, which gives the path of a point on a circle of radius $b$ as it rolls on the outside of a circle of radius $a$. The equations are

$$x = (a + b)\cos t - c \cdot \cos\left[\frac{(a+b)t}{b}\right]$$

$$y = (a + b)\sin t - c \cdot \sin\left[\frac{(a+b)t}{b}\right].$$

Let $a = 1$, $b = 2$, $c = 1$.

59. **[T]** Use technology to sketch the spiral curve given by $x = t \cos(t)$, $y = t \sin(t)$ from $-2\pi \leq t \leq 2\pi$.

60. **[T]** Use technology to graph the curve given by the parametric equations $x = 2 \cot(t)$, $y = 1 - \cos(2t)$, $-\pi/2 \leq t \leq \pi/2$. This curve is known as the witch of Agnesi.

61. **[T]** Sketch the curve given by parametric equations $x = \cosh(t)$
$y = \sinh(t)$, where $-2 \leq t \leq 2$.

# 1.2 | Calculus of Parametric Curves

| Learning Objectives |
| --- |
| **1.2.1** Determine derivatives and equations of tangents for parametric curves. |
| **1.2.2** Find the area under a parametric curve. |
| **1.2.3** Use the equation for arc length of a parametric curve. |
| **1.2.4** Apply the formula for surface area to a volume generated by a parametric curve. |

Now that we have introduced the concept of a parameterized curve, our next step is to learn how to work with this concept in the context of calculus. For example, if we know a parameterization of a given curve, is it possible to calculate the slope of a tangent line to the curve? How about the arc length of the curve? Or the area under the curve?

Another scenario: Suppose we would like to represent the location of a baseball after the ball leaves a pitcher's hand. If the position of the baseball is represented by the plane curve $(x(t), y(t))$, then we should be able to use calculus to find the speed of the ball at any given time. Furthermore, we should be able to calculate just how far that ball has traveled as a function of time.

## Derivatives of Parametric Equations

We start by asking how to calculate the slope of a line tangent to a parametric curve at a point. Consider the plane curve defined by the parametric equations

$$x(t) = 2t + 3, \quad y(t) = 3t - 4, \quad -2 \le t \le 3.$$

The graph of this curve appears in **Figure 1.16**. It is a line segment starting at $(-1, -10)$ and ending at $(9, 5)$.

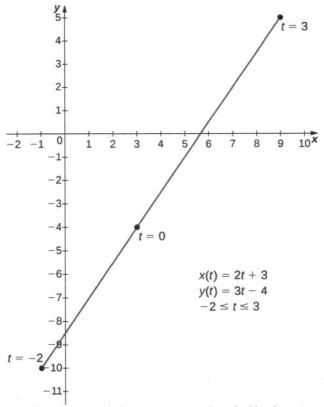

**Figure 1.16** Graph of the line segment described by the given parametric equations.

We can eliminate the parameter by first solving the equation $x(t) = 2t + 3$ for $t$:

$$
\begin{aligned}
x(t) &= 2t + 3 \\
x - 3 &= 2t \\
t &= \frac{x - 3}{2}.
\end{aligned}
$$

Substituting this into $y(t)$, we obtain

$$
\begin{aligned}
y(t) &= 3t - 4 \\
y &= 3\left(\frac{x - 3}{2}\right) - 4 \\
y &= \frac{3x}{2} - \frac{9}{2} - 4 \\
y &= \frac{3x}{2} - \frac{17}{2}.
\end{aligned}
$$

The slope of this line is given by $\dfrac{dy}{dx} = \dfrac{3}{2}$. Next we calculate $x'(t)$ and $y'(t)$. This gives $x'(t) = 2$ and $y'(t) = 3$. Notice that $\dfrac{dy}{dx} = \dfrac{dy/dt}{dx/dt} = \dfrac{3}{2}$. This is no coincidence, as outlined in the following theorem.

### Theorem 1.1: Derivative of Parametric Equations

Consider the plane curve defined by the parametric equations $x = x(t)$ and $y = y(t)$. Suppose that $x'(t)$ and $y'(t)$ exist, and assume that $x'(t) \neq 0$. Then the derivative $\dfrac{dy}{dx}$ is given by

$$
\frac{dy}{dx} = \frac{dy/dt}{dx/dt} = \frac{y'(t)}{x'(t)}. \tag{1.1}
$$

### Proof

This theorem can be proven using the Chain Rule. In particular, assume that the parameter $t$ can be eliminated, yielding a differentiable function $y = F(x)$. Then $y(t) = F(x(t))$. Differentiating both sides of this equation using the Chain Rule yields

$$
y'(t) = F'(x(t))x'(t),
$$

so

$$
F'(x(t)) = \frac{y'(t)}{x'(t)}.
$$

But $F'(x(t)) = \dfrac{dy}{dx}$, which proves the theorem.

$\square$

Equation 1.1 can be used to calculate derivatives of plane curves, as well as critical points. Recall that a critical point of a differentiable function $y = f(x)$ is any point $x = x_0$ such that either $f'(x_0) = 0$ or $f'(x_0)$ does not exist. Equation 1.1 gives a formula for the slope of a tangent line to a curve defined parametrically regardless of whether the curve can be described by a function $y = f(x)$ or not.

## Example 1.4

## Finding the Derivative of a Parametric Curve

Calculate the derivative $\dfrac{dy}{dx}$ for each of the following parametrically defined plane curves, and locate any critical points on their respective graphs.

   a.  $x(t) = t^2 - 3$,   $y(t) = 2t - 1$,   $-3 \le t \le 4$

   b.  $x(t) = 2t + 1$,   $y(t) = t^3 - 3t + 4$,   $-2 \le t \le 5$

   c.  $x(t) = 5\cos t$,   $y(t) = 5\sin t$,   $0 \le t \le 2\pi$

### Solution

   a.  To apply **Equation 1.1**, first calculate $x'(t)$ and $y'(t)$:

$$x'(t) = 2t$$
$$y'(t) = 2.$$

Next substitute these into the equation:

$$\frac{dy}{dx} = \frac{dy/dt}{dx/dt}$$
$$\frac{dy}{dx} = \frac{2}{2t}$$
$$\frac{dy}{dx} = \frac{1}{t}.$$

This derivative is undefined when $t = 0$. Calculating $x(0)$ and $y(0)$ gives $x(0) = (0)^2 - 3 = -3$ and $y(0) = 2(0) - 1 = -1$, which corresponds to the point $(-3, -1)$ on the graph. The graph of this curve is a parabola opening to the right, and the point $(-3, -1)$ is its vertex as shown.

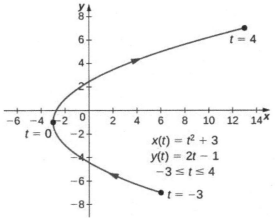

**Figure 1.17** Graph of the parabola described by parametric equations in part a.

   b.  To apply **Equation 1.1**, first calculate $x'(t)$ and $y'(t)$:

$$x'(t) = 2$$
$$y'(t) = 3t^2 - 3.$$

Next substitute these into the equation:

$$\frac{dy}{dx} = \frac{dy/dt}{dx/dt}$$

$$\frac{dy}{dx} = \frac{3t^2 - 3}{2}.$$

This derivative is zero when $t = \pm 1$. When $t = -1$ we have

$$x(-1) = 2(-1) + 1 = -1 \text{ and } y(-1) = (-1)^3 - 3(-1) + 4 = -1 + 3 + 4 = 6,$$

which corresponds to the point $(-1, 6)$ on the graph. When $t = 1$ we have

$$x(1) = 2(1) + 1 = 3 \text{ and } y(1) = (1)^3 - 3(1) + 4 = 1 - 3 + 4 = 2,$$

which corresponds to the point $(3, 2)$ on the graph. The point $(3, 2)$ is a relative minimum and the point $(-1, 6)$ is a relative maximum, as seen in the following graph.

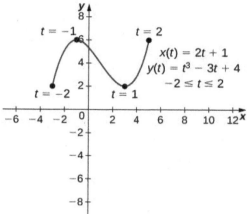

**Figure 1.18** Graph of the curve described by parametric equations in part b.

c.  To apply **Equation 1.1**, first calculate $x'(t)$ and $y'(t)$:

$$x'(t) = -5 \sin t$$
$$y'(t) = 5 \cos t.$$

Next substitute these into the equation:

$$\frac{dy}{dx} = \frac{dy/dt}{dx/dt}$$

$$\frac{dy}{dx} = \frac{5 \cos t}{-5 \sin t}$$

$$\frac{dy}{dx} = -\cot t.$$

This derivative is zero when $\cos t = 0$ and is undefined when $\sin t = 0$. This gives $t = 0, \frac{\pi}{2}, \pi, \frac{3\pi}{2}$, and $2\pi$ as critical points for $t$. Substituting each of these into $x(t)$ and $y(t)$, we obtain

| $t$ | $x(t)$ | $y(t)$ |
|---|---|---|
| 0 | 5 | 0 |
| $\frac{\pi}{2}$ | 0 | 5 |
| $\pi$ | −5 | 0 |
| $\frac{3\pi}{2}$ | 0 | −5 |
| $2\pi$ | 5 | 0 |

These points correspond to the sides, top, and bottom of the circle that is represented by the parametric equations (**Figure 1.19**). On the left and right edges of the circle, the derivative is undefined, and on the top and bottom, the derivative equals zero.

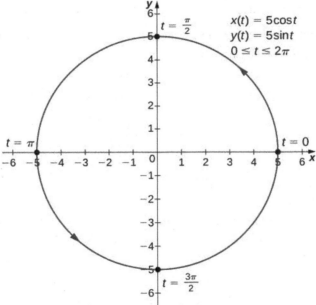

**Figure 1.19** Graph of the curve described by parametric equations in part c.

 **1.4** Calculate the derivative $dy/dx$ for the plane curve defined by the equations

$$x(t) = t^2 - 4t, \quad y(t) = 2t^3 - 6t, \quad -2 \le t \le 3$$

and locate any critical points on its graph.

## Example 1.5

### Finding a Tangent Line

Find the equation of the tangent line to the curve defined by the equations

$$x(t) = t^2 - 3, \quad y(t) = 2t - 1, \quad -3 \le t \le 4 \text{ when } t = 2.$$

### Solution

First find the slope of the tangent line using **Equation 1.1**, which means calculating $x'(t)$ and $y'(t)$:

$$x'(t) = 2t$$
$$y'(t) = 2.$$

Next substitute these into the equation:

$$\frac{dy}{dx} = \frac{dy/dt}{dx/dt}$$
$$\frac{dy}{dx} = \frac{2}{2t}$$
$$\frac{dy}{dx} = \frac{1}{t}.$$

When $t = 2$, $\frac{dy}{dx} = \frac{1}{2}$, so this is the slope of the tangent line. Calculating $x(2)$ and $y(2)$ gives

$$x(2) = (2)^2 - 3 = 1 \text{ and } y(2) = 2(2) - 1 = 3,$$

which corresponds to the point $(1, 3)$ on the graph (**Figure 1.20**). Now use the point-slope form of the equation of a line to find the equation of the tangent line:

$$\begin{aligned} y - y_0 &= m(x - x_0) \\ y - 3 &= \tfrac{1}{2}(x - 1) \\ y - 3 &= \tfrac{1}{2}x - \tfrac{1}{2} \\ y &= \tfrac{1}{2}x + \tfrac{5}{2}. \end{aligned}$$

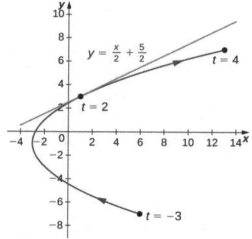

**Figure 1.20** Tangent line to the parabola described by the given parametric equations when $t = 2$.

**1.5** Find the equation of the tangent line to the curve defined by the equations

$$x(t) = t^2 - 4t, \quad y(t) = 2t^3 - 6t, \quad -2 \le t \le 3 \text{ when } t = 5.$$

## Second-Order Derivatives

Our next goal is to see how to take the second derivative of a function defined parametrically. The second derivative of a function $y = f(x)$ is defined to be the derivative of the first derivative; that is,

$$\frac{d^2 y}{dx^2} = \frac{d}{dx}\left[\frac{dy}{dx}\right].$$

Since $\frac{dy}{dx} = \frac{dy/dt}{dx/dt}$, we can replace the $y$ on both sides of this equation with $\frac{dy}{dx}$. This gives us

$$\frac{d^2 y}{dx^2} = \frac{d}{dx}\left(\frac{dy}{dx}\right) = \frac{(d/dt)(dy/dx)}{dx/dt}. \qquad (1.2)$$

If we know $dy/dx$ as a function of $t$, then this formula is straightforward to apply.

### Example 1.6

#### Finding a Second Derivative

Calculate the second derivative $d^2 y/dx^2$ for the plane curve defined by the parametric equations $x(t) = t^2 - 3, \ y(t) = 2t - 1, \ -3 \le t \le 4.$

#### Solution

From **Example 1.4** we know that $\frac{dy}{dx} = \frac{2}{2t} = \frac{1}{t}.$ Using **Equation 1.2**, we obtain

$$\frac{d^2 y}{dx^2} = \frac{(d/dt)(dy/dx)}{dx/dt} = \frac{(d/dt)(1/t)}{2t} = \frac{-t^{-2}}{2t} = -\frac{1}{2t^3}.$$

 **1.6** Calculate the second derivative $d^2 y/dx^2$ for the plane curve defined by the equations

$$x(t) = t^2 - 4t, \quad y(t) = 2t^3 - 6t, \quad -2 \le t \le 3$$

and locate any critical points on its graph.

## Integrals Involving Parametric Equations

Now that we have seen how to calculate the derivative of a plane curve, the next question is this: How do we find the area under a curve defined parametrically? Recall the cycloid defined by the equations $x(t) = t - \sin t, \quad y(t) = 1 - \cos t.$

Suppose we want to find the area of the shaded region in the following graph.

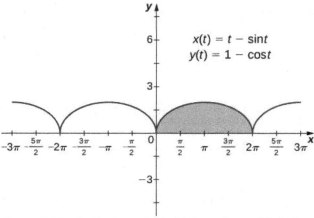

**Figure 1.21** Graph of a cycloid with the arch over $[0, 2\pi]$ highlighted.

To derive a formula for the area under the curve defined by the functions

$$x = x(t), \quad y = y(t), \quad a \le t \le b,$$

we assume that $x(t)$ is differentiable and start with an equal partition of the interval $a \le t \le b$. Suppose $t_0 = a < t_1 < t_2 < \cdots < t_n = b$ and consider the following graph.

**Figure 1.22** Approximating the area under a parametrically defined curve.

We use rectangles to approximate the area under the curve. The height of a typical rectangle in this parametrization is $y(x(\bar{t}_i))$ for some value $\bar{t}_i$ in the $i$th subinterval, and the width can be calculated as $x(t_i) - x(t_{i-1})$. Thus the area of the $i$th rectangle is given by

$$A_i = y(x(\bar{t}_i))(x(t_i) - x(t_{i-1})).$$

Then a Riemann sum for the area is

$$A_n = \sum_{i=1}^{n} y(x(\bar{t}_i))(x(t_i) - x(t_{i-1})).$$

Multiplying and dividing each area by $t_i - t_{i-1}$ gives

$$A_n = \sum_{i=1}^{n} y(x(\bar{t}_i))\left(\frac{x(t_i) - x(t_{i-1})}{t_i - t_{i-1}}\right)(t_i - t_{i-1}) = \sum_{i=1}^{n} y(x(\bar{t}_i))\left(\frac{x(t_i) - x(t_{i-1})}{\Delta t}\right)\Delta t.$$

Taking the limit as $n$ approaches infinity gives

$$A = \lim_{n \to \infty} A_n = \int_a^b y(t)x'(t)\, dt.$$

This leads to the following theorem.

---

**Theorem 1.2: Area under a Parametric Curve**

Consider the non-self-intersecting plane curve defined by the parametric equations

$$x = x(t), \quad y = y(t), \quad a \le t \le b$$

and assume that $x(t)$ is differentiable. The area under this curve is given by

$$A = \int_a^b y(t) x'(t)\, dt.$$

(1.3)

---

## Example 1.7

### Finding the Area under a Parametric Curve

Find the area under the curve of the cycloid defined by the equations

$$x(t) = t - \sin t, \quad y(t) = 1 - \cos t, \quad 0 \le t \le 2\pi.$$

**Solution**

Using Equation 1.3, we have

$$
\begin{aligned}
A &= \int_a^b y(t) x'(t)\, dt \\
&= \int_0^{2\pi} (1 - \cos t)(1 - \cos t)\, dt \\
&= \int_0^{2\pi} (1 - 2\cos t + \cos^2 t)\, dt \\
&= \int_0^{2\pi} \left(1 - 2\cos t + \frac{1 + \cos 2t}{2}\right) dt \\
&= \int_0^{2\pi} \left(\frac{3}{2} - 2\cos t + \frac{\cos 2t}{2}\right) dt \\
&= \frac{3t}{2} - 2\sin t + \frac{\sin 2t}{4} \Big|_0^{2\pi} \\
&= 3\pi.
\end{aligned}
$$

 **1.7** Find the area under the curve of the hypocycloid defined by the equations

$$x(t) = 3\cos t + \cos 3t, \quad y(t) = 3\sin t - \sin 3t, \quad 0 \le t \le \pi.$$

## Arc Length of a Parametric Curve

In addition to finding the area under a parametric curve, we sometimes need to find the arc length of a parametric curve. In the case of a line segment, arc length is the same as the distance between the endpoints. If a particle travels from point $A$ to point $B$ along a curve, then the distance that particle travels is the arc length. To develop a formula for arc length, we start with an approximation by line segments as shown in the following graph.

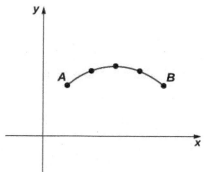

**Figure 1.23** Approximation of a curve by line segments.

Given a plane curve defined by the functions $x = x(t)$, $y = y(t)$, $a \leq t \leq b$, we start by partitioning the interval $[a, b]$ into $n$ equal subintervals: $t_0 = a < t_1 < t_2 < \cdots < t_n = b$. The width of each subinterval is given by $\Delta t = (b - a)/n$. We can calculate the length of each line segment:

$$d_1 = \sqrt{(x(t_1) - x(t_0))^2 + (y(t_1) - y(t_0))^2}$$
$$d_2 = \sqrt{(x(t_2) - x(t_1))^2 + (y(t_2) - y(t_1))^2} \text{ etc.}$$

Then add these up. We let $s$ denote the exact arc length and $s_n$ denote the approximation by $n$ line segments:

$$s \approx \sum_{k=1}^{n} s_k = \sum_{k=1}^{n} \sqrt{(x(t_k) - x(t_{k-1}))^2 + (y(t_k) - y(t_{k-1}))^2}. \tag{1.4}$$

If we assume that $x(t)$ and $y(t)$ are differentiable functions of $t$, then the Mean Value Theorem (**Introduction to the Applications of Derivatives (http://cnx.org/content/m53602/latest/)** ) applies, so in each subinterval $[t_{k-1}, t_k]$ there exist $\hat{t}_k$ and $\tilde{t}_k$ such that

$$x(t_k) - x(t_{k-1}) = x'\left(\hat{t}_k\right)(t_k - t_{k-1}) = x'\left(\hat{t}_k\right)\Delta t$$
$$y(t_k) - y(t_{k-1}) = y'\left(\tilde{t}_k\right)(t_k - t_{k-1}) = y'\left(\tilde{t}_k\right)\Delta t.$$

Therefore **Equation 1.4** becomes

$$\begin{aligned}
s &\approx \sum_{k=1}^{n} s_k \\
&= \sum_{k=1}^{n} \sqrt{\left(x'\left(\hat{t}_k\right)\Delta t\right)^2 + \left(y'\left(\tilde{t}_k\right)\Delta t\right)^2} \\
&= \sum_{k=1}^{n} \sqrt{\left(x'\left(\hat{t}_k\right)\right)^2 (\Delta t)^2 + \left(y'\left(\tilde{t}_k\right)\right)^2 (\Delta t)^2} \\
&= \left(\sum_{k=1}^{n} \sqrt{\left(x'\left(\hat{t}_k\right)\right)^2 + \left(y'\left(\tilde{t}_k\right)\right)^2}\right)\Delta t.
\end{aligned}$$

This is a Riemann sum that approximates the arc length over a partition of the interval $[a, b]$. If we further assume that the derivatives are continuous and let the number of points in the partition increase without bound, the approximation approaches the exact arc length. This gives

$$s = \lim_{n \to \infty} \sum_{k=1}^{n} s_k$$

$$= \lim_{n \to \infty} \left( \sum_{k=1}^{n} \sqrt{\left(x'\left(\hat{t}_k\right)\right)^2 + \left(y'\left(\tilde{t}_k\right)\right)^2} \, \Delta t \right)$$

$$= \int_a^b \sqrt{(x'(t))^2 + (y'(t))^2} \, dt.$$

When taking the limit, the values of $\hat{t}_k$ and $\tilde{t}_k$ are both contained within the same ever-shrinking interval of width $\Delta t$, so they must converge to the same value.

We can summarize this method in the following theorem.

### Theorem 1.3: Arc Length of a Parametric Curve

Consider the plane curve defined by the parametric equations

$$x = x(t), \quad y = y(t), \quad t_1 \le t \le t_2$$

and assume that $x(t)$ and $y(t)$ are differentiable functions of $t$. Then the arc length of this curve is given by

$$s = \int_{t_1}^{t_2} \sqrt{\left(\frac{dx}{dt}\right)^2 + \left(\frac{dy}{dt}\right)^2} \, dt. \tag{1.5}$$

At this point a side derivation leads to a previous formula for arc length. In particular, suppose the parameter can be eliminated, leading to a function $y = F(x)$. Then $y(t) = F(x(t))$ and the Chain Rule gives $y'(t) = F'(x(t))x'(t)$. Substituting this into **Equation 1.5** gives

$$s = \int_{t_1}^{t_2} \sqrt{\left(\frac{dx}{dt}\right)^2 + \left(\frac{dy}{dt}\right)^2} \, dt$$

$$= \int_{t_1}^{t_2} \sqrt{\left(\frac{dx}{dt}\right)^2 + \left(F'(x)\frac{dx}{dt}\right)^2} \, dt$$

$$= \int_{t_1}^{t_2} \sqrt{\left(\frac{dx}{dt}\right)^2 \left(1 + (F'(x))^2\right)} \, dt$$

$$= \int_{t_1}^{t_2} x'(t) \sqrt{1 + \left(\frac{dy}{dx}\right)^2} \, dt.$$

Here we have assumed that $x'(t) > 0$, which is a reasonable assumption. The Chain Rule gives $dx = x'(t)\,dt$, and letting $a = x(t_1)$ and $b = x(t_2)$ we obtain the formula

$$s = \int_a^b \sqrt{1 + \left(\frac{dy}{dx}\right)^2} \, dx,$$

which is the formula for arc length obtained in the **Introduction to the Applications of Integration (http://cnx.org/content/m53638/latest/)** .

### Example 1.8

## Finding the Arc Length of a Parametric Curve

Find the arc length of the semicircle defined by the equations

$$x(t) = 3 \cos t, \quad y(t) = 3 \sin t, \quad 0 \le t \le \pi.$$

### Solution

The values $t = 0$ to $t = \pi$ trace out the red curve in **Figure 1.23**. To determine its length, use **Equation 1.5**:

$$
\begin{aligned}
s &= \int_{t_1}^{t_2} \sqrt{\left(\frac{dx}{dt}\right)^2 + \left(\frac{dy}{dt}\right)^2}\, dt \\
&= \int_0^\pi \sqrt{(-3 \sin t)^2 + (3 \cos t)^2}\, dt \\
&= \int_0^\pi \sqrt{9 \sin^2 t + 9 \cos^2 t}\, dt \\
&= \int_0^\pi \sqrt{9\left(\sin^2 t + \cos^2 t\right)}\, dt \\
&= \int_0^\pi 3\, dt = 3t\big|_0^\pi = 3\pi.
\end{aligned}
$$

Note that the formula for the arc length of a semicircle is $\pi r$ and the radius of this circle is 3. This is a great example of using calculus to derive a known formula of a geometric quantity.

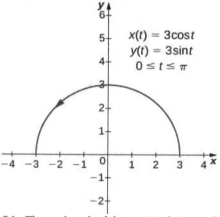

**Figure 1.24** The arc length of the semicircle is equal to its radius times $\pi$.

 **1.8**   Find the arc length of the curve defined by the equations

$$x(t) = 3t^2, \quad y(t) = 2t^3, \quad 1 \le t \le 3.$$

We now return to the problem posed at the beginning of the section about a baseball leaving a pitcher's hand. Ignoring the effect of air resistance (unless it is a curve ball!), the ball travels a parabolic path. Assuming the pitcher's hand is at the origin and the ball travels left to right in the direction of the positive $x$-axis, the parametric equations for this curve can be written as

$$x(t) = 140t, \quad y(t) = -16t^2 + 2t$$

where $t$ represents time. We first calculate the distance the ball travels as a function of time. This distance is represented by the arc length. We can modify the arc length formula slightly. First rewrite the functions $x(t)$ and $y(t)$ using $v$ as an independent variable, so as to eliminate any confusion with the parameter $t$:

$$x(v) = 140v, \quad y(v) = -16v^2 + 2v.$$

Then we write the arc length formula as follows:

$$s(t) = \int_0^t \sqrt{\left(\frac{dx}{dv}\right)^2 + \left(\frac{dy}{dv}\right)^2}\, dv$$

$$= \int_0^t \sqrt{140^2 + (-32v + 2)^2}\, dv.$$

The variable $v$ acts as a dummy variable that disappears after integration, leaving the arc length as a function of time $t$. To integrate this expression we can use a formula from **Appendix A**,

$$\int \sqrt{a^2 + u^2}\, du = \frac{u}{2}\sqrt{a^2 + u^2} + \frac{a^2}{2}\ln\left|u + \sqrt{a^2 + u^2}\right| + C.$$

We set $a = 140$ and $u = -32v + 2$. This gives $du = -32dv$, so $dv = -\frac{1}{32}du$. Therefore

$$\int \sqrt{140^2 + (-32v + 2)^2}\, dv = -\frac{1}{32}\int \sqrt{a^2 + u^2}\, du$$

$$= -\frac{1}{32}\left[\begin{array}{l} \frac{(-32v + 2)}{2}\sqrt{140^2 + (-32v + 2)^2} \\ + \frac{140^2}{2}\ln\left|(-32v + 2) + \sqrt{140^2 + (-32v + 2)^2}\right| \end{array}\right] + C$$

and

$$s(t) = -\frac{1}{32}\left[\frac{(-32t + 2)}{2}\sqrt{140^2 + (-32t + 2)^2} + \frac{140^2}{2}\ln\left|(-32t + 2) + \sqrt{140^2 + (-32t + 2)^2}\right|\right]$$

$$+ \frac{1}{32}\left[\sqrt{140^2 + 2^2} + \frac{140^2}{2}\ln\left|2 + \sqrt{140^2 + 2^2}\right|\right]$$

$$= \left(\frac{t}{2} - \frac{1}{32}\right)\sqrt{1024t^2 - 128t + 19604} - \frac{1225}{4}\ln\left|(-32t + 2) + \sqrt{1024t^2 - 128t + 19604}\right|$$

$$+ \frac{\sqrt{19604}}{32} + \frac{1225}{4}\ln(2 + \sqrt{19604}).$$

This function represents the distance traveled by the ball as a function of time. To calculate the speed, take the derivative of this function with respect to $t$. While this may seem like a daunting task, it is possible to obtain the answer directly from the Fundamental Theorem of Calculus:

$$\frac{d}{dx}\int_a^x f(u)\, du = f(x).$$

Therefore

$$s'(t) = \frac{d}{dt}[s(t)]$$

$$= \frac{d}{dt}\left[\int_0^t \sqrt{140^2 + (-32v + 2)^2}\, dv\right]$$

$$= \sqrt{140^2 + (-32t + 2)^2}$$

$$= \sqrt{1024t^2 - 128t + 19604}$$

$$= 2\sqrt{256t^2 - 32t + 4901}.$$

One third of a second after the ball leaves the pitcher's hand, the distance it travels is equal to

$$s\left(\frac{1}{3}\right) = \left(\frac{1/3}{2} - \frac{1}{32}\right)\sqrt{1024\left(\frac{1}{3}\right)^2 - 128\left(\frac{1}{3}\right) + 19604}$$

$$-\frac{1225}{4}\ln\left|\left(-32\left(\frac{1}{3}\right) + 2\right) + \sqrt{1024\left(\frac{1}{3}\right)^2 - 128\left(\frac{1}{3}\right) + 19604}\right|$$

$$+\frac{\sqrt{19604}}{32} + \frac{1225}{4}\ln(2 + \sqrt{19604})$$

$$\approx 46.69 \text{ feet.}$$

This value is just over three quarters of the way to home plate. The speed of the ball is

$$s'\left(\frac{1}{3}\right) = 2\sqrt{256\left(\frac{1}{3}\right)^2 - 16\left(\frac{1}{3}\right) + 4901} \approx 140.34 \text{ ft/s.}$$

This speed translates to approximately 95 mph—a major-league fastball.

## Surface Area Generated by a Parametric Curve

Recall the problem of finding the surface area of a volume of revolution. In **Curve Length and Surface Area** (http://cnx.org/content/m53644/latest/) , we derived a formula for finding the surface area of a volume generated by a function $y = f(x)$ from $x = a$ to $x = b$, revolved around the $x$-axis:

$$S = 2\pi \int_a^b f(x)\sqrt{1 + (f'(x))^2}dx.$$

We now consider a volume of revolution generated by revolving a parametrically defined curve $x = x(t), \, y = y(t), \, a \le t \le b$ around the $x$-axis as shown in the following figure.

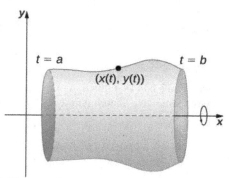

**Figure 1.25** A surface of revolution generated by a parametrically defined curve.

The analogous formula for a parametrically defined curve is

$$S = 2\pi \int_a^b y(t)\sqrt{(x'(t))^2 + (y'(t))^2}dt \qquad (1.6)$$

provided that $y(t)$ is not negative on $[a, b]$.

## Example 1.9

### Finding Surface Area

Find the surface area of a sphere of radius $r$ centered at the origin.

## Solution

We start with the curve defined by the equations

$$x(t) = r \cos t, \quad y(t) = r \sin t, \quad 0 \le t \le \pi.$$

This generates an upper semicircle of radius $r$ centered at the origin as shown in the following graph.

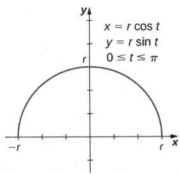

**Figure 1.26** A semicircle generated by parametric equations.

When this curve is revolved around the $x$-axis, it generates a sphere of radius $r$. To calculate the surface area of the sphere, we use **Equation 1.6**:

$$
\begin{aligned}
S &= 2\pi \int_a^b y(t)\sqrt{(x'(t))^2 + (y'(t))^2}\,dt \\
&= 2\pi \int_0^\pi r \sin t \sqrt{(-r \sin t)^2 + (r \cos t)^2}\,dt \\
&= 2\pi \int_0^\pi r \sin t \sqrt{r^2 \sin^2 t + r^2 \cos^2 t}\,dt \\
&= 2\pi \int_0^\pi r \sin t \sqrt{r^2\left(\sin^2 t + \cos^2 t\right)}\,dt \\
&= 2\pi \int_0^\pi r^2 \sin t\,dt \\
&= 2\pi r^2 (-\cos t|_0^\pi) \\
&= 2\pi r^2 (-\cos \pi + \cos 0) \\
&= 4\pi r^2.
\end{aligned}
$$

This is, in fact, the formula for the surface area of a sphere.

**1.9** Find the surface area generated when the plane curve defined by the equations

$$x(t) = t^3, \quad y(t) = t^2, \quad 0 \le t \le 1$$

is revolved around the $x$-axis.

# 1.2 EXERCISES

For the following exercises, each set of parametric equations represents a line. Without eliminating the parameter, find the slope of each line.

62.  $x = 3 + t, \ y = 1 - t$

63.  $x = 8 + 2t, \ y = 1$

64.  $x = 4 - 3t, \ y = -2 + 6t$

65.  $x = -5t + 7, \ y = 3t - 1$

For the following exercises, determine the slope of the tangent line, then find the equation of the tangent line at the given value of the parameter.

66.  $x = 3 \sin t, \ y = 3 \cos t, \quad t = \frac{\pi}{4}$

67.  $x = \cos t, \ y = 8 \sin t, \ t = \frac{\pi}{2}$

68.  $x = 2t, \ y = t^3, \quad t = -1$

69.  $x = t + \frac{1}{t}, \ y = t - \frac{1}{t}, \quad t = 1$

70.  $x = \sqrt{t}, \ y = 2t, \quad t = 4$

For the following exercises, find all points on the curve that have the given slope.

71.  $x = 4 \cos t, \ y = 4 \sin t, \ \text{slope} = 0.5$

72.  $x = 2 \cos t, \ y = 8 \sin t, \ \text{slope} = -1$

73.  $x = t + \frac{1}{t}, \ y = t - \frac{1}{t}, \ \text{slope} = 1$

74.  $x = 2 + \sqrt{t}, \ y = 2 - 4t, \ \text{slope} = 0$

For the following exercises, write the equation of the tangent line in Cartesian coordinates for the given parameter $t$.

75.  $x = e^{\sqrt{t}}, \ y = 1 - \ln t^2, \quad t = 1$

76.  $x = t \ln t, \ y = \sin^2 t, \ t = \frac{\pi}{4}$

77.  $x = e^t, \ y = (t - 1)^2, \quad \text{at}(1, \ 1)$

78.  For $x = \sin(2t), \ y = 2 \sin t$ where $0 \le t < 2\pi$. Find all values of $t$ at which a horizontal tangent line exists.

79.  For $x = \sin(2t), \ y = 2 \sin t$ where $0 \le t < 2\pi$. Find all values of $t$ at which a vertical tangent line exists.

80.  Find all points on the curve $x = 4 \cos(t), \ y = 4 \sin(t)$ that have the slope of $\frac{1}{2}$.

81.  Find $\frac{dy}{dx}$ for $x = \sin(t), \ y = \cos(t)$.

82.  Find the equation of the tangent line to $x = \sin(t), \ y = \cos(t)$ at $t = \frac{\pi}{4}$.

83.  For the curve $x = 4t, \ y = 3t - 2$, find the slope and concavity of the curve at $t = 3$.

84.  For the parametric curve whose equation is $x = 4 \cos \theta, \ y = 4 \sin \theta$, find the slope and concavity of the curve at $\theta = \frac{\pi}{4}$.

85.  Find the slope and concavity for the curve whose equation is $x = 2 + \sec \theta, \ y = 1 + 2 \tan \theta$ at $\theta = \frac{\pi}{6}$.

86.  Find all points on the curve $x = t + 4, \ y = t^3 - 3t$ at which there are vertical and horizontal tangents.

87.  Find all points on the curve $x = \sec \theta, \ y = \tan \theta$ at which horizontal and vertical tangents exist.

For the following exercises, find $d^2 y/dx^2$.

88.  $x = t^4 - 1, \ y = t - t^2$

89.  $x = \sin(\pi t), \ y = \cos(\pi t)$

90.  $x = e^{-t}, \ y = te^{2t}$

For the following exercises, find points on the curve at which tangent line is horizontal or vertical.

91.  $x = t(t^2 - 3), \ y = 3(t^2 - 3)$

92.  $x = \frac{3t}{1 + t^3}, \ y = \frac{3t^2}{1 + t^3}$

For the following exercises, find $dy/dx$ at the value of the parameter.

93.  $x = \cos t, \ y = \sin t, \quad t = \frac{3\pi}{4}$

94. $x = \sqrt{t}, \quad y = 2t + 4, \quad t = 9$

95. $x = 4\cos(2\pi s), \quad y = 3\sin(2\pi s), \quad s = -\frac{1}{4}$

For the following exercises, find $d^2 y/dx^2$ at the given point without eliminating the parameter.

96. $x = \frac{1}{2}t^2, \quad y = \frac{1}{3}t^3, \quad t = 2$

97. $x = \sqrt{t}, \quad y = 2t + 4, \quad t = 1$

98. Find $t$ intervals on which the curve $x = 3t^2, y = t^3 - t$ is concave up as well as concave down.

99. Determine the concavity of the curve $x = 2t + \ln t, y = 2t - \ln t$.

100. Sketch and find the area under one arch of the cycloid $x = r(\theta - \sin \theta), y = r(1 - \cos \theta)$.

101. Find the area bounded by the curve $x = \cos t, y = e^t, 0 \le t \le \frac{\pi}{2}$ and the lines $y = 1$ and $x = 0$.

102. Find the area enclosed by the ellipse $x = a \cos \theta, y = b \sin \theta, 0 \le \theta < 2\pi$.

103. Find the area of the region bounded by $x = 2\sin^2 \theta, y = 2\sin^2 \theta \tan \theta, \text{ for } 0 \le \theta \le \frac{\pi}{2}$.

For the following exercises, find the area of the regions bounded by the parametric curves and the indicated values of the parameter.

104. $x = 2\cot \theta, y = 2\sin^2 \theta, 0 \le \theta \le \pi$

105. **[T]**
$x = 2a\cos t - a\cos(2t), y = 2a\sin t - a\sin(2t), 0 \le t < 2\pi$

106. **[T]** $x = a\sin(2t), y = b\sin(t), 0 \le t < 2\pi$ (the "hourglass")

107. **[T]**
$x = 2a\cos t - a\sin(2t), y = b\sin t, 0 \le t < 2\pi$ (the "teardrop")

For the following exercises, find the arc length of the curve on the indicated interval of the parameter.

108. $x = 4t + 3, \quad y = 3t - 2, \quad 0 \le t \le 2$

109. $x = \frac{1}{3}t^3, \quad y = \frac{1}{2}t^2, \quad 0 \le t \le 1$

110. $x = \cos(2t), \quad y = \sin(2t), \quad 0 \le t \le \frac{\pi}{2}$

111. $x = 1 + t^2, \quad y = (1 + t)^3, \quad 0 \le t \le 1$

112. $x = e^t \cos t, \quad y = e^t \sin t, \quad 0 \le t \le \frac{\pi}{2}$ (express answer as a decimal rounded to three places)

113. $x = a\cos^3 \theta, y = a\sin^3 \theta$ on the interval $[0, 2\pi)$ (the hypocycloid)

114. Find the length of one arch of the cycloid $x = 4(t - \sin t), y = 4(1 - \cos t)$.

115. Find the distance traveled by a particle with position $(x, y)$ as $t$ varies in the given time interval: $x = \sin^2 t, \quad y = \cos^2 t, \quad 0 \le t \le 3\pi$.

116. Find the length of one arch of the cycloid $x = \theta - \sin \theta, y = 1 - \cos \theta$.

117. Show that the total length of the ellipse $x = 4\sin \theta, y = 3\cos \theta$ is
$$L = 16 \int_0^{\pi/2} \sqrt{1 - e^2 \sin^2 \theta} \, d\theta, \quad \text{where} \quad e = \frac{c}{a} \text{ and }$$
$$c = \sqrt{a^2 - b^2}.$$

118. Find the length of the curve $x = e^t - t, y = 4e^{t/2}, -8 \le t \le 3$.

For the following exercises, find the area of the surface obtained by rotating the given curve about the x-axis.

119. $x = t^3, \quad y = t^2, \quad 0 \le t \le 1$

120. $x = a\cos^3 \theta, \quad y = a\sin^3 \theta, \quad 0 \le \theta \le \frac{\pi}{2}$

121. **[T]** Use a CAS to find the area of the surface generated by rotating $x = t + t^3, y = t - \frac{1}{t^2}, 1 \le t \le 2$ about the x-axis. (Answer to three decimal places.)

122. Find the surface area obtained by rotating $x = 3t^2, y = 2t^3, 0 \le t \le 5$ about the y-axis.

123. Find the area of the surface generated by revolving $x = t^2, y = 2t, 0 \le t \le 4$ about the x-axis.

124. Find the surface area generated by revolving $x = t^2, y = 2t^2, 0 \le t \le 1$ about the y-axis.

# 1.3 | Polar Coordinates

The rectangular coordinate system (or Cartesian plane) provides a means of mapping points to ordered pairs and ordered pairs to points. This is called a *one-to-one mapping* from points in the plane to ordered pairs. The polar coordinate system provides an alternative method of mapping points to ordered pairs. In this section we see that in some circumstances, polar coordinates can be more useful than rectangular coordinates.

## Defining Polar Coordinates

To find the coordinates of a point in the polar coordinate system, consider **Figure 1.27**. The point $P$ has Cartesian coordinates $(x, y)$. The line segment connecting the origin to the point $P$ measures the distance from the origin to $P$ and has length $r$. The angle between the positive $x$-axis and the line segment has measure $\theta$. This observation suggests a natural correspondence between the coordinate pair $(x, y)$ and the values $r$ and $\theta$. This correspondence is the basis of the **polar coordinate system**. Note that every point in the Cartesian plane has two values (hence the term *ordered pair*) associated with it. In the polar coordinate system, each point also two values associated with it: $r$ and $\theta$.

**Figure 1.27**   An arbitrary point in the Cartesian plane.

Using right-triangle trigonometry, the following equations are true for the point $P$:

$$\cos\theta = \tfrac{x}{r} \text{ so } x = r\cos\theta$$

$$\sin\theta = \tfrac{y}{r} \text{ so } y = r\sin\theta.$$

Furthermore,

$$r^2 = x^2 + y^2 \text{ and } \tan\theta = \tfrac{y}{x}.$$

Each point $(x, y)$ in the Cartesian coordinate system can therefore be represented as an ordered pair $(r, \theta)$ in the polar coordinate system. The first coordinate is called the **radial coordinate** and the second coordinate is called the **angular coordinate**. Every point in the plane can be represented in this form.

Note that the equation $\tan\theta = y/x$ has an infinite number of solutions for any ordered pair $(x, y)$. However, if we restrict the solutions to values between $0$ and $2\pi$ then we can assign a unique solution to the quadrant in which the original point $(x, y)$ is located. Then the corresponding value of $r$ is positive, so $r^2 = x^2 + y^2$.

### Theorem 1.4: Converting Points between Coordinate Systems

Given a point $P$ in the plane with Cartesian coordinates $(x, y)$ and polar coordinates $(r, \theta)$, the following conversion formulas hold true:

$$x = r \cos \theta \text{ and } y = r \sin \theta, \tag{1.7}$$

$$r^2 = x^2 + y^2 \text{ and } \tan \theta = \frac{y}{x}. \tag{1.8}$$

These formulas can be used to convert from rectangular to polar or from polar to rectangular coordinates.

## Example 1.10

### Converting between Rectangular and Polar Coordinates

Convert each of the following points into polar coordinates.

    a.  $(1, 1)$

    b.  $(-3, 4)$

    c.  $(0, 3)$

    d.  $(5\sqrt{3}, -5)$

Convert each of the following points into rectangular coordinates.

    e.  $(3, \pi/3)$

    f.  $(2, 3\pi/2)$

    g.  $(6, -5\pi/6)$

### Solution

    a.  Use $x = 1$ and $y = 1$ in **Equation 1.8**:

$$
\begin{aligned}
r^2 &= x^2 + y^2 \\
&= 1^2 + 1^2 \quad \text{and} \\
r &= \sqrt{2}
\end{aligned}
\qquad
\begin{aligned}
\tan \theta &= \frac{y}{x} \\
&= \frac{1}{1} = 1 \\
\theta &= \frac{\pi}{4}.
\end{aligned}
$$

Therefore this point can be represented as $\left(\sqrt{2}, \frac{\pi}{4}\right)$ in polar coordinates.

    b.  Use $x = -3$ and $y = 4$ in **Equation 1.8**:

$$
\begin{aligned}
r^2 &= x^2 + y^2 \\
&= (-3)^2 + (4)^2 \quad \text{and} \\
r &= 5
\end{aligned}
\qquad
\begin{aligned}
\tan \theta &= \frac{y}{x} \\
&= -\frac{4}{3} \\
\theta &= -\arctan\left(\frac{4}{3}\right) \\
&\approx 2.21.
\end{aligned}
$$

Therefore this point can be represented as $(5, 2.21)$ in polar coordinates.

c. Use $x = 0$ and $y = 3$ in **Equation 1.8**:

$$\begin{aligned} r^2 &= x^2 + y^2 \\ &= (3)^2 + (0)^2 \\ &= 9 + 0 \\ r &= 3 \end{aligned} \quad \text{and} \quad \begin{aligned} \tan \theta &= \frac{y}{x} \\ &= \frac{3}{0}. \end{aligned}$$

Direct application of the second equation leads to division by zero. Graphing the point $(0, 3)$ on the rectangular coordinate system reveals that the point is located on the positive $y$-axis. The angle between the positive $x$-axis and the positive $y$-axis is $\frac{\pi}{2}$. Therefore this point can be represented as $\left(3, \frac{\pi}{2}\right)$ in polar coordinates.

d. Use $x = 5\sqrt{3}$ and $y = -5$ in **Equation 1.8**:

$$\begin{aligned} r^2 &= x^2 + y^2 \\ &= (5\sqrt{3})^2 + (-5)^2 \\ &= 75 + 25 \\ r &= 10 \end{aligned} \quad \text{and} \quad \begin{aligned} \tan \theta &= \frac{y}{x} \\ &= \frac{-5}{5\sqrt{3}} = -\frac{\sqrt{3}}{3} \\ \theta &= -\frac{\pi}{6}. \end{aligned}$$

Therefore this point can be represented as $\left(10, -\frac{\pi}{6}\right)$ in polar coordinates.

e. Use $r = 3$ and $\theta = \frac{\pi}{3}$ in **Equation 1.7**:

$$\begin{aligned} x &= r\cos\theta \\ &= 3\cos\left(\frac{\pi}{3}\right) \\ &= 3\left(\frac{1}{2}\right) = \frac{3}{2} \end{aligned} \quad \text{and} \quad \begin{aligned} y &= r\sin\theta \\ &= 3\sin\left(\frac{\pi}{3}\right) \\ &= 3\left(\frac{\sqrt{3}}{2}\right) = \frac{3\sqrt{3}}{2}. \end{aligned}$$

Therefore this point can be represented as $\left(\frac{3}{2}, \frac{3\sqrt{3}}{2}\right)$ in rectangular coordinates.

f. Use $r = 2$ and $\theta = \frac{3\pi}{2}$ in **Equation 1.7**:

$$\begin{aligned} x &= r\cos\theta \\ &= 2\cos\left(\frac{3\pi}{2}\right) \\ &= 2(0) = 0 \end{aligned} \quad \text{and} \quad \begin{aligned} y &= r\sin\theta \\ &= 2\sin\left(\frac{3\pi}{2}\right) \\ &= 2(-1) = -2. \end{aligned}$$

Therefore this point can be represented as $(0, -2)$ in rectangular coordinates.

g. Use $r = 6$ and $\theta = -\frac{5\pi}{6}$ in **Equation 1.7**:

$$\begin{aligned} x &= r\cos\theta \\ &= 6\cos\left(-\frac{5\pi}{6}\right) \\ &= 6\left(-\frac{\sqrt{3}}{2}\right) \\ &= -3\sqrt{3} \end{aligned} \quad \text{and} \quad \begin{aligned} y &= r\sin\theta \\ &= 6\sin\left(-\frac{5\pi}{6}\right) \\ &= 6\left(-\frac{1}{2}\right) \\ &= -3. \end{aligned}$$

Therefore this point can be represented as $\left(-3\sqrt{3},\ -3\right)$ in rectangular coordinates.

**1.10** Convert $(-8,\ -8)$ into polar coordinates and $\left(4,\ \frac{2\pi}{3}\right)$ into rectangular coordinates.

The polar representation of a point is not unique. For example, the polar coordinates $\left(2,\ \frac{\pi}{3}\right)$ and $\left(2,\ \frac{7\pi}{3}\right)$ both represent the point $\left(1,\ \sqrt{3}\right)$ in the rectangular system. Also, the value of $r$ can be negative. Therefore, the point with polar coordinates $\left(-2,\ \frac{4\pi}{3}\right)$ also represents the point $\left(1,\ \sqrt{3}\right)$ in the rectangular system, as we can see by using **Equation 1.8**:

$$
\begin{aligned}
x &= r\cos\theta & y &= r\sin\theta \\
&= -2\cos\!\left(\frac{4\pi}{3}\right) & \text{and} \qquad &= -2\sin\!\left(\frac{4\pi}{3}\right) \\
&= -2\!\left(-\tfrac{1}{2}\right) = 1 & &= -2\!\left(-\tfrac{\sqrt{3}}{2}\right) = \sqrt{3}.
\end{aligned}
$$

Every point in the plane has an infinite number of representations in polar coordinates. However, each point in the plane has only one representation in the rectangular coordinate system.

Note that the polar representation of a point in the plane also has a visual interpretation. In particular, $r$ is the directed distance that the point lies from the origin, and $\theta$ measures the angle that the line segment from the origin to the point makes with the positive $x$-axis. Positive angles are measured in a counterclockwise direction and negative angles are measured in a clockwise direction. The polar coordinate system appears in the following figure.

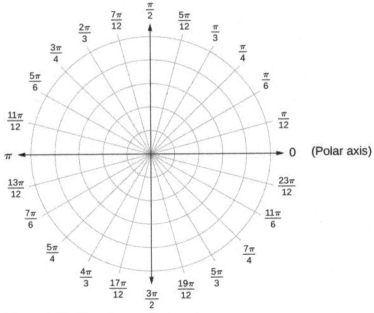

**Figure 1.28** The polar coordinate system.

The line segment starting from the center of the graph going to the right (called the positive $x$-axis in the Cartesian system) is the **polar axis**. The center point is the **pole**, or origin, of the coordinate system, and corresponds to $r = 0$. The innermost circle shown in **Figure 1.28** contains all points a distance of 1 unit from the pole, and is represented by the equation $r = 1$.

Then $r = 2$ is the set of points 2 units from the pole, and so on. The line segments emanating from the pole correspond to fixed angles. To plot a point in the polar coordinate system, start with the angle. If the angle is positive, then measure the angle from the polar axis in a counterclockwise direction. If it is negative, then measure it clockwise. If the value of $r$ is positive, move that distance along the terminal ray of the angle. If it is negative, move along the ray that is opposite the terminal ray of the given angle.

## Example 1.11

### Plotting Points in the Polar Plane

Plot each of the following points on the polar plane.

   a.  $\left(2, \frac{\pi}{4}\right)$

   b.  $\left(-3, \frac{2\pi}{3}\right)$

   c.  $\left(4, \frac{5\pi}{4}\right)$

### Solution

The three points are plotted in the following figure.

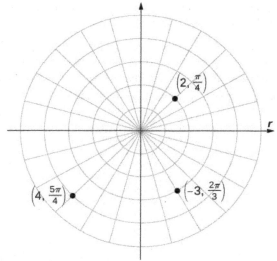

**Figure 1.29**  Three points plotted in the polar coordinate system.

  **1.11**  Plot $\left(4, \frac{5\pi}{3}\right)$ and $\left(-3, -\frac{7\pi}{2}\right)$ on the polar plane.

# Polar Curves

Now that we know how to plot points in the polar coordinate system, we can discuss how to plot curves. In the rectangular coordinate system, we can graph a function $y = f(x)$ and create a curve in the Cartesian plane. In a similar fashion, we can graph a curve that is generated by a function $r = f(\theta)$.

The general idea behind graphing a function in polar coordinates is the same as graphing a function in rectangular coordinates. Start with a list of values for the independent variable ($\theta$ in this case) and calculate the corresponding values of the dependent variable $r$. This process generates a list of ordered pairs, which can be plotted in the polar coordinate system. Finally, connect the points, and take advantage of any patterns that may appear. The function may be periodic, for example, which indicates that only a limited number of values for the independent variable are needed.

### Problem-Solving Strategy: Plotting a Curve in Polar Coordinates

1. Create a table with two columns. The first column is for $\theta$, and the second column is for $r$.

2. Create a list of values for $\theta$.

3. Calculate the corresponding $r$ values for each $\theta$.

4. Plot each ordered pair $(r, \theta)$ on the coordinate axes.

5. Connect the points and look for a pattern.

 Watch this **video (http://www.openstaxcollege.org/l/20_polarcurves)** for more information on sketching polar curves.

## Example 1.12

### Graphing a Function in Polar Coordinates

Graph the curve defined by the function $r = 4 \sin \theta$. Identify the curve and rewrite the equation in rectangular coordinates.

### Solution

Because the function is a multiple of a sine function, it is periodic with period $2\pi$, so use values for $\theta$ between 0 and $2\pi$. The result of steps 1–3 appear in the following table. **Figure 1.30** shows the graph based on this table.

| $\theta$ | $r = 4\sin\theta$ | | $\theta$ | $r = 4\sin\theta$ |
|---|---|---|---|---|
| 0 | 0 | | $\pi$ | 0 |
| $\dfrac{\pi}{6}$ | 2 | | $\dfrac{7\pi}{6}$ | $-2$ |
| $\dfrac{\pi}{4}$ | $2\sqrt{2} \approx 2.8$ | | $\dfrac{5\pi}{4}$ | $-2\sqrt{2} \approx -2.8$ |
| $\dfrac{\pi}{3}$ | $2\sqrt{3} \approx 3.4$ | | $\dfrac{4\pi}{3}$ | $-2\sqrt{3} \approx -3.4$ |
| $\dfrac{\pi}{2}$ | 4 | | $\dfrac{3\pi}{2}$ | 4 |
| $\dfrac{2\pi}{3}$ | $2\sqrt{3} \approx 3.4$ | | $\dfrac{5\pi}{3}$ | $-2\sqrt{3} \approx -3.4$ |
| $\dfrac{3\pi}{4}$ | $2\sqrt{2} \approx 2.8$ | | $\dfrac{7\pi}{4}$ | $-2\sqrt{2} \approx -2.8$ |
| $\dfrac{5\pi}{6}$ | 2 | | $\dfrac{11\pi}{6}$ | $-2$ |
| | | | $2\pi$ | 0 |

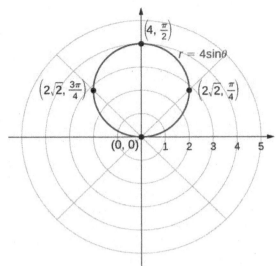

**Figure 1.30** The graph of the function $r = 4 \sin \theta$ is a circle.

This is the graph of a circle. The equation $r = 4 \sin \theta$ can be converted into rectangular coordinates by first multiplying both sides by $r$. This gives the equation $r^2 = 4r \sin \theta$. Next use the facts that $r^2 = x^2 + y^2$ and $y = r \sin \theta$. This gives $x^2 + y^2 = 4y$. To put this equation into standard form, subtract $4y$ from both sides of the equation and complete the square:

$$
\begin{aligned}
x^2 + y^2 - 4y &= 0 \\
x^2 + \left(y^2 - 4y\right) &= 0 \\
x^2 + \left(y^2 - 4y + 4\right) &= 0 + 4 \\
x^2 + (y - 2)^2 &= 4.
\end{aligned}
$$

This is the equation of a circle with radius 2 and center $(0, 2)$ in the rectangular coordinate system.

 **1.12** Create a graph of the curve defined by the function $r = 4 + 4 \cos \theta$.

The graph in **Example 1.12** was that of a circle. The equation of the circle can be transformed into rectangular coordinates using the coordinate transformation formulas in **Equation 1.8**. **Example 1.14** gives some more examples of functions for transforming from polar to rectangular coordinates.

## Example 1.13

### Transforming Polar Equations to Rectangular Coordinates

Rewrite each of the following equations in rectangular coordinates and identify the graph.

a.  $\theta = \dfrac{\pi}{3}$

　　b.　$r = 3$

　　c.　$r = 6\cos\theta - 8\sin\theta$

### Solution

a.　Take the tangent of both sides. This gives $\tan\theta = \tan(\pi/3) = \sqrt{3}$. Since $\tan\theta = y/x$ we can replace the left-hand side of this equation by $y/x$. This gives $y/x = \sqrt{3}$, which can be rewritten as $y = x\sqrt{3}$. This is the equation of a straight line passing through the origin with slope $\sqrt{3}$. In general, any polar equation of the form $\theta = K$ represents a straight line through the pole with slope equal to $\tan K$.

b.　First, square both sides of the equation. This gives $r^2 = 9$. Next replace $r^2$ with $x^2 + y^2$. This gives the equation $x^2 + y^2 = 9$, which is the equation of a circle centered at the origin with radius 3. In general, any polar equation of the form $r = k$ where $k$ is a positive constant represents a circle of radius $k$ centered at the origin. (*Note*: when squaring both sides of an equation it is possible to introduce new points unintentionally. This should always be taken into consideration. However, in this case we do not introduce new points. For example, $\left(-3, \frac{\pi}{3}\right)$ is the same point as $\left(3, \frac{4\pi}{3}\right)$.)

c.　Multiply both sides of the equation by $r$. This leads to $r^2 = 6r\cos\theta - 8r\sin\theta$. Next use the formulas

$$r^2 = x^2 + y^2, \quad x = r\cos\theta, \quad y = r\sin\theta.$$

This gives

$$
\begin{aligned}
r^2 &= 6(r\cos\theta) - 8(r\sin\theta) \\
x^2 + y^2 &= 6x - 8y.
\end{aligned}
$$

To put this equation into standard form, first move the variables from the right-hand side of the equation to the left-hand side, then complete the square.

$$
\begin{aligned}
x^2 + y^2 &= 6x - 8y \\
x^2 - 6x + y^2 + 8y &= 0 \\
\left(x^2 - 6x\right) + \left(y^2 + 8y\right) &= 0 \\
\left(x^2 - 6x + 9\right) + \left(y^2 + 8y + 16\right) &= 9 + 16 \\
(x - 3)^2 + (y + 4)^2 &= 25.
\end{aligned}
$$

This is the equation of a circle with center at $(3, -4)$ and radius 5. Notice that the circle passes through the origin since the center is 5 units away.

 **1.13**　Rewrite the equation $r = \sec\theta\tan\theta$ in rectangular coordinates and identify its graph.

We have now seen several examples of drawing graphs of curves defined by **polar equations**. A summary of some common curves is given in the tables below. In each equation, $a$ and $b$ are arbitrary constants.

| Name | Equation | Example |
|---|---|---|
| Line passing through the pole with slope tan $K$ | $\theta = K$ | |
| Circle | $r = a\cos\theta + b\sin\theta$ | |
| Spiral | $r = a + b\theta$ | |

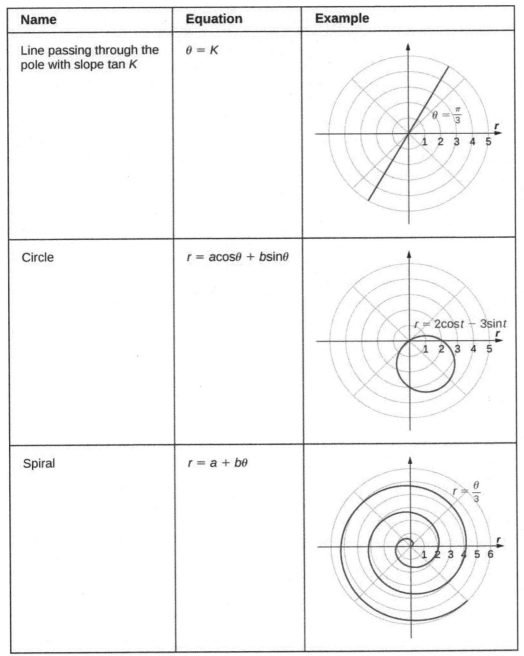

Figure 1.31

| Name | Equation | Example |
|------|----------|---------|
| Cardioid | $r = a(1 + \cos\theta)$<br>$r = a(1 - \cos\theta)$<br>$r = a(1 + \sin\theta)$<br>$r = a(1 - \sin\theta)$ | |
| Limaçon | $r = a\cos\theta + b$<br>$r = a\sin\theta + b$ | |
| Rose | $r = a\cos(b\theta)$<br>$r = a\sin(b\theta)$ | |

Figure 1.32

A **cardioid** is a special case of a **limaçon** (pronounced "lee-mah-son"), in which $a = b$ or $a = -b$. The **rose** is a very interesting curve. Notice that the graph of $r = 3 \sin 2\theta$ has four petals. However, the graph of $r = 3 \sin 3\theta$ has three petals as shown.

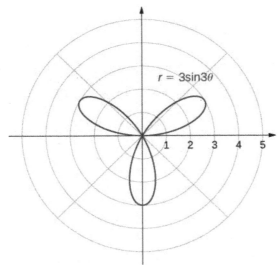

**Figure 1.33** Graph of $r = 3 \sin 3\theta$.

If the coefficient of $\theta$ is even, the graph has twice as many petals as the coefficient. If the coefficient of $\theta$ is odd, then the number of petals equals the coefficient. You are encouraged to explore why this happens. Even more interesting graphs emerge when the coefficient of $\theta$ is not an integer. For example, if it is rational, then the curve is closed; that is, it eventually ends where it started (**Figure 1.34**(a)). However, if the coefficient is irrational, then the curve never closes (**Figure 1.34**(b)). Although it may appear that the curve is closed, a closer examination reveals that the petals just above the positive $x$ axis are slightly thicker. This is because the petal does not quite match up with the starting point.

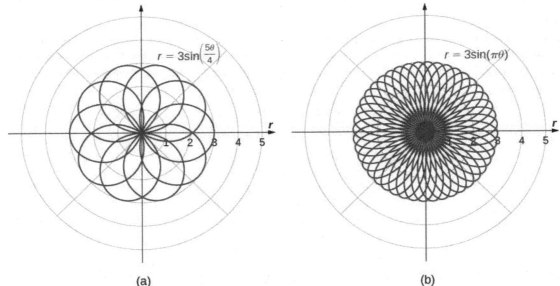

(a)                                                                 (b)

**Figure 1.34** Polar rose graphs of functions with (a) rational coefficient and (b) irrational coefficient. Note that the rose in part (b) would actually fill the entire circle if plotted in full.

Since the curve defined by the graph of $r = 3 \sin(\pi\theta)$ never closes, the curve depicted in **Figure 1.34**(b) is only a partial depiction. In fact, this is an example of a **space-filling curve**. A space-filling curve is one that in fact occupies a two-dimensional subset of the real plane. In this case the curve occupies the circle of radius 3 centered at the origin.

Example 1.14

## Chapter Opener: Describing a Spiral

Recall the chambered nautilus introduced in the chapter opener. This creature displays a spiral when half the outer shell is cut away. It is possible to describe a spiral using rectangular coordinates. **Figure 1.35** shows a spiral in rectangular coordinates. How can we describe this curve mathematically?

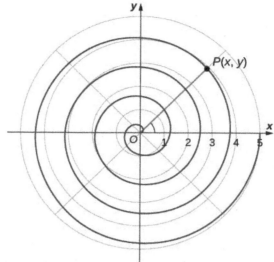

**Figure 1.35** How can we describe a spiral graph mathematically?

## Solution

As the point $P$ travels around the spiral in a counterclockwise direction, its distance $d$ from the origin increases. Assume that the distance $d$ is a constant multiple $k$ of the angle $\theta$ that the line segment $OP$ makes with the positive $x$-axis. Therefore $d(P, O) = k\theta$, where $O$ is the origin. Now use the distance formula and some trigonometry:

$$
\begin{aligned}
d(P, O) &= k\theta \\
\sqrt{(x-0)^2 + (y-0)^2} &= k\arctan\left(\frac{y}{x}\right) \\
\sqrt{x^2 + y^2} &= k\arctan\left(\frac{y}{x}\right) \\
\arctan\left(\frac{y}{x}\right) &= \frac{\sqrt{x^2 + y^2}}{k} \\
y &= x\tan\left(\frac{\sqrt{x^2 + y^2}}{k}\right).
\end{aligned}
$$

Although this equation describes the spiral, it is not possible to solve it directly for either $x$ or $y$. However, if we use polar coordinates, the equation becomes much simpler. In particular, $d(P, O) = r$, and $\theta$ is the second coordinate. Therefore the equation for the spiral becomes $r = k\theta$. Note that when $\theta = 0$ we also have $r = 0$, so the spiral emanates from the origin. We can remove this restriction by adding a constant to the equation. Then the equation for the spiral becomes $r = a + k\theta$ for arbitrary constants $a$ and $k$. This is referred to as an Archimedean spiral, after the Greek mathematician Archimedes.

Another type of spiral is the logarithmic spiral, described by the function $r = a \cdot b^{\theta}$. A graph of the function $r = 1.2\left(1.25^{\theta}\right)$ is given in **Figure 1.36**. This spiral describes the shell shape of the chambered nautilus.

**Figure 1.36** A logarithmic spiral is similar to the shape of the chambered nautilus shell. (credit: modification of work by Jitze Couperus, Flickr)

Suppose a curve is described in the polar coordinate system via the function $r = f(\theta)$. Since we have conversion formulas from polar to rectangular coordinates given by

$$x = r \cos \theta$$
$$y = r \sin \theta,$$

it is possible to rewrite these formulas using the function

$$x = f(\theta) \cos \theta$$
$$y = f(\theta) \sin \theta.$$

This step gives a parameterization of the curve in rectangular coordinates using $\theta$ as the parameter. For example, the spiral formula $r = a + b\theta$ from **Figure 1.31** becomes

$$x = (a + b\theta) \cos \theta$$
$$y = (a + b\theta) \sin \theta.$$

Letting $\theta$ range from $-\infty$ to $\infty$ generates the entire spiral.

## Symmetry in Polar Coordinates

When studying symmetry of functions in rectangular coordinates (i.e., in the form $y = f(x)$), we talk about symmetry with respect to the $y$-axis and symmetry with respect to the origin. In particular, if $f(-x) = f(x)$ for all $x$ in the domain of $f$, then $f$ is an even function and its graph is symmetric with respect to the $y$-axis. If $f(-x) = -f(x)$ for all $x$ in the domain of $f$, then $f$ is an odd function and its graph is symmetric with respect to the origin. By determining which types of symmetry a graph exhibits, we can learn more about the shape and appearance of the graph. Symmetry can also reveal other properties of the function that generates the graph. Symmetry in polar curves works in a similar fashion.

### Theorem 1.5: Symmetry in Polar Curves and Equations

Consider a curve generated by the function $r = f(\theta)$ in polar coordinates.

i. The curve is symmetric about the polar axis if for every point $(r, \theta)$ on the graph, the point $(r, -\theta)$ is also on the graph. Similarly, the equation $r = f(\theta)$ is unchanged by replacing $\theta$ with $-\theta$.

ii. The curve is symmetric about the pole if for every point $(r, \theta)$ on the graph, the point $(r, \pi + \theta)$ is also on the graph. Similarly, the equation $r = f(\theta)$ is unchanged when replacing $r$ with $-r$, or $\theta$ with $\pi + \theta$.

iii. The curve is symmetric about the vertical line $\theta = \frac{\pi}{2}$ if for every point $(r, \theta)$ on the graph, the point $(r, \pi - \theta)$ is also on the graph. Similarly, the equation $r = f(\theta)$ is unchanged when $\theta$ is replaced by $\pi - \theta$.

The following table shows examples of each type of symmetry.

| **Symmetry with respect to the polar axis:** For every point $(r, \theta)$ on the graph, there is also a point reflected directly across the horizontal (polar) axis. | |
|---|---|

| **Symmetry with respect to the pole:** For every point $(r, \theta)$ on the graph, there is also a point on the graph that is reflected through the pole as well. | |
|---|---|

| **Symmetry with respect to the vertical line $\theta = \frac{\pi}{2}$:** For every point $(r, \theta)$ on the graph, there is also a point reflected directly across the vertical axis. | |
|---|---|

## Example 1.15

### Using Symmetry to Graph a Polar Equation

Find the symmetry of the rose defined by the equation $r = 3 \sin(2\theta)$ and create a graph.

### Solution

Suppose the point $(r, \theta)$ is on the graph of $r = 3 \sin(2\theta)$.

i.  To test for symmetry about the polar axis, first try replacing $\theta$ with $-\theta$. This gives $r = 3 \sin(2(-\theta)) = -3 \sin(2\theta)$. Since this changes the original equation, this test is not satisfied. However, returning to the original equation and replacing $r$ with $-r$ and $\theta$ with $\pi - \theta$ yields

$$-r = 3 \sin(2(\pi - \theta))$$
$$-r = 3 \sin(2\pi - 2\theta)$$
$$-r = 3 \sin(-2\theta)$$
$$-r = -3 \sin 2\theta.$$

Multiplying both sides of this equation by $-1$ gives $r = 3 \sin 2\theta$, which is the original equation. This demonstrates that the graph is symmetric with respect to the polar axis.

ii.  To test for symmetry with respect to the pole, first replace $r$ with $-r$, which yields $-r = 3 \sin(2\theta)$. Multiplying both sides by $-1$ gives $r = -3 \sin(2\theta)$, which does not agree with the original equation. Therefore the equation does not pass the test for this symmetry. However, returning to the original equation and replacing $\theta$ with $\theta + \pi$ gives

$$\begin{aligned} r &= 3 \sin(2(\theta + \pi)) \\ &= 3 \sin(2\theta + 2\pi) \\ &= 3(\sin 2\theta \cos 2\pi + \cos 2\theta \sin 2\pi) \\ &= 3 \sin 2\theta. \end{aligned}$$

Since this agrees with the original equation, the graph is symmetric about the pole.

iii.  To test for symmetry with respect to the vertical line $\theta = \frac{\pi}{2}$, first replace both $r$ with $-r$ and $\theta$ with $-\theta$.

$$-r = 3 \sin(2(-\theta))$$
$$-r = 3 \sin(-2\theta)$$
$$-r = -3 \sin 2\theta.$$

Multiplying both sides of this equation by $-1$ gives $r = 3 \sin 2\theta$, which is the original equation. Therefore the graph is symmetric about the vertical line $\theta = \frac{\pi}{2}$.

This graph has symmetry with respect to the polar axis, the origin, and the vertical line going through the pole. To graph the function, tabulate values of $\theta$ between 0 and $\pi/2$ and then reflect the resulting graph.

| $\theta$ | $r$ |
|---|---|
| 0 | 0 |
| $\frac{\pi}{6}$ | $\frac{3\sqrt{3}}{2} \approx 2.6$ |
| $\frac{\pi}{4}$ | 3 |
| $\frac{\pi}{3}$ | $\frac{3\sqrt{3}}{2} \approx 2.6$ |
| $\frac{\pi}{2}$ | 0 |

This gives one petal of the rose, as shown in the following graph.

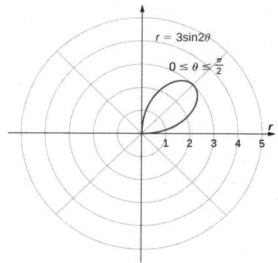

**Figure 1.37**  The graph of the equation between $\theta = 0$ and $\theta = \pi/2$.

Reflecting this image into the other three quadrants gives the entire graph as shown.

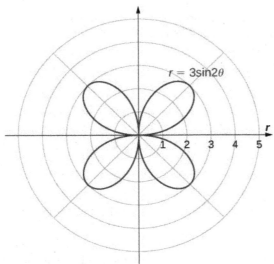

**Figure 1.38** The entire graph of the equation is called a four-petaled rose.

 **1.14** Determine the symmetry of the graph determined by the equation $r = 2\cos(3\theta)$ and create a graph.

# 1.3 EXERCISES

In the following exercises, plot the point whose polar coordinates are given by first constructing the angle $\theta$ and then marking off the distance $r$ along the ray.

125. $\left(3, \frac{\pi}{6}\right)$

126. $\left(-2, \frac{5\pi}{3}\right)$

127. $\left(0, \frac{7\pi}{6}\right)$

128. $\left(-4, \frac{3\pi}{4}\right)$

129. $\left(1, \frac{\pi}{4}\right)$

130. $\left(2, \frac{5\pi}{6}\right)$

131. $\left(1, \frac{\pi}{2}\right)$

For the following exercises, consider the polar graph below. Give two sets of polar coordinates for each point.

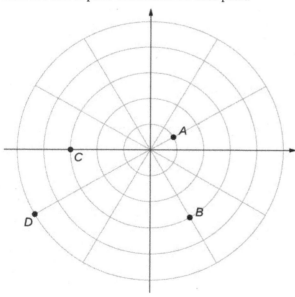

132. Coordinates of point $A$.

133. Coordinates of point $B$.

134. Coordinates of point $C$.

135. Coordinates of point $D$.

For the following exercises, the rectangular coordinates of a point are given. Find two sets of polar coordinates for the

point in $(0, 2\pi]$. Round to three decimal places.

136. $(2, 2)$

137. $(3, -4)$  $(3, -4)$

138. $(8, 15)$

139. $(-6, 8)$

140. $(4, 3)$

141. $\left(3, -\sqrt{3}\right)$

For the following exercises, find rectangular coordinates for the given point in polar coordinates.

142. $\left(2, \frac{5\pi}{4}\right)$

143. $\left(-2, \frac{\pi}{6}\right)$

144. $\left(5, \frac{\pi}{3}\right)$

145. $\left(1, \frac{7\pi}{6}\right)$

146. $\left(-3, \frac{3\pi}{4}\right)$

147. $\left(0, \frac{\pi}{2}\right)$

148. $(-4.5, 6.5)$

For the following exercises, determine whether the graphs of the polar equation are symmetric with respect to the $x$-axis, the $y$-axis, or the origin.

149. $r = 3\sin(2\theta)$

150. $r^2 = 9\cos\theta$

151. $r = \cos\left(\frac{\theta}{5}\right)$

152. $r = 2\sec\theta$

153. $r = 1 + \cos\theta$

For the following exercises, describe the graph of each polar equation. Confirm each description by converting into a rectangular equation.

154. $r = 3$

155. $\theta = \frac{\pi}{4}$

156. $r = \sec \theta$

157. $r = \csc \theta$

For the following exercises, convert the rectangular equation to polar form and sketch its graph.

158. $x^2 + y^2 = 16$

159. $x^2 - y^2 = 16$

160. $x = 8$

For the following exercises, convert the rectangular equation to polar form and sketch its graph.

161. $3x - y = 2$

162. $y^2 = 4x$

For the following exercises, convert the polar equation to rectangular form and sketch its graph.

163. $r = 4 \sin \theta$

164. $r = 6 \cos \theta$

165. $r = \theta$

166. $r = \cot \theta \csc \theta$

For the following exercises, sketch a graph of the polar equation and identify any symmetry.

167. $r = 1 + \sin \theta$

168. $r = 3 - 2 \cos \theta$

169. $r = 2 - 2 \sin \theta$

170. $r = 5 - 4 \sin \theta$

171. $r = 3 \cos(2\theta)$

172. $r = 3 \sin(2\theta)$

173. $r = 2 \cos(3\theta)$

174. $r = 3 \cos\left(\frac{\theta}{2}\right)$

175. $r^2 = 4 \cos(2\theta)$

176. $r^2 = 4 \sin \theta$

177. $r = 2\theta$

178. **[T]** The graph of $r = 2 \cos(2\theta)\sec(\theta)$. is called a *strophoid*. Use a graphing utility to sketch the graph, and, from the graph, determine the asymptote.

179. **[T]** Use a graphing utility and sketch the graph of $r = \dfrac{6}{2 \sin \theta - 3 \cos \theta}$.

180. **[T]** Use a graphing utility to graph $r = \dfrac{1}{1 - \cos \theta}$.

181. **[T]** Use technology to graph $r = e^{\sin(\theta)} - 2 \cos(4\theta)$.

182. **[T]** Use technology to plot $r = \sin\left(\frac{3\theta}{7}\right)$ (use the interval $0 \le \theta \le 14\pi$).

183. Without using technology, sketch the polar curve $\theta = \frac{2\pi}{3}$.

184. **[T]** Use a graphing utility to plot $r = \theta \sin \theta$ for $-\pi \le \theta \le \pi$.

185. **[T]** Use technology to plot $r = e^{-0.1\theta}$ for $-10 \le \theta \le 10$.

186. **[T]** There is a curve known as the "*Black Hole.*" Use technology to plot $r = e^{-0.01\theta}$ for $-100 \le \theta \le 100$.

187. **[T]** Use the results of the preceding two problems to explore the graphs of $r = e^{-0.001\theta}$ and $r = e^{-0.0001\theta}$ for $|\theta| > 100$.

# 1.4 | Area and Arc Length in Polar Coordinates

In the rectangular coordinate system, the definite integral provides a way to calculate the area under a curve. In particular, if we have a function $y = f(x)$ defined from $x = a$ to $x = b$ where $f(x) > 0$ on this interval, the area between the curve and the $x$-axis is given by $A = \int_a^b f(x)\, dx$. This fact, along with the formula for evaluating this integral, is summarized in the Fundamental Theorem of Calculus. Similarly, the arc length of this curve is given by $L = \int_a^b \sqrt{1 + (f'(x))^2}\, dx$. In this section, we study analogous formulas for area and arc length in the polar coordinate system.

## Areas of Regions Bounded by Polar Curves

We have studied the formulas for area under a curve defined in rectangular coordinates and parametrically defined curves. Now we turn our attention to deriving a formula for the area of a region bounded by a polar curve. Recall that the proof of the Fundamental Theorem of Calculus used the concept of a Riemann sum to approximate the area under a curve by using rectangles. For polar curves we use the Riemann sum again, but the rectangles are replaced by sectors of a circle.

Consider a curve defined by the function $r = f(\theta)$, where $\alpha \le \theta \le \beta$. Our first step is to partition the interval $[\alpha, \beta]$ into $n$ equal-width subintervals. The width of each subinterval is given by the formula $\Delta\theta = (\beta - \alpha)/n$, and the $i$th partition point $\theta_i$ is given by the formula $\theta_i = \alpha + i\Delta\theta$. Each partition point $\theta = \theta_i$ defines a line with slope $\tan\theta_i$ passing through the pole as shown in the following graph.

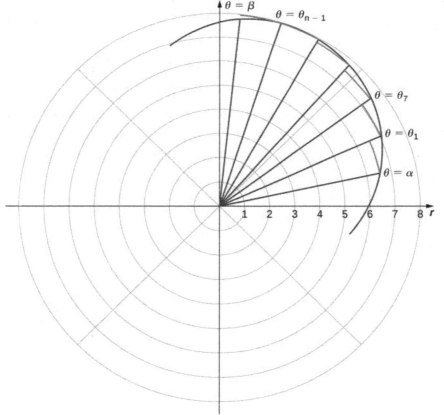

**Figure 1.39**   A partition of a typical curve in polar coordinates.

The line segments are connected by arcs of constant radius. This defines sectors whose areas can be calculated by using a geometric formula. The area of each sector is then used to approximate the area between successive line segments. We then sum the areas of the sectors to approximate the total area. This approach gives a Riemann sum approximation for the total area. The formula for the area of a sector of a circle is illustrated in the following figure.

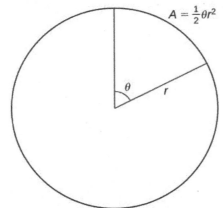

**Figure 1.40** The area of a sector of a circle is given by $A = \frac{1}{2}\theta r^2$.

Recall that the area of a circle is $A = \pi r^2$. When measuring angles in radians, 360 degrees is equal to $2\pi$ radians. Therefore a fraction of a circle can be measured by the central angle $\theta$. The fraction of the circle is given by $\frac{\theta}{2\pi}$, so the area of the sector is this fraction multiplied by the total area:

$$A = \left(\frac{\theta}{2\pi}\right)\pi r^2 = \frac{1}{2}\theta r^2.$$

Since the radius of a typical sector in **Figure 1.39** is given by $r_i = f(\theta_i)$, the area of the $i$th sector is given by

$$A_i = \frac{1}{2}(\Delta\theta)(f(\theta_i))^2.$$

Therefore a Riemann sum that approximates the area is given by

$$A_n = \sum_{i=1}^{n} A_i \approx \sum_{i=1}^{n} \frac{1}{2}(\Delta\theta)(f(\theta_i))^2.$$

We take the limit as $n \to \infty$ to get the exact area:

$$A = \lim_{n \to \infty} A_n = \frac{1}{2}\int_{\alpha}^{\beta}(f(\theta))^2\, d\theta.$$

This gives the following theorem.

**Theorem 1.6: Area of a Region Bounded by a Polar Curve**

Suppose $f$ is continuous and nonnegative on the interval $\alpha \le \theta \le \beta$ with $0 < \beta - \alpha \le 2\pi$. The area of the region bounded by the graph of $r = f(\theta)$ between the radial lines $\theta = \alpha$ and $\theta = \beta$ is

$$A = \frac{1}{2}\int_{\alpha}^{\beta}[f(\theta)]^2\, d\theta = \frac{1}{2}\int_{\alpha}^{\beta} r^2\, d\theta.$$

(1.9)

## Example 1.16

### Finding an Area of a Polar Region

Find the area of one petal of the rose defined by the equation $r = 3\sin(2\theta)$.

### Solution

The graph of $r = 3\sin(2\theta)$ follows.

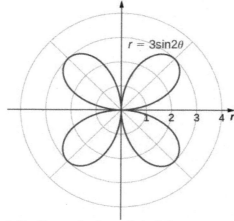

**Figure 1.41** The graph of $r = 3\sin(2\theta)$.

When $\theta = 0$ we have $r = 3\sin(2(0)) = 0$. The next value for which $r = 0$ is $\theta = \pi/2$. This can be seen by solving the equation $3\sin(2\theta) = 0$ for $\theta$. Therefore the values $\theta = 0$ to $\theta = \pi/2$ trace out the first petal of the rose. To find the area inside this petal, use **Equation 1.9** with $f(\theta) = 3\sin(2\theta)$, $\alpha = 0$, and $\beta = \pi/2$:

$$
\begin{aligned}
A &= \frac{1}{2}\int_{\alpha}^{\beta} [f(\theta)]^2 \, d\theta \\
&= \frac{1}{2}\int_{0}^{\pi/2} [3\sin(2\theta)]^2 \, d\theta \\
&= \frac{1}{2}\int_{0}^{\pi/2} 9\sin^2(2\theta) \, d\theta.
\end{aligned}
$$

To evaluate this integral, use the formula $\sin^2\alpha = (1 - \cos(2\alpha))/2$ with $\alpha = 2\theta$:

$$
\begin{aligned}
A \;&= \frac{1}{2}\int_{0}^{\pi/2} 9\sin^{2}(2\theta)\,d\theta \\
&= \frac{9}{2}\int_{0}^{\pi/2} \frac{(1-\cos(4\theta))}{2}\,d\theta \\
&= \frac{9}{4}\left(\int_{0}^{\pi/2} 1-\cos(4\theta)\,d\theta\right) \\
&= \frac{9}{4}\left(\theta - \frac{\sin(4\theta)}{4}\right)\Big|_{0}^{\pi/2} \\
&= \frac{9}{4}\left(\frac{\pi}{2} - \frac{\sin 2\pi}{4}\right) - \frac{9}{4}\left(0 - \frac{\sin 4(0)}{4}\right) \\
&= \frac{9\pi}{8}.
\end{aligned}
$$

 **1.15** Find the area inside the cardioid defined by the equation $r = 1 - \cos\theta$.

Example 1.16 involved finding the area inside one curve. We can also use **Area of a Region Bounded by a Polar Curve** to find the area between two polar curves. However, we often need to find the points of intersection of the curves and determine which function defines the outer curve or the inner curve between these two points.

## Example 1.17

### Finding the Area between Two Polar Curves

Find the area outside the cardioid $r = 2 + 2\sin\theta$ and inside the circle $r = 6\sin\theta$.

### Solution

First draw a graph containing both curves as shown.

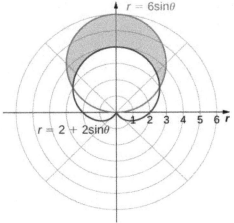

**Figure 1.42** The region between the curves $r = 2 + 2\sin\theta$ and $r = 6\sin\theta$.

To determine the limits of integration, first find the points of intersection by setting the two functions equal to each other and solving for $\theta$:

$$
\begin{aligned}
6 \sin \theta &= 2 + 2 \sin \theta \\
4 \sin \theta &= 2 \\
\sin \theta &= \tfrac{1}{2}.
\end{aligned}
$$

This gives the solutions $\theta = \frac{\pi}{6}$ and $\theta = \frac{5\pi}{6}$, which are the limits of integration. The circle $r = 3 \sin \theta$ is the red graph, which is the outer function, and the cardioid $r = 2 + 2 \sin \theta$ is the blue graph, which is the inner function. To calculate the area between the curves, start with the area inside the circle between $\theta = \frac{\pi}{6}$ and $\theta = \frac{5\pi}{6}$, then subtract the area inside the cardioid between $\theta = \frac{\pi}{6}$ and $\theta = \frac{5\pi}{6}$:

$$
\begin{aligned}
A &= \text{circle} - \text{cardioid} \\
&= \tfrac{1}{2} \int_{\pi/6}^{5\pi/6} [6 \sin \theta]^2 \, d\theta - \tfrac{1}{2} \int_{\pi/6}^{5\pi/6} [2 + 2 \sin \theta]^2 \, d\theta \\
&= \tfrac{1}{2} \int_{\pi/6}^{5\pi/6} 36 \sin^2 \theta \, d\theta - \tfrac{1}{2} \int_{\pi/6}^{5\pi/6} 4 + 8 \sin \theta + 4 \sin^2 \theta \, d\theta \\
&= 18 \int_{\pi/6}^{5\pi/6} \frac{1 - \cos(2\theta)}{2} d\theta - 2 \int_{\pi/6}^{5\pi/6} 1 + 2 \sin \theta + \frac{1 - \cos(2\theta)}{2} d\theta \\
&= 9 \left[ \theta - \frac{\sin(2\theta)}{2} \right]_{\pi/6}^{5\pi/6} - 2 \left[ \frac{3\theta}{2} - 2 \cos \theta - \frac{\sin(2\theta)}{4} \right]_{\pi/6}^{5\pi/6} \\
&= 9 \left( \frac{5\pi}{6} - \frac{\sin 2(5\pi/6)}{2} \right) - 9 \left( \frac{\pi}{6} - \frac{\sin 2(\pi/6)}{2} \right) \\
&\quad - \left( 3 \left( \frac{5\pi}{6} \right) - 4 \cos \frac{5\pi}{6} - \frac{\sin 2(5\pi/6)}{2} \right) + \left( 3 \left( \frac{\pi}{6} \right) - 4 \cos \frac{\pi}{6} - \frac{\sin 2(\pi/6)}{2} \right) \\
&= 4\pi.
\end{aligned}
$$

**1.16**　Find the area inside the circle $r = 4 \cos \theta$ and outside the circle $r = 2$.

In Example 1.17 we found the area inside the circle and outside the cardioid by first finding their intersection points. Notice that solving the equation directly for $\theta$ yielded two solutions: $\theta = \frac{\pi}{6}$ and $\theta = \frac{5\pi}{6}$. However, in the graph there are three intersection points. The third intersection point is the origin. The reason why this point did not show up as a solution is because the origin is on both graphs but for different values of $\theta$. For example, for the cardioid we get

$$
\begin{aligned}
2 + 2 \sin \theta &= 0 \\
\sin \theta &= -1,
\end{aligned}
$$

so the values for $\theta$ that solve this equation are $\theta = \frac{3\pi}{2} + 2n\pi$, where $n$ is any integer. For the circle we get

$$6 \sin \theta = 0.$$

The solutions to this equation are of the form $\theta = n\pi$ for any integer value of $n$. These two solution sets have no points in common. Regardless of this fact, the curves intersect at the origin. This case must always be taken into consideration.

# Arc Length in Polar Curves

Here we derive a formula for the arc length of a curve defined in polar coordinates.

In rectangular coordinates, the arc length of a parameterized curve $(x(t), y(t))$ for $a \le t \le b$ is given by

$$L = \int_a^b \sqrt{\left(\frac{dx}{dt}\right)^2 + \left(\frac{dy}{dt}\right)^2}\, dt.$$

In polar coordinates we define the curve by the equation $r = f(\theta)$, where $\alpha \le \theta \le \beta$. In order to adapt the arc length formula for a polar curve, we use the equations

$$x = r \cos \theta = f(\theta) \cos \theta \text{ and } y = r \sin \theta = f(\theta) \sin \theta,$$

and we replace the parameter $t$ by $\theta$. Then

$$\frac{dx}{d\theta} = f'(\theta) \cos \theta - f(\theta) \sin \theta$$

$$\frac{dy}{d\theta} = f'(\theta) \sin \theta + f(\theta) \cos \theta.$$

We replace $dt$ by $d\theta$, and the lower and upper limits of integration are $\alpha$ and $\beta$, respectively. Then the arc length formula becomes

$$
\begin{aligned}
L &= \int_a^b \sqrt{\left(\frac{dx}{dt}\right)^2 + \left(\frac{dy}{dt}\right)^2}\, dt \\
&= \int_\alpha^\beta \sqrt{\left(\frac{dx}{d\theta}\right)^2 + \left(\frac{dy}{d\theta}\right)^2}\, d\theta \\
&= \int_\alpha^\beta \sqrt{(f'(\theta) \cos \theta - f(\theta) \sin \theta)^2 + (f'(\theta) \sin \theta + f(\theta) \cos \theta)^2}\, d\theta \\
&= \int_\alpha^\beta \sqrt{(f'(\theta))^2 \left(\cos^2 \theta + \sin^2 \theta\right) + (f(\theta))^2 \left(\cos^2 \theta + \sin^2 \theta\right)}\, d\theta \\
&= \int_\alpha^\beta \sqrt{(f'(\theta))^2 + (f(\theta))^2}\, d\theta \\
&= \int_\alpha^\beta \sqrt{r^2 + \left(\frac{dr}{d\theta}\right)^2}\, d\theta.
\end{aligned}
$$

This gives us the following theorem.

---

**Theorem 1.7: Arc Length of a Curve Defined by a Polar Function**

Let $f$ be a function whose derivative is continuous on an interval $\alpha \le \theta \le \beta$. The length of the graph of $r = f(\theta)$ from $\theta = \alpha$ to $\theta = \beta$ is

$$L = \int_\alpha^\beta \sqrt{[f(\theta)]^2 + [f'(\theta)]^2}\, d\theta = \int_\alpha^\beta \sqrt{r^2 + \left(\frac{dr}{d\theta}\right)^2}\, d\theta. \qquad (1.10)$$

---

## Example 1.18

### Finding the Arc Length of a Polar Curve

Find the arc length of the cardioid $r = 2 + 2\cos\theta$.

**Solution**

When $\theta = 0$, $r = 2 + 2\cos 0 = 4$. Furthermore, as $\theta$ goes from $0$ to $2\pi$, the cardioid is traced out exactly once. Therefore these are the limits of integration. Using $f(\theta) = 2 + 2\cos\theta$, $\alpha = 0$, and $\beta = 2\pi$, **Equation 1.10** becomes

$$
\begin{aligned}
L &= \int_{\alpha}^{\beta} \sqrt{[f(\theta)]^2 + [f'(\theta)]^2} \, d\theta \\
&= \int_{0}^{2\pi} \sqrt{[2 + 2\cos\theta]^2 + [-2\sin\theta]^2} \, d\theta \\
&= \int_{0}^{2\pi} \sqrt{4 + 8\cos\theta + 4\cos^2\theta + 4\sin^2\theta} \, d\theta \\
&= \int_{0}^{2\pi} \sqrt{4 + 8\cos\theta + 4\left(\cos^2\theta + \sin^2\theta\right)} \, d\theta \\
&= \int_{0}^{2\pi} \sqrt{8 + 8\cos\theta} \, d\theta \\
&= 2\int_{0}^{2\pi} \sqrt{2 + 2\cos\theta} \, d\theta.
\end{aligned}
$$

Next, using the identity $\cos(2\alpha) = 2\cos^2\alpha - 1$, add 1 to both sides and multiply by 2. This gives $2 + 2\cos(2\alpha) = 4\cos^2\alpha$. Substituting $\alpha = \theta/2$ gives $2 + 2\cos\theta = 4\cos^2(\theta/2)$, so the integral becomes

$$
\begin{aligned}
L &= 2\int_{0}^{2\pi} \sqrt{2 + 2\cos\theta} \, d\theta \\
&= 2\int_{0}^{2\pi} \sqrt{4\cos^2\left(\frac{\theta}{2}\right)} \, d\theta \\
&= 2\int_{0}^{2\pi} 2\left|\cos\left(\frac{\theta}{2}\right)\right| \, d\theta.
\end{aligned}
$$

The absolute value is necessary because the cosine is negative for some values in its domain. To resolve this issue, change the limits from $0$ to $\pi$ and double the answer. This strategy works because cosine is positive between $0$ and $\frac{\pi}{2}$. Thus,

$$
\begin{aligned}
L &= 4\int_{0}^{2\pi} \left|\cos\left(\frac{\theta}{2}\right)\right| \, d\theta \\
&= 8\int_{0}^{\pi} \cos\left(\frac{\theta}{2}\right) \, d\theta \\
&= 8\left(2\sin\left(\frac{\theta}{2}\right)\right)\Big|_{0}^{\pi} \\
&= 16.
\end{aligned}
$$

 **1.17**    Find the total arc length of $r = 3\sin\theta$.

# 1.4 EXERCISES

For the following exercises, determine a definite integral that represents the area.

188. Region enclosed by $r = 4$

189. Region enclosed by $r = 3 \sin \theta$

190. Region in the first quadrant within the cardioid $r = 1 + \sin \theta$

191. Region enclosed by one petal of $r = 8 \sin(2\theta)$

192. Region enclosed by one petal of $r = \cos(3\theta)$

193. Region below the polar axis and enclosed by $r = 1 - \sin \theta$

194. Region in the first quadrant enclosed by $r = 2 - \cos \theta$

195. Region enclosed by the inner loop of $r = 2 - 3 \sin \theta$

196. Region enclosed by the inner loop of $r = 3 - 4 \cos \theta$

197. Region enclosed by $r = 1 - 2 \cos \theta$ and outside the inner loop

198. Region common to $r = 3 \sin \theta$ and $r = 2 - \sin \theta$

199. Region common to $r = 2$ and $r = 4 \cos \theta$

200. Region common to $r = 3 \cos \theta$ and $r = 3 \sin \theta$

For the following exercises, find the area of the described region.

201. Enclosed by $r = 6 \sin \theta$

202. Above the polar axis enclosed by $r = 2 + \sin \theta$

203. Below the polar axis and enclosed by $r = 2 - \cos \theta$

204. Enclosed by one petal of $r = 4 \cos(3\theta)$

205. Enclosed by one petal of $r = 3 \cos(2\theta)$

206. Enclosed by $r = 1 + \sin \theta$

207. Enclosed by the inner loop of $r = 3 + 6 \cos \theta$

208. Enclosed by $r = 2 + 4 \cos \theta$ and outside the inner loop

209. Common interior of $r = 4 \sin(2\theta)$ and $r = 2$

210. Common interior of $r = 3 - 2 \sin \theta$ and $r = -3 + 2 \sin \theta$

211. Common interior of $r = 6 \sin \theta$ and $r = 3$

212. Inside $r = 1 + \cos \theta$ and outside $r = \cos \theta$

213. Common interior of $r = 2 + 2 \cos \theta$ and $r = 2 \sin \theta$

For the following exercises, find a definite integral that represents the arc length.

214. $r = 4 \cos \theta$ on the interval $0 \le \theta \le \frac{\pi}{2}$

215. $r = 1 + \sin \theta$ on the interval $0 \le \theta \le 2\pi$

216. $r = 2 \sec \theta$ on the interval $0 \le \theta \le \frac{\pi}{3}$

217. $r = e^{\theta}$ on the interval $0 \le \theta \le 1$

For the following exercises, find the length of the curve over the given interval.

218. $r = 6$ on the interval $0 \le \theta \le \frac{\pi}{2}$

219. $r = e^{3\theta}$ on the interval $0 \le \theta \le 2$

220. $r = 6 \cos \theta$ on the interval $0 \le \theta \le \frac{\pi}{2}$

221. $r = 8 + 8 \cos \theta$ on the interval $0 \le \theta \le \pi$

222. $r = 1 - \sin \theta$ on the interval $0 \le \theta \le 2\pi$

For the following exercises, use the integration capabilities of a calculator to approximate the length of the curve.

223. [T] $r = 3\theta$ on the interval $0 \le \theta \le \frac{\pi}{2}$

224. [T] $r = \frac{2}{\theta}$ on the interval $\pi \le \theta \le 2\pi$

225. [T] $r = \sin^2\left(\frac{\theta}{2}\right)$ on the interval $0 \le \theta \le \pi$

226. [T] $r = 2\theta^2$ on the interval $0 \le \theta \le \pi$

227. [T] $r = \sin(3 \cos \theta)$ on the interval $0 \le \theta \le \pi$

For the following exercises, use the familiar formula from

geometry to find the area of the region described and then confirm by using the definite integral.

**228.** $r = 3 \sin \theta$ on the interval $0 \leq \theta \leq \pi$

**229.** $r = \sin \theta + \cos \theta$ on the interval $0 \leq \theta \leq \pi$

**230.** $r = 6 \sin \theta + 8 \cos \theta$ on the interval $0 \leq \theta \leq \pi$

For the following exercises, use the familiar formula from geometry to find the length of the curve and then confirm using the definite integral.

**231.** $r = 3 \sin \theta$ on the interval $0 \leq \theta \leq \pi$

**232.** $r = \sin \theta + \cos \theta$ on the interval $0 \leq \theta \leq \pi$

**233.** $r = 6 \sin \theta + 8 \cos \theta$ on the interval $0 \leq \theta \leq \pi$

**234.** Verify that if $y = r \sin \theta = f(\theta) \sin \theta$ then $\frac{dy}{d\theta} = f'(\theta) \sin \theta + f(\theta) \cos \theta.$

For the following exercises, find the slope of a tangent line to a polar curve $r = f(\theta)$. Let $x = r \cos \theta = f(\theta) \cos \theta$ and $y = r \sin \theta = f(\theta) \sin \theta$, so the polar equation $r = f(\theta)$ is now written in parametric form.

**235.** Use the definition of the derivative $\frac{dy}{dx} = \frac{dy/d\theta}{dx/d\theta}$ and the product rule to derive the derivative of a polar equation.

**236.** $r = 1 - \sin \theta$; $\left( \frac{1}{2}, \frac{\pi}{6} \right)$

**237.** $r = 4 \cos \theta$; $\left( 2, \frac{\pi}{3} \right)$

**238.** $r = 8 \sin \theta$; $\left( 4, \frac{5\pi}{6} \right)$

**239.** $r = 4 + \sin \theta$; $\left( 3, \frac{3\pi}{2} \right)$

**240.** $r = 6 + 3 \cos \theta$; $(3, \pi)$

**241.** $r = 4 \cos(2\theta)$; tips of the leaves

**242.** $r = 2 \sin(3\theta)$; tips of the leaves

**243.** $r = 2\theta$; $\left( \frac{\pi}{2}, \frac{\pi}{4} \right)$

**244.** Find the points on the interval $-\pi \leq \theta \leq \pi$ at which the cardioid $r = 1 - \cos \theta$ has a vertical or horizontal tangent line.

**245.** For the cardioid $r = 1 + \sin \theta$, find the slope of the tangent line when $\theta = \frac{\pi}{3}$.

For the following exercises, find the slope of the tangent line to the given polar curve at the point given by the value of $\theta$.

**246.** $r = 3 \cos \theta$, $\theta = \frac{\pi}{3}$

**247.** $r = \theta$, $\theta = \frac{\pi}{2}$

**248.** $r = \ln \theta$, $\theta = e$

**249.** **[T]** Use technology: $r = 2 + 4 \cos \theta$ at $\theta = \frac{\pi}{6}$

For the following exercises, find the points at which the following polar curves have a horizontal or vertical tangent line.

**250.** $r = 4 \cos \theta$

**251.** $r^2 = 4 \cos(2\theta)$

**252.** $r = 2 \sin(2\theta)$

**253.** The cardioid $r = 1 + \sin \theta$

**254.** Show that the curve $r = \sin \theta \tan \theta$ (called a *cissoid of Diocles*) has the line $x = 1$ as a vertical asymptote.

# 1.5 | Conic Sections

## Learning Objectives

**1.5.1** Identify the equation of a parabola in standard form with given focus and directrix.

**1.5.2** Identify the equation of an ellipse in standard form with given foci.

**1.5.3** Identify the equation of a hyperbola in standard form with given foci.

**1.5.4** Recognize a parabola, ellipse, or hyperbola from its eccentricity value.

**1.5.5** Write the polar equation of a conic section with eccentricity $e$.

**1.5.6** Identify when a general equation of degree two is a parabola, ellipse, or hyperbola.

Conic sections have been studied since the time of the ancient Greeks, and were considered to be an important mathematical concept. As early as 320 BCE, such Greek mathematicians as Menaechmus, Appollonius, and Archimedes were fascinated by these curves. Appollonius wrote an entire eight-volume treatise on conic sections in which he was, for example, able to derive a specific method for identifying a conic section through the use of geometry. Since then, important applications of conic sections have arisen (for example, in astronomy), and the properties of conic sections are used in radio telescopes, satellite dish receivers, and even architecture. In this section we discuss the three basic conic sections, some of their properties, and their equations.

Conic sections get their name because they can be generated by intersecting a plane with a cone. A cone has two identically shaped parts called **nappes**. One nappe is what most people mean by "cone," having the shape of a party hat. A right circular cone can be generated by revolving a line passing through the origin around the *y*-axis as shown.

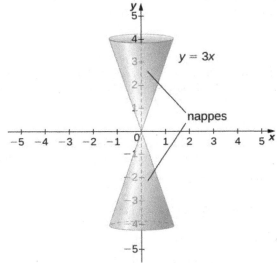

**Figure 1.43** A cone generated by revolving the line $y = 3x$ around the $y$-axis.

Conic sections are generated by the intersection of a plane with a cone (**Figure 1.44**). If the plane is parallel to the axis of revolution (the *y*-axis), then the **conic section** is a hyperbola. If the plane is parallel to the generating line, the conic section is a parabola. If the plane is perpendicular to the axis of revolution, the conic section is a circle. If the plane intersects one nappe at an angle to the axis (other than $90°$), then the conic section is an ellipse.

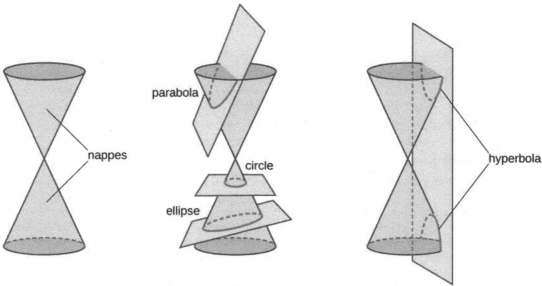

**Figure 1.44** The four conic sections. Each conic is determined by the angle the plane makes with the axis of the cone.

## Parabolas

A parabola is generated when a plane intersects a cone parallel to the generating line. In this case, the plane intersects only one of the nappes. A parabola can also be defined in terms of distances.

---
### Definition

A parabola is the set of all points whose distance from a fixed point, called the **focus**, is equal to the distance from a fixed line, called the **directrix**. The point halfway between the focus and the directrix is called the **vertex** of the parabola.

---

A graph of a typical parabola appears in **Figure 1.45**. Using this diagram in conjunction with the distance formula, we can derive an equation for a parabola. Recall the distance formula: Given point $P$ with coordinates $(x_1, y_1)$ and point $Q$ with coordinates $(x_2, y_2),$ the distance between them is given by the formula

$$d(P, Q) = \sqrt{(x_2 - x_1)^2 + (y_2 - y_1)^2}.$$

Then from the definition of a parabola and **Figure 1.45**, we get

$$d(F, P) = d(P, Q)$$
$$\sqrt{(0 - x)^2 + (p - y)^2} = \sqrt{(x - x)^2 + (-p - y)^2}.$$

Squaring both sides and simplifying yields

$$x^2 + (p - y)^2 = 0^2 + (-p - y)^2$$
$$x^2 + p^2 - 2py + y^2 = p^2 + 2py + y^2$$
$$x^2 - 2py = 2py$$
$$x^2 = 4py.$$

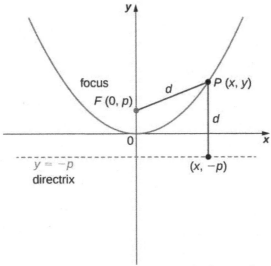

**Figure 1.45** A typical parabola in which the distance from the focus to the vertex is represented by the variable $p$.

Now suppose we want to relocate the vertex. We use the variables $(h, k)$ to denote the coordinates of the vertex. Then if the focus is directly above the vertex, it has coordinates $(h, k + p)$ and the directrix has the equation $y = k - p$. Going through the same derivation yields the formula $(x - h)^2 = 4p(y - k)$. Solving this equation for $y$ leads to the following theorem.

### Theorem 1.8: Equations for Parabolas

Given a parabola opening upward with vertex located at $(h, k)$ and focus located at $(h, k + p)$, where $p$ is a constant, the equation for the parabola is given by

$$y = \frac{1}{4p}(x - h)^2 + k. \tag{1.11}$$

This is the **standard form** of a parabola.

We can also study the cases when the parabola opens down or to the left or the right. The equation for each of these cases can also be written in standard form as shown in the following graphs.

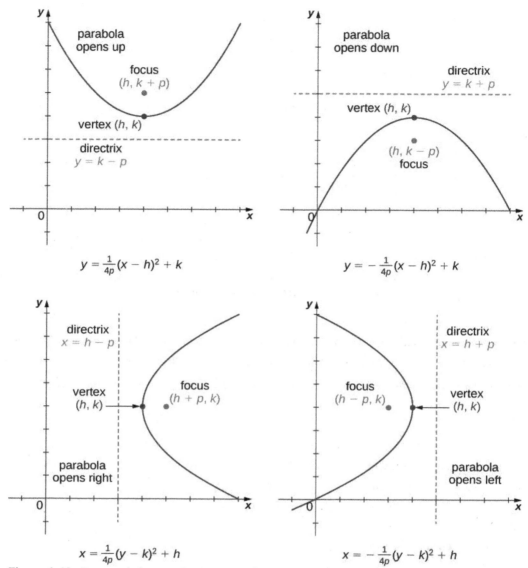

**Figure 1.46** Four parabolas, opening in various directions, along with their equations in standard form.

In addition, the equation of a parabola can be written in the **general form**, though in this form the values of $h$, $k$, and $p$ are not immediately recognizable. The general form of a parabola is written as

$$ax^2 + bx + cy + d = 0 \quad \text{or} \quad ay^2 + bx + cy + d = 0.$$

The first equation represents a parabola that opens either up or down. The second equation represents a parabola that opens either to the left or to the right. To put the equation into standard form, use the method of completing the square.

### Example 1.19

#### Converting the Equation of a Parabola from General into Standard Form

Put the equation $x^2 - 4x - 8y + 12 = 0$ into standard form and graph the resulting parabola.

## Solution

Since $y$ is not squared in this equation, we know that the parabola opens either upward or downward. Therefore we need to solve this equation for $y$, which will put the equation into standard form. To do that, first add $8y$ to both sides of the equation:

$$8y = x^2 - 4x + 12.$$

The next step is to complete the square on the right-hand side. Start by grouping the first two terms on the right-hand side using parentheses:

$$8y = \left(x^2 - 4x\right) + 12.$$

Next determine the constant that, when added inside the parentheses, makes the quantity inside the parentheses a perfect square trinomial. To do this, take half the coefficient of $x$ and square it. This gives $\left(\frac{-4}{2}\right)^2 = 4$. Add 4 inside the parentheses and subtract 4 outside the parentheses, so the value of the equation is not changed:

$$8y = \left(x^2 - 4x + 4\right) + 12 - 4.$$

Now combine like terms and factor the quantity inside the parentheses:

$$8y = (x - 2)^2 + 8.$$

Finally, divide by 8:

$$y = \frac{1}{8}(x - 2)^2 + 1.$$

This equation is now in standard form. Comparing this to **Equation 1.11** gives $h = 2$, $\quad k = 1$, $\quad$ and $\quad p = 2$. The parabola opens up, with vertex at $(2, 1)$, focus at $(2, 3)$, and directrix $y = -1$. The graph of this parabola appears as follows.

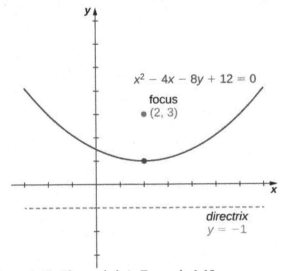

**Figure 1.47** The parabola in **Example 1.19**.

 **1.18** Put the equation $2y^2 - x + 12y + 16 = 0$ into standard form and graph the resulting parabola.

The axis of symmetry of a vertical (opening up or down) parabola is a vertical line passing through the vertex. The parabola has an interesting reflective property. Suppose we have a satellite dish with a parabolic cross section. If a beam of electromagnetic waves, such as light or radio waves, comes into the dish in a straight line from a satellite (parallel to the axis of symmetry), then the waves reflect off the dish and collect at the focus of the parabola as shown.

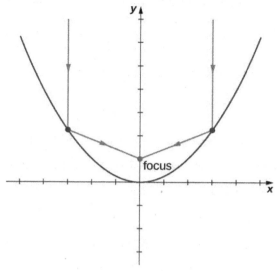

Consider a parabolic dish designed to collect signals from a satellite in space. The dish is aimed directly at the satellite, and a receiver is located at the focus of the parabola. Radio waves coming in from the satellite are reflected off the surface of the parabola to the receiver, which collects and decodes the digital signals. This allows a small receiver to gather signals from a wide angle of sky. Flashlights and headlights in a car work on the same principle, but in reverse: the source of the light (that is, the light bulb) is located at the focus and the reflecting surface on the parabolic mirror focuses the beam straight ahead. This allows a small light bulb to illuminate a wide angle of space in front of the flashlight or car.

## Ellipses

An ellipse can also be defined in terms of distances. In the case of an ellipse, there are two foci (plural of focus), and two directrices (plural of directrix). We look at the directrices in more detail later in this section.

**Definition**

An *ellipse* is the set of all points for which the sum of their distances from two fixed points (the foci) is constant.

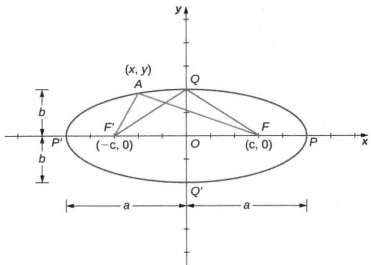

**Figure 1.48** A typical ellipse in which the sum of the distances from any point on the ellipse to the foci is constant.

A graph of a typical ellipse is shown in **Figure 1.48**. In this figure the foci are labeled as $F$ and $F'$. Both are the same fixed distance from the origin, and this distance is represented by the variable $c$. Therefore the coordinates of $F$ are $(c, 0)$ and the coordinates of $F'$ are $(-c, 0)$. The points $P$ and $P'$ are located at the ends of the **major axis** of the ellipse, and have coordinates $(a, 0)$ and $(-a, 0)$, respectively. The major axis is always the longest distance across the ellipse, and can be horizontal or vertical. Thus, the length of the major axis in this ellipse is $2a$. Furthermore, $P$ and $P'$ are called the vertices of the ellipse. The points $Q$ and $Q'$ are located at the ends of the **minor axis** of the ellipse, and have coordinates $(0, b)$ and $(0, -b)$, respectively. The minor axis is the shortest distance across the ellipse. The minor axis is perpendicular to the major axis.

According to the definition of the ellipse, we can choose any point on the ellipse and the sum of the distances from this point to the two foci is constant. Suppose we choose the point $P$. Since the coordinates of point $P$ are $(a, 0)$, the sum of the distances is

$$d(P, F) + d(P, F') = (a - c) + (a + c) = 2a.$$

Therefore the sum of the distances from an arbitrary point $A$ with coordinates $(x, y)$ is also equal to $2a$. Using the distance formula, we get

$$d(A, F) + d(A, F') = 2a$$
$$\sqrt{(x - c)^2 + y^2} + \sqrt{(x + c)^2 + y^2} = 2a.$$

Subtract the second radical from both sides and square both sides:

$$\sqrt{(x - c)^2 + y^2} = 2a - \sqrt{(x + c)^2 + y^2}$$
$$(x - c)^2 + y^2 = 4a^2 - 4a\sqrt{(x + c)^2 + y^2} + (x + c)^2 + y^2$$
$$x^2 - 2cx + c^2 + y^2 = 4a^2 - 4a\sqrt{(x + c)^2 + y^2} + x^2 + 2cx + c^2 + y^2$$
$$-2cx = 4a^2 - 4a\sqrt{(x + c)^2 + y^2} + 2cx.$$

Now isolate the radical on the right-hand side and square again:

$$-2cx = 4a^2 - 4a\sqrt{(x+c)^2 + y^2} + 2cx$$

$$4a\sqrt{(x+c)^2 + y^2} = 4a^2 + 4cx$$

$$\sqrt{(x+c)^2 + y^2} = a + \frac{cx}{a}$$

$$(x+c)^2 + y^2 = a^2 + 2cx + \frac{c^2 x^2}{a^2}$$

$$x^2 + 2cx + c^2 + y^2 = a^2 + 2cx + \frac{c^2 x^2}{a^2}$$

$$x^2 + c^2 + y^2 = a^2 + \frac{c^2 x^2}{a^2}.$$

Isolate the variables on the left-hand side of the equation and the constants on the right-hand side:

$$x^2 - \frac{c^2 x^2}{a^2} + y^2 = a^2 - c^2$$

$$\frac{(a^2 - c^2)x^2}{a^2} + y^2 = a^2 - c^2.$$

Divide both sides by $a^2 - c^2$. This gives the equation

$$\frac{x^2}{a^2} + \frac{y^2}{a^2 - c^2} = 1.$$

If we refer back to **Figure 1.48**, then the length of each of the two green line segments is equal to $a$. This is true because the sum of the distances from the point $Q$ to the foci $F$ and $F'$ is equal to $2a$, and the lengths of these two line segments are equal. This line segment forms a right triangle with hypotenuse length $a$ and leg lengths $b$ and $c$. From the Pythagorean theorem, $a^2 + b^2 = c^2$ and $b^2 = a^2 - c^2$. Therefore the equation of the ellipse becomes

$$\frac{x^2}{a^2} + \frac{y^2}{b^2} = 1.$$

Finally, if the center of the ellipse is moved from the origin to a point $(h, k)$, we have the following standard form of an ellipse.

## Theorem 1.9: Equation of an Ellipse in Standard Form

Consider the ellipse with center $(h, k)$, a horizontal major axis with length $2a$, and a vertical minor axis with length $2b$. Then the equation of this ellipse in standard form is

$$\frac{(x-h)^2}{a^2} + \frac{(y-k)^2}{b^2} = 1 \tag{1.12}$$

and the foci are located at $(h \pm c, k)$, where $c^2 = a^2 - b^2$. The equations of the directrices are $x = h \pm \frac{a^2}{c}$.

If the major axis is vertical, then the equation of the ellipse becomes

$$\frac{(x-h)^2}{b^2} + \frac{(y-k)^2}{a^2} = 1 \tag{1.13}$$

and the foci are located at $(h, k \pm c)$, where $c^2 = a^2 - b^2$. The equations of the directrices in this case are $y = k \pm \frac{a^2}{c}$.

If the major axis is horizontal, then the ellipse is called horizontal, and if the major axis is vertical, then the ellipse is called vertical. The equation of an ellipse is in general form if it is in the form $Ax^2 + By^2 + Cx + Dy + E = 0$, where $A$ and $B$ are either both positive or both negative. To convert the equation from general to standard form, use the method of completing the square.

## Example 1.20

### Finding the Standard Form of an Ellipse

Put the equation $9x^2 + 4y^2 - 36x + 24y + 36 = 0$ into standard form and graph the resulting ellipse.

#### Solution

First subtract 36 from both sides of the equation:

$$9x^2 + 4y^2 - 36x + 24y = -36.$$

Next group the $x$ terms together and the $y$ terms together, and factor out the common factor:

$$\left(9x^2 - 36x\right) + \left(4y^2 + 24y\right) = -36$$
$$9\left(x^2 - 4x\right) + 4\left(y^2 + 6y\right) = -36.$$

We need to determine the constant that, when added inside each set of parentheses, results in a perfect square. In the first set of parentheses, take half the coefficient of $x$ and square it. This gives $\left(\frac{-4}{2}\right)^2 = 4$. In the second set of parentheses, take half the coefficient of $y$ and square it. This gives $\left(\frac{6}{2}\right)^2 = 9$. Add these inside each pair of parentheses. Since the first set of parentheses has a 9 in front, we are actually adding 36 to the left-hand side. Similarly, we are adding 36 to the second set as well. Therefore the equation becomes

$$9\left(x^2 - 4x + 4\right) + 4\left(y^2 + 6y + 9\right) = -36 + 36 + 36$$
$$9\left(x^2 - 4x + 4\right) + 4\left(y^2 + 6y + 9\right) = 36.$$

Now factor both sets of parentheses and divide by 36:

$$9(x - 2)^2 + 4(y + 3)^2 = 36$$
$$\frac{9(x - 2)^2}{36} + \frac{4(y + 3)^2}{36} = 1$$
$$\frac{(x - 2)^2}{4} + \frac{(y + 3)^2}{9} = 1.$$

The equation is now in standard form. Comparing this to **Equation 1.14** gives $h = 2$, $k = -3$, $a = 3$, and $b = 2$. This is a vertical ellipse with center at $(2, -3)$, major axis 6, and minor axis 4. The graph of this ellipse appears as follows.

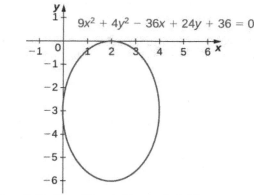

Figure 1.49   The ellipse in Example 1.20.

**1.19**   Put the equation $9x^2 + 16y^2 + 18x - 64y - 71 = 0$ into standard form and graph the resulting ellipse.

According to Kepler's first law of planetary motion, the orbit of a planet around the Sun is an ellipse with the Sun at one of the foci as shown in Figure 1.50(a). Because Earth's orbit is an ellipse, the distance from the Sun varies throughout the year. A commonly held misconception is that Earth is closer to the Sun in the summer. In fact, in summer for the northern hemisphere, Earth is farther from the Sun than during winter. The difference in season is caused by the tilt of Earth's axis in the orbital plane. Comets that orbit the Sun, such as Halley's Comet, also have elliptical orbits, as do moons orbiting the planets and satellites orbiting Earth.

Ellipses also have interesting reflective properties: A light ray emanating from one focus passes through the other focus after mirror reflection in the ellipse. The same thing occurs with a sound wave as well. The National Statuary Hall in the U.S. Capitol in Washington, DC, is a famous room in an elliptical shape as shown in Figure 1.50(b). This hall served as the meeting place for the U.S. House of Representatives for almost fifty years. The location of the two foci of this semi-elliptical room are clearly identified by marks on the floor, and even if the room is full of visitors, when two people stand on these spots and speak to each other, they can hear each other much more clearly than they can hear someone standing close by. Legend has it that John Quincy Adams had his desk located on one of the foci and was able to eavesdrop on everyone else in the House without ever needing to stand. Although this makes a good story, it is unlikely to be true, because the original ceiling produced so many echoes that the entire room had to be hung with carpets to dampen the noise. The ceiling was rebuilt in 1902 and only then did the now-famous whispering effect emerge. Another famous whispering gallery—the site of many marriage proposals—is in Grand Central Station in New York City.

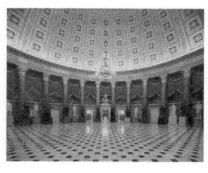

(a)                                                                                               (b)

Figure 1.50   (a) Earth's orbit around the Sun is an ellipse with the Sun at one focus. (b) Statuary Hall in the U.S. Capitol is a whispering gallery with an elliptical cross section.

# Hyperbolas

A hyperbola can also be defined in terms of distances. In the case of a hyperbola, there are two foci and two directrices. Hyperbolas also have two asymptotes.

### Definition

A hyperbola is the set of all points where the difference between their distances from two fixed points (the foci) is constant.

A graph of a typical hyperbola appears as follows.

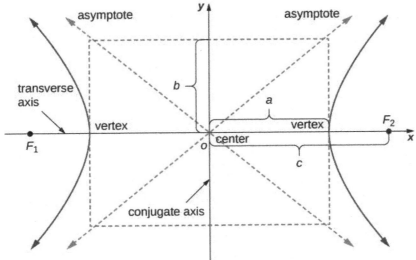

**Figure 1.51** A typical hyperbola in which the difference of the distances from any point on the ellipse to the foci is constant. The transverse axis is also called the major axis, and the conjugate axis is also called the minor axis.

The derivation of the equation of a hyperbola in standard form is virtually identical to that of an ellipse. One slight hitch lies in the definition: The difference between two numbers is always positive. Let $P$ be a point on the hyperbola with coordinates $(x, y)$. Then the definition of the hyperbola gives $|d(P, F_1) - d(P, F_2)| = $ constant. To simplify the derivation, assume that $P$ is on the right branch of the hyperbola, so the absolute value bars drop. If it is on the left branch, then the subtraction is reversed. The vertex of the right branch has coordinates $(a, 0)$, so

$$d(P, F_1) - d(P, F_2) = (c + a) - (c - a) = 2a.$$

This equation is therefore true for any point on the hyperbola. Returning to the coordinates $(x, y)$ for $P$:

$$d(P, F_1) - d(P, F_2) = 2a$$
$$\sqrt{(x + c)^2 + y^2} - \sqrt{(x - c)^2 + y^2} = 2a.$$

Add the second radical from both sides and square both sides:

$$\sqrt{(x - c)^2 + y^2} = 2a + \sqrt{(x + c)^2 + y^2}$$
$$(x - c)^2 + y^2 = 4a^2 + 4a\sqrt{(x + c)^2 + y^2} + (x + c)^2 + y^2$$
$$x^2 - 2cx + c^2 + y^2 = 4a^2 + 4a\sqrt{(x + c)^2 + y^2} + x^2 + 2cx + c^2 + y^2$$
$$-2cx = 4a^2 + 4a\sqrt{(x + c)^2 + y^2} + 2cx.$$

Now isolate the radical on the right-hand side and square again:

$$
\begin{aligned}
-2cx &= 4a^2 + 4a\sqrt{(x+c)^2 + y^2} + 2cx \\
4a\sqrt{(x+c)^2 + y^2} &= -4a^2 - 4cx \\
\sqrt{(x+c)^2 + y^2} &= -a - \frac{cx}{a} \\
(x+c)^2 + y^2 &= a^2 + 2cx + \frac{c^2 x^2}{a^2} \\
x^2 + 2cx + c^2 + y^2 &= a^2 + 2cx + \frac{c^2 x^2}{a^2} \\
x^2 + c^2 + y^2 &= a^2 + \frac{c^2 x^2}{a^2}.
\end{aligned}
$$

Isolate the variables on the left-hand side of the equation and the constants on the right-hand side:

$$
\begin{aligned}
x^2 - \frac{c^2 x^2}{a^2} + y^2 &= a^2 - c^2 \\
\frac{(a^2 - c^2)x^2}{a^2} + y^2 &= a^2 - c^2.
\end{aligned}
$$

Finally, divide both sides by $a^2 - c^2$. This gives the equation

$$
\frac{x^2}{a^2} + \frac{y^2}{a^2 - c^2} = 1.
$$

We now define $b$ so that $b^2 = c^2 - a^2$. This is possible because $c > a$. Therefore the equation of the ellipse becomes

$$
\frac{x^2}{a^2} - \frac{y^2}{b^2} = 1.
$$

Finally, if the center of the hyperbola is moved from the origin to the point $(h, k)$, we have the following standard form of a hyperbola.

---

### Theorem 1.10: Equation of a Hyperbola in Standard Form

Consider the hyperbola with center $(h, k)$, a horizontal major axis, and a vertical minor axis. Then the equation of this ellipse is

$$
\frac{(x-h)^2}{a^2} - \frac{(y-k)^2}{b^2} = 1 \tag{1.14}
$$

and the foci are located at $(h \pm c, k)$, where $c^2 = a^2 + b^2$. The equations of the asymptotes are given by $y = k \pm \frac{b}{a}(x - h)$. The equations of the directrices are

$$
x = k \pm \frac{a^2}{\sqrt{a^2 + b^2}} = h \pm \frac{a^2}{c}.
$$

If the major axis is vertical, then the equation of the hyperbola becomes

$$
\frac{(y-k)^2}{a^2} - \frac{(x-h)^2}{b^2} = 1 \tag{1.15}
$$

and the foci are located at $(h, k \pm c)$, where $c^2 = a^2 + b^2$. The equations of the asymptotes are given by $y = k \pm \frac{a}{b}(x - h)$. The equations of the directrices are

$$y = k \pm \frac{a^2}{\sqrt{a^2 + b^2}} = k \pm \frac{a^2}{c}.$$

If the major axis (transverse axis) is horizontal, then the hyperbola is called horizontal, and if the major axis is vertical then the hyperbola is called vertical. The equation of a hyperbola is in general form if it is in the form $Ax^2 + By^2 + Cx + Dy + E = 0$, where $A$ and $B$ have opposite signs. In order to convert the equation from general to standard form, use the method of completing the square.

## Example 1.21

### Finding the Standard Form of a Hyperbola

Put the equation $9x^2 - 16y^2 + 36x + 32y - 124 = 0$ into standard form and graph the resulting hyperbola. What are the equations of the asymptotes?

**Solution**

First add 124 to both sides of the equation:

$$9x^2 - 16y^2 + 36x + 32y = 124.$$

Next group the $x$ terms together and the $y$ terms together, then factor out the common factors:

$$\left(9x^2 + 36x\right) - \left(16y^2 - 32y\right) = 124$$
$$9\left(x^2 + 4x\right) - 16\left(y^2 - 2y\right) = 124.$$

We need to determine the constant that, when added inside each set of parentheses, results in a perfect square. In the first set of parentheses, take half the coefficient of $x$ and square it. This gives $\left(\frac{4}{2}\right)^2 = 4$. In the second set of parentheses, take half the coefficient of $y$ and square it. This gives $\left(\frac{-2}{2}\right)^2 = 1$. Add these inside each pair of parentheses. Since the first set of parentheses has a 9 in front, we are actually adding 36 to the left-hand side. Similarly, we are subtracting 16 from the second set of parentheses. Therefore the equation becomes

$$9\left(x^2 + 4x + 4\right) - 16\left(y^2 - 2y + 1\right) = 124 + 36 - 16$$
$$9\left(x^2 + 4x + 4\right) - 16\left(y^2 - 2y + 1\right) = 144.$$

Next factor both sets of parentheses and divide by 144:

$$9(x + 2)^2 - 16(y - 1)^2 = 144$$
$$\frac{9(x + 2)^2}{144} - \frac{16(y - 1)^2}{144} = 1$$
$$\frac{(x + 2)^2}{16} - \frac{(y - 1)^2}{9} = 1.$$

The equation is now in standard form. Comparing this to **Equation 1.15** gives $h = -2$, $k = 1$, $a = 4$, and $b = 3$. This is a horizontal hyperbola with center at $(-2, 1)$ and asymptotes given by the equations $y = 1 \pm \frac{3}{4}(x + 2)$. The graph of this hyperbola appears in the following figure.

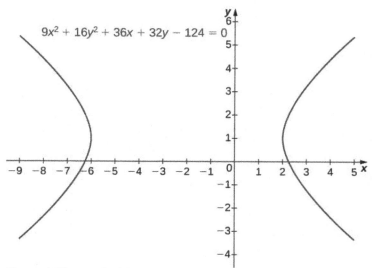

**Figure 1.52**  Graph of the hyperbola in Example 1.21.

 **1.20**  Put the equation $4y^2 - 9x^2 + 16y + 18x - 29 = 0$ into standard form and graph the resulting hyperbola. What are the equations of the asymptotes?

Hyperbolas also have interesting reflective properties. A ray directed toward one focus of a hyperbola is reflected by a hyperbolic mirror toward the other focus. This concept is illustrated in the following figure.

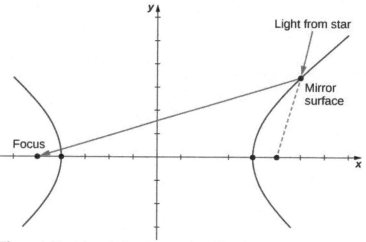

**Figure 1.53**  A hyperbolic mirror used to collect light from distant stars.

This property of the hyperbola has important applications. It is used in radio direction finding (since the difference in signals from two towers is constant along hyperbolas), and in the construction of mirrors inside telescopes (to reflect light coming from the parabolic mirror to the eyepiece). Another interesting fact about hyperbolas is that for a comet entering the solar system, if the speed is great enough to escape the Sun's gravitational pull, then the path that the comet takes as it passes through the solar system is hyperbolic.

## Eccentricity and Directrix

An alternative way to describe a conic section involves the directrices, the foci, and a new property called eccentricity. We will see that the value of the eccentricity of a conic section can uniquely define that conic.

---

### Definition

The **eccentricity** $e$ of a conic section is defined to be the distance from any point on the conic section to its focus, divided by the perpendicular distance from that point to the nearest directrix. This value is constant for any conic section, and can define the conic section as well:

1. If $e = 1$, the conic is a parabola.

2. If $e < 1$, it is an ellipse.

3. If $e > 1$, it is a hyperbola.

The eccentricity of a circle is zero. The directrix of a conic section is the line that, together with the point known as the focus, serves to define a conic section. Hyperbolas and noncircular ellipses have two foci and two associated directrices. Parabolas have one focus and one directrix.

---

The three conic sections with their directrices appear in the following figure.

**Figure 1.54** The three conic sections with their foci and directrices.

Recall from the definition of a parabola that the distance from any point on the parabola to the focus is equal to the distance from that same point to the directrix. Therefore, by definition, the eccentricity of a parabola must be 1. The equations of the directrices of a horizontal ellipse are $x = \pm \frac{a^2}{c}$. The right vertex of the ellipse is located at $(a, 0)$ and the right focus is $(c, 0)$. Therefore the distance from the vertex to the focus is $a - c$ and the distance from the vertex to the right directrix is $\frac{a^2}{c} - c$. This gives the eccentricity as

$$e = \frac{a - c}{\frac{a^2}{c} - a} = \frac{c(a - c)}{a^2 - ac} = \frac{c(a - c)}{a(a - c)} = \frac{c}{a}.$$

Since $c < a$, this step proves that the eccentricity of an ellipse is less than 1. The directrices of a horizontal hyperbola are also located at $x = \pm \frac{a^2}{c}$, and a similar calculation shows that the eccentricity of a hyperbola is also $e = \frac{c}{a}$. However in this case we have $c > a$, so the eccentricity of a hyperbola is greater than 1.

## Example 1.22

### Determining Eccentricity of a Conic Section

Determine the eccentricity of the ellipse described by the equation

$$\frac{(x-3)^2}{16} + \frac{(y+2)^2}{25} = 1.$$

### Solution

From the equation we see that $a = 5$ and $b = 4$. The value of $c$ can be calculated using the equation $a^2 = b^2 + c^2$ for an ellipse. Substituting the values of $a$ and $b$ and solving for $c$ gives $c = 3$. Therefore the eccentricity of the ellipse is $e = \frac{c}{a} = \frac{3}{5} = 0.6$.

 **1.21** Determine the eccentricity of the hyperbola described by the equation

$$\frac{(y-3)^2}{49} - \frac{(x+2)^2}{25} = 1.$$

## Polar Equations of Conic Sections

Sometimes it is useful to write or identify the equation of a conic section in polar form. To do this, we need the concept of the focal parameter. The **focal parameter** of a conic section $p$ is defined as the distance from a focus to the nearest directrix. The following table gives the focal parameters for the different types of conics, where $a$ is the length of the semi-major axis (i.e., half the length of the major axis), $c$ is the distance from the origin to the focus, and $e$ is the eccentricity. In the case of a parabola, $a$ represents the distance from the vertex to the focus.

| Conic | e | p |
|---|---|---|
| Ellipse | $0 < e < 1$ | $\frac{a^2 - c^2}{c} = \frac{a\left(1 - e^2\right)}{c}$ |
| Parabola | $e = 1$ | $2a$ |
| Hyperbola | $e > 1$ | $\frac{c^2 - a^2}{c} = \frac{a\left(e^2 - 1\right)}{e}$ |

**Table 1.7** Eccentricities and Focal Parameters of the Conic Sections

Using the definitions of the focal parameter and eccentricity of the conic section, we can derive an equation for any conic section in polar coordinates. In particular, we assume that one of the foci of a given conic section lies at the pole. Then using the definition of the various conic sections in terms of distances, it is possible to prove the following theorem.

### Theorem 1.11: Polar Equation of Conic Sections

The polar equation of a conic section with focal parameter $p$ is given by

$$r = \frac{ep}{1 \pm e \cos \theta} \text{ or } r = \frac{ep}{1 \pm e \sin \theta}.$$

In the equation on the left, the major axis of the conic section is horizontal, and in the equation on the right, the major axis is vertical. To work with a conic section written in polar form, first make the constant term in the denominator equal to 1. This can be done by dividing both the numerator and the denominator of the fraction by the constant that appears in front of the plus or minus in the denominator. Then the coefficient of the sine or cosine in the denominator is the eccentricity. This value identifies the conic. If cosine appears in the denominator, then the conic is horizontal. If sine appears, then the conic is vertical. If both appear then the axes are rotated. The center of the conic is not necessarily at the origin. The center is at the origin only if the conic is a circle (i.e., $e = 0$).

## Example 1.23

### Graphing a Conic Section in Polar Coordinates

Identify and create a graph of the conic section described by the equation

$$r = \frac{3}{1 + 2\cos\theta}.$$

**Solution**

The constant term in the denominator is 1, so the eccentricity of the conic is 2. This is a hyperbola. The focal parameter $p$ can be calculated by using the equation $ep = 3$. Since $e = 2$, this gives $p = \frac{3}{2}$. The cosine function appears in the denominator, so the hyperbola is horizontal. Pick a few values for $\theta$ and create a table of values. Then we can graph the hyperbola (**Figure 1.55**).

| $\theta$ | $r$ | $\theta$ | $r$ |
|---|---|---|---|
| 0 | 1 | $\pi$ | $-3$ |
| $\frac{\pi}{4}$ | $\frac{3}{1+\sqrt{2}} \approx 1.2426$ | $\frac{5\pi}{4}$ | $\frac{3}{1-\sqrt{2}} \approx -7.2426$ |
| $\frac{\pi}{2}$ | 3 | $\frac{3\pi}{2}$ | 3 |
| $\frac{3\pi}{4}$ | $\frac{3}{1-\sqrt{2}} \approx -7.2426$ | $\frac{7\pi}{4}$ | $\frac{3}{1+\sqrt{2}} \approx 1.2426$ |

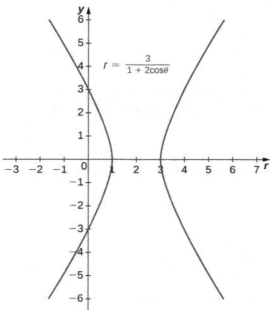

**Figure 1.55** Graph of the hyperbola described in **Example** 1.23.

 **1.22** Identify and create a graph of the conic section described by the equation

$$r = \frac{4}{1 - 0.8 \sin \theta}.$$

## General Equations of Degree Two

A general equation of degree two can be written in the form

$$Ax^2 + Bxy + Cy^2 + Dx + Ey + F = 0.$$

The graph of an equation of this form is a conic section. If $B \neq 0$ then the coordinate axes are rotated. To identify the conic section, we use the **discriminant** of the conic section $4AC - B^2$. One of the following cases must be true:

1.  $4AC - B^2 > 0$. If so, the graph is an ellipse.

2.  $4AC - B^2 = 0$. If so, the graph is a parabola.

3.  $4AC - B^2 < 0$. If so, the graph is a hyperbola.

The simplest example of a second-degree equation involving a cross term is $xy = 1$. This equation can be solved for $y$ to obtain $y = \frac{1}{x}$. The graph of this function is called a *rectangular hyperbola* as shown.

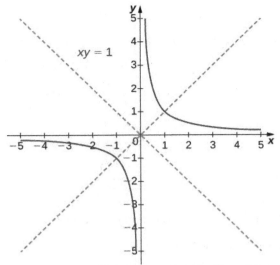

**Figure 1.56** Graph of the equation $xy = 1$; The red lines indicate the rotated axes.

The asymptotes of this hyperbola are the $x$ and $y$ coordinate axes. To determine the angle $\theta$ of rotation of the conic section, we use the formula $\cot 2\theta = \dfrac{A - C}{B}$. In this case $A = C = 0$ and $B = 1$, so $\cot 2\theta = (0 - 0)/1 = 0$ and $\theta = 45°$.

The method for graphing a conic section with rotated axes involves determining the coefficients of the conic in the rotated coordinate system. The new coefficients are labeled $A'$, $B'$, $C'$, $D'$, $E'$, and $F'$, and are given by the formulas

$$
\begin{aligned}
A' &= A \cos^2\theta + B \cos\theta \sin\theta + C \sin^2\theta \\
B' &= 0 \\
C' &= A \sin^2\theta - B \sin\theta \cos\theta + C \cos^2\theta \\
D' &= D \cos\theta + E \sin\theta \\
E' &= -D \sin\theta + E \cos\theta \\
F' &= F.
\end{aligned}
$$

The procedure for graphing a rotated conic is the following:

1. Identify the conic section using the discriminant $4AC - B^2$.

2. Determine $\theta$ using the formula $\cot 2\theta = \dfrac{A - C}{B}$.

3. Calculate $A'$, $B'$, $C'$, $D'$, $E'$, and $F'$.

4. Rewrite the original equation using $A'$, $B'$, $C'$, $D'$, $E'$, and $F'$.

5. Draw a graph using the rotated equation.

## Example 1.24

### Identifying a Rotated Conic

Identify the conic and calculate the angle of rotation of axes for the curve described by the equation

$$13x^2 - 6\sqrt{3}xy + 7y^2 - 256 = 0.$$

### Solution

In this equation, $A = 13$, $B = -6\sqrt{3}$, $C = 7$, $D = 0$, $E = 0$, and $F = -256$. The discriminant of this equation is $4AC - B^2 = 4(13)(7) - \left(-6\sqrt{3}\right)^2 = 364 - 108 = 256$. Therefore this conic is an ellipse. To calculate the angle of rotation of the axes, use $\cot 2\theta = \dfrac{A - C}{B}$. This gives

$$
\begin{aligned}
\cot 2\theta &= \frac{A - C}{B} \\
&= \frac{13 - 7}{-6\sqrt{3}} \\
&= -\frac{\sqrt{3}}{3}.
\end{aligned}
$$

Therefore $2\theta = 120°$ and $\theta = 60°$, which is the angle of the rotation of the axes.

To determine the rotated coefficients, use the formulas given above:

$$
\begin{aligned}
A' &= A\cos^2\theta + B\cos\theta\sin\theta + C\sin^2\theta \\
&= 13\cos^2 60 + \left(-6\sqrt{3}\right)\cos 60\sin 60 + 7\sin^2 60 \\
&= 13\left(\tfrac{1}{2}\right)^2 - 6\sqrt{3}\left(\tfrac{1}{2}\right)\left(\tfrac{\sqrt{3}}{2}\right) + 7\left(\tfrac{\sqrt{3}}{2}\right)^2 \\
&= 4, \\
B' &= 0, \\
C' &= A\sin^2\theta - B\sin\theta\cos\theta + C\cos^2\theta \\
&= 13\sin^2 60 + \left(-6\sqrt{3}\right)\sin 60\cos 60 = 7\cos^2 60 \\
&= \left(\tfrac{\sqrt{3}}{2}\right)^2 + 6\sqrt{3}\left(\tfrac{\sqrt{3}}{2}\right)\left(\tfrac{1}{2}\right) + 7\left(\tfrac{1}{2}\right)^2 \\
&= 16, \\
D' &= D\cos\theta + E\sin\theta \\
&= (0)\cos 60 + (0)\sin 60 \\
&= 0, \\
E' &= -D\sin\theta + E\cos\theta \\
&= -(0)\sin 60 + (0)\cos 60 \\
&= 0, \\
F' &= F \\
&= -256.
\end{aligned}
$$

The equation of the conic in the rotated coordinate system becomes

$$
\begin{aligned}
4(x')^2 + 16(y')^2 &= 256 \\
\frac{(x')^2}{64} + \frac{(y')^2}{16} &= 1.
\end{aligned}
$$

A graph of this conic section appears as follows.

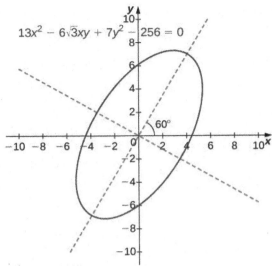

**Figure 1.57** Graph of the ellipse described by the equation $13x^2 - 6\sqrt{3}xy + 7y^2 - 256 = 0$. The axes are rotated $60°$. The red dashed lines indicate the rotated axes.

 **1.23** Identify the conic and calculate the angle of rotation of axes for the curve described by the equation

$$3x^2 + 5xy - 2y^2 - 125 = 0.$$

# 1.5 EXERCISES

For the following exercises, determine the equation of the parabola using the information given.

255. Focus $(4, 0)$ and directrix $x = -4$

256. Focus $(0, -3)$ and directrix $y = 3$

257. Focus $(0, 0.5)$ and directrix $y = -0.5$

258. Focus $(2, 3)$ and directrix $x = -2$

259. Focus $(0, 2)$ and directrix $y = 4$

260. Focus $(-1, 4)$ and directrix $x = 5$

261. Focus $(-3, 5)$ and directrix $y = 1$

262. Focus $\left(\frac{5}{2}, -4\right)$ and directrix $x = \frac{7}{2}$

For the following exercises, determine the equation of the ellipse using the information given.

263. Endpoints of major axis at $(4, 0), (-4, 0)$ and foci located at $(2, 0), (-2, 0)$

264. Endpoints of major axis at $(0, 5), (0, -5)$ and foci located at $(0, 3), (0, -3)$

265. Endpoints of major axis at $(0, 2), (0, -2)$ and foci located at $(3, 0), (-3, 0)$

266. Endpoints of major axis at $(-3, 3), (7, 3)$ and foci located at $(-2, 3), (6, 3)$

267. Endpoints of major axis at $(-3, 5), (-3, -3)$ and foci located at $(-3, 3), (-3, -1)$

268. Endpoints of major axis at $(0, 0), (0, 4)$ and foci located at $(5, 2), (-5, 2)$

269. Foci located at $(2, 0), (-2, 0)$ and eccentricity of $\frac{1}{2}$

270. Foci located at $(0, -3), (0, 3)$ and eccentricity of $\frac{3}{4}$

For the following exercises, determine the equation of the hyperbola using the information given.

271. Vertices located at $(5, 0), (-5, 0)$ and foci located at $(6, 0), (-6, 0)$

272. Vertices located at $(0, 2), (0, -2)$ and foci located at $(0, 3), (0, -3)$

273. Endpoints of the conjugate axis located at $(0, 3), (0, -3)$ and foci located $(4, 0), (-4, 0)$

274. Vertices located at $(0, 1), (6, 1)$ and focus located at $(8, 1)$

275. Vertices located at $(-2, 0), (-2, -4)$ and focus located at $(-2, -8)$

276. Endpoints of the conjugate axis located at $(3, 2), (3, 4)$ and focus located at $(3, 7)$

277. Foci located at $(6, -0), (6, 0)$ and eccentricity of 3

278. $(0, 10), (0, -10)$ and eccentricity of 2.5

For the following exercises, consider the following polar equations of conics. Determine the eccentricity and identify the conic.

279. $r = \dfrac{-1}{1 + \cos \theta}$

280. $r = \dfrac{8}{2 - \sin \theta}$

281. $r = \dfrac{5}{2 + \sin \theta}$

282. $r = \dfrac{5}{-1 + 2 \sin \theta}$

283. $r = \dfrac{3}{2 - 6 \sin \theta}$

284. $r = \dfrac{3}{-4 + 3 \sin \theta}$

For the following exercises, find a polar equation of the conic with focus at the origin and eccentricity and directrix as given.

285. Directrix: $x = 4; e = \frac{1}{5}$

286. Directrix: $x = -4; e = 5$

287. Directrix: $y = 2; e = 2$

288. Directrix: $y = -2$; $e = \frac{1}{2}$

For the following exercises, sketch the graph of each conic.

289. $r = \dfrac{1}{1 + \sin \theta}$

290. $r = \dfrac{1}{1 - \cos \theta}$

291. $r = \dfrac{4}{1 + \cos \theta}$

292. $r = \dfrac{10}{5 + 4 \sin \theta}$

293. $r = \dfrac{15}{3 - 2 \cos \theta}$

294. $r = \dfrac{32}{3 + 5 \sin \theta}$

295. $r(2 + \sin \theta) = 4$

296. $r = \dfrac{3}{2 + 6 \sin \theta}$

297. $r = \dfrac{3}{-4 + 2 \sin \theta}$

298. $\dfrac{x^2}{9} + \dfrac{y^2}{4} = 1$

299. $\dfrac{x^2}{4} + \dfrac{y^2}{16} = 1$

300. $4x^2 + 9y^2 = 36$

301. $25x^2 - 4y^2 = 100$

302. $\dfrac{x^2}{16} - \dfrac{y^2}{9} = 1$

303. $x^2 = 12y$

304. $y^2 = 20x$

305. $12x = 5y^2$

For the following equations, determine which of the conic sections is described.

306. $xy = 4$

307. $x^2 + 4xy - 2y^2 - 6 = 0$

308. $x^2 + 2\sqrt{3}xy + 3y^2 - 6 = 0$

309. $x^2 - xy + y^2 - 2 = 0$

310. $34x^2 - 24xy + 41y^2 - 25 = 0$

311. $52x^2 - 72xy + 73y^2 + 40x + 30y - 75 = 0$

312. The mirror in an automobile headlight has a parabolic cross section, with the lightbulb at the focus. On a schematic, the equation of the parabola is given as $x^2 = 4y$. At what coordinates should you place the lightbulb?

313. A satellite dish is shaped like a paraboloid of revolution. The receiver is to be located at the focus. If the dish is 12 feet across at its opening and 4 feet deep at its center, where should the receiver be placed?

314. Consider the satellite dish of the preceding problem. If the dish is 8 feet across at the opening and 2 feet deep, where should we place the receiver?

315. A searchlight is shaped like a paraboloid of revolution. A light source is located 1 foot from the base along the axis of symmetry. If the opening of the searchlight is 3 feet across, find the depth.

316. Whispering galleries are rooms designed with elliptical ceilings. A person standing at one focus can whisper and be heard by a person standing at the other focus because all the sound waves that reach the ceiling are reflected to the other person. If a whispering gallery has a length of 120 feet and the foci are located 30 feet from the center, find the height of the ceiling at the center.

317. A person is standing 8 feet from the nearest wall in a whispering gallery. If that person is at one focus and the other focus is 80 feet away, what is the length and the height at the center of the gallery?

For the following exercises, determine the polar equation form of the orbit given the length of the major axis and eccentricity for the orbits of the comets or planets. Distance is given in astronomical units (AU).

318. Halley's Comet: length of major axis = 35.88, eccentricity = 0.967

319. Hale-Bopp Comet: length of major axis = 525.91, eccentricity = 0.995

320. Mars: length of major axis = 3.049, eccentricity = 0.0934

321. Jupiter: length of major axis = 10.408, eccentricity = 0.0484

# CHAPTER 1 REVIEW

## KEY TERMS

**angular coordinate** $\theta$ the angle formed by a line segment connecting the origin to a point in the polar coordinate system with the positive radial ($x$) axis, measured counterclockwise

**cardioid** a plane curve traced by a point on the perimeter of a circle that is rolling around a fixed circle of the same radius; the equation of a cardioid is $r = a(1 + \sin\theta)$ or $r = a(1 + \cos\theta)$

**conic section** a conic section is any curve formed by the intersection of a plane with a cone of two nappes

**cusp** a pointed end or part where two curves meet

**cycloid** the curve traced by a point on the rim of a circular wheel as the wheel rolls along a straight line without slippage

**directrix** a directrix (plural: directrices) is a line used to construct and define a conic section; a parabola has one directrix; ellipses and hyperbolas have two

**discriminant** the value $4AC - B^2$, which is used to identify a conic when the equation contains a term involving $xy$, is called a discriminant

**eccentricity** the eccentricity is defined as the distance from any point on the conic section to its focus divided by the perpendicular distance from that point to the nearest directrix

**focal parameter** the focal parameter is the distance from a focus of a conic section to the nearest directrix

**focus** a focus (plural: foci) is a point used to construct and define a conic section; a parabola has one focus; an ellipse and a hyperbola have two

**general form** an equation of a conic section written as a general second-degree equation

**limaçon** the graph of the equation $r = a + b\sin\theta$ or $r = a + b\cos\theta$. If $a = b$ then the graph is a cardioid

**major axis** the major axis of a conic section passes through the vertex in the case of a parabola or through the two vertices in the case of an ellipse or hyperbola; it is also an axis of symmetry of the conic; also called the transverse axis

**minor axis** the minor axis is perpendicular to the major axis and intersects the major axis at the center of the conic, or at the vertex in the case of the parabola; also called the conjugate axis

**nappe** a nappe is one half of a double cone

**orientation** the direction that a point moves on a graph as the parameter increases

**parameter** an independent variable that both $x$ and $y$ depend on in a parametric curve; usually represented by the variable $t$

**parameterization of a curve** rewriting the equation of a curve defined by a function $y = f(x)$ as parametric equations

**parametric curve** the graph of the parametric equations $x(t)$ and $y(t)$ over an interval $a \leq t \leq b$ combined with the equations

**parametric equations** the equations $x = x(t)$ and $y = y(t)$ that define a parametric curve

**polar axis** the horizontal axis in the polar coordinate system corresponding to $r \geq 0$

**polar coordinate system** a system for locating points in the plane. The coordinates are $r$, the radial coordinate, and $\theta$, the angular coordinate

**polar equation** an equation or function relating the radial coordinate to the angular coordinate in the polar coordinate system

**pole** the central point of the polar coordinate system, equivalent to the origin of a Cartesian system

**radial coordinate** $r$ the coordinate in the polar coordinate system that measures the distance from a point in the plane to the pole

**rose** graph of the polar equation $r = a \cos 2\theta$ or $r = a \sin 2\theta$ for a positive constant $a$

**space-filling curve** a curve that completely occupies a two-dimensional subset of the real plane

**standard form** an equation of a conic section showing its properties, such as location of the vertex or lengths of major and minor axes

**vertex** a vertex is an extreme point on a conic section; a parabola has one vertex at its turning point. An ellipse has two vertices, one at each end of the major axis; a hyperbola has two vertices, one at the turning point of each branch

# KEY EQUATIONS

- **Derivative of parametric equations**

$$\frac{dy}{dx} = \frac{dy/dt}{dx/dt} = \frac{y'(t)}{x'(t)}$$

- **Second-order derivative of parametric equations**

$$\frac{d^2 y}{dx^2} = \frac{d}{dx}\left(\frac{dy}{dx}\right) = \frac{(d/dt)(dy/dx)}{dx/dt}$$

- **Area under a parametric curve**

$$A = \int_a^b y(t) x'(t)\, dt$$

- **Arc length of a parametric curve**

$$s = \int_{t_1}^{t_2} \sqrt{\left(\frac{dx}{dt}\right)^2 + \left(\frac{dy}{dt}\right)^2}\, dt$$

- **Surface area generated by a parametric curve**

$$S = 2\pi \int_a^b y(t) \sqrt{(x'(t))^2 + (y'(t))^2}\, dt$$

- **Area of a region bounded by a polar curve**

$$A = \frac{1}{2} \int_\alpha^\beta [f(\theta)]^2\, d\theta = \frac{1}{2} \int_\alpha^\beta r^2\, d\theta$$

- **Arc length of a polar curve**

$$L = \int_\alpha^\beta \sqrt{[f(\theta)]^2 + [f'(\theta)]^2}\, d\theta = \int_\alpha^\beta \sqrt{r^2 + \left(\frac{dr}{d\theta}\right)^2}\, d\theta$$

# KEY CONCEPTS

## 1.1 Parametric Equations

- Parametric equations provide a convenient way to describe a curve. A parameter can represent time or some other meaningful quantity.

- It is often possible to eliminate the parameter in a parameterized curve to obtain a function or relation describing that curve.

- There is always more than one way to parameterize a curve.

- Parametric equations can describe complicated curves that are difficult or perhaps impossible to describe using rectangular coordinates.

## 1.2 Calculus of Parametric Curves

- The derivative of the parametrically defined curve $x = x(t)$ and $y = y(t)$ can be calculated using the formula $\frac{dy}{dx} = \frac{y'(t)}{x'(t)}$. Using the derivative, we can find the equation of a tangent line to a parametric curve.

- The area between a parametric curve and the $x$-axis can be determined by using the formula $A = \int_{t_1}^{t_2} y(t)x'(t)\, dt$.

- The arc length of a parametric curve can be calculated by using the formula $s = \int_{t_1}^{t_2} \sqrt{\left(\frac{dx}{dt}\right)^2 + \left(\frac{dy}{dt}\right)^2}\, dt$.

- The surface area of a volume of revolution revolved around the $x$-axis is given by $S = 2\pi \int_a^b y(t)\sqrt{(x'(t))^2 + (y'(t))^2}\, dt$. If the curve is revolved around the $y$-axis, then the formula is $S = 2\pi \int_a^b x(t)\sqrt{(x'(t))^2 + (y'(t))^2}\, dt$.

## 1.3 Polar Coordinates

- The polar coordinate system provides an alternative way to locate points in the plane.
- Convert points between rectangular and polar coordinates using the formulas

$$x = r\cos\theta \text{ and } y = r\sin\theta$$

and

$$r = \sqrt{x^2 + y^2} \text{ and } \tan\theta = \frac{y}{x}.$$

- To sketch a polar curve from a given polar function, make a table of values and take advantage of periodic properties.
- Use the conversion formulas to convert equations between rectangular and polar coordinates.
- Identify symmetry in polar curves, which can occur through the pole, the horizontal axis, or the vertical axis.

## 1.4 Area and Arc Length in Polar Coordinates

- The area of a region in polar coordinates defined by the equation $r = f(\theta)$ with $\alpha \le \theta \le \beta$ is given by the integral

$$A = \frac{1}{2}\int_\alpha^\beta [f(\theta)]^2\, d\theta.$$

- To find the area between two curves in the polar coordinate system, first find the points of intersection, then subtract the corresponding areas.
- The arc length of a polar curve defined by the equation $r = f(\theta)$ with $\alpha \le \theta \le \beta$ is given by the integral

$$L = \int_\alpha^\beta \sqrt{[f(\theta)]^2 + [f'(\theta)]^2}\, d\theta = \int_\alpha^\beta \sqrt{r^2 + \left(\frac{dr}{d\theta}\right)^2}\, d\theta.$$

## 1.5 Conic Sections

- The equation of a vertical parabola in standard form with given focus and directrix is $y = \frac{1}{4p}(x - h)^2 + k$ where $p$ is the distance from the vertex to the focus and $(h, k)$ are the coordinates of the vertex.

- The equation of a horizontal ellipse in standard form is $\frac{(x-h)^2}{a^2} + \frac{(y-k)^2}{b^2} = 1$ where the center has coordinates $(h, k)$, the major axis has length $2a$, the minor axis has length $2b$, and the coordinates of the foci are $(h \pm c, k)$, where $c^2 = a^2 - b^2$.

- The equation of a horizontal hyperbola in standard form is $\frac{(x-h)^2}{a^2} - \frac{(y-k)^2}{b^2} = 1$ where the center has coordinates $(h, k)$, the vertices are located at $(h \pm a, k)$, and the coordinates of the foci are $(h \pm c, k)$, where $c^2 = a^2 + b^2$.

- The eccentricity of an ellipse is less than 1, the eccentricity of a parabola is equal to 1, and the eccentricity of a hyperbola is greater than 1. The eccentricity of a circle is 0.

- The polar equation of a conic section with eccentricity $e$ is $r = \frac{ep}{1 \pm e \cos\theta}$ or $r = \frac{ep}{1 \pm e \sin\theta}$, where $p$ represents the focal parameter.

- To identify a conic generated by the equation $Ax^2 + Bxy + Cy^2 + Dx + Ey + F = 0$, first calculate the discriminant $D = 4AC - B^2$. If $D > 0$ then the conic is an ellipse, if $D = 0$ then the conic is a parabola, and if $D < 0$ then the conic is a hyperbola.

# CHAPTER 1 REVIEW EXERCISES

*True or False?* Justify your answer with a proof or a counterexample.

**322.** The rectangular coordinates of the point $\left(4, \frac{5\pi}{6}\right)$ are $\left(2\sqrt{3}, -2\right)$.

**323.** The equations $x = \cosh(3t)$, $y = 2\sinh(3t)$ represent a hyperbola.

**324.** The arc length of the spiral given by $r = \frac{\theta}{2}$ for $0 \le \theta \le 3\pi$ is $\frac{9}{4}\pi^3$.

**325.** Given $x = f(t)$ and $y = g(t)$, if $\frac{dx}{dy} = \frac{dy}{dx}$, then $f(t) = g(t) + C$, where C is a constant.

For the following exercises, sketch the parametric curve and eliminate the parameter to find the Cartesian equation of the curve.

**326.** $x = 1 + t$, $y = t^2 - 1$, $-1 \le t \le 1$

**327.** $x = e^t$, $y = 1 - e^{3t}$, $0 \le t \le 1$

**328.** $x = \sin\theta$, $y = 1 - \csc\theta$, $0 \le \theta \le 2\pi$

**329.** $x = 4\cos\phi$, $y = 1 - \sin\phi$, $0 \le \phi \le 2\pi$

For the following exercises, sketch the polar curve and determine what type of symmetry exists, if any.

**330.** $r = 4\sin\left(\frac{\theta}{3}\right)$

**331.** $r = 5\cos(5\theta)$

For the following exercises, find the polar equation for the curve given as a Cartesian equation.

**332.** $x + y = 5$

**333.** $y^2 = 4 + x^2$

For the following exercises, find the equation of the tangent line to the given curve. Graph both the function and its tangent line.

**334.** $x = \ln(t)$, $y = t^2 - 1$, $t = 1$

**335.** $r = 3 + \cos(2\theta)$, $\theta = \frac{3\pi}{4}$

**336.** Find $\frac{dy}{dx}$, $\frac{dx}{dy}$, and $\frac{d^2x}{dy^2}$ of $y = \left(2 + e^{-t}\right)$, $x = 1 - \sin(t)$

For the following exercises, find the area of the region.

**337.** $x = t^2$, $y = \ln(t)$, $0 \le t \le e$

**338.** $r = 1 - \sin \theta$ in the first quadrant

For the following exercises, find the arc length of the curve over the given interval.

**339.** $x = 3t + 4, \quad y = 9t - 2, \quad 0 \le t \le 3$

**340.** $r = 6 \cos \theta, \quad 0 \le \theta \le 2\pi.$ Check your answer by geometry.

For the following exercises, find the Cartesian equation describing the given shapes.

**341.** A parabola with focus $(2, -5)$ and directrix $x = 6$

**342.** An ellipse with a major axis length of 10 and foci at $(-7, 2)$ and $(1, 2)$

**343.** A hyperbola with vertices at $(3, -2)$ and $(-5, -2)$ and foci at $(-2, -6)$ and $(-2, 4)$

For the following exercises, determine the eccentricity and identify the conic. Sketch the conic.

**344.** $r = \dfrac{6}{1 + 3 \cos(\theta)}$

**345.** $r = \dfrac{4}{3 - 2 \cos \theta}$

**346.** $r = \dfrac{7}{5 - 5 \cos \theta}$

**347.** Determine the Cartesian equation describing the orbit of Pluto, the most eccentric orbit around the Sun. The length of the major axis is 39.26 AU and minor axis is 38.07 AU. What is the eccentricity?

**348.** The C/1980 E1 comet was observed in 1980. Given an eccentricity of 1.057 and a perihelion (point of closest approach to the Sun) of 3.364 AU, find the Cartesian equations describing the comet's trajectory. Are we guaranteed to see this comet again? (*Hint*: Consider the Sun at point $(0, 0)$.)

# 2 | VECTORS IN SPACE

**Figure 2.1** The Karl G. Jansky Very Large Array, located in Socorro, New Mexico, consists of a large number of radio telescopes that can collect radio waves and collate them as if they were gathering waves over a huge area with no gaps in coverage. (credit: modification of work by CGP Grey, Wikimedia Commons)

## Chapter Outline

## Introduction

Modern astronomical observatories often consist of a large number of parabolic reflectors, connected by computers, used to analyze radio waves. Each dish focuses the incoming parallel beams of radio waves to a precise focal point, where they can be synchronized by computer. If the surface of one of the parabolic reflectors is described by the equation $\frac{x^2}{100} + \frac{y^2}{100} = \frac{z}{4}$, where is the focal point of the reflector? (See **Example 2.58**.)

We are now about to begin a new part of the calculus course, when we study functions of two or three independent variables in multidimensional space. Many of the computations are similar to those in the study of single-variable functions, but there are also a lot of differences. In this first chapter, we examine coordinate systems for working in three-dimensional space, along with vectors, which are a key mathematical tool for dealing with quantities in more than one dimension. Let's start here with the basic ideas and work our way up to the more general and powerful tools of mathematics in later chapters.

# 2.1 | Vectors in the Plane

## Learning Objectives

**2.1.1** Describe a plane vector, using correct notation.
**2.1.2** Perform basic vector operations (scalar multiplication, addition, subtraction).
**2.1.3** Express a vector in component form.
**2.1.4** Explain the formula for the magnitude of a vector.
**2.1.5** Express a vector in terms of unit vectors.
**2.1.6** Give two examples of vector quantities.

When describing the movement of an airplane in flight, it is important to communicate two pieces of information: the direction in which the plane is traveling and the plane's speed. When measuring a force, such as the thrust of the plane's engines, it is important to describe not only the strength of that force, but also the direction in which it is applied. Some quantities, such as or force, are defined in terms of both size (also called *magnitude*) and direction. A quantity that has magnitude and direction is called a **vector**. In this text, we denote vectors by boldface letters, such as **v**.

### Definition

A vector is a quantity that has both magnitude and direction.

## Vector Representation

A vector in a plane is represented by a directed line segment (an arrow). The endpoints of the segment are called the **initial point** and the **terminal point** of the vector. An arrow from the initial point to the terminal point indicates the direction of the vector. The length of the line segment represents its **magnitude**. We use the notation $\| \mathbf{v} \|$ to denote the magnitude of the vector **v**. A vector with an initial point and terminal point that are the same is called the **zero vector**, denoted **0**. The zero vector is the only vector without a direction, and by convention can be considered to have any direction convenient to the problem at hand.

Vectors with the same magnitude and direction are called equivalent vectors. We treat equivalent vectors as equal, even if they have different initial points. Thus, if **v** and **w** are equivalent, we write

$$\mathbf{v} = \mathbf{w}.$$

### Definition

Vectors are said to be **equivalent vectors** if they have the same magnitude and direction.

The arrows in Figure 2.2(b) are equivalent. Each arrow has the same length and direction. A closely related concept is the idea of parallel vectors. Two vectors are said to be parallel if they have the same or opposite directions. We explore this idea in more detail later in the chapter. A vector is defined by its magnitude and direction, regardless of where its initial point is located.

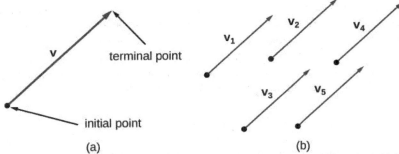

**Figure 2.2** (a) A vector is represented by a directed line segment from its initial point to its terminal point. (b) Vectors $\mathbf{v}_1$ through $\mathbf{v}_5$ are equivalent.

The use of boldface, lowercase letters to name vectors is a common representation in print, but there are alternative notations. When writing the name of a vector by hand, for example, it is easier to sketch an arrow over the variable than to simulate boldface type: $\vec{v}$ . When a vector has initial point $P$ and terminal point $Q$, the notation $\vec{PQ}$ is useful because it indicates the direction and location of the vector.

## Example 2.1

### Sketching Vectors

Sketch a vector in the plane from initial point $P(1, 1)$ to terminal point $Q(8, 5)$.

### Solution

See **Figure 2.3**. Because the vector goes from point $P$ to point $Q$, we name it $\vec{PQ}$.

**Figure 2.3** The vector with initial point $(1, 1)$ and terminal point $(8, 5)$ is named $\vec{PQ}$.

 **2.1** Sketch the vector $\vec{ST}$ where $S$ is point $(3, -1)$ and $T$ is point $(-2, 3)$.

## Combining Vectors

Vectors have many real-life applications, including situations involving force or velocity. For example, consider the forces acting on a boat crossing a river. The boat's motor generates a force in one direction, and the current of the river generates a force in another direction. Both forces are vectors. We must take both the magnitude and direction of each force into account if we want to know where the boat will go.

A second example that involves vectors is a quarterback throwing a football. The quarterback does not throw the ball parallel to the ground; instead, he aims up into the air. The velocity of his throw can be represented by a vector. If we know how hard he throws the ball (magnitude—in this case, speed), and the angle (direction), we can tell how far the ball will travel down the field.

A real number is often called a **scalar** in mathematics and physics. Unlike vectors, scalars are generally considered to have a magnitude only, but no direction. Multiplying a vector by a scalar changes the vector's magnitude. This is called scalar multiplication. Note that changing the magnitude of a vector does not indicate a change in its direction. For example, wind blowing from north to south might increase or decrease in speed while maintaining its direction from north to south.

---

**Definition**

The product $k\mathbf{v}$ of a vector $\mathbf{v}$ and a scalar $k$ is a vector with a magnitude that is $|k|$ times the magnitude of $\mathbf{v}$, and with a direction that is the same as the direction of $\mathbf{v}$ if $k > 0$, and opposite the direction of $\mathbf{v}$ if $k < 0$. This is called **scalar multiplication**. If $k = 0$ or $\mathbf{v} = \mathbf{0}$, then $k\mathbf{v} = \mathbf{0}$.

---

As you might expect, if $k = -1$, we denote the product $k\mathbf{v}$ as

$$k\mathbf{v} = (-1)\mathbf{v} = -\mathbf{v}.$$

Note that $-\mathbf{v}$ has the same magnitude as $\mathbf{v}$, but has the opposite direction (**Figure 2.4**).

**Figure 2.4** (a) The original vector $\mathbf{v}$ has length $n$ units. (b) The length of $2\mathbf{v}$ equals $2n$ units. (c) The length of $\mathbf{v}/2$ is $n/2$ units. (d) The vectors $\mathbf{v}$ and $-\mathbf{v}$ have the same length but opposite directions.

Another operation we can perform on vectors is to add them together in vector addition, but because each vector may have its own direction, the process is different from adding two numbers. The most common graphical method for adding two vectors is to place the initial point of the second vector at the terminal point of the first, as in **Figure 2.5**(a). To see why this makes sense, suppose, for example, that both vectors represent displacement. If an object moves first from the initial point to the terminal point of vector $\mathbf{v}$, then from the initial point to the terminal point of vector $\mathbf{w}$, the overall displacement is the same as if the object had made just one movement from the initial point to the terminal point of the vector $\mathbf{v} + \mathbf{w}$. For obvious reasons, this approach is called the **triangle method**. Notice that if we had switched the order, so that $\mathbf{w}$ was our first vector and $\mathbf{v}$ was our second vector, we would have ended up in the same place. (Again, see **Figure 2.5**(a).) Thus, $\mathbf{v} + \mathbf{w} = \mathbf{w} + \mathbf{v}$.

A second method for adding vectors is called the **parallelogram method**. With this method, we place the two vectors so they have the same initial point, and then we draw a parallelogram with the vectors as two adjacent sides, as in **Figure 2.5**(b). The length of the diagonal of the parallelogram is the sum. Comparing **Figure 2.5**(b) and **Figure 2.5**(a), we can see that we get the same answer using either method. The vector $\mathbf{v} + \mathbf{w}$ is called the **vector sum**.

---

**Definition**

The sum of two vectors $\mathbf{v}$ and $\mathbf{w}$ can be constructed graphically by placing the initial point of $\mathbf{w}$ at the terminal point of **v**. Then, the vector sum, **v** + **w**, is the vector with an initial point that coincides with the initial point of **v** and has a terminal point that coincides with the terminal point of **w**. This operation is known as **vector addition**.

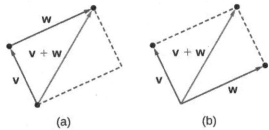

(a)                              (b)

**Figure 2.5** (a) When adding vectors by the triangle method, the initial point of **w** is the terminal point of **v**. (b) When adding vectors by the parallelogram method, the vectors **v** and **w** have the same initial point.

It is also appropriate here to discuss vector subtraction. We define **v** − **w** as **v** + (−**w**) = **v** + (−1)**w**. The vector **v** − **w** is called the **vector difference**. Graphically, the vector **v** − **w** is depicted by drawing a vector from the terminal point of **w** to the terminal point of **v** (Figure 2.6).

(a)                              (b)

**Figure 2.6** (a) The vector difference **v** − **w** is depicted by drawing a vector from the terminal point of **w** to the terminal point of **v**. (b) The vector **v** − **w** is equivalent to the vector **v** + (−**w**).

In Figure 2.5(a), the initial point of **v** + **w** is the initial point of **v**. The terminal point of **v** + **w** is the terminal point of **w**. These three vectors form the sides of a triangle. It follows that the length of any one side is less than the sum of the lengths of the remaining sides. So we have

$$\| \mathbf{v} + \mathbf{w} \| \leq \| \mathbf{v} \| + \| \mathbf{w} \| .$$

This is known more generally as the **triangle inequality**. There is one case, however, when the resultant vector **u** + **v** has the same magnitude as the sum of the magnitudes of **u** and **v**. This happens only when **u** and **v** have the same direction.

## Example 2.2

### Combining Vectors

Given the vectors **v** and **w** shown in Figure 2.7, sketch the vectors

a.   3**w**

b.   **v** + **w**

c.   $2\mathbf{v} - \mathbf{w}$

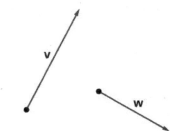

Figure 2.7   Vectors $\mathbf{v}$ and $\mathbf{w}$ lie in the same plane.

## Solution

a.   The vector $3\mathbf{w}$ has the same direction as $\mathbf{w}$; it is three times as long as $\mathbf{w}$.

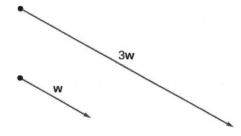

Vector $3\mathbf{w}$ has the same direction as $\mathbf{w}$ and is three times as long.

b.   Use either addition method to find $\mathbf{v} + \mathbf{w}$.

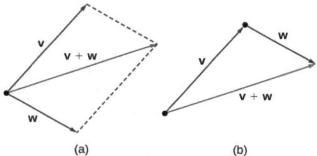

(a)                                   (b)

Figure 2.8   To find $\mathbf{v} + \mathbf{w}$,   align the vectors at their initial points or place the initial point of one vector at the terminal point of the other. (a) The vector $\mathbf{v} + \mathbf{w}$ is the diagonal of the parallelogram with sides $\mathbf{v}$ and $\mathbf{w}$ (b) The vector $\mathbf{v} + \mathbf{w}$ is the third side of a triangle formed with $\mathbf{w}$ placed at the terminal point of $\mathbf{v}$.

c.   To find $2\mathbf{v} - \mathbf{w}$,   we can first rewrite the expression as $2\mathbf{v} + (-\mathbf{w})$. Then we can draw the vector $-\mathbf{w}$, then add it to the vector $2\mathbf{v}$.

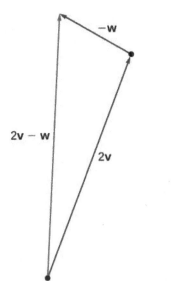

**Figure 2.9** To find $2\mathbf{v} - \mathbf{w}$, simply add $2\mathbf{v} + (-\mathbf{w})$.

 **2.2** Using vectors $\mathbf{v}$ and $\mathbf{w}$ from **Example 2.2**, sketch the vector $2\mathbf{w} - \mathbf{v}$.

## Vector Components

Working with vectors in a plane is easier when we are working in a coordinate system. When the initial points and terminal points of vectors are given in Cartesian coordinates, computations become straightforward.

### Example 2.3

#### Comparing Vectors

Are $\mathbf{v}$ and $\mathbf{w}$ equivalent vectors?

   a.  $\mathbf{v}$ has initial point $(3, 2)$ and terminal point $(7, 2)$

       $\mathbf{w}$ has initial point $(1, -4)$ and terminal point $(1, 0)$

   b.  $\mathbf{v}$ has initial point $(0, 0)$ and terminal point $(1, 1)$

       $\mathbf{w}$ has initial point $(-2, 2)$ and terminal point $(-1, 3)$

#### Solution

   a.  The vectors are each $4$ units long, but they are oriented in different directions. So $\mathbf{v}$ and $\mathbf{w}$ are not equivalent (**Figure 2.10**).

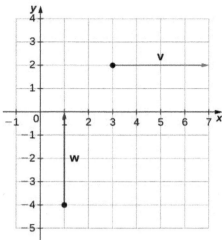

Figure 2.10 These vectors are not equivalent.

b. Based on **Figure 2.11**, and using a bit of geometry, it is clear these vectors have the same length and the same direction, so **v** and **w** are equivalent.

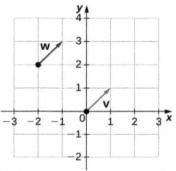

Figure 2.11 These vectors are equivalent.

 **2.3** Which of the following vectors are equivalent?

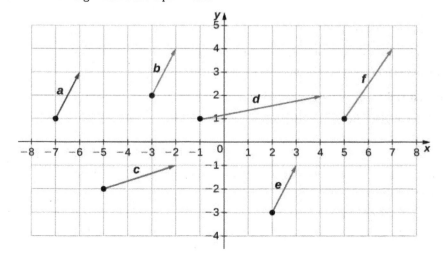

We have seen how to plot a vector when we are given an initial point and a terminal point. However, because a vector can be placed anywhere in a plane, it may be easier to perform calculations with a vector when its initial point coincides with the origin. We call a vector with its initial point at the origin a **standard-position vector**. Because the initial point of any vector in standard position is known to be $(0, 0)$, we can describe the vector by looking at the coordinates of its terminal point. Thus, if vector **v** has its initial point at the origin and its terminal point at $(x, y)$, we write the vector in component form as

$$\mathbf{v} = \langle x, y \rangle.$$

When a vector is written in component form like this, the scalars $x$ and $y$ are called the **components** of **v**.

---

**Definition**

The vector with initial point $(0, 0)$ and terminal point $(x, y)$ can be written in component form as

$$\mathbf{v} = \langle x, y \rangle.$$

The scalars $x$ and $y$ are called the components of **v**.

---

Recall that vectors are named with lowercase letters in bold type or by drawing an arrow over their name. We have also learned that we can name a vector by its component form, with the coordinates of its terminal point in angle brackets. However, when writing the component form of a vector, it is important to distinguish between $\langle x, y \rangle$ and $(x, y)$. The first ordered pair uses angle brackets to describe a vector, whereas the second uses parentheses to describe a point in a plane. The initial point of $\langle x, y \rangle$ is $(0, 0)$; the terminal point of $\langle x, y \rangle$ is $(x, y)$.

When we have a vector not already in standard position, we can determine its component form in one of two ways. We can use a geometric approach, in which we sketch the vector in the coordinate plane, and then sketch an equivalent standard-position vector. Alternatively, we can find it algebraically, using the coordinates of the initial point and the terminal point. To find it algebraically, we subtract the $x$-coordinate of the initial point from the $x$-coordinate of the terminal point to get the $x$ component, and we subtract the $y$-coordinate of the initial point from the $y$-coordinate of the terminal point to get the $y$ component.

---

**Rule: Component Form of a Vector**

Let **v** be a vector with initial point $(x_i, y_i)$ and terminal point $(x_t, y_t)$. Then we can express **v** in component form as $\mathbf{v} = \langle x_t - x_i, y_t - y_i \rangle$.

---

## Example 2.4

### Expressing Vectors in Component Form

Express vector **v** with initial point $(-3, 4)$ and terminal point $(1, 2)$ in component form.

### Solution

   a.  Geometric

       1.  Sketch the vector in the coordinate plane (**Figure 2.12**).

       2.  The terminal point is 4 units to the right and 2 units down from the initial point.

       3.  Find the point that is 4 units to the right and 2 units down from the origin.

       4.  In standard position, this vector has initial point $(0, 0)$ and terminal point $(4, -2)$:

$$\mathbf{v} = \langle\, 4, -2 \,\rangle .$$

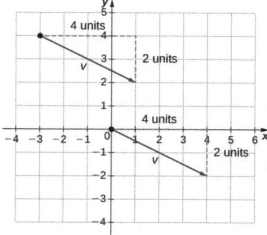

Figure 2.12 These vectors are equivalent.

b. Algebraic

In the first solution, we used a sketch of the vector to see that the terminal point lies 4 units to the right. We can accomplish this algebraically by finding the difference of the *x*-coordinates:

$$x_t - x_i = 1 - (-3) = 4.$$

Similarly, the difference of the *y*-coordinates shows the vertical length of the vector.

$$y_t - y_i = 2 - 4 = -2.$$

So, in component form,

$$\begin{aligned}
\mathbf{v} &= \langle\, x_t - x_i,\, y_t - y_i \,\rangle \\
&= \langle\, 1 - (-3),\, 2 - 4 \,\rangle \\
&= \langle\, 4, -2 \,\rangle .
\end{aligned}$$

 **2.4** Vector **w** has initial point $(-4, -5)$ and terminal point $(-1, 2)$. Express **w** in component form.

To find the magnitude of a vector, we calculate the distance between its initial point and its terminal point. The magnitude of vector $\mathbf{v} = \langle\, x, y \,\rangle$ is denoted $\|\,\mathbf{v}\,\|$, or $|\mathbf{v}|$, and can be computed using the formula

$$\|\,\mathbf{v}\,\| = \sqrt{x^2 + y^2}.$$

Note that because this vector is written in component form, it is equivalent to a vector in standard position, with its initial point at the origin and terminal point $(x, y)$. Thus, it suffices to calculate the magnitude of the vector in standard position.

Using the distance formula to calculate the distance between initial point $(0, 0)$ and terminal point $(x, y)$, we have

$$\begin{aligned}
\|\,\mathbf{v}\,\| &= \sqrt{(x - 0)^2 + (y - 0)^2} \\
&= \sqrt{x^2 + y^2}.
\end{aligned}$$

Based on this formula, it is clear that for any vector **v**, $\|\,\mathbf{v}\,\| \geq 0$, and $\|\,\mathbf{v}\,\| = 0$ if and only if $\mathbf{v} = \mathbf{0}$.

The magnitude of a vector can also be derived using the Pythagorean theorem, as in the following figure.

**Figure 2.13** If you use the components of a vector to define a right triangle, the magnitude of the vector is the length of the triangle's hypotenuse.

We have defined scalar multiplication and vector addition geometrically. Expressing vectors in component form allows us to perform these same operations algebraically.

---

### Definition

Let $\mathbf{v} = \langle x_1, y_1 \rangle$ and $\mathbf{w} = \langle x_2, y_2 \rangle$ be vectors, and let $k$ be a scalar.

**Scalar multiplication:** $k\mathbf{v} = \langle kx_1, ky_1 \rangle$

**Vector addition:** $\mathbf{v} + \mathbf{w} = \langle x_1, y_1 \rangle + \langle x_2, y_2 \rangle = \langle x_1 + x_2, y_1 + y_2 \rangle$

---

## Example 2.5

### Performing Operations in Component Form

Let $\mathbf{v}$ be the vector with initial point $(2, 5)$ and terminal point $(8, 13)$, and let $\mathbf{w} = \langle -2, 4 \rangle$.

    a.  Express $\mathbf{v}$ in component form and find $\| \mathbf{v} \|$. Then, using algebra, find

    b.  $\mathbf{v} + \mathbf{w}$,

    c.  $3\mathbf{v}$, and

    d.  $\mathbf{v} - 2\mathbf{w}$.

### Solution

    a.  To place the initial point of $\mathbf{v}$ at the origin, we must translate the vector $2$ units to the left and $5$ units down (**Figure 2.15**). Using the algebraic method, we can express $\mathbf{v}$ as $\mathbf{v} = \langle 8 - 2, 13 - 5 \rangle = \langle 6, 8 \rangle$:

$$\| \mathbf{v} \| = \sqrt{6^2 + 8^2} = \sqrt{36 + 64} = \sqrt{100} = 10.$$

**Figure 2.14** In component form, $\mathbf{v} = \langle\, 6, 8\,\rangle$.

b. To find $\mathbf{v} + \mathbf{w}$, add the $x$-components and the $y$-components separately:

$$\mathbf{v} + \mathbf{w} = \langle\, 6, 8\,\rangle + \langle\, -2, 4\,\rangle = \langle\, 4, 12\,\rangle.$$

c. To find $3\mathbf{v}$, multiply $\mathbf{v}$ by the scalar $k = 3$:

$$3\mathbf{v} = 3 \cdot \langle\, 6, 8\,\rangle = \langle\, 3 \cdot 6, 3 \cdot 8\,\rangle = \langle\, 18, 24\,\rangle.$$

d. To find $\mathbf{v} - 2\mathbf{w}$, find $-2\mathbf{w}$ and add it to $\mathbf{v}$:

$$\mathbf{v} - 2\mathbf{w} = \langle\, 6, 8\,\rangle - 2 \cdot \langle\, -2, 4\,\rangle = \langle\, 6, 8\,\rangle + \langle\, 4, -8\,\rangle = \langle\, 10, 0\,\rangle.$$

 **2.5** Let $\mathbf{a} = \langle\, 7, 1\,\rangle$ and let $\mathbf{b}$ be the vector with initial point $(3, 2)$ and terminal point $(-1, -1)$.

a. Find $\|\,\mathbf{a}\,\|$.

b. Express $\mathbf{b}$ in component form.

c. Find $3\mathbf{a} - 4\mathbf{b}$.

Now that we have established the basic rules of vector arithmetic, we can state the properties of vector operations. We will prove two of these properties. The others can be proved in a similar manner.

### Theorem 2.1: Properties of Vector Operations

Let $\mathbf{u}$, $\mathbf{v}$, and $\mathbf{w}$ be vectors in a plane. Let $r$ and $s$ be scalars.

| | | |
|---|---|---|
| i. | $\mathbf{u} + \mathbf{v} = \mathbf{v} + \mathbf{u}$ | Commutative property |
| ii. | $(\mathbf{u} + \mathbf{v}) + \mathbf{w} = \mathbf{u} + (\mathbf{v} + \mathbf{w})$ | Associative property |
| iii. | $\mathbf{u} + 0 = \mathbf{u}$ | Additive identity property |
| iv. | $\mathbf{u} + (-\mathbf{u}) = 0$ | Additive inverse property |
| v. | $r(s\mathbf{u}) = (rs)\mathbf{u}$ | Associativity of scalar multiplication |
| vi. | $(r + s)\mathbf{u} = r\mathbf{u} + s\mathbf{u}$ | Distributive property |
| vii. | $r(\mathbf{u} + \mathbf{v}) = r\mathbf{u} + r\mathbf{v}$ | Distributive property |
| viii. | $1\mathbf{u} = \mathbf{u},\ 0\mathbf{u} = 0$ | Identity and zero properties |

## Proof of Commutative Property

Let $\mathbf{u} = \langle\, x_1, y_1 \,\rangle$ and $\mathbf{v} = \langle\, x_2, y_2 \,\rangle$. Apply the commutative property for real numbers:

$$\mathbf{u} + \mathbf{v} = \langle\, x_1 + x_2, y_1 + y_2 \,\rangle = \langle\, x_2 + x_1, y_2 + y_1 \,\rangle = \mathbf{v} + \mathbf{u}.$$

☐

## Proof of Distributive Property

Apply the distributive property for real numbers:

$$
\begin{aligned}
r(\mathbf{u} + \mathbf{v}) &= r \cdot \langle\, x_1 + x_2, y_1 + y_2 \,\rangle \\
&= \langle\, r(x_1 + x_2), r(y_1 + y_2) \,\rangle \\
&= \langle\, rx_1 + rx_2, ry_1 + ry_2 \,\rangle \\
&= \langle\, rx_1, ry_1 \,\rangle + \langle\, rx_2, ry_2 \,\rangle \\
&= r\mathbf{u} + r\mathbf{v}.
\end{aligned}
$$

☐

 **2.6** Prove the additive inverse property.

We have found the components of a vector given its initial and terminal points. In some cases, we may only have the magnitude and direction of a vector, not the points. For these vectors, we can identify the horizontal and vertical components using trigonometry (**Figure 2.15**).

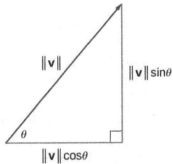

**Figure 2.15** The components of a vector form the legs of a right triangle, with the vector as the hypotenuse.

Consider the angle $\theta$ formed by the vector $\mathbf{v}$ and the positive $x$-axis. We can see from the triangle that the components of vector $\mathbf{v}$ are $\langle\, \|\mathbf{v}\| \cos\theta, \|\mathbf{v}\| \sin\theta \,\rangle$. Therefore, given an angle and the magnitude of a vector, we can use the cosine and sine of the angle to find the components of the vector.

## Example 2.6

### Finding the Component Form of a Vector Using Trigonometry

Find the component form of a vector with magnitude 4 that forms an angle of $-45°$ with the $x$-axis.

### Solution

Let $x$ and $y$ represent the components of the vector (**Figure 2.16**). Then $x = 4\cos(-45°) = 2\sqrt{2}$ and $y = 4\sin(-45°) = -2\sqrt{2}$. The component form of the vector is $\langle\, 2\sqrt{2}, -2\sqrt{2} \,\rangle$.

**Figure 2.16** Use trigonometric ratios, $x = \| \mathbf{v} \| \cos \theta$ and $y = \| \mathbf{v} \| \sin \theta$, to identify the components of the vector.

 **2.7** Find the component form of vector $\mathbf{v}$ with magnitude $10$ that forms an angle of $120°$ with the positive $x$-axis.

## Unit Vectors

A **unit vector** is a vector with magnitude $1$. For any nonzero vector $\mathbf{v}$, we can use scalar multiplication to find a unit vector $\mathbf{u}$ that has the same direction as $\mathbf{v}$. To do this, we multiply the vector by the reciprocal of its magnitude:

$$\mathbf{u} = \frac{1}{\| \mathbf{v} \|} \mathbf{v}.$$

Recall that when we defined scalar multiplication, we noted that $\| k\mathbf{v} \| = |k| \cdot \| \mathbf{v} \|$. For $\mathbf{u} = \frac{1}{\| \mathbf{v} \|} \mathbf{v}$, it follows that $\| \mathbf{u} \| = \frac{1}{\| \mathbf{v} \|} (\| \mathbf{v} \|) = 1$. We say that $\mathbf{u}$ is the *unit vector in the direction of* $\mathbf{v}$ (**Figure 2.17**). The process of using scalar multiplication to find a unit vector with a given direction is called **normalization**.

**Figure 2.17** The vector $\mathbf{v}$ and associated unit vector $\mathbf{u} = \frac{1}{\| \mathbf{v} \|} \mathbf{v}$. In this case, $\| \mathbf{v} \| > 1$.

---

### Example 2.7

#### Finding a Unit Vector

Let $\mathbf{v} = \langle 1, 2 \rangle$.

    a. Find a unit vector with the same direction as $\mathbf{v}$.

    b. Find a vector $\mathbf{w}$ with the same direction as $\mathbf{v}$ such that $\| \mathbf{w} \| = 7$.

#### Solution

a.  First, find the magnitude of **v**, then divide the components of **v** by the magnitude:

$$\| \mathbf{v} \| = \sqrt{1^2 + 2^2} = \sqrt{1 + 4} = \sqrt{5}$$

$$\mathbf{u} = \frac{1}{\| \mathbf{v} \|}\mathbf{v} = \frac{1}{\sqrt{5}} \langle 1, 2 \rangle = \langle \frac{1}{\sqrt{5}}, \frac{2}{\sqrt{5}} \rangle.$$

b.  The vector **u** is in the same direction as **v** and $\| \mathbf{u} \| = 1$. Use scalar multiplication to increase the length of **u** without changing direction:

$$\mathbf{w} = 7\mathbf{u} = 7 \langle \frac{1}{\sqrt{5}}, \frac{2}{\sqrt{5}} \rangle = \langle \frac{7}{\sqrt{5}}, \frac{14}{\sqrt{5}} \rangle.$$

**2.8**  Let $\mathbf{v} = \langle 9, 2 \rangle$. Find a vector with magnitude 5 in the opposite direction as **v**.

We have seen how convenient it can be to write a vector in component form. Sometimes, though, it is more convenient to write a vector as a sum of a horizontal vector and a vertical vector. To make this easier, let's look at standard unit vectors. The **standard unit vectors** are the vectors $\mathbf{i} = \langle 1, 0 \rangle$ and $\mathbf{j} = \langle 0, 1 \rangle$ (**Figure 2.18**).

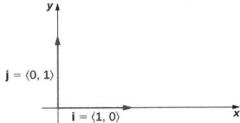

**Figure 2.18**  The standard unit vectors **i** and **j**.

By applying the properties of vectors, it is possible to express any vector in terms of **i** and **j** in what we call a *linear combination*:

$$\mathbf{v} = \langle x, y \rangle = \langle x, 0 \rangle + \langle 0, y \rangle = x \langle 1, 0 \rangle + y \langle 0, 1 \rangle = x\mathbf{i} + y\mathbf{j}.$$

Thus, **v** is the sum of a horizontal vector with magnitude $x$, and a vertical vector with magnitude $y$, as in the following figure.

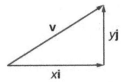

**Figure 2.19**  The vector **v** is the sum of $x\mathbf{i}$ and $y\mathbf{j}$.

## Example 2.8

### Using Standard Unit Vectors

a.  Express the vector $\mathbf{w} = \langle 3, -4 \rangle$ in terms of standard unit vectors.

b.  Vector $\mathbf{u}$ is a unit vector that forms an angle of $60°$ with the positive $x$-axis. Use standard unit vectors to describe $\mathbf{u}$.

### Solution

a.  Resolve vector $\mathbf{w}$ into a vector with a zero $y$-component and a vector with a zero $x$-component:

$$\mathbf{w} = \langle 3, -4 \rangle = 3\mathbf{i} - 4\mathbf{j}.$$

b.  Because $\mathbf{u}$ is a unit vector, the terminal point lies on the unit circle when the vector is placed in standard position (Figure 2.20).

$$u = \langle \cos 60°, \sin 60° \rangle$$
$$= \langle \tfrac{1}{2}, \tfrac{\sqrt{3}}{2} \rangle$$
$$= \tfrac{1}{2}\mathbf{i} + \tfrac{\sqrt{3}}{2}\mathbf{j}.$$

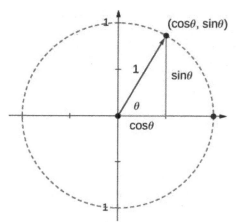

**Figure 2.20** The terminal point of $\mathbf{u}$ lies on the unit circle $(\cos \theta, \sin \theta)$.

 **2.9** Let $\mathbf{a} = \langle 16, -11 \rangle$ and let $\mathbf{b}$ be a unit vector that forms an angle of $225°$ with the positive $x$-axis. Express $\mathbf{a}$ and $\mathbf{b}$ in terms of the standard unit vectors.

## Applications of Vectors

Because vectors have both direction and magnitude, they are valuable tools for solving problems involving such applications as motion and force. Recall the boat example and the quarterback example we described earlier. Here we look at two other examples in detail.

### Example 2.9

## Finding Resultant Force

Jane's car is stuck in the mud. Lisa and Jed come along in a truck to help pull her out. They attach one end of a tow strap to the front of the car and the other end to the truck's trailer hitch, and the truck starts to pull. Meanwhile, Jane and Jed get behind the car and push. The truck generates a horizontal force of 300 lb on the car. Jane and Jed are pushing at a slight upward angle and generate a force of 150 lb on the car. These forces can be represented by vectors, as shown in **Figure 2.21**. The angle between these vectors is 15°. Find the resultant force (the vector sum) and give its magnitude to the nearest tenth of a pound and its direction angle from the positive $x$-axis.

**Figure 2.21** Two forces acting on a car in different directions.

### Solution

To find the effect of combining the two forces, add their representative vectors. First, express each vector in component form or in terms of the standard unit vectors. For this purpose, it is easiest if we align one of the vectors with the positive $x$-axis. The horizontal vector, then, has initial point $(0, 0)$ and terminal point $(300, 0)$. It can be expressed as $\langle 300, 0 \rangle$ or $300\mathbf{i}$.

The second vector has magnitude 150 and makes an angle of 15° with the first, so we can express it as $\langle 150\cos(15°), 150\sin(15°) \rangle$, or $150\cos(15°)\mathbf{i} + 150\sin(15°)\mathbf{j}$. Then, the sum of the vectors, or resultant vector, is $\mathbf{r} = \langle 300, 0 \rangle + \langle 150\cos(15°), 150\sin(15°) \rangle$, and we have

$$\| \mathbf{r} \| = \sqrt{(300 + 150\cos(15°))^2 + (150\sin(15°))^2}$$
$$\approx 446.6.$$

The angle $\theta$ made by $\mathbf{r}$ and the positive $x$-axis has $\tan\theta = \dfrac{150\sin 15°}{(300 + 150\cos 15°)} \approx 0.09$, so $\theta \approx \tan^{-1}(0.09) \approx 5°$, which means the resultant force $\mathbf{r}$ has an angle of 5° above the horizontal axis.

## Example 2.10

### Finding Resultant Velocity

An airplane flies due west at an airspeed of 425 mph. The wind is blowing from the northeast at 40 mph. What is the ground speed of the airplane? What is the bearing of the airplane?

### Solution

Let's start by sketching the situation described (**Figure 2.22**).

**Figure 2.22** Initially, the plane travels due west. The wind is from the northeast, so it is blowing to the southwest. The angle between the plane's course and the wind is $45°$. (Figure not drawn to scale.)

Set up a sketch so that the initial points of the vectors lie at the origin. Then, the plane's velocity vector is $\mathbf{p} = -425\mathbf{i}$. The vector describing the wind makes an angle of $225°$ with the positive $x$-axis:

$$\mathbf{w} = \langle\, 40\cos(225°),\, 40\sin(225°)\,\rangle = \langle\, -\frac{40}{\sqrt{2}},\, -\frac{40}{\sqrt{2}}\,\rangle = -\frac{40}{\sqrt{2}}\mathbf{i} - \frac{40}{\sqrt{2}}\mathbf{j}.$$

When the airspeed and the wind act together on the plane, we can add their vectors to find the resultant force:

$$\mathbf{p} + \mathbf{w} = -425\mathbf{i} + \left(-\frac{40}{\sqrt{2}}\mathbf{i} - \frac{40}{\sqrt{2}}\mathbf{j}\right) = \left(-425 - \frac{40}{\sqrt{2}}\right)\mathbf{i} - \frac{40}{\sqrt{2}}\mathbf{j}.$$

The magnitude of the resultant vector shows the effect of the wind on the ground speed of the airplane:

$$\| \mathbf{p} + \mathbf{w} \| = \sqrt{\left(-425 - \frac{40}{\sqrt{2}}\right)^2 + \left(-\frac{40}{\sqrt{2}}\right)^2} \approx 454.17 \text{ mph}$$

As a result of the wind, the plane is traveling at approximately $454$ mph relative to the ground.

To determine the bearing of the airplane, we want to find the direction of the vector $\mathbf{p} + \mathbf{w}$:

$$\tan\theta = \frac{-\frac{40}{\sqrt{2}}}{\left(-425 - \frac{40}{\sqrt{2}}\right)} \approx 0.06$$

$$\theta \approx 3.57°.$$

The overall direction of the plane is $3.57°$ south of west.

 **2.10** An airplane flies due north at an airspeed of $550$ mph. The wind is blowing from the northwest at $50$ mph. What is the ground speed of the airplane?

# 2.1 EXERCISES

For the following exercises, consider points $P(-1, 3)$, $Q(1, 5)$, and $R(-3, 7)$. Determine the requested vectors and express each of them a. in component form and b. by using the standard unit vectors.

1. $\vec{PQ}$

2. $\vec{PR}$

3. $\vec{QP}$

4. $\vec{RP}$

5. $\vec{PQ} + \vec{PR}$

6. $\vec{PQ} - \vec{PR}$

7. $2\vec{PQ} - 2\vec{PR}$

8. $2\vec{PQ} + \frac{1}{2}\vec{PR}$

9. The unit vector in the direction of $\vec{PQ}$

10. The unit vector in the direction of $\vec{PR}$

11. A vector $\mathbf{v}$ has initial point $(-1, -3)$ and terminal point $(2, 1)$. Find the unit vector in the direction of $\mathbf{v}$. Express the answer in component form.

12. A vector $\mathbf{v}$ has initial point $(-2, 5)$ and terminal point $(3, -1)$. Find the unit vector in the direction of $\mathbf{v}$. Express the answer in component form.

13. The vector $\mathbf{v}$ has initial point $P(1, 0)$ and terminal point $Q$ that is on the $y$-axis and above the initial point. Find the coordinates of terminal point $Q$ such that the magnitude of the vector $\mathbf{v}$ is $\sqrt{5}$.

14. The vector $\mathbf{v}$ has initial point $P(1, 1)$ and terminal point $Q$ that is on the $x$-axis and left of the initial point. Find the coordinates of terminal point $Q$ such that the magnitude of the vector $\mathbf{v}$ is $\sqrt{10}$.

For the following exercises, use the given vectors $\mathbf{a}$ and $\mathbf{b}$.

   a. Determine the vector sum $\mathbf{a} + \mathbf{b}$ and express it in both the component form and by using the standard unit vectors.

   b. Find the vector difference $\mathbf{a} - \mathbf{b}$ and express it in both the component form and by using the standard unit vectors.

   c. Verify that the vectors $\mathbf{a}$, $\mathbf{b}$, and $\mathbf{a} + \mathbf{b}$, and, respectively, $\mathbf{a}$, $\mathbf{b}$, and $\mathbf{a} - \mathbf{b}$ satisfy the triangle inequality.

   d. Determine the vectors $2\mathbf{a}$, $-\mathbf{b}$, and $2\mathbf{a} - \mathbf{b}$. Express the vectors in both the component form and by using standard unit vectors.

15. $\mathbf{a} = 2\mathbf{i} + \mathbf{j}$, $\mathbf{b} = \mathbf{i} + 3\mathbf{j}$

16. $\mathbf{a} = 2\mathbf{i}$, $\mathbf{b} = -2\mathbf{i} + 2\mathbf{j}$

17. Let $\mathbf{a}$ be a standard-position vector with terminal point $(-2, -4)$. Let $\mathbf{b}$ be a vector with initial point $(1, 2)$ and terminal point $(-1, 4)$. Find the magnitude of vector $-3\mathbf{a} + \mathbf{b} - 4\mathbf{i} + \mathbf{j}$.

18. Let $\mathbf{a}$ be a standard-position vector with terminal point at $(2, 5)$. Let $\mathbf{b}$ be a vector with initial point $(-1, 3)$ and terminal point $(1, 0)$. Find the magnitude of vector $\mathbf{a} - 3\mathbf{b} + 14\mathbf{i} - 14\mathbf{j}$.

19. Let $\mathbf{u}$ and $\mathbf{v}$ be two nonzero vectors that are nonequivalent. Consider the vectors $\mathbf{a} = 4\mathbf{u} + 5\mathbf{v}$ and $\mathbf{b} = \mathbf{u} + 2\mathbf{v}$ defined in terms of $\mathbf{u}$ and $\mathbf{v}$. Find the scalar $\lambda$ such that vectors $\mathbf{a} + \lambda\mathbf{b}$ and $\mathbf{u} - \mathbf{v}$ are equivalent.

20. Let $\mathbf{u}$ and $\mathbf{v}$ be two nonzero vectors that are nonequivalent. Consider the vectors $\mathbf{a} = 2\mathbf{u} - 4\mathbf{v}$ and $\mathbf{b} = 3\mathbf{u} - 7\mathbf{v}$ defined in terms of $\mathbf{u}$ and $\mathbf{v}$. Find the scalars $\alpha$ and $\beta$ such that vectors $\alpha\mathbf{a} + \beta\mathbf{b}$ and $\mathbf{u} - \mathbf{v}$ are equivalent.

21. Consider the vector $\mathbf{a}(t) = \langle \cos t, \sin t \rangle$ with components that depend on a real number $t$. As the number $t$ varies, the components of $\mathbf{a}(t)$ change as well, depending on the functions that define them.

   a. Write the vectors $\mathbf{a}(0)$ and $\mathbf{a}(\pi)$ in component form.

   b. Show that the magnitude $\| \mathbf{a}(t) \|$ of vector $\mathbf{a}(t)$ remains constant for any real number $t$.

   c. As $t$ varies, show that the terminal point of vector $\mathbf{a}(t)$ describes a circle centered at the origin of radius 1.

22. Consider vector $\mathbf{a}(x) = \langle x, \sqrt{1-x^2} \rangle$ with components that depend on a real number $x \in [-1, 1]$. As the number $x$ varies, the components of $\mathbf{a}(x)$ change as well, depending on the functions that define them.
   a. Write the vectors $\mathbf{a}(0)$ and $\mathbf{a}(1)$ in component form.
   b. Show that the magnitude $\| \mathbf{a}(x) \|$ of vector $\mathbf{a}(x)$ remains constant for any real number $x$
   c. As $x$ varies, show that the terminal point of vector $\mathbf{a}(x)$ describes a circle centered at the origin of radius 1.

23. Show that vectors $\mathbf{a}(t) = \langle \cos t, \sin t \rangle$ and $\mathbf{a}(x) = \langle x, \sqrt{1-x^2} \rangle$ are equivalent for $x = r$ and $t = 2k\pi$, where $k$ is an integer.

24. Show that vectors $\mathbf{a}(t) = \langle \cos t, \sin t \rangle$ and $\mathbf{a}(x) = \langle x, \sqrt{1-x^2} \rangle$ are opposite for $x = r$ and $t = \pi + 2k\pi$, where $k$ is an integer.

For the following exercises, find vector $\mathbf{v}$ with the given magnitude and in the same direction as vector $\mathbf{u}$.

25. $\| \mathbf{v} \| = 7, \mathbf{u} = \langle 3, 4 \rangle$

26. $\| \mathbf{v} \| = 3, \mathbf{u} = \langle -2, 5 \rangle$

27. $\| \mathbf{v} \| = 7, \mathbf{u} = \langle 3, -5 \rangle$

28. $\| \mathbf{v} \| = 10, \mathbf{u} = \langle 2, -1 \rangle$

For the following exercises, find the component form of vector $\mathbf{u}$, given its magnitude and the angle the vector makes with the positive $x$-axis. Give exact answers when possible.

29. $\| \mathbf{u} \| = 2, \quad \theta = 30°$

30. $\| \mathbf{u} \| = 6, \quad \theta = 60°$

31. $\| \mathbf{u} \| = 5, \quad \theta = \frac{\pi}{2}$

32. $\| \mathbf{u} \| = 8, \quad \theta = \pi$

33. $\| \mathbf{u} \| = 10, \quad \theta = \frac{5\pi}{6}$

34. $\| \mathbf{u} \| = 50, \quad \theta = \frac{3\pi}{4}$

For the following exercises, vector $\mathbf{u}$ is given. Find the

angle $\theta \in [0, 2\pi)$ that vector $\mathbf{u}$ makes with the positive direction of the $x$-axis, in a counter-clockwise direction.

35. $\mathbf{u} = 5\sqrt{2}\mathbf{i} - 5\sqrt{2}\mathbf{j}$

36. $\mathbf{u} = -\sqrt{3}\mathbf{i} - \mathbf{j}$

37. Let $\mathbf{a} = \langle a_1, a_2 \rangle$, $\mathbf{b} = \langle b_1, b_2 \rangle$, and $\mathbf{c} = \langle c_1, c_2 \rangle$ be three nonzero vectors. If $a_1 b_2 - a_2 b_1 \neq 0$, then show there are two scalars, $\alpha$ and $\beta$, such that $\mathbf{c} = \alpha \mathbf{a} + \beta \mathbf{b}$.

38. Consider vectors $\mathbf{a} = \langle 2, -4 \rangle$, $\mathbf{b} = \langle -1, 2 \rangle$, and $\mathbf{c} = \mathbf{0}$ Determine the scalars $\alpha$ and $\beta$ such that $\mathbf{c} = \alpha \mathbf{a} + \beta \mathbf{b}$.

39. Let $P(x_0, f(x_0))$ be a fixed point on the graph of the differential function $f$ with a domain that is the set of real numbers.
   a. Determine the real number $z_0$ such that point $Q(x_0 + 1, z_0)$ is situated on the line tangent to the graph of $f$ at point $P$.
   b. Determine the unit vector $\mathbf{u}$ with initial point $P$ and terminal point $Q$.

40. Consider the function $f(x) = x^4$, where $x \in \mathbb{R}$.
   a. Determine the real number $z_0$ such that point $Q(2, z_0)$ s situated on the line tangent to the graph of $f$ at point $P(1, 1)$.
   b. Determine the unit vector $\mathbf{u}$ with initial point $P$ and terminal point $Q$.

41. Consider $f$ and $g$ two functions defined on the same set of real numbers $D$. Let $\mathbf{a} = \langle x, f(x) \rangle$ and $\mathbf{b} = \langle x, g(x) \rangle$ be two vectors that describe the graphs of the functions, where $x \in D$. Show that if the graphs of the functions $f$ and $g$ do not intersect, then the vectors $\mathbf{a}$ and $\mathbf{b}$ are not equivalent.

42. Find $x \in \mathbb{R}$ such that vectors $\mathbf{a} = \langle x, \sin x \rangle$ and $\mathbf{b} = \langle x, \cos x \rangle$ are equivalent.

43. Calculate the coordinates of point $D$ such that $ABCD$ is a parallelogram, with $A(1, 1)$, $B(2, 4)$, and $C(7, 4)$.

44. Consider the points $A(2, 1)$, $B(10, 6)$, $C(13, 4)$, and $D(16, -2)$. Determine the component form of vector $\overrightarrow{AD}$.

45. The speed of an object is the magnitude of its related velocity vector. A football thrown by a quarterback has an initial speed of 70 mph and an angle of elevation of 30°. Determine the velocity vector in mph and express it in component form. (Round to two decimal places.)

46. A baseball player throws a baseball at an angle of 30° with the horizontal. If the initial speed of the ball is 100 mph, find the horizontal and vertical components of the initial velocity vector of the baseball. (Round to two decimal places.)

47. A bullet is fired with an initial velocity of 1500 ft/sec at an angle of 60° with the horizontal. Find the horizontal and vertical components of the velocity vector of the bullet. (Round to two decimal places.)

48. [T] A 65-kg sprinter exerts a force of 798 N at a 19° angle with respect to the ground on the starting block at the instant a race begins. Find the horizontal component of the force. (Round to two decimal places.)

49. [T] Two forces, a horizontal force of 45 lb and another of 52 lb, act on the same object. The angle between these forces is 25°. Find the magnitude and direction angle from the positive x-axis of the resultant force that acts on the object. (Round to two decimal places.)

50. [T] Two forces, a vertical force of 26 lb and another of 45 lb, act on the same object. The angle between these forces is 55°. Find the magnitude and direction angle from the positive x-axis of the resultant force that acts on the object. (Round to two decimal places.)

51. [T] Three forces act on object. Two of the forces have the magnitudes 58 N and 27 N, and make angles 53° and 152°, respectively, with the positive x-axis. Find the magnitude and the direction angle from the positive x-axis of the third force such that the resultant force acting on the object is zero. (Round to two decimal places.)

52. Three forces with magnitudes 80 lb, 120 lb, and 60 lb act on an object at angles of 45°, 60° and 30°, respectively, with the positive x-axis. Find the magnitude and direction angle from the positive x-axis of the resultant force. (Round to two decimal places.)

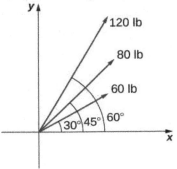

53. [T] An airplane is flying in the direction of 43° east of north (also abbreviated as N43E) at a speed of 550 mph. A wind with speed 25 mph comes from the southwest at a bearing of N15E. What are the ground speed and new direction of the airplane?

54. **[T]** A boat is traveling in the water at 30 mph in a direction of N20E (that is, 20° east of north). A strong current is moving at 15 mph in a direction of N45E. What are the new speed and direction of the boat?

55. **[T]** A 50-lb weight is hung by a cable so that the two portions of the cable make angles of 40° and 53°, respectively, with the horizontal. Find the magnitudes of the forces of tension $T_1$ and $T_2$ in the cables if the resultant force acting on the object is zero. (Round to two decimal places.)

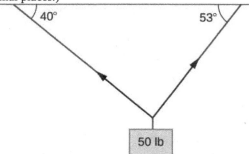

56. **[T]** A 62-lb weight hangs from a rope that makes the angles of 29° and 61°, respectively, with the horizontal. Find the magnitudes of the forces of tension $T_1$ and $T_2$ in the cables if the resultant force acting on the object is zero. (Round to two decimal places.)

57. **[T]** A 1500-lb boat is parked on a ramp that makes an angle of 30° with the horizontal. The boat's weight vector points downward and is a sum of two vectors: a horizontal vector $v_1$ that is parallel to the ramp and a vertical vector $v_2$ that is perpendicular to the inclined surface. The magnitudes of vectors $v_1$ and $v_2$ are the horizontal and vertical component, respectively, of the boat's weight vector. Find the magnitudes of $v_1$ and $v_2$. (Round to the nearest integer.)

58. **[T]** An 85-lb box is at rest on a 26° incline. Determine the magnitude of the force parallel to the incline necessary to keep the box from sliding. (Round to the nearest integer.)

59. A guy-wire supports a pole that is 75 ft high. One end of the wire is attached to the top of the pole and the other end is anchored to the ground 50 ft from the base of the pole. Determine the horizontal and vertical components of the force of tension in the wire if its magnitude is 50 lb. (Round to the nearest integer.)

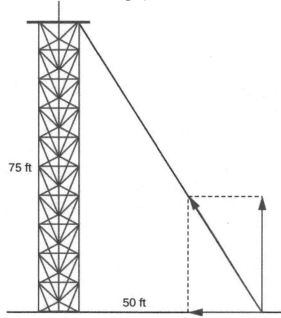

60. A telephone pole guy-wire has an angle of elevation of 35° with respect to the ground. The force of tension in the guy-wire is 120 lb. Find the horizontal and vertical components of the force of tension. (Round to the nearest integer.)

# 2.2 | Vectors in Three Dimensions

## Learning Objectives

2.2.1  Describe three-dimensional space mathematically.

2.2.2  Locate points in space using coordinates.

2.2.3  Write the distance formula in three dimensions.

2.2.4  Write the equations for simple planes and spheres.

2.2.5  Perform vector operations in $\mathbb{R}^3$.

Vectors are useful tools for solving two-dimensional problems. Life, however, happens in three dimensions. To expand the use of vectors to more realistic applications, it is necessary to create a framework for describing three-dimensional space. For example, although a two-dimensional map is a useful tool for navigating from one place to another, in some cases the topography of the land is important. Does your planned route go through the mountains? Do you have to cross a river? To appreciate fully the impact of these geographic features, you must use three dimensions. This section presents a natural extension of the two-dimensional Cartesian coordinate plane into three dimensions.

## Three-Dimensional Coordinate Systems

As we have learned, the two-dimensional rectangular coordinate system contains two perpendicular axes: the horizontal $x$-axis and the vertical $y$-axis. We can add a third dimension, the $z$-axis, which is perpendicular to both the $x$-axis and the $y$-axis. We call this system the three-dimensional rectangular coordinate system. It represents the three dimensions we encounter in real life.

### Definition

The **three-dimensional rectangular coordinate system** consists of three perpendicular axes: the $x$-axis, the $y$-axis, and the $z$-axis. Because each axis is a number line representing all real numbers in $\mathbb{R}$, the three-dimensional system is often denoted by $\mathbb{R}^3$.

In **Figure 2.23**(a), the positive $z$-axis is shown above the plane containing the $x$- and $y$-axes. The positive $x$-axis appears to the left and the positive $y$-axis is to the right. A natural question to ask is: How was arrangement determined? The system displayed follows the **right-hand rule**. If we take our right hand and align the fingers with the positive $x$-axis, then curl the fingers so they point in the direction of the positive $y$-axis, our thumb points in the direction of the positive $z$-axis. In this text, we always work with coordinate systems set up in accordance with the right-hand rule. Some systems do follow a left-hand rule, but the right-hand rule is considered the standard representation.

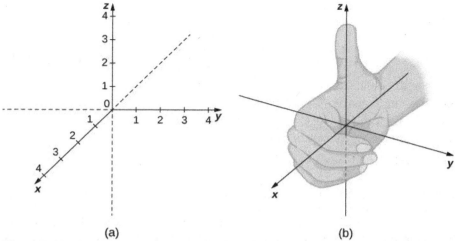

(a)                                        (b)

Figure 2.23   (a) We can extend the two-dimensional rectangular coordinate system by adding a third axis, the z-axis, that is perpendicular to both the x-axis and the y-axis. (b) The right-hand rule is used to determine the placement of the coordinate axes in the standard Cartesian plane.

In two dimensions, we describe a point in the plane with the coordinates $(x, y)$. Each coordinate describes how the point aligns with the corresponding axis. In three dimensions, a new coordinate, $z$, is appended to indicate alignment with the z-axis: $(x, y, z)$. A point in space is identified by all three coordinates (**Figure 2.24**). To plot the point $(x, y, z)$, go $x$ units along the x-axis, then $y$ units in the direction of the y-axis, then $z$ units in the direction of the z-axis.

Figure 2.24   To plot the point $(x, y, z)$ go $x$ units along the x-axis, then $y$ units in the direction of the y-axis, then $z$ units in the direction of the z-axis.

## Example 2.11

### Locating Points in Space

Sketch the point $(1, -2, 3)$ in three-dimensional space.

### Solution

To sketch a point, start by sketching three sides of a rectangular prism along the coordinate axes: one unit in the positive $x$ direction, 2 units in the negative $y$ direction, and 3 units in the positive $z$ direction. Complete the prism to plot the point (**Figure 2.25**).

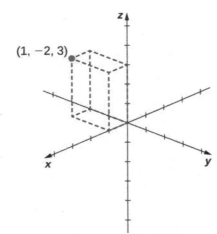

**Figure 2.25** Sketching the point $(1, -2, 3)$.

 **2.11** Sketch the point $(-2, 3, -1)$ in three-dimensional space.

In two-dimensional space, the coordinate plane is defined by a pair of perpendicular axes. These axes allow us to name any location within the plane. In three dimensions, we define **coordinate planes** by the coordinate axes, just as in two dimensions. There are three axes now, so there are three intersecting pairs of axes. Each pair of axes forms a coordinate plane: the $xy$-plane, the $xz$-plane, and the $yz$-plane (**Figure 2.26**). We define the $xy$-plane formally as the following set: $\{(x, y, 0) : x, y \in \mathbb{R}\}$. Similarly, the $xz$-plane and the $yz$-plane are defined as $\{(x, 0, z) : x, z \in \mathbb{R}\}$ and $\{(0, y, z) : y, z \in \mathbb{R}\}$, respectively.

To visualize this, imagine you're building a house and are standing in a room with only two of the four walls finished. (Assume the two finished walls are adjacent to each other.) If you stand with your back to the corner where the two finished walls meet, facing out into the room, the floor is the $xy$-plane, the wall to your right is the $xz$-plane, and the wall to your left is the $yz$-plane.

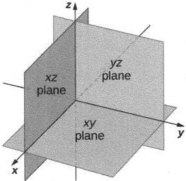

**Figure 2.26** The plane containing the $x$- and $y$-axes is called the $xy$-plane. The plane containing the $x$- and $z$-axes is called the $xz$-plane, and the $y$- and $z$-axes define the $yz$-plane.

In two dimensions, the coordinate axes partition the plane into four quadrants. Similarly, the coordinate planes divide space between them into eight regions about the origin, called **octants**. The octants fill $\mathbb{R}^3$ in the same way that quadrants fill

$\mathbb{R}^2$ , as shown in **Figure 2.27**.

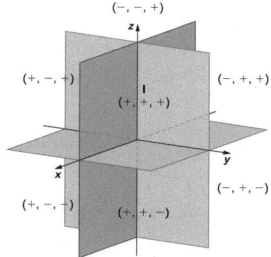

**Figure 2.27** Points that lie in octants have three nonzero coordinates.

Most work in three-dimensional space is a comfortable extension of the corresponding concepts in two dimensions. In this section, we use our knowledge of circles to describe spheres, then we expand our understanding of vectors to three dimensions. To accomplish these goals, we begin by adapting the distance formula to three-dimensional space.

If two points lie in the same coordinate plane, then it is straightforward to calculate the distance between them. We that the distance $d$ between two points $(x_1, y_1)$ and $(x_2, y_2)$ in the $xy$-coordinate plane is given by the formula

$$d = \sqrt{(x_2 - x_1)^2 + (y_2 - y_1)^2}.$$

The formula for the distance between two points in space is a natural extension of this formula.

---

**Theorem 2.2: The Distance between Two Points in Space**

The distance $d$ between points $(x_1, y_1, z_1)$ and $(x_2, y_2, z_2)$ is given by the formula

$$d = \sqrt{(x_2 - x_1)^2 + (y_2 - y_1)^2 + (z_2 - z_1)^2}. \tag{2.1}$$

---

The proof of this theorem is left as an exercise. (*Hint:* First find the distance $d_1$ between the points $(x_1, y_1, z_1)$ and $(x_2, y_2, z_1)$ as shown in **Figure 2.28**.)

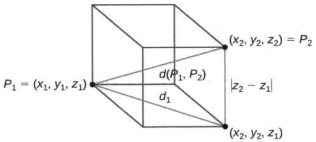

**Figure 2.28** The distance between $P_1$ and $P_2$ is the length of the diagonal of the rectangular prism having $P_1$ and $P_2$ as opposite corners.

## Example 2.12

### Distance in Space

Find the distance between points $P_1 = (3, -1, 5)$ and $P_2 = (2, 1, -1)$.

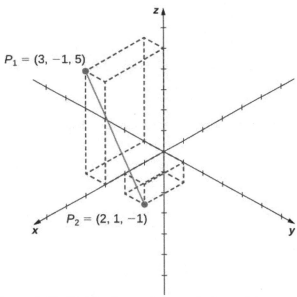

**Figure 2.29** Find the distance between the two points.

### Solution

Substitute values directly into the distance formula:

$$d(P_1, P_2) = \sqrt{(x_2 - x_1)^2 + (y_2 - y_1)^2 + (z_2 - z_1)^2}$$
$$= \sqrt{(2 - 3)^2 + (1 - (-1))^2 + (-1 - 5)^2}$$
$$= \sqrt{1^2 + 2^2 + (-6)^2}$$
$$= \sqrt{41}.$$

  **2.12** Find the distance between points $P_1 = (1, -5, 4)$ and $P_2 = (4, -1, -1)$.

Before moving on to the next section, let's get a feel for how $\mathbb{R}^3$ differs from $\mathbb{R}^2$. For example, in $\mathbb{R}^2$, lines that are not parallel must always intersect. This is not the case in $\mathbb{R}^3$. For example, consider the line shown in **Figure 2.30**. These two lines are not parallel, nor do they intersect.

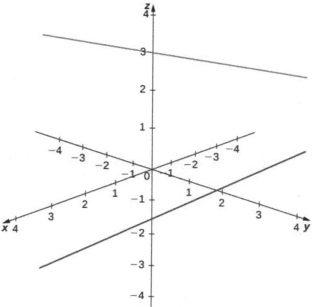

**Figure 2.30** These two lines are not parallel, but still do not intersect.

You can also have circles that are interconnected but have no points in common, as in **Figure 2.31**.

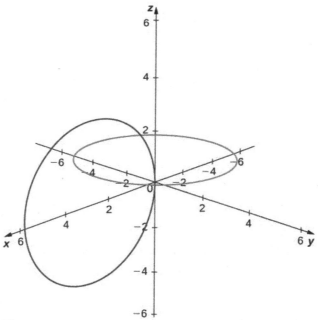

**Figure 2.31** These circles are interconnected, but have no points in common.

We have a lot more flexibility working in three dimensions than we do if we stuck with only two dimensions.

# Writing Equations in $\mathbb{R}^3$

Now that we can represent points in space and find the distance between them, we can learn how to write equations of geometric objects such as lines, planes, and curved surfaces in $\mathbb{R}^3$. First, we start with a simple equation. Compare the graphs of the equation $x = 0$ in $\mathbb{R}$, $\mathbb{R}^2$, and $\mathbb{R}^3$ (Figure 2.32). From these graphs, we can see the same equation can describe a point, a line, or a plane.

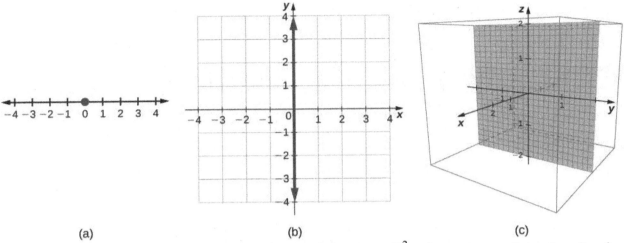

(a)        (b)        (c)

Figure 2.32 (a) In $\mathbb{R}$, the equation $x = 0$ describes a single point. (b) In $\mathbb{R}^2$, the equation $x = 0$ describes a line, the y-axis. (c) In $\mathbb{R}^3$, the equation $x = 0$ describes a plane, the yz-plane.

In space, the equation $x = 0$ describes all points $(0, y, z)$. This equation defines the yz-plane. Similarly, the xy-plane contains all points of the form $(x, y, 0)$. The equation $z = 0$ defines the xy-plane and the equation $y = 0$ describes the xz-plane (Figure 2.33).

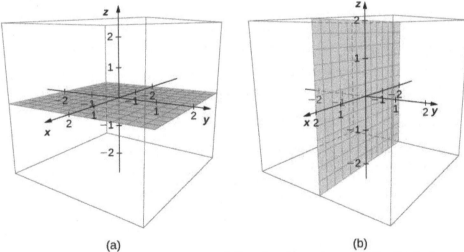

(a)        (b)

Figure 2.33 (a) In space, the equation $z = 0$ describes the xy-plane. (b) All points in the xz-plane satisfy the equation $y = 0$.

Understanding the equations of the coordinate planes allows us to write an equation for any plane that is parallel to one of the coordinate planes. When a plane is parallel to the xy-plane, for example, the z-coordinate of each point in the plane has the same constant value. Only the x- and y-coordinates of points in that plane vary from point to point.

**Rule: Equations of Planes Parallel to Coordinate Planes**

1. The plane in space that is parallel to the $xy$-plane and contains point $(a, b, c)$ can be represented by the equation $z = c$.

2. The plane in space that is parallel to the $xz$-plane and contains point $(a, b, c)$ can be represented by the equation $y = b$.

3. The plane in space that is parallel to the $yz$-plane and contains point $(a, b, c)$ can be represented by the equation $x = a$.

## Example 2.13

### Writing Equations of Planes Parallel to Coordinate Planes

a. Write an equation of the plane passing through point $(3, 11, 7)$ that is parallel to the $yz$-plane.

b. Find an equation of the plane passing through points $(6, -2, 9)$, $(0, -2, 4)$, and $(1, -2, -3)$.

**Solution**

a. When a plane is parallel to the $yz$-plane, only the $y$- and $z$-coordinates may vary. The $x$-coordinate has the same constant value for all points in this plane, so this plane can be represented by the equation $x = 3$.

b. Each of the points $(6, -2, 9)$, $(0, -2, 4)$, and $(1, -2, -3)$ has the same $y$-coordinate. This plane can be represented by the equation $y = -2$.

 **2.13** Write an equation of the plane passing through point $(1, -6, -4)$ that is parallel to the $xy$-plane.

As we have seen, in $\mathbb{R}^2$ the equation $x = 5$ describes the vertical line passing through point $(5, 0)$. This line is parallel to the $y$-axis. In a natural extension, the equation $x = 5$ in $\mathbb{R}^3$ describes the plane passing through point $(5, 0, 0)$, which is parallel to the $yz$-plane. Another natural extension of a familiar equation is found in the equation of a sphere.

**Definition**

A **sphere** is the set of all points in space equidistant from a fixed point, the center of the sphere (Figure 2.34), just as the set of all points in a plane that are equidistant from the center represents a circle. In a sphere, as in a circle, the distance from the center to a point on the sphere is called the *radius*.

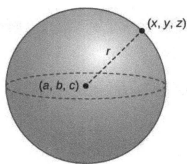

**Figure 2.34** Each point $(x, y, z)$ on the surface of a sphere is $r$ units away from the center $(a, b, c)$.

The equation of a circle is derived using the distance formula in two dimensions. In the same way, the equation of a sphere is based on the three-dimensional formula for distance.

---

**Rule: Equation of a Sphere**

The sphere with center $(a, b, c)$ and radius $r$ can be represented by the equation

$$(x - a)^2 + (y - b)^2 + (z - c)^2 = r^2. \tag{2.2}$$

This equation is known as the **standard equation of a sphere**.

## Example 2.14

### Finding an Equation of a Sphere

Find the standard equation of the sphere with center $(10, 7, 4)$ and point $(-1, 3, -2)$, as shown in **Figure 2.35**.

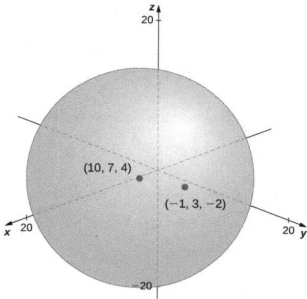

**Figure 2.35** The sphere centered at $(10, 7, 4)$ containing point $(-1, 3, -2)$.

### Solution

Use the distance formula to find the radius $r$ of the sphere:

$$\begin{aligned} r &= \sqrt{(-1-10)^2 + (3-7)^2 + (-2-4)^2} \\ &= \sqrt{(-11)^2 + (-4)^2 + (-6)^2} \\ &= \sqrt{173}. \end{aligned}$$

The standard equation of the sphere is

$$(x-10)^2 + (y-7)^2 + (z-4)^2 = 173.$$

 **2.14** Find the standard equation of the sphere with center $(-2, 4, -5)$ containing point $(4, 4, -1)$.

## Example 2.15

### Finding the Equation of a Sphere

Let $P = (-5, 2, 3)$ and $Q = (3, 4, -1)$, and suppose line segment $PQ$ forms the diameter of a sphere

(**Figure 2.36**). Find the equation of the sphere.

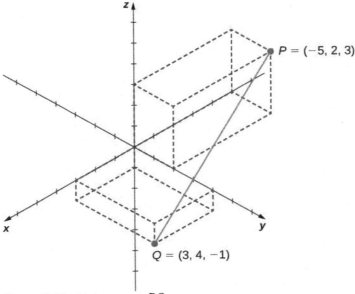

**Figure 2.36** Line segment $PQ$.

## Solution

Since $PQ$ is a diameter of the sphere, we know the center of the sphere is the midpoint of $PQ$. Then,

$$C = \left(\frac{-5+3}{2}, \frac{2+4}{2}, \frac{3+(-1)}{2}\right)$$
$$= (-1, 3, 1).$$

Furthermore, we know the radius of the sphere is half the length of the diameter. This gives

$$r = \frac{1}{2}\sqrt{(-5-3)^2 + (2-4)^2 + (3-(-1))^2}$$
$$= \frac{1}{2}\sqrt{64 + 4 + 16}$$
$$= \sqrt{21}.$$

Then, the equation of the sphere is $(x+1)^2 + (y-3)^2 + (z-1)^2 = 21$.

 **2.15** Find the equation of the sphere with diameter $PQ$, where $P = (2, -1, -3)$ and $Q = (-2, 5, -1)$.

## Example 2.16

### Graphing Other Equations in Three Dimensions

Describe the set of points that satisfies $(x-4)(z-2) = 0$, and graph the set.

### Solution

We must have either $x - 4 = 0$ or $z - 2 = 0$, so the set of points forms the two planes $x = 4$ and $z = 2$ (**Figure 2.37**).

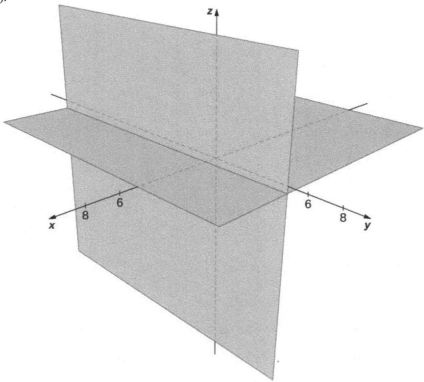

**Figure 2.37** The set of points satisfying $(x - 4)(z - 2) = 0$ forms the two planes $x = 4$ and $z = 2$.

 **2.16** Describe the set of points that satisfies $(y + 2)(z - 3) = 0$, and graph the set.

---

### Example 2.17

### Graphing Other Equations in Three Dimensions

Describe the set of points in three-dimensional space that satisfies $(x - 2)^2 + (y - 1)^2 = 4$, and graph the set.

### Solution

The $x$- and $y$-coordinates form a circle in the $xy$-plane of radius 2, centered at $(2, 1)$. Since there is no restriction on the $z$-coordinate, the three-dimensional result is a circular cylinder of radius 2 centered on the line with $x = 2$ and $y = 1$. The cylinder extends indefinitely in the $z$-direction (**Figure 2.38**).

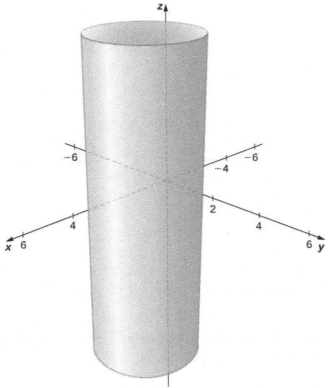

**Figure 2.38** The set of points satisfying
$(x-2)^2 + (y-1)^2 = 4.$ This is a cylinder of radius 2 centered
on the line with $x = 2$ and $y = 1.$

 **2.17** Describe the set of points in three dimensional space that satisfies $x^2 + (z-2)^2 = 16,$ and graph the surface.

## Working with Vectors in $\mathbb{R}^3$

Just like two-dimensional vectors, three-dimensional vectors are quantities with both magnitude and direction, and they are represented by directed line segments (arrows). With a three-dimensional vector, we use a three-dimensional arrow.

Three-dimensional vectors can also be represented in component form. The notation $\mathbf{v} = \langle x, y, z \rangle$ is a natural extension of the two-dimensional case, representing a vector with the initial point at the origin, $(0, 0, 0),$ and terminal point $(x, y, z).$ The zero vector is $\mathbf{0} = \langle 0, 0, 0 \rangle.$ So, for example, the three dimensional vector $\mathbf{v} = \langle 2, 4, 1 \rangle$ is represented by a directed line segment from point $(0, 0, 0)$ to point $(2, 4, 1)$ (**Figure 2.39**).

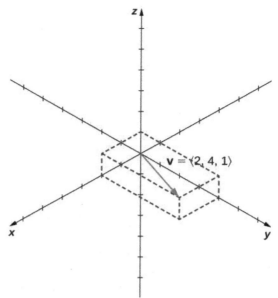

**Figure 2.39** Vector $\mathbf{v} = \langle\, 2, 4, 1\, \rangle$ is represented by a directed line segment from point $(0, 0, 0)$ to point $(2, 4, 1)$.

Vector addition and scalar multiplication are defined analogously to the two-dimensional case. If $\mathbf{v} = \langle\, x_1, y_1, z_1\, \rangle$ and $\mathbf{w} = \langle\, x_2, y_2, z_2\, \rangle$ are vectors, and $k$ is a scalar, then

$$\mathbf{v} + \mathbf{w} = \langle\, x_1 + x_2,\, y_1 + y_2,\, z_1 + z_2\, \rangle \text{ and } k\mathbf{v} = \langle\, kx_1,\, ky_1,\, kz_1\, \rangle\,.$$

If $k = -1$, then $k\mathbf{v} = (-1)\mathbf{v}$ is written as $-\mathbf{v}$, and vector subtraction is defined by $\mathbf{v} - \mathbf{w} = \mathbf{v} + (-\mathbf{w}) = \mathbf{v} + (-1)\mathbf{w}$.

The standard unit vectors extend easily into three dimensions as well—$\mathbf{i} = \langle\, 1, 0, 0\, \rangle$, $\mathbf{j} = \langle\, 0, 1, 0\, \rangle$, and $\mathbf{k} = \langle\, 0, 0, 1\, \rangle$ —and we use them in the same way we used the standard unit vectors in two dimensions. Thus, we can represent a vector in $\mathbb{R}^3$ in the following ways:

$$\mathbf{v} = \langle\, x, y, z\, \rangle = x\mathbf{i} + y\mathbf{j} + z\mathbf{k}.$$

## Example 2.18

### Vector Representations

Let $\overrightarrow{PQ}$ be the vector with initial point $P = (3, 12, 6)$ and terminal point $Q = (-4, -3, 2)$ as shown in Figure 2.40. Express $\overrightarrow{PQ}$ in both component form and using standard unit vectors.

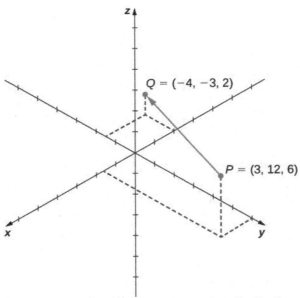

**Figure 2.40** The vector with initial point $P = (3, 12, 6)$ and terminal point $Q = (-4, -3, 2)$.

### Solution

In component form,

$$\vec{PQ} = \langle x_2 - x_1, y_2 - y_1, z_2 - z_1 \rangle$$
$$= \langle -4 - 3, -3 - 12, 2 - 6 \rangle = \langle -7, -15, -4 \rangle .$$

In standard unit form,

$$\vec{PQ} = -7\mathbf{i} - 15\mathbf{j} - 4\mathbf{k}.$$

 **2.18** Let $S = (3, 8, 2)$ and $T = (2, -1, 3)$. Express $\vec{ST}$ in component form and in standard unit form.

As described earlier, vectors in three dimensions behave in the same way as vectors in a plane. The geometric interpretation of vector addition, for example, is the same in both two- and three-dimensional space (Figure 2.41).

**Figure 2.41** To add vectors in three dimensions, we follow the same procedures we learned for two dimensions.

We have already seen how some of the algebraic properties of vectors, such as vector addition and scalar multiplication, can be extended to three dimensions. Other properties can be extended in similar fashion. They are summarized here for our reference.

**Rule: Properties of Vectors in Space**

Let $\mathbf{v} = \langle x_1, y_1, z_1 \rangle$ and $\mathbf{w} = \langle x_2, y_2, z_2 \rangle$ be vectors, and let $k$ be a scalar.

**Scalar multiplication:** $k\mathbf{v} = \langle kx_1, ky_1, kz_1 \rangle$

**Vector addition:** $\mathbf{v} + \mathbf{w} = \langle x_1, y_1, z_1 \rangle + \langle x_2, y_2, z_2 \rangle = \langle x_1 + x_2, y_1 + y_2, z_1 + z_2 \rangle$

**Vector subtraction:** $\mathbf{v} - \mathbf{w} = \langle x_1, y_1, z_1 \rangle - \langle x_2, y_2, z_2 \rangle = \langle x_1 - x_2, y_1 - y_2, z_1 - z_2 \rangle$

**Vector magnitude:** $\| \mathbf{v} \| = \sqrt{x_1{}^2 + y_1{}^2 + z_1{}^2}$

**Unit vector in the direction of v:** $\dfrac{1}{\| \mathbf{v} \|}\mathbf{v} = \dfrac{1}{\| \mathbf{v} \|} \langle x_1, y_1, z_1 \rangle = \langle \dfrac{x_1}{\| \mathbf{v} \|}, \dfrac{y_1}{\| \mathbf{v} \|}, \dfrac{z_1}{\| \mathbf{v} \|} \rangle$, if $\mathbf{v} \neq \mathbf{0}$

We have seen that vector addition in two dimensions satisfies the commutative, associative, and additive inverse properties. These properties of vector operations are valid for three-dimensional vectors as well. Scalar multiplication of vectors satisfies the distributive property, and the zero vector acts as an additive identity. The proofs to verify these properties in three dimensions are straightforward extensions of the proofs in two dimensions.

### Example 2.19

#### Vector Operations in Three Dimensions

Let $\mathbf{v} = \langle -2, 9, 5 \rangle$ and $\mathbf{w} = \langle 1, -1, 0 \rangle$ (**Figure 2.42**). Find the following vectors.

a. $3\mathbf{v} - 2\mathbf{w}$

b. $5 \| \mathbf{w} \|$

c. $\| 5\mathbf{w} \|$

d. A unit vector in the direction of $\mathbf{v}$

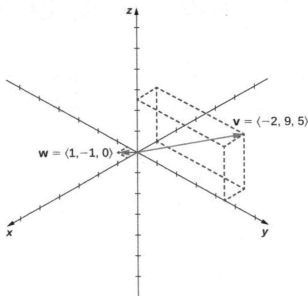

**Figure 2.42** The vectors $\mathbf{v} = \langle -2, 9, 5 \rangle$ and $\mathbf{w} = \langle 1, -1, 0 \rangle$.

## Solution

a. First, use scalar multiplication of each vector, then subtract:

$$\begin{aligned}
3\mathbf{v} - 2\mathbf{w} &= 3\langle -2, 9, 5 \rangle - 2\langle 1, -1, 0 \rangle \\
&= \langle -6, 27, 15 \rangle - \langle 2, -2, 0 \rangle \\
&= \langle -6 - 2,\, 27 - (-2),\, 15 - 0 \rangle \\
&= \langle -8, 29, 15 \rangle.
\end{aligned}$$

b. Write the equation for the magnitude of the vector, then use scalar multiplication:

$$5 \| \mathbf{w} \| = 5\sqrt{1^2 + (-1)^2 + 0^2} = 5\sqrt{2}.$$

c. First, use scalar multiplication, then find the magnitude of the new vector. Note that the result is the same as for part b.:

$$\| 5\mathbf{w} \| = \| \langle 5, -5, 0 \rangle \| = \sqrt{5^2 + (-5)^2 + 0^2} = \sqrt{50} = 5\sqrt{2}.$$

d. Recall that to find a unit vector in two dimensions, we divide a vector by its magnitude. The procedure is the same in three dimensions:

$$\begin{aligned}
\frac{\mathbf{v}}{\| \mathbf{v} \|} &= \frac{1}{\| \mathbf{v} \|} \langle -2, 9, 5 \rangle \\
&= \frac{1}{\sqrt{(-2)^2 + 9^2 + 5^2}} \langle -2, 9, 5 \rangle \\
&= \frac{1}{\sqrt{110}} \langle -2, 9, 5 \rangle \\
&= \langle \frac{-2}{\sqrt{110}}, \frac{9}{\sqrt{110}}, \frac{5}{\sqrt{110}} \rangle.
\end{aligned}$$

**2.19** Let $\mathbf{v} = \langle -1, -1, 1 \rangle$ and $\mathbf{w} = \langle 2, 0, 1 \rangle$. Find a unit vector in the direction of $5\mathbf{v} + 3\mathbf{w}$.

### Example 2.20

## Throwing a Forward Pass

A quarterback is standing on the football field preparing to throw a pass. His receiver is standing 20 yd down the field and 15 yd to the quarterback's left. The quarterback throws the ball at a velocity of 60 mph toward the receiver at an upward angle of 30° (see the following figure). Write the initial velocity vector of the ball, **v,** in component form.

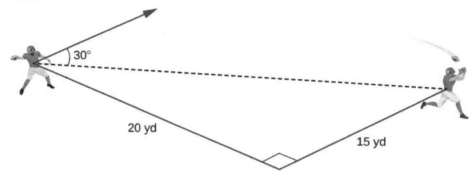

## Solution

The first thing we want to do is find a vector in the same direction as the velocity vector of the ball. We then scale the vector appropriately so that it has the right magnitude. Consider the vector **w** extending from the quarterback's arm to a point directly above the receiver's head at an angle of 30° (see the following figure). This vector would have the same direction as **v,** but it may not have the right magnitude.

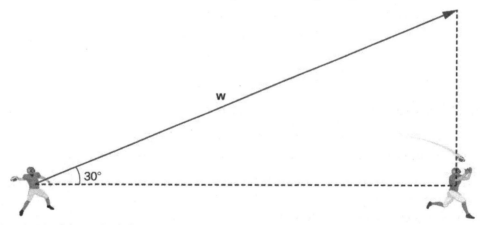

The receiver is 20 yd down the field and 15 yd to the quarterback's left. Therefore, the straight-line distance from the quarterback to the receiver is

$$\text{Dist from QB to receiver} = \sqrt{15^2 + 20^2} = \sqrt{225 + 400} = \sqrt{625} = 25 \text{ yd.}$$

We have $\dfrac{25}{\| \mathbf{w} \|} = \cos 30°.$ Then the magnitude of **w** is given by

$$\| \mathbf{w} \| = \frac{25}{\cos 30°} = \frac{25 \cdot 2}{\sqrt{3}} = \frac{50}{\sqrt{3}} \text{ yd}$$

and the vertical distance from the receiver to the terminal point of **w** is

$$\text{Vert dist from receiver to terminal point of } \mathbf{w} = \| \mathbf{w} \| \sin 30° = \frac{50}{\sqrt{3}} \cdot \frac{1}{2} = \frac{25}{\sqrt{3}} \text{ yd.}$$

Then $\mathbf{w} = \langle 20, 15, \frac{25}{\sqrt{3}} \rangle$, and has the same direction as $\mathbf{v}$.

Recall, though, that we calculated the magnitude of $\mathbf{w}$ to be $\| \mathbf{w} \| = \frac{50}{\sqrt{3}}$, and $\mathbf{v}$ has magnitude 60 mph.

So, we need to multiply vector $\mathbf{w}$ by an appropriate constant, $k$. We want to find a value of $k$ so that $\| k\mathbf{w} \| = 60$ mph. We have

$$\| k\mathbf{w} \| = k \| \mathbf{w} \| = k\frac{50}{\sqrt{3}} \text{ mph,}$$

so we want

$$k\frac{50}{\sqrt{3}} = 60$$

$$k = \frac{60\sqrt{3}}{50}$$

$$k = \frac{6\sqrt{3}}{5}.$$

Then

$$\mathbf{v} = k\mathbf{w} = k \langle 20, 15, \frac{25}{\sqrt{3}} \rangle = \frac{6\sqrt{3}}{5} \langle 20, 15, \frac{25}{\sqrt{3}} \rangle = \langle 24\sqrt{3}, 18\sqrt{3}, 30 \rangle.$$

Let's double-check that $\| \mathbf{v} \| = 60$. We have

$$\| \mathbf{v} \| = \sqrt{(24\sqrt{3})^2 + (18\sqrt{3})^2 + (30)^2} = \sqrt{1728 + 972 + 900} = \sqrt{3600} = 60 \text{ mph.}$$

So, we have found the correct components for $\mathbf{v}$.

 **2.20** Assume the quarterback and the receiver are in the same place as in the previous example. This time, however, the quarterback throws the ball at velocity of 40 mph and an angle of 45°. Write the initial velocity vector of the ball, $\mathbf{v}$, in component form.

# 2.2 EXERCISES

**61.** Consider a rectangular box with one of the vertices at the origin, as shown in the following figure. If point $A(2, 3, 5)$ is the opposite vertex to the origin, then find

    a. the coordinates of the other six vertices of the box and

    b. the length of the diagonal of the box determined by the vertices $O$ and $A$.

**62.** Find the coordinates of point $P$ and determine its distance to the origin.

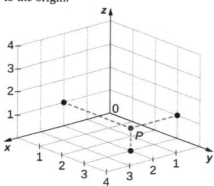

For the following exercises, describe and graph the set of points that satisfies the given equation.

**63.** $(y - 5)(z - 6) = 0$

**64.** $(z - 2)(z - 5) = 0$

**65.** $(y - 1)^2 + (z - 1)^2 = 1$

**66.** $(x - 2)^2 + (z - 5)^2 = 4$

**67.** Write the equation of the plane passing through point $(1, 1, 1)$ that is parallel to the $xy$-plane.

**68.** Write the equation of the plane passing through point $(1, -3, 2)$ that is parallel to the $xz$-plane.

**69.** Find an equation of the plane passing through points $(1, -3, -2)$, $(0, 3, -2)$, and $(1, 0, -2)$.

**70.** Find an equation of the plane passing through points $(1, 9, 2)$, $(1, 3, 6)$, and $(1, -7, 8)$.

For the following exercises, find the equation of the sphere in standard form that satisfies the given conditions.

**71.** Center $C(-1, 7, 4)$ and radius 4

**72.** Center $C(-4, 7, 2)$ and radius 6

**73.** Diameter $PQ$, where $P(-1, 5, 7)$ and $Q(-5, 2, 9)$

**74.** Diameter $PQ$, where $P(-16, -3, 9)$ and $Q(-2, 3, 5)$

For the following exercises, find the center and radius of the sphere with an equation in general form that is given.

**75.** $P(1, 2, 3)$ $x^2 + y^2 + z^2 - 4z + 3 = 0$

**76.** $x^2 + y^2 + z^2 - 6x + 8y - 10z + 25 = 0$

For the following exercises, express vector $\overrightarrow{PQ}$ with the initial point at $P$ and the terminal point at $Q$

    a. in component form and

    b. by using standard unit vectors.

**77.** $P(3, 0, 2)$ and $Q(-1, -1, 4)$

**78.** $P(0, 10, 5)$ and $Q(1, 1, -3)$

**79.** $P(-2, 5, -8)$ and $M(1, -7, 4)$, where $M$ is the midpoint of the line segment $PQ$

**80.** $Q(0, 7, -6)$ and $M(-1, 3, 2)$, where $M$ is the midpoint of the line segment $PQ$

**81.** Find terminal point $Q$ of vector $\overrightarrow{PQ} = \langle 7, -1, 3 \rangle$ with the initial point at $P(-2, 3, 5)$.

**82.** Find initial point $P$ of vector $\overrightarrow{PQ} = \langle -9, 1, 2 \rangle$ with the terminal point at $Q(10, 0, -1)$.

For the following exercises, use the given vectors **a** and

**b** to find and express the vectors $\mathbf{a} + \mathbf{b}$, $4\mathbf{a}$, and $-5\mathbf{a} + 3\mathbf{b}$ in component form.

83. $\mathbf{a} = \langle -1, -2, 4 \rangle$, $\mathbf{b} = \langle -5, 6, -7 \rangle$

84. $\mathbf{a} = \langle 3, -2, 4 \rangle$, $\mathbf{b} = \langle -5, 6, -9 \rangle$

85. $\mathbf{a} = -\mathbf{k}$, $\mathbf{b} = -\mathbf{i}$

86. $\mathbf{a} = \mathbf{i} + \mathbf{j} + \mathbf{k}$, $\mathbf{b} = 2\mathbf{i} - 3\mathbf{j} + 2\mathbf{k}$

For the following exercises, vectors **u** and **v** are given. Find the magnitudes of vectors $\mathbf{u} - \mathbf{v}$ and $-2\mathbf{u}$.

87. $\mathbf{u} = 2\mathbf{i} + 3\mathbf{j} + 4\mathbf{k}$, $\mathbf{v} = -\mathbf{i} + 5\mathbf{j} - \mathbf{k}$

88. $\mathbf{u} = \mathbf{i} + \mathbf{j}$, $\mathbf{v} = \mathbf{j} - \mathbf{k}$

89. $\mathbf{u} = \langle 2\cos t, -2\sin t, 3 \rangle$, $\mathbf{v} = \langle 0, 0, 3 \rangle$, where $t$ is a real number.

90. $\mathbf{u} = \langle 0, 1, \sinh t \rangle$, $\mathbf{v} = \langle 1, 1, 0 \rangle$, where $t$ is a real number.

For the following exercises, find the unit vector in the direction of the given vector **a** and express it using standard unit vectors.

91. $\mathbf{a} = 3\mathbf{i} - 4\mathbf{j}$

92. $\mathbf{a} = \langle 4, -3, 6 \rangle$

93. $\mathbf{a} = \overrightarrow{PQ}$, where $P(-2, 3, 1)$ and $Q(0, -4, 4)$

94. $\mathbf{a} = \overrightarrow{OP}$, where $P(-1, -1, 1)$

95. $\mathbf{a} = \mathbf{u} - \mathbf{v} + \mathbf{w}$, where $\mathbf{u} = \mathbf{i} - \mathbf{j} - \mathbf{k}$, $\mathbf{v} = 2\mathbf{i} - \mathbf{j} + \mathbf{k}$, and $\mathbf{w} = -\mathbf{i} + \mathbf{j} + 3\mathbf{k}$

96. $\mathbf{a} = 2\mathbf{u} + \mathbf{v} - \mathbf{w}$, where $\mathbf{u} = \mathbf{i} - \mathbf{k}$, $\mathbf{v} = 2\mathbf{j}$, and $\mathbf{w} = \mathbf{i} - \mathbf{j}$

97. Determine whether $\overrightarrow{AB}$ and $\overrightarrow{PQ}$ are equivalent vectors, where $A(1, 1, 1)$, $B(3, 3, 3)$, $P(1, 4, 5)$, and $Q(3, 6, 7)$.

98. Determine whether the vectors $\overrightarrow{AB}$ and $\overrightarrow{PQ}$ are equivalent, where $A(1, 4, 1)$, $B(-2, 2, 0)$, $P(2, 5, 7)$, and $Q(-3, 2, 1)$.

For the following exercises, find vector **u** with a magnitude that is given and satisfies the given conditions.

99. $\mathbf{v} = \langle 7, -1, 3 \rangle$, $\| \mathbf{u} \| = 10$, **u** and **v** have the same direction

100. $\mathbf{v} = \langle 2, 4, 1 \rangle$, $\| \mathbf{u} \| = 15$, **u** and **v** have the same direction

101. $\mathbf{v} = \langle 2\sin t, 2\cos t, 1 \rangle$, $\| \mathbf{u} \| = 2$, **u** and **v** have opposite directions for any $t$, where $t$ is a real number

102. $\mathbf{v} = \langle 3\sinh t, 0, 3 \rangle$, $\| \mathbf{u} \| = 5$, **u** and **v** have opposite directions for any $t$, where $t$ is a real number

103. Determine a vector of magnitude 5 in the direction of vector $\overrightarrow{AB}$, where $A(2, 1, 5)$ and $B(3, 4, -7)$.

104. Find a vector of magnitude 2 that points in the opposite direction than vector $\overrightarrow{AB}$, where $A(-1, -1, 1)$ and $B(0, 1, 1)$. Express the answer in component form.

105. Consider the points $A(2, \alpha, 0)$, $B(0, 1, \beta)$, and $C(1, 1, \beta)$, where $\alpha$ and $\beta$ are negative real numbers. Find $\alpha$ and $\beta$ such that $\| \overrightarrow{OA} - \overrightarrow{OB} + \overrightarrow{OC} \| = \| \overrightarrow{OB} \| = 4$.

106. Consider points $A(\alpha, 0, 0)$, $B(0, \beta, 0)$, and $C(\alpha, \beta, \beta)$, where $\alpha$ and $\beta$ are positive real numbers. Find $\alpha$ and $\beta$ such that $\| \overrightarrow{OA} + \overrightarrow{OB} \| = \sqrt{2}$ and $\| \overrightarrow{OC} \| = \sqrt{3}$.

107. Let $P(x, y, z)$ be a point situated at an equal distance from points $A(1, -1, 0)$ and $B(-1, 2, 1)$. Show that point $P$ lies on the plane of equation $-2x + 3y + z = 2$.

108. Let $P(x, y, z)$ be a point situated at an equal distance from the origin and point $A(4, 1, 2)$. Show that the coordinates of point $P$ satisfy the equation $8x + 2y + 4z = 21$.

109. The points $A$, $B$, and $C$ are collinear (in this order) if the relation $\| \overrightarrow{AB} \| + \| \overrightarrow{BC} \| = \| \overrightarrow{AC} \|$ is satisfied. Show that $A(5, 3, -1)$, $B(-5, -3, 1)$, and $C(-15, -9, 3)$ are collinear points.

110. Show that points $A(1, 0, 1)$, $B(0, 1, 1)$, and $C(1, 1, 1)$ are not collinear.

111. **[T]** A force **F** of $50\,\text{N}$ acts on a particle in the direction of the vector $\overrightarrow{OP}$, where $P(3, 4, 0)$.

    a. Express the force as a vector in component form.

    b. Find the angle between force **F** and the positive direction of the $x$-axis. Express the answer in degrees rounded to the nearest integer.

112. **[T]** A force **F** of $40\,\text{N}$ acts on a box in the direction of the vector $\overrightarrow{OP}$, where $P(1, 0, 2)$.

    a. Express the force as a vector by using standard unit vectors.

    b. Find the angle between force **F** and the positive direction of the $x$-axis.

113. If **F** is a force that moves an object from point $P_1(x_1, y_1, z_1)$ to another point $P_2(x_2, y_2, z_2)$, then the displacement vector is defined as $\mathbf{D} = (x_2 - x_1)\mathbf{i} + (y_2 - y_1)\mathbf{j} + (z_2 - z_1)\mathbf{k}$. A metal container is lifted $10$ m vertically by a constant force **F**. Express the displacement vector **D** by using standard unit vectors.

114. A box is pulled $4$ yd horizontally in the $x$-direction by a constant force **F**. Find the displacement vector in component form.

115. The sum of the forces acting on an object is called the *resultant* or *net force*. An object is said to be in static equilibrium if the resultant force of the forces that act on it is zero. Let $\mathbf{F}_1 = \langle 10, 6, 3 \rangle$, $\mathbf{F}_2 = \langle 0, 4, 9 \rangle$, and $\mathbf{F}_3 = \langle 10, -3, -9 \rangle$ be three forces acting on a box. Find the force $\mathbf{F}_4$ acting on the box such that the box is in static equilibrium. Express the answer in component form.

116. **[T]** Let $\mathbf{F}_k = \langle 1, k, k^2 \rangle$, $k = 1, ..., n$ be $n$ forces acting on a particle, with $n \geq 2$.

    a. Find the net force $\mathbf{F} = \sum_{k=1}^{n} F_k$. Express the answer using standard unit vectors.

    b. Use a computer algebra system (CAS) to find $n$ such that $\| \mathbf{F} \| < 100$.

117. The force of gravity **F** acting on an object is given by $\mathbf{F} = m\mathbf{g}$, where $m$ is the mass of the object (expressed in kilograms) and **g** is acceleration resulting from gravity, with $\| \mathbf{g} \| = 9.8$ N/kg. A 2-kg disco ball hangs by a chain from the ceiling of a room.

    a. Find the force of gravity **F** acting on the disco ball and find its magnitude.

    b. Find the force of tension **T** in the chain and its magnitude.

    Express the answers using standard unit vectors.

**Figure 2.43** (credit: modification of work by Kenneth Lu, Flickr)

118. A 5-kg pendant chandelier is designed such that the alabaster bowl is held by four chains of equal length, as shown in the following figure.

    a. Find the magnitude of the force of gravity acting on the chandelier.

    b. Find the magnitudes of the forces of tension for each of the four chains (assume chains are essentially vertical).

119. **[T]** A 30-kg block of cement is suspended by three cables of equal length that are anchored at points $P(-2, 0, 0)$, $Q(1, \sqrt{3}, 0)$, and $R(1, -\sqrt{3}, 0)$. The load is located at $S(0, 0, -2\sqrt{3})$, as shown in the following figure. Let $\mathbf{F}_1$, $\mathbf{F}_2$, and $\mathbf{F}_3$ be the forces of tension resulting from the load in cables $RS$, $QS$, and $PS$, respectively.

   a. Find the gravitational force $\mathbf{F}$ acting on the block of cement that counterbalances the sum $\mathbf{F}_1 + \mathbf{F}_2 + \mathbf{F}_3$ of the forces of tension in the cables.

   b. Find forces $\mathbf{F}_1$, $\mathbf{F}_2$, and $\mathbf{F}_3$. Express the answer in component form.

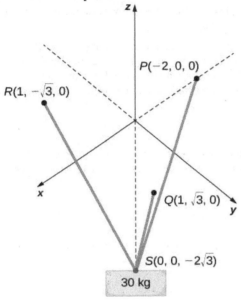

120. Two soccer players are practicing for an upcoming game. One of them runs 10 m from point $A$ to point $B$. She then turns left at $90°$ and runs 10 m until she reaches point $C$. Then she kicks the ball with a speed of 10 m/sec at an upward angle of $45°$ to her teammate, who is located at point $A$. Write the velocity of the ball in component form.

121. Let $\mathbf{r}(t) = \langle x(t), y(t), z(t) \rangle$ be the position vector of a particle at the time $t \in [0, T]$, where $x$, $y$, and $z$ are smooth functions on $[0, T]$. The instantaneous velocity of the particle at time $t$ is defined by vector $\mathbf{v}(t) = \langle x'(t), y'(t), z'(t) \rangle$, with components that are the derivatives with respect to $t$, of the functions $x$, $y$, and $z$, respectively. The magnitude $\| \mathbf{v}(t) \|$ of the instantaneous velocity vector is called the *speed of the particle at time* t. Vector $\mathbf{a}(t) = \langle x''(t), y''(t), z''(t) \rangle$, with components that are the second derivatives with respect to $t$, of the functions $x$, $y$, and $z$, respectively, gives the acceleration of the particle at time $t$. Consider $\mathbf{r}(t) = \langle \cos t, \sin t, 2t \rangle$ the position vector of a particle at time $t \in [0, 30]$, where the components of $\mathbf{r}$ are expressed in centimeters and time is expressed in seconds.

   a. Find the instantaneous velocity, speed, and acceleration of the particle after the first second. Round your answer to two decimal places.

   b. Use a CAS to visualize the path of the particle—that is, the set of all points of coordinates $(\cos t, \sin t, 2t)$, where $t \in [0, 30]$.

122. **[T]** Let $\mathbf{r}(t) = \langle t, 2t^2, 4t^2 \rangle$ be the position vector of a particle at time $t$ (in seconds), where $t \in [0, 10]$ (here the components of $\mathbf{r}$ are expressed in centimeters).

   a. Find the instantaneous velocity, speed, and acceleration of the particle after the first two seconds. Round your answer to two decimal places.

   b. Use a CAS to visualize the path of the particle defined by the points $(t, 2t^2, 4t^2)$, where $t \in [0, 60]$.

# 2.3 | The Dot Product

| Learning Objectives |
| --- |
| **2.3.1** Calculate the dot product of two given vectors. |
| **2.3.2** Determine whether two given vectors are perpendicular. |
| **2.3.3** Find the direction cosines of a given vector. |
| **2.3.4** Explain what is meant by the vector projection of one vector onto another vector, and describe how to compute it. |
| **2.3.5** Calculate the work done by a given force. |

If we apply a force to an object so that the object moves, we say that *work* is done by the force. In Introduction to Applications of Integration (http://cnx.org/content/m53638/latest/) on integration applications, we looked at a constant force and we assumed the force was applied in the direction of motion of the object. Under those conditions, work can be expressed as the product of the force acting on an object and the distance the object moves. In this chapter, however, we have seen that both force and the motion of an object can be represented by vectors.

In this section, we develop an operation called the *dot product*, which allows us to calculate work in the case when the force vector and the motion vector have different directions. The dot product essentially tells us how much of the force vector is applied in the direction of the motion vector. The dot product can also help us measure the angle formed by a pair of vectors and the position of a vector relative to the coordinate axes. It even provides a simple test to determine whether two vectors meet at a right angle.

## The Dot Product and Its Properties

We have already learned how to add and subtract vectors. In this chapter, we investigate two types of vector multiplication. The first type of vector multiplication is called the dot product, based on the notation we use for it, and it is defined as follows:

> **Definition**
>
> The **dot product** of vectors $\mathbf{u} = \langle u_1, u_2, u_3 \rangle$ and $\mathbf{v} = \langle v_1, v_2, v_3 \rangle$ is given by the sum of the products of the components
>
> $$\mathbf{u} \cdot \mathbf{v} = u_1 v_1 + u_2 v_2 + u_3 v_3. \tag{2.3}$$

Note that if $\mathbf{u}$ and $\mathbf{v}$ are two-dimensional vectors, we calculate the dot product in a similar fashion. Thus, if $\mathbf{u} = \langle u_1, u_2 \rangle$ and $\mathbf{v} = \langle v_1, v_2 \rangle$, then

$$\mathbf{u} \cdot \mathbf{v} = u_1 v_1 + u_2 v_2.$$

When two vectors are combined under addition or subtraction, the result is a vector. When two vectors are combined using the dot product, the result is a scalar. For this reason, the dot product is often called the *scalar product*. It may also be called the *inner product*.

> ## Example 2.21
>
> ### Calculating Dot Products
>
> a.  Find the dot product of $\mathbf{u} = \langle 3, 5, 2 \rangle$ and $\mathbf{v} = \langle -1, 3, 0 \rangle$.
>
> b.  Find the scalar product of $\mathbf{p} = 10\mathbf{i} - 4\mathbf{j} + 7\mathbf{k}$ and $\mathbf{q} = -2\mathbf{i} + \mathbf{j} + 6\mathbf{k}$.
>
> ### Solution

a.  Substitute the vector components into the formula for the dot product:

$$\mathbf{u} \cdot \mathbf{v} = u_1 v_1 + u_2 v_2 + u_3 v_3$$
$$= 3(-1) + 5(3) + 2(0) = -3 + 15 + 0 = 12.$$

b.  The calculation is the same if the vectors are written using standard unit vectors. We still have three components for each vector to substitute into the formula for the dot product:

$$\mathbf{p} \cdot \mathbf{q} = u_1 v_1 + u_2 v_2 + u_3 v_3$$
$$= 10(-2) + (-4)(1) + (7)(6) = -20 - 4 + 42 = 18.$$

 **2.21**  Find $\mathbf{u} \cdot \mathbf{v}$, where $\mathbf{u} = \langle\, 2, 9, -1 \,\rangle$ and $\mathbf{v} = \langle\, -3, 1, -4 \,\rangle$.

Like vector addition and subtraction, the dot product has several algebraic properties. We prove three of these properties and leave the rest as exercises.

---

### Theorem 2.3: Properties of the Dot Product

Let $\mathbf{u}$, $\mathbf{v}$, and $\mathbf{w}$ be vectors, and let $c$ be a scalar.

|  |  |  |
|---|---|---|
| i. | $\mathbf{u} \cdot \mathbf{v} = \mathbf{v} \cdot \mathbf{u}$ | Commutative property |
| ii. | $\mathbf{u} \cdot (\mathbf{v} + \mathbf{w}) = \mathbf{u} \cdot \mathbf{v} + \mathbf{u} \cdot \mathbf{w}$ | Distributive property |
| iii. | $c(\mathbf{u} \cdot \mathbf{v}) = (c\mathbf{u}) \cdot \mathbf{v} = \mathbf{u} \cdot (c\mathbf{v})$ | Associative property |
| iv. | $\mathbf{v} \cdot \mathbf{v} = \|\mathbf{v}\|^2$ | Property of magnitude |

---

### Proof

Let $\mathbf{u} = \langle\, u_1, u_2, u_3 \,\rangle$ and $\mathbf{v} = \langle\, v_1, v_2, v_3 \,\rangle$. Then

$$\mathbf{u} \cdot \mathbf{v} = \langle\, u_1, u_2, u_3 \,\rangle \cdot \langle\, v_1, v_2, v_3 \,\rangle$$
$$= u_1 v_1 + u_2 v_2 + u_3 v_3$$
$$= v_1 u_1 + v_2 u_2 + v_3 u_3$$
$$= \langle\, v_1, v_2, v_3 \,\rangle \cdot \langle\, u_1, u_2, u_3 \,\rangle$$
$$= \mathbf{v} \cdot \mathbf{u}.$$

The associative property looks like the associative property for real-number multiplication, but pay close attention to the difference between scalar and vector objects:

$$c(\mathbf{u} \cdot \mathbf{v}) = c(u_1 v_1 + u_2 v_2 + u_3 v_3)$$
$$= c(u_1 v_1) + c(u_2 v_2) + c(u_3 v_3)$$
$$= (c u_1)v_1 + (c u_2)v_2 + (c u_3)v_3$$
$$= \langle\, c u_1, c u_2, c u_3 \,\rangle \cdot \langle\, v_1, v_2, v_3 \,\rangle$$
$$= c \langle\, u_1, u_2, u_3 \,\rangle \cdot \langle\, v_1, v_2, v_3 \,\rangle$$
$$= (c\mathbf{u}) \cdot \mathbf{v}.$$

The proof that $c(\mathbf{u} \cdot \mathbf{v}) = \mathbf{u} \cdot (c\mathbf{v})$ is similar.

The fourth property shows the relationship between the magnitude of a vector and its dot product with itself:

$$\begin{aligned}
\mathbf{v} \cdot \mathbf{v} &= \langle v_1, v_2, v_3 \rangle \cdot \langle v_1, v_2, v_3 \rangle \\
&= (v_1)^2 + (v_2)^2 + (v_3)^2 \\
&= \left[ \sqrt{(v_1)^2 + (v_2)^2 + (v_3)^2} \right]^2 \\
&= \| \mathbf{v} \|^2.
\end{aligned}$$

$\square$

Note that the definition of the dot product yields $0 \cdot \mathbf{v} = 0$. By property iv., if $\mathbf{v} \cdot \mathbf{v} = 0,$ then $\mathbf{v} = 0$.

### Example 2.22

#### Using Properties of the Dot Product

Let $\mathbf{a} = \langle 1, 2, -3 \rangle$, $\mathbf{b} = \langle 0, 2, 4 \rangle$, and $\mathbf{c} = \langle 5, -1, 3 \rangle$. Find each of the following products.

a. $(\mathbf{a} \cdot \mathbf{b})\mathbf{c}$

b. $\mathbf{a} \cdot (2\mathbf{c})$

c. $\| \mathbf{b} \|^2$

#### Solution

a. Note that this expression asks for the scalar multiple of $\mathbf{c}$ by $\mathbf{a} \cdot \mathbf{b}$:

$$\begin{aligned}
(\mathbf{a} \cdot \mathbf{b})\mathbf{c} &= (\langle 1, 2, -3 \rangle \cdot \langle 0, 2, 4 \rangle)\langle 5, -1, 3 \rangle \\
&= (1(0) + 2(2) + (-3)(4))\langle 5, -1, 3 \rangle \\
&= -8 \langle 5, -1, 3 \rangle \\
&= \langle -40, 8, -24 \rangle.
\end{aligned}$$

b. This expression is a dot product of vector $\mathbf{a}$ and scalar multiple $2\mathbf{c}$:

$$\begin{aligned}
\mathbf{a} \cdot (2\mathbf{c}) &= 2(\mathbf{a} \cdot \mathbf{c}) \\
&= 2(\langle 1, 2, -3 \rangle \cdot \langle 5, -1, 3 \rangle) \\
&= 2(1(5) + 2(-1) + (-3)(3)) \\
&= 2(-6) = -12.
\end{aligned}$$

c. Simplifying this expression is a straightforward application of the dot product:

$$\| \mathbf{b} \|^2 = \mathbf{b} \cdot \mathbf{b} = \langle 0, 2, 4 \rangle \cdot \langle 0, 2, 4 \rangle = 0^2 + 2^2 + 4^2 = 0 + 4 + 16 = 20.$$

 **2.22** Find the following products for $\mathbf{p} = \langle 7, 0, 2 \rangle$, $\mathbf{q} = \langle -2, 2, -2 \rangle$, and $\mathbf{r} = \langle 0, 2, -3 \rangle$.

a. $(\mathbf{r} \cdot \mathbf{p})\mathbf{q}$

b. $\| \mathbf{p} \|^2$

## Using the Dot Product to Find the Angle between Two Vectors

When two nonzero vectors are placed in standard position, whether in two dimensions or three dimensions, they form an angle between them (**Figure 2.44**). The dot product provides a way to find the measure of this angle. This property is a result of the fact that we can express the dot product in terms of the cosine of the angle formed by two vectors.

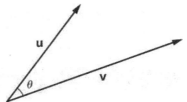

**Figure 2.44** Let $\theta$ be the angle between two nonzero vectors $\mathbf{u}$ and $\mathbf{v}$ such that $0 \le \theta \le \pi$.

### Theorem 2.4: Evaluating a Dot Product

The dot product of two vectors is the product of the magnitude of each vector and the cosine of the angle between them:

$$\mathbf{u} \cdot \mathbf{v} = \|\mathbf{u}\| \ \|\mathbf{v}\| \cos\theta. \tag{2.4}$$

### Proof

Place vectors $\mathbf{u}$ and $\mathbf{v}$ in standard position and consider the vector $\mathbf{v} - \mathbf{u}$ (Figure 2.45). These three vectors form a triangle with side lengths $\|\mathbf{u}\|$, $\|\mathbf{v}\|$, and $\|\mathbf{v} - \mathbf{u}\|$.

**Figure 2.45** The lengths of the sides of the triangle are given by the magnitudes of the vectors that form the triangle.

Recall from trigonometry that the law of cosines describes the relationship among the side lengths of the triangle and the angle $\theta$. Applying the law of cosines here gives

$$\|\mathbf{v} - \mathbf{u}\|^2 = \|\mathbf{u}\|^2 + \|\mathbf{v}\|^2 - 2\|\mathbf{u}\| \ \|\mathbf{v}\| \cos\theta.$$

The dot product provides a way to rewrite the left side of this equation:

$$\begin{aligned}
\|\mathbf{v} - \mathbf{u}\|^2 &= (\mathbf{v} - \mathbf{u}) \cdot (\mathbf{v} - \mathbf{u}) \\
&= (\mathbf{v} - \mathbf{u}) \cdot \mathbf{v} - (\mathbf{v} - \mathbf{u}) \cdot \mathbf{u} \\
&= \mathbf{v} \cdot \mathbf{v} - \mathbf{u} \cdot \mathbf{v} - \mathbf{v} \cdot \mathbf{u} + \mathbf{u} \cdot \mathbf{u} \\
&= \mathbf{v} \cdot \mathbf{v} - \mathbf{u} \cdot \mathbf{v} - \mathbf{u} \cdot \mathbf{v} + \mathbf{u} \cdot \mathbf{u} \\
&= \|\mathbf{v}\|^2 - 2\mathbf{u} \cdot \mathbf{v} + \|\mathbf{u}\|^2.
\end{aligned}$$

Substituting into the law of cosines yields

$$\begin{aligned}
\|\mathbf{v} - \mathbf{u}\|^2 &= \|\mathbf{u}\|^2 + \|\mathbf{v}\|^2 - 2\|\mathbf{u}\| \ \|\mathbf{v}\| \cos\theta \\
\|\mathbf{v}\|^2 - 2\mathbf{u} \cdot \mathbf{v} + \|\mathbf{u}\|^2 &= \|\mathbf{u}\|^2 + \|\mathbf{v}\|^2 - 2\|\mathbf{u}\| \ \|\mathbf{v}\| \cos\theta \\
-2\mathbf{u} \cdot \mathbf{v} &= -2\|\mathbf{u}\| \ \|\mathbf{v}\| \cos\theta \\
\mathbf{u} \cdot \mathbf{v} &= \|\mathbf{u}\| \ \|\mathbf{v}\| \cos\theta.
\end{aligned}$$

$\square$

We can use this form of the dot product to find the measure of the angle between two nonzero vectors. The following equation rearranges Equation 2.3 to solve for the cosine of the angle:

$$\cos\theta = \frac{\mathbf{u} \cdot \mathbf{v}}{\|\mathbf{u}\| \ \|\mathbf{v}\|}. \tag{2.5}$$

Using this equation, we can find the cosine of the angle between two nonzero vectors. Since we are considering the smallest angle between the vectors, we assume $0° \leq \theta \leq 180°$ (or $0 \leq \theta \leq \pi$ if we are working in radians). The inverse cosine is unique over this range, so we are then able to determine the measure of the angle $\theta$.

## Example 2.23

### Finding the Angle between Two Vectors

Find the measure of the angle between each pair of vectors.

    a.   $\mathbf{i} + \mathbf{j} + \mathbf{k}$ and $2\mathbf{i} - \mathbf{j} - 3\mathbf{k}$

    b.   $\langle 2, 5, 6 \rangle$ and $\langle -2, -4, 4 \rangle$

**Solution**

    a.   To find the cosine of the angle formed by the two vectors, substitute the components of the vectors into **Equation 2.5**:

$$\begin{aligned} \cos \theta &= \frac{(\mathbf{i} + \mathbf{j} + \mathbf{k}) \cdot (2\mathbf{i} - \mathbf{j} - 3\mathbf{k})}{\| \mathbf{i} + \mathbf{j} + \mathbf{k} \| \cdot \| 2\mathbf{i} - \mathbf{j} - 3\mathbf{k} \|} \\ &= \frac{1(2) + (1)(-1) + (1)(-3)}{\sqrt{1^2 + 1^2 + 1^2} \sqrt{2^2 + (-1)^2 + (-3)^2}} \\ &= \frac{-2}{\sqrt{3}\sqrt{14}} = \frac{-2}{\sqrt{42}}. \end{aligned}$$

Therefore, $\theta = \arccos \frac{-2}{\sqrt{42}}$ rad.

    b.   Start by finding the value of the cosine of the angle between the vectors:

$$\begin{aligned} \cos \theta &= \frac{\langle 2, 5, 6 \rangle \cdot \langle -2, -4, 4 \rangle}{\| \langle 2, 5, 6 \rangle \| \cdot \| \langle -2, -4, 4 \rangle \|} \\ &= \frac{2(-2) + (5)(-4) + (6)(4)}{\sqrt{2^2 + 5^2 + 6^2} \sqrt{(-2)^2 + (-4)^2 + 4^2}} \\ &= \frac{0}{\sqrt{65}\sqrt{36}} = 0. \end{aligned}$$

Now, $\cos \theta = 0$ and $0 \leq \theta \leq \pi$, so $\theta = \pi/2$.

 **2.23**   Find the measure of the angle, in radians, formed by vectors $\mathbf{a} = \langle 1, 2, 0 \rangle$ and $\mathbf{b} = \langle 2, 4, 1 \rangle$. Round to the nearest hundredth.

The angle between two vectors can be acute $(0 < \cos \theta < 1)$, obtuse $(-1 < \cos \theta < 0)$, or straight $(\cos \theta = -1)$. If $\cos \theta = 1$, then both vectors have the same direction. If $\cos \theta = 0$, then the vectors, when placed in standard position, form a right angle (**Figure 2.46**). We can formalize this result into a theorem regarding orthogonal (perpendicular) vectors.

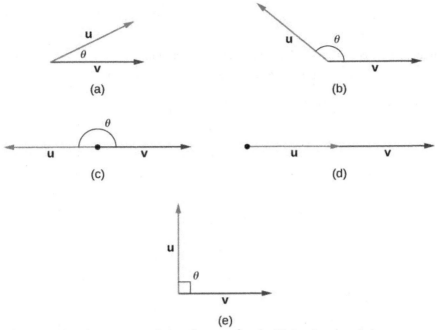

**Figure 2.46** (a) An acute angle has $0 < \cos \theta < 1$. (b) An obtuse angle has $-1 < \cos \theta < 0$. (c) A straight line has $\cos \theta = -1$. (d) If the vectors have the same direction, $\cos \theta = 1$. (e) If the vectors are orthogonal (perpendicular), $\cos \theta = 0$.

---

**Theorem 2.5: Orthogonal Vectors**

The nonzero vectors $\mathbf{u}$ and $\mathbf{v}$ are **orthogonal vectors** if and only if $\mathbf{u} \cdot \mathbf{v} = 0$.

---

**Proof**

Let $\mathbf{u}$ and $\mathbf{v}$ be nonzero vectors, and let $\theta$ denote the angle between them. First, assume $\mathbf{u} \cdot \mathbf{v} = 0$. Then

$$\| \mathbf{u} \| \, \| \mathbf{v} \| \cos \theta = 0.$$

However, $\| \mathbf{u} \| \neq 0$ and $\| \mathbf{v} \| \neq 0$, so we must have $\cos \theta = 0$. Hence, $\theta = 90°$, and the vectors are orthogonal.

Now assume $\mathbf{u}$ and $\mathbf{v}$ are orthogonal. Then $\theta = 90°$ and we have

$$\mathbf{u} \cdot \mathbf{v} = \| \mathbf{u} \| \, \| \mathbf{v} \| \cos \theta = \| \mathbf{u} \| \, \| \mathbf{v} \| \cos 90° = \| \mathbf{u} \| \, \| \mathbf{v} \| (0) = 0.$$

$\square$

The terms *orthogonal*, *perpendicular*, and *normal* each indicate that mathematical objects are intersecting at right angles. The use of each term is determined mainly by its context. We say that vectors are orthogonal and lines are perpendicular. The term *normal* is used most often when measuring the angle made with a plane or other surface.

---

## Example 2.24

### Identifying Orthogonal Vectors

Determine whether $\mathbf{p} = \langle \, 1, 0, 5 \, \rangle$ and $\mathbf{q} = \langle \, 10, 3, -2 \, \rangle$ are orthogonal vectors.

### Solution

Using the definition, we need only check the dot product of the vectors:

$$\mathbf{p} \cdot \mathbf{q} = 1(10) + (0)(3) + (5)(-2) = 10 + 0 - 10 = 0.$$

Because $\mathbf{p} \cdot \mathbf{q} = 0,$ the vectors are orthogonal (Figure 2.47).

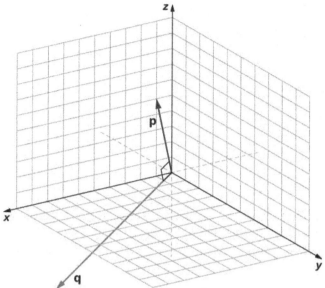

**Figure 2.47** Vectors $\mathbf{p}$ and $\mathbf{q}$ form a right angle when their initial points are aligned.

 **2.24** For which value of $x$ is $\mathbf{p} = \langle\, 2,\ 8,\ -1\, \rangle$ orthogonal to $\mathbf{q} = \langle\, x,\ -1,\ 2\, \rangle$ ?

---

### Example 2.25

### Measuring the Angle Formed by Two Vectors

Let $\mathbf{v} = \langle\, 2,\ 3,\ 3\, \rangle$. Find the measures of the angles formed by the following vectors.

   a.  $\mathbf{v}$ and $\mathbf{i}$

   b.  $\mathbf{v}$ and $\mathbf{j}$

   c.  $\mathbf{v}$ and $\mathbf{k}$

### Solution

   a.  Let $\alpha$ be the angle formed by $\mathbf{v}$ and $\mathbf{i}$:

$$\cos \alpha = \frac{\mathbf{v} \cdot \mathbf{i}}{\|\mathbf{v}\| \cdot \|\mathbf{i}\|}$$

$$= \frac{\langle 2, 3, 3 \rangle \cdot \langle 1, 0, 0 \rangle}{\sqrt{2^2 + 3^2 + 3^2}\sqrt{1}}$$

$$= \frac{2}{\sqrt{22}}.$$

$$\alpha = \arccos \frac{2}{\sqrt{22}} \approx 1.130 \text{ rad.}$$

b.  Let $\beta$ represent the angle formed by $\mathbf{v}$ and $\mathbf{j}$:

$$\cos \beta = \frac{\mathbf{v} \cdot \mathbf{j}}{\|\mathbf{v}\| \cdot \|\mathbf{j}\|}$$

$$= \frac{\langle 2, 3, 3 \rangle \cdot \langle 0, 1, 0 \rangle}{\sqrt{2^2 + 3^2 + 3^2}\sqrt{1}}$$

$$= \frac{3}{\sqrt{22}}.$$

$$\beta = \arccos \frac{3}{\sqrt{22}} \approx 0.877 \text{ rad.}$$

c.  Let $\gamma$ represent the angle formed by $\mathbf{v}$ and $\mathbf{k}$:

$$\cos \gamma = \frac{\mathbf{v} \cdot \mathbf{k}}{\|\mathbf{v}\| \cdot \|\mathbf{k}\|}$$

$$= \frac{\langle 2, 3, 3 \rangle \cdot \langle 0, 0, 1 \rangle}{\sqrt{2^2 + 3^2 + 3^2}\sqrt{1}}$$

$$= \frac{3}{\sqrt{22}}.$$

$$\gamma = \arccos \frac{3}{\sqrt{22}} \approx 0.877 \text{ rad.}$$

 **2.25**  Let $\mathbf{v} = \langle 3, -5, 1 \rangle$. Find the measure of the angles formed by each pair of vectors.

a.  $\mathbf{v}$ and $\mathbf{i}$

b.  $\mathbf{v}$ and $\mathbf{j}$

c.  $\mathbf{v}$ and $\mathbf{k}$

The angle a vector makes with each of the coordinate axes, called a direction angle, is very important in practical computations, especially in a field such as engineering. For example, in astronautical engineering, the angle at which a rocket is launched must be determined very precisely. A very small error in the angle can lead to the rocket going hundreds of miles off course. Direction angles are often calculated by using the dot product and the cosines of the angles, called the direction cosines. Therefore, we define both these angles and their cosines.

## Definition

The angles formed by a nonzero vector and the coordinate axes are called the **direction angles** for the vector (Figure 2.48). The cosines for these angles are called the **direction cosines**.

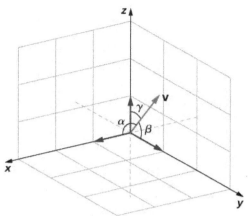

**Figure 2.48** Angle $\alpha$ is formed by vector **v** and unit vector **i**. Angle $\beta$ is formed by vector **v** and unit vector **j**. Angle $\gamma$ is formed by vector **v** and unit vector **k**.

In **Example 2.25**, the direction cosines of $\mathbf{v} = \langle\, 2, 3, 3\, \rangle$ are $\cos\alpha = \frac{2}{\sqrt{22}}$, $\cos\beta = \frac{3}{\sqrt{22}}$, and $\cos\gamma = \frac{3}{\sqrt{22}}$. The direction angles of **v** are $\alpha = 1.130\,\text{rad}$, $\beta = 0.877\,\text{rad}$, and $\gamma = 0.877\,\text{rad}$.

So far, we have focused mainly on vectors related to force, movement, and position in three-dimensional physical space. However, vectors are often used in more abstract ways. For example, suppose a fruit vendor sells apples, bananas, and oranges. On a given day, he sells 30 apples, 12 bananas, and 18 oranges. He might use a quantity vector, $\mathbf{q} = \langle\, 30, 12, 18\, \rangle$, to represent the quantity of fruit he sold that day. Similarly, he might want to use a price vector, $\mathbf{p} = \langle\, 0.50, 0.25, 1\, \rangle$, to indicate that he sells his apples for 50¢ each, bananas for 25¢ each, and oranges for $1 apiece.

In this example, although we could still graph these vectors, we do not interpret them as literal representations of position in the physical world. We are simply using vectors to keep track of particular pieces of information about apples, bananas, and oranges.

This idea might seem a little strange, but if we simply regard vectors as a way to order and store data, we find they can be quite a powerful tool. Going back to the fruit vendor, let's think about the dot product, $\mathbf{q} \cdot \mathbf{p}$. We compute it by multiplying the number of apples sold (30) by the price per apple (50¢), the number of bananas sold by the price per banana, and the number of oranges sold by the price per orange. We then add all these values together. So, in this example, the dot product tells us how much money the fruit vendor had in sales on that particular day.

When we use vectors in this more general way, there is no reason to limit the number of components to three. What if the fruit vendor decides to start selling grapefruit? In that case, he would want to use four-dimensional quantity and price vectors to represent the number of apples, bananas, oranges, and grapefruit sold, and their unit prices. As you might expect, to calculate the dot product of four-dimensional vectors, we simply add the products of the components as before, but the sum has four terms instead of three.

## Example 2.26

### Using Vectors in an Economic Context

AAA Party Supply Store sells invitations, party favors, decorations, and food service items such as paper plates and napkins. When AAA buys its inventory, it pays 25¢ per package for invitations and party favors. Decorations cost AAA 50¢ each, and food service items cost 20¢ per package. AAA sells invitations for $2.50 per package and party favors for $1.50 per package. Decorations sell for $4.50 each and food service items for $1.25 per package.

During the month of May, AAA Party Supply Store sells 1258 invitations, 342 party favors, 2426 decorations, and 1354 food service items. Use vectors and dot products to calculate how much money AAA made in sales during the month of May. How much did the store make in profit?

**Solution**

The cost, price, and quantity vectors are

$$\mathbf{c} = \langle\ 0.25,\ 0.25,\ 0.50,\ 0.20\ \rangle$$
$$\mathbf{p} = \langle\ 2.50,\ 1.50,\ 4.50,\ 1.25\ \rangle$$
$$\mathbf{q} = \langle\ 1258,\ 342,\ 2426,\ 1354\ \rangle .$$

AAA sales for the month of May can be calculated using the dot product $\mathbf{p}\cdot\mathbf{q}$. We have

$$\begin{aligned}
\mathbf{p}\cdot\mathbf{q} &= \langle\ 2.50,\ 1.50,\ 4.50,\ 1.25\ \rangle \cdot \langle\ 1258,\ 342,\ 2426,\ 1354\ \rangle \\
&= 3145 + 513 + 10917 + 1692.5 \\
&= 16267.5.
\end{aligned}$$

So, AAA took in $16,267.50 during the month of May.

To calculate the profit, we must first calculate how much AAA paid for the items sold. We use the dot product $\mathbf{c}\cdot\mathbf{q}$ to get

$$\begin{aligned}
\mathbf{c}\cdot\mathbf{q} &= \langle\ 0.25,\ 0.25,\ 0.50,\ 0.20\ \rangle \cdot \langle\ 1258,\ 342,\ 2426,\ 1354\ \rangle \\
&= 314.5 + 85.5 + 1213 + 270.8 \\
&= 1883.8.
\end{aligned}$$

So, AAA paid $1,883.30 for the items they sold. Their profit, then, is given by

$$\begin{aligned}
\mathbf{p}\cdot\mathbf{q} - \mathbf{c}\cdot\mathbf{q} &= 16267.5 - 1883.8 \\
&= 14383.7.
\end{aligned}$$

Therefore, AAA Party Supply Store made $14,383.70 in May.

 **2.26** On June 1, AAA Party Supply Store decided to increase the price they charge for party favors to $2 per package. They also changed suppliers for their invitations, and are now able to purchase invitations for only 10¢ per package. All their other costs and prices remain the same. If AAA sells 1408 invitations, 147 party favors, 2112 decorations, and 1894 food service items in the month of June, use vectors and dot products to calculate their total sales and profit for June.

## Projections

As we have seen, addition combines two vectors to create a resultant vector. But what if we are given a vector and we need to find its component parts? We use vector projections to perform the opposite process; they can break down a vector into its components. The magnitude of a vector projection is a scalar projection. For example, if a child is pulling the handle of a wagon at a 55° angle, we can use projections to determine how much of the force on the handle is actually moving the wagon forward (**Figure 2.49**). We return to this example and learn how to solve it after we see how to calculate projections.

**Figure 2.49** When a child pulls a wagon, only the horizontal component of the force propels the wagon forward.

**Definition**

The **vector projection** of **v** onto **u** is the vector labeled $\text{proj}_\mathbf{u}\mathbf{v}$ in Figure 2.50. It has the same initial point as **u** and **v** and the same direction as **u**, and represents the component of **v** that acts in the direction of **u**. If $\theta$ represents the angle between **u** and **v**, then, by properties of triangles, we know the length of $\text{proj}_\mathbf{u}\mathbf{v}$ is $\| \text{proj}_\mathbf{u}\mathbf{v} \| = \| \mathbf{v} \| \cos\theta$. When expressing $\cos\theta$ in terms of the dot product, this becomes

$$\| \text{proj}_\mathbf{u}\mathbf{v} \| = \| \mathbf{v} \| \cos\theta$$
$$= \| \mathbf{v} \| \left( \frac{\mathbf{u} \cdot \mathbf{v}}{\| \mathbf{u} \| \; \| \mathbf{v} \|} \right)$$
$$= \frac{\mathbf{u} \cdot \mathbf{v}}{\| \mathbf{u} \|}.$$

We now multiply by a unit vector in the direction of **u** to get $\text{proj}_\mathbf{u}\mathbf{v}$:

$$\text{proj}_\mathbf{u}\mathbf{v} = \frac{\mathbf{u} \cdot \mathbf{v}}{\| \mathbf{u} \|} \left( \frac{1}{\| \mathbf{u} \|}\mathbf{u} \right) = \frac{\mathbf{u} \cdot \mathbf{v}}{\| \mathbf{u} \|^2}\mathbf{u}. \qquad (2.6)$$

The length of this vector is also known as the **scalar projection** of **v** onto **u** and is denoted by

$$\| \text{proj}_\mathbf{u}\mathbf{v} \| = \text{comp}_\mathbf{u}\mathbf{v} = \frac{\mathbf{u} \cdot \mathbf{v}}{\| \mathbf{u} \|}. \qquad (2.7)$$

**Figure 2.50** The projection of **v** onto **u** shows the component of vector **v** in the direction of **u**.

## Example 2.27

### Finding Projections

Find the projection of **v** onto **u**.

    a.   $\mathbf{v} = \langle 3, 5, 1 \rangle$ and $\mathbf{u} = \langle -1, 4, 3 \rangle$

    b.   $\mathbf{v} = 3\mathbf{i} - 2\mathbf{j}$ and $\mathbf{u} = \mathbf{i} + 6\mathbf{j}$

### Solution

    a.  Substitute the components of **v** and **u** into the formula for the projection:

$$\text{proj}_{\mathbf{u}} \mathbf{v} = \frac{\mathbf{u} \cdot \mathbf{v}}{\|\mathbf{u}\|^2}\mathbf{u}$$

$$= \frac{\langle -1, 4, 3 \rangle \cdot \langle 3, 5, 1 \rangle}{\|\langle -1, 4, 3 \rangle\|^2}\langle -1, 4, 3 \rangle$$

$$= \frac{-3 + 20 + 3}{(-1)^2 + 4^2 + 3^2}\langle -1, 4, 3 \rangle$$

$$= \frac{20}{26}\langle -1, 4, 3 \rangle$$

$$= \langle -\frac{10}{13}, \frac{40}{13}, \frac{30}{13} \rangle.$$

b.  To find the two-dimensional projection, simply adapt the formula to the two-dimensional case:

$$\text{proj}_{\mathbf{u}} \mathbf{v} = \frac{\mathbf{u} \cdot \mathbf{v}}{\|\mathbf{u}\|^2}\mathbf{u}$$

$$= \frac{(\mathbf{i} + 6\mathbf{j}) \cdot (3\mathbf{i} - 2\mathbf{j})}{\|\mathbf{i} + 6\mathbf{j}\|^2}(\mathbf{i} + 6\mathbf{j})$$

$$= \frac{1(3) + 6(-2)}{1^2 + 6^2}(\mathbf{i} + 6\mathbf{j})$$

$$= -\frac{9}{37}(\mathbf{i} + 6\mathbf{j})$$

$$= -\frac{9}{37}\mathbf{i} - \frac{54}{37}\mathbf{j}.$$

Sometimes it is useful to decompose vectors—that is, to break a vector apart into a sum. This process is called the *resolution of a vector into components*. Projections allow us to identify two orthogonal vectors having a desired sum. For example, let $\mathbf{v} = \langle 6, -4 \rangle$ and let $\mathbf{u} = \langle 3, 1 \rangle$. We want to decompose the vector $\mathbf{v}$ into orthogonal components such that one of the component vectors has the same direction as $\mathbf{u}$.

We first find the component that has the same direction as $\mathbf{u}$ by projecting $\mathbf{v}$ onto $\mathbf{u}$. Let $\mathbf{p} = \text{proj}_{\mathbf{u}} \mathbf{v}$. Then, we have

$$\mathbf{p} = \frac{\mathbf{u} \cdot \mathbf{v}}{\|\mathbf{u}\|^2}\mathbf{u}$$

$$= \frac{18 - 4}{9 + 1}\mathbf{u}$$

$$= \frac{7}{5}\mathbf{u} = \frac{7}{5}\langle 3, 1 \rangle = \langle \frac{21}{5}, \frac{7}{5} \rangle.$$

Now consider the vector $\mathbf{q} = \mathbf{v} - \mathbf{p}$. We have

$$\mathbf{q} = \mathbf{v} - \mathbf{p}$$

$$= \langle 6, -4 \rangle - \langle \frac{21}{5}, \frac{7}{5} \rangle$$

$$= \langle \frac{9}{5}, -\frac{27}{5} \rangle.$$

Clearly, by the way we defined $\mathbf{q}$, we have $\mathbf{v} = \mathbf{q} + \mathbf{p}$, and

$$\mathbf{q} \cdot \mathbf{p} = \langle \frac{9}{5}, -\frac{27}{5} \rangle \cdot \langle \frac{21}{5}, \frac{7}{5} \rangle$$

$$= \frac{9(21)}{25} + \frac{-27(7)}{25}$$

$$= \frac{189}{25} - \frac{189}{25} = 0.$$

Therefore, $\mathbf{q}$ and $\mathbf{p}$ are orthogonal.

## Example 2.28

### Resolving Vectors into Components

Express $\mathbf{v} = \langle\, 8,\, -3,\, -3\, \rangle$ as a sum of orthogonal vectors such that one of the vectors has the same direction as $\mathbf{u} = \langle\, 2,\, 3,\, 2\, \rangle$.

### Solution

Let $\mathbf{p}$ represent the projection of $\mathbf{v}$ onto $\mathbf{u}$:

$$
\begin{aligned}
\mathbf{p} &= \operatorname{proj}_{\mathbf{u}} \mathbf{v} \\
&= \frac{\mathbf{u} \cdot \mathbf{v}}{\|\,\mathbf{u}\,\|^{2}} \mathbf{u} \\
&= \frac{\langle\, 2,\, 3,\, 2\, \rangle \cdot \langle\, 8,\, -3,\, -3\, \rangle}{\|\,\langle\, 2,\, 3,\, 2\, \rangle\,\|^{2}} \langle\, 2,\, 3,\, 2\, \rangle \\
&= \frac{16 - 9 - 6}{2^{2} + 3^{2} + 2^{2}} \langle\, 2,\, 3,\, 2\, \rangle \\
&= \frac{1}{17} \langle\, 2,\, 3,\, 2\, \rangle \\
&= \langle\, \tfrac{2}{17},\, \tfrac{3}{17},\, \tfrac{2}{17}\, \rangle.
\end{aligned}
$$

Then,

$$
\mathbf{q} = \mathbf{v} - \mathbf{p} = \langle\, 8,\, -3,\, -3\, \rangle - \langle\, \tfrac{2}{17},\, \tfrac{3}{17},\, \tfrac{2}{17}\, \rangle = \langle\, \tfrac{134}{17},\, -\tfrac{54}{17},\, -\tfrac{53}{17}\, \rangle.
$$

To check our work, we can use the dot product to verify that $\mathbf{p}$ and $\mathbf{q}$ are orthogonal vectors:

$$
\mathbf{p} \cdot \mathbf{q} = \langle\, \tfrac{2}{17},\, \tfrac{3}{17},\, \tfrac{2}{17}\, \rangle \cdot \langle\, \tfrac{134}{17},\, -\tfrac{54}{17},\, -\tfrac{53}{17}\, \rangle = \frac{268}{17} - \frac{162}{17} - \frac{106}{17} = 0.
$$

Then,

$$
\mathbf{v} = \mathbf{p} + \mathbf{q} = \langle\, \tfrac{2}{17},\, \tfrac{3}{17},\, \tfrac{2}{17}\, \rangle + \langle\, \tfrac{134}{17},\, -\tfrac{54}{17},\, -\tfrac{53}{17}\, \rangle.
$$

 **2.27** Express $\mathbf{v} = 5\mathbf{i} - \mathbf{j}$ as a sum of orthogonal vectors such that one of the vectors has the same direction as $\mathbf{u} = 4\mathbf{i} + 2\mathbf{j}$.

## Example 2.29

### Scalar Projection of Velocity

A container ship leaves port traveling $15°$ north of east. Its engine generates a speed of 20 knots along that path (see the following figure). In addition, the ocean current moves the ship northeast at a speed of 2 knots. Considering both the engine and the current, how fast is the ship moving in the direction $15°$ north of east? Round the answer to two decimal places.

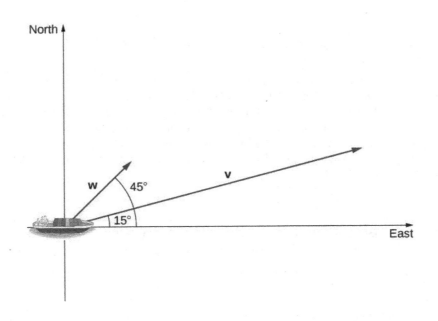

## Solution

Let **v** be the velocity vector generated by the engine, and let **w** be the velocity vector of the current. We already know $\|\mathbf{v}\| = 20$ along the desired route. We just need to add in the scalar projection of **w** onto **v**. We get

$$
\begin{aligned}
\text{comp}_\mathbf{v}\,\mathbf{w} &= \frac{\mathbf{v} \cdot \mathbf{w}}{\|\mathbf{v}\|} \\
&= \frac{\|\mathbf{v}\|\ \|\mathbf{w}\|\ \cos(30°)}{\|\mathbf{v}\|} \\
&= \|\mathbf{w}\|\ \cos(30°) \\
&= 2\frac{\sqrt{3}}{2} = \sqrt{3} \approx 1.73 \text{ knots.}
\end{aligned}
$$

The ship is moving at 21.73 knots in the direction $15°$ north of east.

 **2.28** Repeat the previous example, but assume the ocean current is moving southeast instead of northeast, as shown in the following figure.

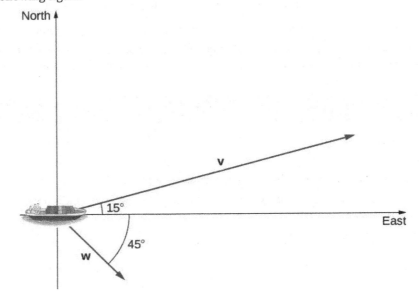

# Work

Now that we understand dot products, we can see how to apply them to real-life situations. The most common application of the dot product of two vectors is in the calculation of work.

From physics, we know that work is done when an object is moved by a force. When the force is constant and applied in the same direction the object moves, then we define the work done as the product of the force and the distance the object travels: $W = Fd$. We saw several examples of this type in earlier chapters. Now imagine the direction of the force is different from the direction of motion, as with the example of a child pulling a wagon. To find the work done, we need to multiply the component of the force that acts in the direction of the motion by the magnitude of the displacement. The dot product allows us to do just that. If we represent an applied force by a vector **F** and the displacement of an object by a vector **s**, then the **work done by the force** is the dot product of **F** and **s**.

---

**Definition**

When a constant force is applied to an object so the object moves in a straight line from point $P$ to point $Q$, the work $W$ done by the force **F**, acting at an angle $\theta$ from the line of motion, is given by

$$W = \mathbf{F} \cdot \overrightarrow{PQ} = \| \mathbf{F} \| \ \| \overrightarrow{PQ} \| \cos \theta. \tag{2.8}$$

---

Let's revisit the problem of the child's wagon introduced earlier. Suppose a child is pulling a wagon with a force having a magnitude of 8 lb on the handle at an angle of 55°. If the child pulls the wagon 50 ft, find the work done by the force (**Figure 2.51**).

**Figure 2.51** The horizontal component of the force is the projection of **F** onto the positive $x$-axis.

We have

$$W = \| \mathbf{F} \| \ \| \overrightarrow{PQ} \| \cos \theta = 8(50)(\cos(55°)) \approx 229 \text{ ft} \cdot \text{lb}.$$

In U.S. standard units, we measure the magnitude of force $\| \mathbf{F} \|$ in pounds. The magnitude of the displacement vector $\| \overrightarrow{PQ} \|$ tells us how far the object moved, and it is measured in feet. The customary unit of measure for work, then, is the foot-pound. One foot-pound is the amount of work required to move an object weighing 1 lb a distance of 1 ft straight up. In the metric system, the unit of measure for force is the newton (N), and the unit of measure of magnitude for work is a newton-meter (N·m), or a joule (J).

---

**Example 2.30**

**Calculating Work**

A conveyor belt generates a force $\mathbf{F} = 5\mathbf{i} - 3\mathbf{j} + \mathbf{k}$ that moves a suitcase from point $(1, 1, 1)$ to point $(9, 4, 7)$ along a straight line. Find the work done by the conveyor belt. The distance is measured in meters and the force is measured in newtons.

**Solution**

The displacement vector $\vec{PQ}$ has initial point $(1, 1, 1)$ and terminal point $(9, 4, 7)$:

$$\vec{PQ} = \langle 9 - 1, 4 - 1, 7 - 1 \rangle = \langle 8, 3, 6 \rangle = 8\mathbf{i} + 3\mathbf{j} + 6\mathbf{k}.$$

Work is the dot product of force and displacement:

$$\begin{aligned} W &= \mathbf{F} \cdot \vec{PQ} \\ &= (5\mathbf{i} - 3\mathbf{j} + \mathbf{k}) \cdot (8\mathbf{i} + 3\mathbf{j} + 6\mathbf{k}) \\ &= 5(8) + (-3)(3) + 1(6) \\ &= 37 \mathrm{N} \cdot \mathrm{m} \\ &= 37 \, \mathrm{J}. \end{aligned}$$

 **2.29** A constant force of 30 lb is applied at an angle of 60° to pull a handcart 10 ft across the ground (**Figure 2.52**). What is the work done by this force?

**Figure 2.52**

# 2.3 EXERCISES

For the following exercises, the vectors **u** and **v** are given. Calculate the dot product **u** · **v**.

123. $\mathbf{u} = \langle 3, 0 \rangle$, $\mathbf{v} = \langle 2, 2 \rangle$

124. $\mathbf{u} = \langle 3, -4 \rangle$, $\mathbf{v} = \langle 4, 3 \rangle$

125. $\mathbf{u} = \langle 2, 2, -1 \rangle$, $\mathbf{v} = \langle -1, 2, 2 \rangle$

126. $\mathbf{u} = \langle 4, 5, -6 \rangle$, $\mathbf{v} = \langle 0, -2, -3 \rangle$

For the following exercises, the vectors **a**, **b**, and **c** are given. Determine the vectors $(\mathbf{a} \cdot \mathbf{b})\mathbf{c}$ and $(\mathbf{a} \cdot \mathbf{c})\mathbf{b}$. Express the vectors in component form.

127. $\mathbf{a} = \langle 2, 0, -3 \rangle$, $\mathbf{b} = \langle -4, -7, 1 \rangle$, $\mathbf{c} = \langle 1, 1, -1 \rangle$

128. $\mathbf{a} = \langle 0, 1, 2 \rangle$, $\mathbf{b} = \langle -1, 0, 1 \rangle$, $\mathbf{c} = \langle 1, 0, -1 \rangle$

129. $\mathbf{a} = \mathbf{i} + \mathbf{j}$, $\mathbf{b} = \mathbf{i} - \mathbf{k}$, $\mathbf{c} = \mathbf{i} - 2\mathbf{k}$

130. $\mathbf{a} = \mathbf{i} - \mathbf{j} + \mathbf{k}$, $\mathbf{b} = \mathbf{j} + 3\mathbf{k}$, $\mathbf{c} = -\mathbf{i} + 2\mathbf{j} - 4\mathbf{k}$

For the following exercises, the two-dimensional vectors **a** and **b** are given.

  a. Find the measure of the angle $\theta$ between **a** and **b**. Express the answer in radians rounded to two decimal places, if it is not possible to express it exactly.
  b. Is $\theta$ an acute angle?

131. **[T]** $\mathbf{a} = \langle 3, -1 \rangle$, $\mathbf{b} = \langle -4, 0 \rangle$

132. **[T]** $\mathbf{a} = \langle 2, 1 \rangle$, $\mathbf{b} = \langle -1, 3 \rangle$

133. $\mathbf{u} = 3\mathbf{i}$, $\mathbf{v} = 4\mathbf{i} + 4\mathbf{j}$

134. $\mathbf{u} = 5\mathbf{i}$, $\mathbf{v} = -6\mathbf{i} + 6\mathbf{j}$

For the following exercises, find the measure of the angle between the three-dimensional vectors **a** and **b**. Express the answer in radians rounded to two decimal places, if it is not possible to express it exactly.

135. $\mathbf{a} = \langle 3, -1, 2 \rangle$, $\mathbf{b} = \langle 1, -1, -2 \rangle$

136. $\mathbf{a} = \langle 0, -1, -3 \rangle$, $\mathbf{b} = \langle 2, 3, -1 \rangle$

137. $\mathbf{a} = \mathbf{i} + \mathbf{j}$, $\mathbf{b} = \mathbf{j} - \mathbf{k}$

138. $\mathbf{a} = \mathbf{i} - 2\mathbf{j} + \mathbf{k}$, $\mathbf{b} = \mathbf{i} + \mathbf{j} - 2\mathbf{k}$

139. **[T]** $\mathbf{a} = 3\mathbf{i} - \mathbf{j} - 2\mathbf{k}$, $\mathbf{b} = \mathbf{v} + \mathbf{w}$, where $\mathbf{v} = -2\mathbf{i} - 3\mathbf{j} + 2\mathbf{k}$ and $\mathbf{w} = \mathbf{i} + 2\mathbf{k}$

140. **[T]** $\mathbf{a} = 3\mathbf{i} - \mathbf{j} + 2\mathbf{k}$, $\mathbf{b} = \mathbf{v} - \mathbf{w}$, where $\mathbf{v} = 2\mathbf{i} + \mathbf{j} + 4\mathbf{k}$ and $\mathbf{w} = 6\mathbf{i} + \mathbf{j} + 2\mathbf{k}$

For the following exercises determine whether the given vectors are orthogonal.

141. $\mathbf{a} = \langle x, y \rangle$, $\mathbf{b} = \langle -y, x \rangle$, where $x$ and $y$ are nonzero real numbers

142. $\mathbf{a} = \langle x, x \rangle$, $\mathbf{b} = \langle -y, y \rangle$, where $x$ and $y$ are nonzero real numbers

143. $\mathbf{a} = 3\mathbf{i} - \mathbf{j} - 2\mathbf{k}$, $\mathbf{b} = -2\mathbf{i} - 3\mathbf{j} + \mathbf{k}$

144. $\mathbf{a} = \mathbf{i} - \mathbf{j}$, $\mathbf{b} = 7\mathbf{i} + 2\mathbf{j} - \mathbf{k}$

145. Find all two-dimensional vectors **a** orthogonal to vector $\mathbf{b} = \langle 3, 4 \rangle$. Express the answer in component form.

146. Find all two-dimensional vectors **a** orthogonal to vector $\mathbf{b} = \langle 5, -6 \rangle$. Express the answer by using standard unit vectors.

147. Determine all three-dimensional vectors **u** orthogonal to vector $\mathbf{v} = \langle 1, 1, 0 \rangle$. Express the answer by using standard unit vectors.

148. Determine all three-dimensional vectors **u** orthogonal to vector $\mathbf{v} = \mathbf{i} - \mathbf{j} - \mathbf{k}$. Express the answer in component form.

149. Determine the real number $\alpha$ such that vectors $\mathbf{a} = 2\mathbf{i} + 3\mathbf{j}$ and $\mathbf{b} = 9\mathbf{i} + \alpha\mathbf{j}$ are orthogonal.

150. Determine the real number $\alpha$ such that vectors $\mathbf{a} = -3\mathbf{i} + 2\mathbf{j}$ and $\mathbf{b} = 2\mathbf{i} + \alpha\mathbf{j}$ are orthogonal.

151. **[T]** Consider the points $P(4, 5)$ and $Q(5, -7)$.

  a. Determine vectors $\overrightarrow{OP}$ and $\overrightarrow{OQ}$. Express the answer by using standard unit vectors.
  b. Determine the measure of angle $O$ in triangle $OPQ$. Express the answer in degrees rounded to two decimal places.

152. **[T]** Consider points $A(1, 1)$, $B(2, -7)$, and $C(6, 3)$.

    a. Determine vectors $\vec{BA}$ and $\vec{BC}$. Express the answer in component form.

    b. Determine the measure of angle $B$ in triangle $ABC$. Express the answer in degrees rounded to two decimal places.

153. Determine the measure of angle $A$ in triangle $ABC$, where $A(1, 1, 8)$, $B(4, -3, -4)$, and $C(-3, 1, 5)$. Express your answer in degrees rounded to two decimal places.

154. Consider points $P(3, 7, -2)$ and $Q(1, 1, -3)$. Determine the angle between vectors $\vec{OP}$ and $\vec{OQ}$. Express the answer in degrees rounded to two decimal places.

For the following exercises, determine which (if any) pairs of the following vectors are orthogonal.

155. $\mathbf{u} = \langle 3, 7, -2 \rangle$, $\mathbf{v} = \langle 5, -3, -3 \rangle$, $\mathbf{w} = \langle 0, 1, -1 \rangle$

156. $\mathbf{u} = \mathbf{i} - \mathbf{k}$, $\mathbf{v} = 5\mathbf{j} - 5\mathbf{k}$, $\mathbf{w} = 10\mathbf{j}$

157. Use vectors to show that a parallelogram with equal diagonals is a square.

158. Use vectors to show that the diagonals of a rhombus are perpendicular.

159. Show that $\mathbf{u} \cdot (\mathbf{v} + \mathbf{w}) = \mathbf{u} \cdot \mathbf{v} + \mathbf{u} \cdot \mathbf{w}$ is true for any vectors $\mathbf{u}$, $\mathbf{v}$, and $\mathbf{w}$.

160. Verify the identity $\mathbf{u} \cdot (\mathbf{v} + \mathbf{w}) = \mathbf{u} \cdot \mathbf{v} + \mathbf{u} \cdot \mathbf{w}$ for vectors $\mathbf{u} = \langle 1, 0, 4 \rangle$, $\mathbf{v} = \langle -2, 3, 5 \rangle$, and $\mathbf{w} = \langle 4, -2, 6 \rangle$.

For the following problems, the vector $\mathbf{u}$ is given.

    a. Find the direction cosines for the vector u.

    b. Find the direction angles for the vector u expressed in degrees. (Round the answer to the nearest integer.)

161. $\mathbf{u} = \langle 2, 2, 1 \rangle$

162. $\mathbf{u} = \mathbf{i} - 2\mathbf{j} + 2\mathbf{k}$

163. $\mathbf{u} = \langle -1, 5, 2 \rangle$

164. $\mathbf{u} = \langle 2, 3, 4 \rangle$

165. Consider $\mathbf{u} = \langle a, b, c \rangle$ a nonzero three-dimensional vector. Let $\cos \alpha$, $\cos \beta$, and $\cos \gamma$ be the directions of the cosines of $\mathbf{u}$. Show that $\cos^2 \alpha + \cos^2 \beta + \cos^2 \gamma = 1$.

166. Determine the direction cosines of vector $\mathbf{u} = \mathbf{i} + 2\mathbf{j} + 2\mathbf{k}$ and show they satisfy $\cos^2 \alpha + \cos^2 \beta + \cos^2 \gamma = 1$.

For the following exercises, the vectors $\mathbf{u}$ and $\mathbf{v}$ are given.

    a. Find the vector projection $\mathbf{w} = \text{proj}_{\mathbf{u}} \mathbf{v}$ of vector $\mathbf{v}$ onto vector $\mathbf{u}$. Express your answer in component form.

    b. Find the scalar projection $\text{comp}_{\mathbf{u}} \mathbf{v}$ of vector $\mathbf{v}$ onto vector $\mathbf{u}$.

167. $\mathbf{u} = 5\mathbf{i} + 2\mathbf{j}$, $\mathbf{v} = 2\mathbf{i} + 3\mathbf{j}$

168. $\mathbf{u} = \langle -4, 7 \rangle$, $\mathbf{v} = \langle 3, 5 \rangle$

169. $\mathbf{u} = 3\mathbf{i} + 2\mathbf{k}$, $\mathbf{v} = 2\mathbf{j} + 4\mathbf{k}$

170. $\mathbf{u} = \langle 4, 4, 0 \rangle$, $\mathbf{v} = \langle 0, 4, 1 \rangle$

171. Consider the vectors $\mathbf{u} = 4\mathbf{i} - 3\mathbf{j}$ and $\mathbf{v} = 3\mathbf{i} + 2\mathbf{j}$.

    a. Find the component form of vector $\mathbf{w} = \text{proj}_{\mathbf{u}} \mathbf{v}$ that represents the projection of $\mathbf{v}$ onto $\mathbf{u}$.

    b. Write the decomposition $\mathbf{v} = \mathbf{w} + \mathbf{q}$ of vector $\mathbf{v}$ into the orthogonal components $\mathbf{w}$ and $\mathbf{q}$, where $\mathbf{w}$ is the projection of $\mathbf{v}$ onto $\mathbf{u}$ and $\mathbf{q}$ is a vector orthogonal to the direction of $\mathbf{u}$.

172. Consider vectors $\mathbf{u} = 2\mathbf{i} + 4\mathbf{j}$ and $\mathbf{v} = 4\mathbf{j} + 2\mathbf{k}$.

    a. Find the component form of vector $\mathbf{w} = \text{proj}_{\mathbf{u}} \mathbf{v}$ that represents the projection of $\mathbf{v}$ onto $\mathbf{u}$.

    b. Write the decomposition $\mathbf{v} = \mathbf{w} + \mathbf{q}$ of vector $\mathbf{v}$ into the orthogonal components $\mathbf{w}$ and $\mathbf{q}$, where $\mathbf{w}$ is the projection of $\mathbf{v}$ onto $\mathbf{u}$ and $\mathbf{q}$ is a vector orthogonal to the direction of $\mathbf{u}$.

**173.** A methane molecule has a carbon atom situated at the origin and four hydrogen atoms located at points $P(1, 1, -1)$, $Q(1, -1, 1)$, $R(-1, 1, 1)$, and $S(-1, -1, -1)$ (see figure).

   a. Find the distance between the hydrogen atoms located at $P$ and $R$.

   b. Find the angle between vectors $\overrightarrow{OS}$ and $\overrightarrow{OR}$ that connect the carbon atom with the hydrogen atoms located at $S$ and $R$, which is also called the *bond angle*. Express the answer in degrees rounded to two decimal places.

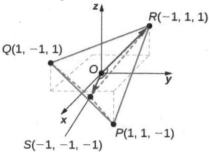

**174.** **[T]** Find the vectors that join the center of a clock to the hours 1:00, 2:00, and 3:00. Assume the clock is circular with a radius of 1 unit.

**175.** Find the work done by force $\mathbf{F} = \langle 5, 6, -2 \rangle$ (measured in Newtons) that moves a particle from point $P(3, -1, 0)$ to point $Q(2, 3, 1)$ along a straight line (the distance is measured in meters).

**176.** **[T]** A sled is pulled by exerting a force of 100 N on a rope that makes an angle of $25°$ with the horizontal. Find the work done in pulling the sled 40 m. (Round the answer to one decimal place.)

**177.** **[T]** A father is pulling his son on a sled at an angle of $20°$ with the horizontal with a force of 25 lb (see the following image). He pulls the sled in a straight path of 50 ft. How much work was done by the man pulling the sled? (Round the answer to the nearest integer.)

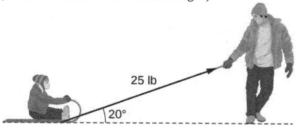

**178.** **[T]** A car is towed using a force of 1600 N. The rope used to pull the car makes an angle of 25° with the horizontal. Find the work done in towing the car 2 km. Express the answer in joules $(1J = 1N \cdot m)$ rounded to the nearest integer.

**179.** **[T]** A boat sails north aided by a wind blowing in a direction of N30°E with a magnitude of 500 lb. How much work is performed by the wind as the boat moves 100 ft? (Round the answer to two decimal places.)

**180.** Vector $\mathbf{p} = \langle 150, 225, 375 \rangle$ represents the price of certain models of bicycles sold by a bicycle shop. Vector $\mathbf{n} = \langle 10, 7, 9 \rangle$ represents the number of bicycles sold of each model, respectively. Compute the dot product $\mathbf{p} \cdot \mathbf{n}$ and state its meaning.

**181.** **[T]** Two forces $\mathbf{F}_1$ and $\mathbf{F}_2$ are represented by vectors with initial points that are at the origin. The first force has a magnitude of 20 lb and the terminal point of the vector is point $P(1, 1, 0)$. The second force has a magnitude of 40 lb and the terminal point of its vector is point $Q(0, 1, 1)$. Let $\mathbf{F}$ be the resultant force of forces $\mathbf{F}_1$ and $\mathbf{F}_2$.

   a. Find the magnitude of $\mathbf{F}$. (Round the answer to one decimal place.)

   b. Find the direction angles of $\mathbf{F}$. (Express the answer in degrees rounded to one decimal place.)

**182.** **[T]** Consider $\mathbf{r}(t) = \langle \cos t, \sin t, 2t \rangle$ the position vector of a particle at time $t \in [0, 30]$, where the components of $\mathbf{r}$ are expressed in centimeters and time in seconds. Let $\overrightarrow{OP}$ be the position vector of the particle after 1 sec.

   a. Show that all vectors $\overrightarrow{PQ}$, where $Q(x, y, z)$ is an arbitrary point, orthogonal to the instantaneous velocity vector $\mathbf{v}(1)$ of the particle after 1 sec, can be expressed as $\overrightarrow{PQ} = \langle x - \cos 1, y - \sin 1, z - 2 \rangle$, where $x \sin 1 - y \cos 1 - 2z + 4 = 0$. The set of point $Q$ describes a plane called the *normal plane* to the path of the particle at point $P$.

   b. Use a CAS to visualize the instantaneous velocity vector and the normal plane at point $P$ along with the path of the particle.

# 2.4 | The Cross Product

## Learning Objectives

**2.4.1** Calculate the cross product of two given vectors.

**2.4.2** Use determinants to calculate a cross product.

**2.4.3** Find a vector orthogonal to two given vectors.

**2.4.4** Determine areas and volumes by using the cross product.

**2.4.5** Calculate the torque of a given force and position vector.

Imagine a mechanic turning a wrench to tighten a bolt. The mechanic applies a force at the end of the wrench. This creates rotation, or torque, which tightens the bolt. We can use vectors to represent the force applied by the mechanic, and the distance (radius) from the bolt to the end of the wrench. Then, we can represent torque by a vector oriented along the axis of rotation. Note that the torque vector is orthogonal to both the force vector and the radius vector.

In this section, we develop an operation called the *cross product*, which allows us to find a vector orthogonal to two given vectors. Calculating torque is an important application of cross products, and we examine torque in more detail later in the section.

## The Cross Product and Its Properties

The dot product is a multiplication of two vectors that results in a scalar. In this section, we introduce a product of two vectors that generates a third vector orthogonal to the first two. Consider how we might find such a vector. Let $\mathbf{u} = \langle u_1, u_2, u_3 \rangle$ and $\mathbf{v} = \langle v_1, v_2, v_3 \rangle$ be nonzero vectors. We want to find a vector $\mathbf{w} = \langle w_1, w_2, w_3 \rangle$ orthogonal to both $\mathbf{u}$ and $\mathbf{v}$ —that is, we want to find $\mathbf{w}$ such that $\mathbf{u} \cdot \mathbf{w} = 0$ and $\mathbf{v} \cdot \mathbf{w} = 0$. Therefore, $w_1$, $w_2$, and $w_3$ must satisfy

$$u_1 w_1 + u_2 w_2 + u_3 w_3 = 0$$
$$v_1 w_1 + v_2 w_2 + v_3 w_3 = 0.$$

If we multiply the top equation by $v_3$ and the bottom equation by $u_3$ and subtract, we can eliminate the variable $w_3$, which gives

$$(u_1 v_3 - v_1 u_3)w_1 + (u_2 v_3 - v_2 u_3)w_2 = 0.$$

If we select

$$w_1 = u_2 v_3 - u_3 v_2$$
$$w_2 = -(u_1 v_3 - u_3 v_1),$$

we get a possible solution vector. Substituting these values back into the original equations gives

$$w_3 = u_1 v_2 - u_2 v_1.$$

That is, vector

$$\mathbf{w} = \langle u_2 v_3 - u_3 v_2, -(u_1 v_3 - u_3 v_1), u_1 v_2 - u_2 v_1 \rangle$$

is orthogonal to both $\mathbf{u}$ and $\mathbf{v}$, which leads us to define the following operation, called the cross product.

---

**Definition** _____

Let $\mathbf{u} = \langle u_1, u_2, u_3 \rangle$ and $\mathbf{v} = \langle v_1, v_2, v_3 \rangle$. Then, the **cross product** $\mathbf{u} \times \mathbf{v}$ is vector

$$\mathbf{u} \times \mathbf{v} = (u_2 v_3 - u_3 v_2)\mathbf{i} - (u_1 v_3 - u_3 v_1)\mathbf{j} + (u_1 v_2 - u_2 v_1)\mathbf{k} \qquad (2.9)$$
$$= \langle u_2 v_3 - u_3 v_2, -(u_1 v_3 - u_3 v_1), u_1 v_2 - u_2 v_1 \rangle.$$

---

From the way we have developed $\mathbf{u} \times \mathbf{v}$, it should be clear that the cross product is orthogonal to both $\mathbf{u}$ and $\mathbf{v}$. However, it never hurts to check. To show that $\mathbf{u} \times \mathbf{v}$ is orthogonal to $\mathbf{u}$, we calculate the dot product of $\mathbf{u}$ and $\mathbf{u} \times \mathbf{v}$.

$$
\begin{aligned}
\mathbf{u} \cdot (\mathbf{u} \times \mathbf{v}) &= \langle u_1, u_2, u_3 \rangle \cdot \langle u_2 v_3 - u_3 v_2, -u_1 v_3 + u_3 v_1, u_1 v_2 - u_2 v_1 \rangle \\
&= u_1 (u_2 v_3 - u_3 v_2) + u_2 (-u_1 v_3 + u_3 v_1) + u_3 (u_1 v_2 - u_2 v_1) \\
&= u_1 u_2 v_3 - u_1 u_3 v_2 - u_1 u_2 v_3 + u_2 u_3 v_1 + u_1 u_3 v_2 - u_2 u_3 v_1 \\
&= (u_1 u_2 v_3 - u_1 u_2 v_3) + (-u_1 u_3 v_2 + u_1 u_3 v_2) + (u_2 u_3 v_1 - u_2 u_3 v_1) \\
&= 0
\end{aligned}
$$

In a similar manner, we can show that the cross product is also orthogonal to $\mathbf{v}$.

## Example 2.31

### Finding a Cross Product

Let $\mathbf{p} = \langle -1, 2, 5 \rangle$ and $\mathbf{q} = \langle 4, 0, -3 \rangle$ (Figure 2.53). Find $\mathbf{p} \times \mathbf{q}$.

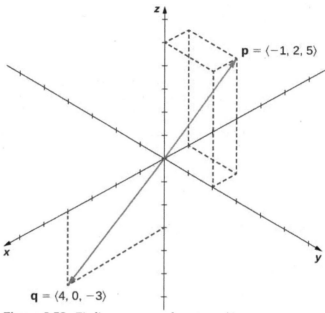

**Figure 2.53** Finding a cross product to two given vectors.

### Solution

Substitute the components of the vectors into Equation 2.9:

$$
\begin{aligned}
\mathbf{p} \times \mathbf{q} &= \langle -1, 2, 5 \rangle \times \langle 4, 0, -3 \rangle \\
&= \langle p_2 q_3 - p_3 q_2, \ p_1 q_3 - p_3 q_1, \ p_1 q_2 - p_2 q_1 \rangle \\
&= \langle 2(-3) - 5(0), \ -(-1)(-3) + 5(4), \ (-1)(0) - 2(4) \rangle \\
&= \langle -6, 17, -8 \rangle .
\end{aligned}
$$

 **2.30** Find $\mathbf{p} \times \mathbf{q}$ for $\mathbf{p} = \langle 5, 1, 2 \rangle$ and $\mathbf{q} = \langle -2, 0, 1 \rangle$. Express the answer using standard unit vectors.

Although it may not be obvious from Equation 2.9, the direction of $\mathbf{u} \times \mathbf{v}$ is given by the right-hand rule. If we hold the right hand out with the fingers pointing in the direction of $\mathbf{u}$, then curl the fingers toward vector $\mathbf{v}$, the thumb points in the direction of the cross product, as shown.

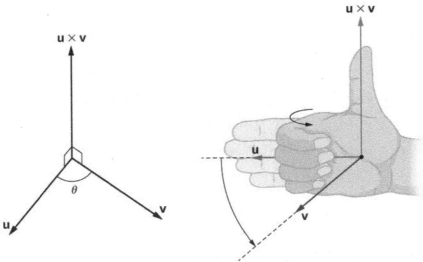

Figure 2.54 The direction of **u** × **v** is determined by the right-hand rule.

Notice what this means for the direction of **v** × **u**. If we apply the right-hand rule to **v** × **u**, we start with our fingers pointed in the direction of **v**, then curl our fingers toward the vector **u**. In this case, the thumb points in the opposite direction of **u** × **v**. (Try it!)

## Example 2.32

### Anticommutativity of the Cross Product

Let **u** = $\langle 0, 2, 1 \rangle$ and **v** = $\langle 3, -1, 0 \rangle$. Calculate **u** × **v** and **v** × **u** and graph them.

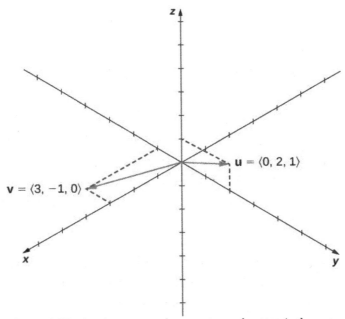

Figure 2.55 Are the cross products **u** × **v** and **v** × **u** in the same direction?

### Solution

We have

$$\mathbf{u} \times \mathbf{v} = \langle (0+1), -(0-3), (0-6) \rangle = \langle 1, 3, -6 \rangle$$
$$\mathbf{v} \times \mathbf{u} = \langle (-1-0), -(3-0), (6-0) \rangle = \langle -1, -3, 6 \rangle .$$

We see that, in this case, $\mathbf{u} \times \mathbf{v} = -(\mathbf{v} \times \mathbf{u})$ (Figure 2.56). We prove this in general later in this section.

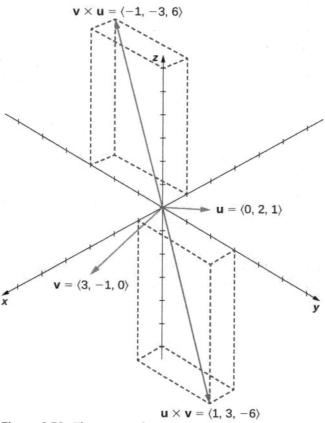

**Figure 2.56** The cross products $\mathbf{u} \times \mathbf{v}$ and $\mathbf{v} \times \mathbf{u}$ are both orthogonal to $\mathbf{u}$ and $\mathbf{v}$, but in opposite directions.

 **2.31** Suppose vectors $\mathbf{u}$ and $\mathbf{v}$ lie in the $xy$-plane (the $z$-component of each vector is zero). Now suppose the $x$- and $y$-components of $\mathbf{u}$ and the $y$-component of $\mathbf{v}$ are all positive, whereas the $x$-component of $\mathbf{v}$ is negative. Assuming the coordinate axes are oriented in the usual positions, in which direction does $\mathbf{u} \times \mathbf{v}$ point?

The cross products of the standard unit vectors $\mathbf{i}, \mathbf{j},$ and $\mathbf{k}$ can be useful for simplifying some calculations, so let's consider these cross products. A straightforward application of the definition shows that

$$\mathbf{i} \times \mathbf{i} = \mathbf{j} \times \mathbf{j} = \mathbf{k} \times \mathbf{k} = \mathbf{0}.$$

(The cross product of two vectors is a vector, so each of these products results in the zero vector, not the scalar 0.) It's up to you to verify the calculations on your own.

Furthermore, because the cross product of two vectors is orthogonal to each of these vectors, we know that the cross product of **i** and **j** is parallel to **k**. Similarly, the vector product of **i** and **k** is parallel to **j**, and the vector product of **j** and **k** is parallel to **i**. We can use the right-hand rule to determine the direction of each product. Then we have

$$\mathbf{i} \times \mathbf{j} = \mathbf{k} \qquad \mathbf{j} \times \mathbf{i} = -\mathbf{k}$$
$$\mathbf{j} \times \mathbf{k} = \mathbf{i} \qquad \mathbf{k} \times \mathbf{j} = -\mathbf{i}$$
$$\mathbf{k} \times \mathbf{i} = \mathbf{j} \qquad \mathbf{i} \times \mathbf{k} = -\mathbf{j}.$$

These formulas come in handy later.

## Example 2.33

### Cross Product of Standard Unit Vectors

Find $\mathbf{i} \times (\mathbf{j} \times \mathbf{k})$.

### Solution

We know that $\mathbf{j} \times \mathbf{k} = \mathbf{i}$. Therefore, $\mathbf{i} \times (\mathbf{j} \times \mathbf{k}) = \mathbf{i} \times \mathbf{i} = \mathbf{0}$.

 **2.32** Find $(\mathbf{i} \times \mathbf{j}) \times (\mathbf{k} \times \mathbf{i})$.

As we have seen, the dot product is often called the *scalar product* because it results in a scalar. The cross product results in a vector, so it is sometimes called the **vector product**. These operations are both versions of vector multiplication, but they have very different properties and applications. Let's explore some properties of the cross product. We prove only a few of them. Proofs of the other properties are left as exercises.

### Theorem 2.6: Properties of the Cross Product

Let **u**, **v**, and **w** be vectors in space, and let $c$ be a scalar.

|  |  |  |
|---|---|---|
| i. | $\mathbf{u} \times \mathbf{v} = -(\mathbf{v} \times \mathbf{u})$ | Anticommutative property |
| ii. | $\mathbf{u} \times (\mathbf{v} + \mathbf{w}) = \mathbf{u} \times \mathbf{v} + \mathbf{u} \times \mathbf{w}$ | Distributive property |
| iii. | $c(\mathbf{u} \times \mathbf{v}) = (c\mathbf{u}) \times \mathbf{v} = \mathbf{u} \times (c\mathbf{v})$ | Multiplication by a constant |
| iv. | $\mathbf{u} \times \mathbf{0} = \mathbf{0} \times \mathbf{u} = \mathbf{0}$ | Cross product of the zero vector |
| v. | $\mathbf{v} \times \mathbf{v} = \mathbf{0}$ | Cross product of a vector with itself |
| vi. | $\mathbf{u} \cdot (\mathbf{v} \times \mathbf{w}) = (\mathbf{u} \times \mathbf{v}) \cdot \mathbf{w}$ | Scalar triple product |

### Proof

For property i., we want to show $\mathbf{u} \times \mathbf{v} = -(\mathbf{v} \times \mathbf{u})$. We have

$$\begin{aligned}
\mathbf{u} \times \mathbf{v} &= \langle u_1, u_2, u_3 \rangle \times \langle v_1, v_2, v_3 \rangle \\
&= \langle u_2 v_3 - u_3 v_2, -u_1 v_3 + u_3 v_1, u_1 v_2 - u_2 v_1 \rangle \\
&= -\langle u_3 v_2 - u_2 v_3, -u_3 v_1 + u_1 v_3, u_2 v_1 - u_1 v_2 \rangle \\
&= -\langle v_1, v_2, v_3 \rangle \times \langle u_1, u_2, u_3 \rangle \\
&= -(\mathbf{v} \times \mathbf{u}).
\end{aligned}$$

Unlike most operations we've seen, the cross product is not commutative. This makes sense if we think about the right-hand rule.

For property iv., this follows directly from the definition of the cross product. We have

$$\mathbf{u} \times \mathbf{0} = \langle u_2(0) - u_3(0), -(u_2(0) - u_3(0)), u_1(0) - u_2(0) \rangle$$
$$= \langle 0, 0, 0 \rangle = \mathbf{0}.$$

Then, by property i., $\mathbf{0} \times \mathbf{u} = \mathbf{0}$ as well. Remember that the dot product of a vector and the zero vector is the *scalar* 0, whereas the cross product of a vector with the zero vector is the *vector* $\mathbf{0}$.

Property vi. looks like the associative property, but note the change in operations:

$$\mathbf{u} \cdot (\mathbf{v} \times \mathbf{w}) = \mathbf{u} \cdot \langle v_2 w_3 - v_3 w_2, -v_1 w_3 + v_3 w_1, v_1 w_2 - v_2 w_1 \rangle$$
$$= u_1(v_2 w_3 - v_3 w_2) + u_2(-v_1 w_3 + v_3 w_1) + u_3(v_1 w_2 - v_2 w_1)$$
$$= u_1 v_2 w_3 - u_1 v_3 w_2 - u_2 v_1 w_3 + u_2 v_3 w_1 + u_3 v_1 w_2 - u_3 v_2 w_1$$
$$= (u_2 v_3 - u_3 v_2)w_1 + (u_3 v_1 - u_1 v_3)w_2 + (u_1 v_2 - u_2 v_1)w_3$$
$$= \langle u_2 v_3 - u_3 v_2, u_3 v_1 - u_1 v_3, u_1 v_2 - u_2 v_1 \rangle \cdot \langle w_1, w_2, w_3 \rangle$$
$$= (\mathbf{u} \times \mathbf{v}) \cdot \mathbf{w}.$$

$\square$

## Example 2.34

### Using the Properties of the Cross Product

Use the cross product properties to calculate $(2\mathbf{i} \times 3\mathbf{j}) \times \mathbf{j}$.

### Solution

$$(2\mathbf{i} \times 3\mathbf{j}) \times \mathbf{j} = 2(\mathbf{i} \times 3\mathbf{j}) \times \mathbf{j}$$
$$= 2(3)(\mathbf{i} \times \mathbf{j}) \times \mathbf{j}$$
$$= (6\mathbf{k}) \times \mathbf{j}$$
$$= 6(\mathbf{k} \times \mathbf{j})$$
$$= 6(-\mathbf{i}) = -6\mathbf{i}.$$

 **2.33** Use the properties of the cross product to calculate $(\mathbf{i} \times \mathbf{k}) \times (\mathbf{k} \times \mathbf{j})$.

So far in this section, we have been concerned with the direction of the vector $\mathbf{u} \times \mathbf{v}$, but we have not discussed its magnitude. It turns out there is a simple expression for the magnitude of $\mathbf{u} \times \mathbf{v}$ involving the magnitudes of $\mathbf{u}$ and $\mathbf{v}$, and the sine of the angle between them.

### Theorem 2.7: Magnitude of the Cross Product

Let $\mathbf{u}$ and $\mathbf{v}$ be vectors, and let $\theta$ be the angle between them. Then, $\| \mathbf{u} \times \mathbf{v} \| = \| \mathbf{u} \| \cdot \| \mathbf{v} \| \cdot \sin\theta$.

### Proof

Let $\mathbf{u} = \langle u_1, u_2, u_3 \rangle$ and $\mathbf{v} = \langle v_1, v_2, v_3 \rangle$ be vectors, and let $\theta$ denote the angle between them. Then

$$\begin{aligned}
\| \mathbf{u} \times \mathbf{v} \|^2 &= (u_2 v_3 - u_3 v_2)^2 + (u_3 v_1 - u_1 v_3)^2 + (u_1 v_2 - u_2 v_1)^2 \\
&= u_2^2 v_3^2 - 2u_2 u_3 v_2 v_3 + u_3^2 v_2^2 + u_3^2 v_1^2 - 2u_1 u_3 v_1 v_3 + u_1^2 v_3^2 + u_1^2 v_2^2 - 2u_1 u_2 v_1 v_2 + u_2^2 v_1^2 \\
&= u_1^2 v_1^2 + u_1^2 v_2^2 + u_1^2 v_3^2 + u_2^2 v_1^2 + u_2^2 v_2^2 + u_2^2 v_3^2 + u_3^2 v_1^2 + u_3^2 v_2^2 + u_3^2 v_3^2 \\
&\quad - \left( u_1^2 v_1^2 + u_2^2 v_2^2 + u_3^2 v_3^2 + 2u_1 u_2 v_1 v_2 + 2u_1 u_3 v_1 v_3 + 2u_2 u_3 v_2 v_3 \right) \\
&= \left( u_1^2 + u_2^2 + u_3^2 \right)\left( v_1^2 + v_2^2 + v_3^2 \right) - (u_1 v_1 + u_2 v_2 + u_3 v_3)^2 \\
&= \| \mathbf{u} \|^2 \| \mathbf{v} \|^2 - (\mathbf{u} \cdot \mathbf{v})^2 \\
&= \| \mathbf{u} \|^2 \| \mathbf{v} \|^2 - \| \mathbf{u} \|^2 \| \mathbf{v} \|^2 \cos^2 \theta \\
&= \| \mathbf{u} \|^2 \| \mathbf{v} \|^2 \left( 1 - \cos^2 \theta \right) \\
&= \| \mathbf{u} \|^2 \| \mathbf{v} \|^2 \left( \sin^2 \theta \right).
\end{aligned}$$

Taking square roots and noting that $\sqrt{\sin^2 \theta} = \sin \theta$ for $0 \le \theta \le 180°,$ we have the desired result:

$$\| \mathbf{u} \times \mathbf{v} \| = \| \mathbf{u} \| \, \| \mathbf{v} \| \sin \theta.$$

□

This definition of the cross product allows us to visualize or interpret the product geometrically. It is clear, for example, that the cross product is defined only for vectors in three dimensions, not for vectors in two dimensions. In two dimensions, it is impossible to generate a vector simultaneously orthogonal to two nonparallel vectors.

### Example 2.35

#### Calculating the Cross Product

Use **Properties of the Cross Product** to find the magnitude of the cross product of $\mathbf{u} = \langle 0, 4, 0 \rangle$ and $\mathbf{v} = \langle 0, 0, -3 \rangle$.

#### Solution

We have

$$\begin{aligned}
\| \mathbf{u} \times \mathbf{v} \| &= \| \mathbf{u} \| \cdot \| \mathbf{v} \| \cdot \sin \theta \\
&= \sqrt{0^2 + 4^2 + 0^2} \cdot \sqrt{0^2 + 0^2 + (-3)^2} \cdot \sin \frac{\pi}{2} \\
&= 4(3)(1) = 12.
\end{aligned}$$

 **2.34** Use **Properties of the Cross Product** to find the magnitude of $\mathbf{u} \times \mathbf{v}$, where $\mathbf{u} = \langle -8, 0, 0 \rangle$ and $\mathbf{v} = \langle 0, 2, 0 \rangle$.

## Determinants and the Cross Product

Using **Equation 2.9** to find the cross product of two vectors is straightforward, and it presents the cross product in the useful component form. The formula, however, is complicated and difficult to remember. Fortunately, we have an alternative. We can calculate the cross product of two vectors using **determinant** notation.

A $2 \times 2$ determinant is defined by

$$\begin{vmatrix} a_1 & a_2 \\ b_1 & b_2 \end{vmatrix} = a_1 b_2 - b_1 a_2.$$

For example,

$$\begin{vmatrix} 3 & -2 \\ 5 & 1 \end{vmatrix} = 3(1) - 5(-2) = 3 + 10 = 13.$$

A $3 \times 3$ determinant is defined in terms of $2 \times 2$ determinants as follows:

$$\begin{vmatrix} a_1 & a_2 & a_3 \\ b_1 & b_2 & b_3 \\ c_1 & c_2 & c_3 \end{vmatrix} = a_1 \begin{vmatrix} b_2 & b_3 \\ c_2 & c_3 \end{vmatrix} - a_2 \begin{vmatrix} b_1 & b_3 \\ c_1 & c_3 \end{vmatrix} + a_3 \begin{vmatrix} b_1 & b_2 \\ c_1 & c_2 \end{vmatrix}. \tag{2.10}$$

Equation 2.10 is referred to as the *expansion of the determinant along the first row*. Notice that the multipliers of each of the $2 \times 2$ determinants on the right side of this expression are the entries in the first row of the $3 \times 3$ determinant. Furthermore, each of the $2 \times 2$ determinants contains the entries from the $3 \times 3$ determinant that would remain if you crossed out the row and column containing the multiplier. Thus, for the first term on the right, $a_1$ is the multiplier, and the $2 \times 2$ determinant contains the entries that remain if you cross out the first row and first column of the $3 \times 3$ determinant. Similarly, for the second term, the multiplier is $a_2$, and the $2 \times 2$ determinant contains the entries that remain if you cross out the first row and second column of the $3 \times 3$ determinant. Notice, however, that the coefficient of the second term is negative. The third term can be calculated in similar fashion.

## Example 2.36

### Using Expansion Along the First Row to Compute a $3 \times 3$ Determinant

Evaluate the determinant $\begin{vmatrix} 2 & 5 & -1 \\ -1 & 1 & 3 \\ -2 & 3 & 4 \end{vmatrix}$.

#### Solution

We have

$$\begin{aligned}
\begin{vmatrix} 2 & 5 & -1 \\ -1 & 1 & 3 \\ -2 & 3 & 4 \end{vmatrix} &= 2\begin{vmatrix} 1 & 3 \\ 3 & 4 \end{vmatrix} - 5\begin{vmatrix} -1 & 3 \\ -2 & 4 \end{vmatrix} - 1\begin{vmatrix} -1 & 1 \\ -2 & 3 \end{vmatrix} \\
&= 2(4 - 9) - 5(-4 + 6) - 1(-3 + 2) \\
&= 2(-5) - 5(2) - 1(-1) = -10 - 10 + 1 \\
&= -19.
\end{aligned}$$

 **2.35** Evaluate the determinant $\begin{vmatrix} 1 & -2 & -1 \\ 3 & 2 & -3 \\ 1 & 5 & 4 \end{vmatrix}$.

Technically, determinants are defined only in terms of arrays of real numbers. However, the determinant notation provides a useful mnemonic device for the cross product formula.

### Rule: Cross Product Calculated by a Determinant

Let $\mathbf{u} = \langle u_1, u_2, u_3 \rangle$ and $\mathbf{v} = \langle v_1, v_2, v_3 \rangle$ be vectors. Then the cross product $\mathbf{u} \times \mathbf{v}$ is given by

$$\mathbf{u} \times \mathbf{v} = \begin{vmatrix} \mathbf{i} & \mathbf{j} & \mathbf{k} \\ u_1 & u_2 & u_3 \\ v_1 & v_2 & v_3 \end{vmatrix} = \begin{vmatrix} u_2 & u_3 \\ v_2 & v_3 \end{vmatrix}\mathbf{i} - \begin{vmatrix} u_1 & u_3 \\ v_1 & v_3 \end{vmatrix}\mathbf{j} + \begin{vmatrix} u_1 & u_2 \\ v_1 & v_2 \end{vmatrix}\mathbf{k}.$$

### Example 2.37

**Using Determinant Notation to find $\mathbf{p} \times \mathbf{q}$**

Let $\mathbf{p} = \langle -1, 2, 5 \rangle$ and $\mathbf{q} = \langle 4, 0, -3 \rangle$. Find $\mathbf{p} \times \mathbf{q}$.

**Solution**

We set up our determinant by putting the standard unit vectors across the first row, the components of $\mathbf{u}$ in the second row, and the components of $\mathbf{v}$ in the third row. Then, we have

$$\mathbf{p} \times \mathbf{q} = \begin{vmatrix} \mathbf{i} & \mathbf{j} & \mathbf{k} \\ -1 & 2 & 5 \\ 4 & 0 & -3 \end{vmatrix} = \begin{vmatrix} 2 & 5 \\ 0 & -3 \end{vmatrix} \mathbf{i} - \begin{vmatrix} -1 & 5 \\ 4 & -3 \end{vmatrix} \mathbf{j} + \begin{vmatrix} -1 & 2 \\ 4 & 0 \end{vmatrix} \mathbf{k}$$

$$= (-6 - 0)\mathbf{i} - (3 - 20)\mathbf{j} + (0 - 8)\mathbf{k}$$

$$= -6\mathbf{i} + 17\mathbf{j} - 8\mathbf{k}.$$

Notice that this answer confirms the calculation of the cross product in Example 2.31.

 **2.36** Use determinant notation to find $\mathbf{a} \times \mathbf{b}$, where $\mathbf{a} = \langle 8, 2, 3 \rangle$ and $\mathbf{b} = \langle -1, 0, 4 \rangle$.

## Using the Cross Product

The cross product is very useful for several types of calculations, including finding a vector orthogonal to two given vectors, computing areas of triangles and parallelograms, and even determining the volume of the three-dimensional geometric shape made of parallelograms known as a *parallelepiped*. The following examples illustrate these calculations.

### Example 2.38

**Finding a Unit Vector Orthogonal to Two Given Vectors**

Let $\mathbf{a} = \langle 5, 2, -1 \rangle$ and $\mathbf{b} = \langle 0, -1, 4 \rangle$. Find a unit vector orthogonal to both $\mathbf{a}$ and $\mathbf{b}$.

**Solution**

The cross product $\mathbf{a} \times \mathbf{b}$ is orthogonal to both vectors $\mathbf{a}$ and $\mathbf{b}$. We can calculate it with a determinant:

$$\mathbf{a} \times \mathbf{b} = \begin{vmatrix} \mathbf{i} & \mathbf{j} & \mathbf{k} \\ 5 & 2 & -1 \\ 0 & -1 & 4 \end{vmatrix} = \begin{vmatrix} 2 & -1 \\ -1 & 4 \end{vmatrix} \mathbf{i} - \begin{vmatrix} 5 & -1 \\ 0 & 4 \end{vmatrix} \mathbf{j} + \begin{vmatrix} 5 & 2 \\ 0 & -1 \end{vmatrix} \mathbf{k}$$

$$= (8 - 1)\mathbf{i} - (20 - 0)\mathbf{j} + (-5 - 0)\mathbf{k}$$

$$= 7\mathbf{i} - 20\mathbf{j} - 5\mathbf{k}.$$

Normalize this vector to find a unit vector in the same direction:

$$\| \mathbf{a} \times \mathbf{b} \| = \sqrt{(7)^2 + (-20)^2 + (-5)^2} = \sqrt{474}.$$

Thus, $\langle \frac{7}{\sqrt{474}}, \frac{-20}{\sqrt{474}}, \frac{-5}{\sqrt{474}} \rangle$ is a unit vector orthogonal to $\mathbf{a}$ and $\mathbf{b}$.

**2.37**   Find a unit vector orthogonal to both **a** and **b**,   where $\mathbf{a} = \langle\, 4, 0, 3\, \rangle$   and $\mathbf{b} = \langle\, 1, 1, 4\, \rangle$.

To use the cross product for calculating areas, we state and prove the following theorem.

---

### Theorem 2.8: Area of a Parallelogram

If we locate vectors **u** and **v** such that they form adjacent sides of a parallelogram, then the area of the parallelogram is given by   $\| \mathbf{u} \times \mathbf{v} \|$   (Figure 2.57).

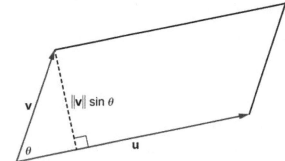

**Figure 2.57**   The parallelogram with adjacent sides **u** and **v** has base   $\| \mathbf{u} \|$   and height   $\| \mathbf{v} \| \sin\theta$.

### Proof

We show that the magnitude of the cross product is equal to the base times height of the parallelogram.

$$\begin{aligned}
\text{Area of a parallelogram} \;&= \text{base} \times \text{height} \\
&= \| \mathbf{u} \| \,(\, \| \mathbf{v} \| \, \sin\theta) \\
&= \| \mathbf{u} \times \mathbf{v} \|
\end{aligned}$$

$\square$

---

### Example 2.39

## Finding the Area of a Triangle

Let $P = (1, 0, 0)$, $Q = (0, 1, 0)$,  and $R = (0, 0, 1)$  be the vertices of a triangle (Figure 2.58). Find its area.

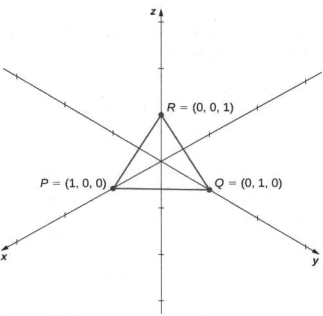

**Figure 2.58** Finding the area of a triangle by using the cross product.

**Solution**

We have $\vec{PQ} = \langle 0-1, 1-0, 0-0 \rangle = \langle -1, 1, 0 \rangle$ and $\vec{PR} = \langle 0-1, 0-0, 1-0 \rangle = \langle -1, 0, 1 \rangle$. The area of the parallelogram with adjacent sides $\vec{PQ}$ and $\vec{PR}$ is given by $\| \vec{PQ} \times \vec{PR} \|$:

$$\vec{PQ} \times \vec{PR} = \begin{vmatrix} \mathbf{i} & \mathbf{j} & \mathbf{k} \\ -1 & 1 & 0 \\ -1 & 0 & 1 \end{vmatrix} = (1-0)\mathbf{i} - (-1-0)\mathbf{j} + (0-(-1))\mathbf{k} = \mathbf{i} + \mathbf{j} + \mathbf{k}$$

$$\| \vec{PQ} \times \vec{PR} \| = \| \langle 1, 1, 1 \rangle \| = \sqrt{1^2 + 1^2 + 1^2} = \sqrt{3}.$$

The area of $\triangle PQR$ is half the area of the parallelogram, or $\sqrt{3}/2$.

 **2.38** Find the area of the parallelogram $PQRS$ with vertices $P(1, 1, 0)$, $Q(7, 1, 0)$, $R(9, 4, 2)$, and $S(3, 4, 2)$.

## The Triple Scalar Product

Because the cross product of two vectors is a vector, it is possible to combine the dot product and the cross product. The dot product of a vector with the cross product of two other vectors is called the triple scalar product because the result is a scalar.

**Definition**

The **triple scalar product** of vectors $\mathbf{u}$, $\mathbf{v}$, and $\mathbf{w}$ is $\mathbf{u} \cdot (\mathbf{v} \times \mathbf{w})$.

### Theorem 2.9: Calculating a Triple Scalar Product

The triple scalar product of vectors $\mathbf{u} = u_1\mathbf{i} + u_2\mathbf{j} + u_3\mathbf{k}$, $\mathbf{v} = v_1\mathbf{i} + v_2\mathbf{j} + v_3\mathbf{k}$, and $\mathbf{w} = w_1\mathbf{i} + w_2\mathbf{j} + w_3\mathbf{k}$ is the determinant of the $3 \times 3$ matrix formed by the components of the vectors:

$$\mathbf{u} \cdot (\mathbf{v} \times \mathbf{w}) = \begin{vmatrix} u_1 & u_2 & u_3 \\ v_1 & v_2 & v_3 \\ w_1 & w_2 & w_3 \end{vmatrix}.$$

### Proof

The calculation is straightforward.

$$\begin{aligned} \mathbf{u} \cdot (\mathbf{v} \times \mathbf{w}) &= \langle u_1, u_2, u_3 \rangle \cdot \langle v_2 w_3 - v_3 w_2, -v_1 w_3 + v_3 w_1, v_1 w_2 - v_2 w_1 \rangle \\ &= u_1(v_2 w_3 - v_3 w_2) + u_2(-v_1 w_3 + v_3 w_1) + u_3(v_1 w_2 - v_2 w_1) \\ &= u_1(v_2 w_3 - v_3 w_2) - u_2(v_1 w_3 - v_3 w_1) + u_3(v_1 w_2 - v_2 w_1) \\ &= \begin{vmatrix} u_1 & u_2 & u_3 \\ v_1 & v_2 & v_3 \\ w_1 & w_2 & w_3 \end{vmatrix} \end{aligned}$$

□

### Example 2.40

#### Calculating the Triple Scalar Product

Let $\mathbf{u} = \langle 1, 3, 5 \rangle$, $\mathbf{v} = \langle 2, -1, 0 \rangle$ and $\mathbf{w} = \langle -3, 0, -1 \rangle$. Calculate the triple scalar product $\mathbf{u} \cdot (\mathbf{v} \times \mathbf{w})$.

#### Solution

Apply **Calculating a Triple Scalar Product** directly:

$$\begin{aligned} \mathbf{u} \cdot (\mathbf{v} \times \mathbf{w}) &= \begin{vmatrix} 1 & 3 & 5 \\ 2 & -1 & 0 \\ -3 & 0 & -1 \end{vmatrix} \\ &= 1\begin{vmatrix} -1 & 0 \\ 0 & -1 \end{vmatrix} - 3\begin{vmatrix} 2 & 0 \\ -3 & -1 \end{vmatrix} + 5\begin{vmatrix} 2 & -1 \\ -3 & 0 \end{vmatrix} \\ &= (1 - 0) - 3(-2 - 0) + 5(0 - 3) \\ &= 1 + 6 - 15 = -8. \end{aligned}$$

 **2.39** Calculate the triple scalar product $\mathbf{a} \cdot (\mathbf{b} \times \mathbf{c})$, where $\mathbf{a} = \langle 2, -4, 1 \rangle$, $\mathbf{b} = \langle 0, 3, -1 \rangle$, and $\mathbf{c} = \langle 5, -3, 3 \rangle$.

When we create a matrix from three vectors, we must be careful about the order in which we list the vectors. If we list them in a matrix in one order and then rearrange the rows, the absolute value of the determinant remains unchanged. However, each time two rows switch places, the determinant changes sign:

$$\begin{vmatrix} a_1 & a_2 & a_3 \\ b_1 & b_2 & b_3 \\ c_1 & c_2 & c_3 \end{vmatrix} = d \qquad \begin{vmatrix} b_1 & b_2 & b_3 \\ a_1 & a_2 & a_3 \\ c_1 & c_2 & c_3 \end{vmatrix} = -d \qquad \begin{vmatrix} b_1 & b_2 & b_3 \\ c_1 & c_2 & c_3 \\ a_1 & a_2 & a_3 \end{vmatrix} = d \qquad \begin{vmatrix} c_1 & c_2 & c_3 \\ b_1 & b_2 & b_3 \\ a_1 & a_2 & a_3 \end{vmatrix} = -d.$$

Verifying this fact is straightforward, but rather messy. Let's take a look at this with an example:

$$\begin{vmatrix} 1 & 2 & 1 \\ -2 & 0 & 3 \\ 4 & 1 & -1 \end{vmatrix} = \begin{vmatrix} 0 & 3 \\ 1 & -1 \end{vmatrix} - 2\begin{vmatrix} -2 & 3 \\ 4 & -1 \end{vmatrix} + \begin{vmatrix} -2 & 0 \\ 4 & 1 \end{vmatrix}$$

$$= (0 - 3) - 2(2 - 12) + (-2 - 0) = -3 + 20 - 2 = 15.$$

Switching the top two rows we have

$$\begin{vmatrix} -2 & 0 & 3 \\ 1 & 2 & 1 \\ 4 & 1 & -1 \end{vmatrix} = -2\begin{vmatrix} 2 & 1 \\ 1 & -1 \end{vmatrix} + 3\begin{vmatrix} 1 & 2 \\ 4 & 1 \end{vmatrix} = -2(-2 - 1) + 3(1 - 8) = 6 - 21 = -15.$$

Rearranging vectors in the triple products is equivalent to reordering the rows in the matrix of the determinant. Let $\mathbf{u} = u_1\mathbf{i} + u_2\mathbf{j} + u_3\mathbf{k}$, $\mathbf{v} = v_1\mathbf{i} + v_2\mathbf{j} + v_3\mathbf{k}$, and $\mathbf{w} = w_1\mathbf{i} + w_2\mathbf{j} + w_3\mathbf{k}$. Applying **Calculating a Triple Scalar Product**, we have

$$\mathbf{u} \cdot (\mathbf{v} \times \mathbf{w}) = \begin{vmatrix} u_1 & u_2 & u_3 \\ v_1 & v_2 & v_3 \\ w_1 & w_2 & w_3 \end{vmatrix} \quad \text{and} \quad \mathbf{u} \cdot (\mathbf{w} \times \mathbf{v}) = \begin{vmatrix} u_1 & u_2 & u_3 \\ w_1 & w_2 & w_3 \\ v_1 & v_2 & v_3 \end{vmatrix}.$$

We can obtain the determinant for calculating $\mathbf{u} \cdot (\mathbf{w} \times \mathbf{v})$ by switching the bottom two rows of $\mathbf{u} \cdot (\mathbf{v} \times \mathbf{w})$. Therefore, $\mathbf{u} \cdot (\mathbf{v} \times \mathbf{w}) = -\mathbf{u} \cdot (\mathbf{w} \times \mathbf{v})$.

Following this reasoning and exploring the different ways we can interchange variables in the triple scalar product lead to the following identities:

$$\mathbf{u} \cdot (\mathbf{v} \times \mathbf{w}) = -\mathbf{u} \cdot (\mathbf{w} \times \mathbf{v})$$
$$\mathbf{u} \cdot (\mathbf{v} \times \mathbf{w}) = \mathbf{v} \cdot (\mathbf{w} \times \mathbf{u}) = \mathbf{w} \cdot (\mathbf{u} \times \mathbf{v}).$$

Let $\mathbf{u}$ and $\mathbf{v}$ be two vectors in standard position. If $\mathbf{u}$ and $\mathbf{v}$ are not scalar multiples of each other, then these vectors form adjacent sides of a parallelogram. We saw in **Area of a Parallelogram** that the area of this parallelogram is $\| \mathbf{u} \times \mathbf{v} \|$.

Now suppose we add a third vector $\mathbf{w}$ that does not lie in the same plane as $\mathbf{u}$ and $\mathbf{v}$ but still shares the same initial point. Then these vectors form three edges of a **parallelepiped**, a three-dimensional prism with six faces that are each parallelograms, as shown in **Figure 2.59**. The volume of this prism is the product of the figure's height and the area of its base. The triple scalar product of $\mathbf{u}$, $\mathbf{v}$, and $\mathbf{w}$ provides a simple method for calculating the volume of the parallelepiped defined by these vectors.

### Theorem 2.10: Volume of a Parallelepiped

The volume of a parallelepiped with adjacent edges given by the vectors $\mathbf{u}$, $\mathbf{v}$, and $\mathbf{w}$ is the absolute value of the triple scalar product:

$$V = |\mathbf{u} \cdot (\mathbf{v} \times \mathbf{w})|.$$

See **Figure 2.59**.

Note that, as the name indicates, the triple scalar product produces a scalar. The volume formula just presented uses the absolute value of a scalar quantity.

**Figure 2.59** The height of the parallelepiped is given by $\| \operatorname{proj}_{\mathbf{v} \times \mathbf{w}} \mathbf{u} \|$ .

## Proof

The area of the base of the parallelepiped is given by $\| \mathbf{v} \times \mathbf{w} \|$ . The height of the figure is given by $\| \operatorname{proj}_{\mathbf{v} \times \mathbf{w}} \mathbf{u} \|$ . The volume of the parallelepiped is the product of the height and the area of the base, so we have

$$
\begin{aligned}
V &= \| \operatorname{proj}_{\mathbf{v} \times \mathbf{w}} \mathbf{u} \| \ \| \mathbf{v} \times \mathbf{w} \| \\
&= \left| \frac{\mathbf{u} \cdot (\mathbf{v} \times \mathbf{w})}{\| \mathbf{v} \times \mathbf{w} \|} \right| \| \mathbf{v} \times \mathbf{w} \| \\
&= |\mathbf{u} \cdot (\mathbf{v} \times \mathbf{w})|.
\end{aligned}
$$

□

### Example 2.41

### Calculating the Volume of a Parallelepiped

Let $\mathbf{u} = \langle -1, -2, 1 \rangle$, $\mathbf{v} = \langle 4, 3, 2 \rangle$, and $\mathbf{w} = \langle 0, -5, -2 \rangle$. Find the volume of the parallelepiped with adjacent edges $\mathbf{u}$, $\mathbf{v}$, and $\mathbf{w}$ (**Figure 2.60**).

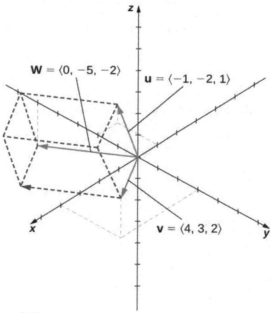

**Figure 2.60**

### Solution

We have

$$\mathbf{u} \cdot (\mathbf{v} \times \mathbf{w}) = \begin{vmatrix} -1 & -2 & 1 \\ 4 & 3 & 2 \\ 0 & -5 & -2 \end{vmatrix} = (-1)\begin{vmatrix} 3 & 2 \\ -5 & -2 \end{vmatrix} + 2\begin{vmatrix} 4 & 2 \\ 0 & -2 \end{vmatrix} + \begin{vmatrix} 4 & 3 \\ 0 & -5 \end{vmatrix}$$
$$= (-1)(-6 + 10) + 2(-8 - 0) + (-20 - 0)$$
$$= -4 - 16 - 20$$
$$= -40.$$

Thus, the volume of the parallelepiped is $|-40| = 40$ units$^3$.

 **2.40** Find the volume of the parallelepiped formed by the vectors $\mathbf{a} = 3\mathbf{i} + 4\mathbf{j} - \mathbf{k}$, $\mathbf{b} = 2\mathbf{i} - \mathbf{j} - \mathbf{k}$, and $\mathbf{c} = 3\mathbf{j} + \mathbf{k}$.

## Applications of the Cross Product

The cross product appears in many practical applications in mathematics, physics, and engineering. Let's examine some of these applications here, including the idea of torque, with which we began this section. Other applications show up in later chapters, particularly in our study of vector fields such as gravitational and electromagnetic fields (**Introduction to Vector Calculus**).

### Example 2.42

**Using the Triple Scalar Product**

Use the triple scalar product to show that vectors $\mathbf{u} = \langle 2, 0, 5 \rangle$, $\mathbf{v} = \langle 2, 2, 4 \rangle$, and $\mathbf{w} = \langle 1, -1, 3 \rangle$ are coplanar—that is, show that these vectors lie in the same plane.

**Solution**

Start by calculating the triple scalar product to find the volume of the parallelepiped defined by $\mathbf{u}$, $\mathbf{v}$, and $\mathbf{w}$:

$$\mathbf{u} \cdot (\mathbf{v} \times \mathbf{w}) = \begin{vmatrix} 2 & 0 & 5 \\ 2 & 2 & 4 \\ 1 & -1 & 3 \end{vmatrix}$$
$$= [2(2)(3) + (0)(4)(1) + 5(2)(-1)] - [5(2)(1) + (2)(4)(-1) + (0)(2)(3)]$$
$$= 2 - 2$$
$$= 0.$$

The volume of the parallelepiped is $0$ units$^3$, so one of the dimensions must be zero. Therefore, the three vectors all lie in the same plane.

 **2.41** Are the vectors $\mathbf{a} = \mathbf{i} + \mathbf{j} - \mathbf{k}$, $\mathbf{b} = \mathbf{i} - \mathbf{j} + \mathbf{k}$, and $\mathbf{c} = \mathbf{i} + \mathbf{j} + \mathbf{k}$ coplanar?

## Example 2.43

### Finding an Orthogonal Vector

Only a single plane can pass through any set of three noncolinear points. Find a vector orthogonal to the plane containing points $P = (9, -3, -2)$, $Q = (1, 3, 0)$, and $R = (-2, 5, 0)$.

### Solution

The plane must contain vectors $\vec{PQ}$ and $\vec{QR}$:

$$\vec{PQ} = \langle\, 1 - 9,\, 3 - (-3),\, 0 - (-2) \,\rangle = \langle\, -8, 6, 2 \,\rangle$$
$$\vec{QR} = \langle\, -2 - 1,\, 5 - 3,\, 0 - 0 \,\rangle = \langle\, -3, 2, 0 \,\rangle.$$

The cross product $\vec{PQ} \times \vec{QR}$ produces a vector orthogonal to both $\vec{PQ}$ and $\vec{QR}$. Therefore, the cross product is orthogonal to the plane that contains these two vectors:

$$\vec{PQ} \times \vec{QR} = \begin{vmatrix} \mathbf{i} & \mathbf{j} & \mathbf{k} \\ -8 & 6 & 2 \\ -3 & 2 & 0 \end{vmatrix}$$
$$= 0\mathbf{i} - 6\mathbf{j} - 16\mathbf{k} - (-18\mathbf{k} + 4\mathbf{i} + 0\mathbf{j})$$
$$= -4\mathbf{i} - 6\mathbf{j} + 2\mathbf{k}.$$

We have seen how to use the triple scalar product and how to find a vector orthogonal to a plane. Now we apply the cross product to real-world situations.

Sometimes a force causes an object to rotate. For example, turning a screwdriver or a wrench creates this kind of rotational effect, called torque.

### Definition

**Torque**, $\tau$ (the Greek letter *tau*), measures the tendency of a force to produce rotation about an axis of rotation. Let $\mathbf{r}$ be a vector with an initial point located on the axis of rotation and with a terminal point located at the point where the force is applied, and let vector $\mathbf{F}$ represent the force. Then torque is equal to the cross product of $\mathbf{r}$ and $\mathbf{F}$:

$$\tau = \mathbf{r} \times \mathbf{F}.$$

See Figure 2.61.

**Figure 2.61** Torque measures how a force causes an object to rotate.

Think about using a wrench to tighten a bolt. The torque $\tau$ applied to the bolt depends on how hard we push the wrench (force) and how far up the handle we apply the force (distance). The torque increases with a greater force on the wrench at a greater distance from the bolt. Common units of torque are the newton-meter or foot-pound. Although torque is dimensionally equivalent to work (it has the same units), the two concepts are distinct. Torque is used specifically in the context of rotation, whereas work typically involves motion along a line.

## Example 2.44

### Evaluating Torque

A bolt is tightened by applying a force of 6 N to a 0.15-m wrench (**Figure 2.62**). The angle between the wrench and the force vector is 40°. Find the magnitude of the torque about the center of the bolt. Round the answer to two decimal places.

**Figure 2.62** Torque describes the twisting action of the wrench.

### Solution

Substitute the given information into the equation defining torque:

$$\| \tau \| = \| \mathbf{r} \times \mathbf{F} \| = \| \mathbf{r} \| \; \| \mathbf{F} \| \sin \theta = (0.15 \text{ m})(6 \text{ N})\sin 40° \approx 0.58 \text{ N} \cdot \text{m}.$$

  **2.42**   Calculate the force required to produce 15 N · m torque at an angle of 30 ° from a 150-cm rod.

# 2.4 EXERCISES

For the following exercises, the vectors **u** and **v** are given.

    a.  Find the cross product **u** × **v** of the vectors **u** and **v**. Express the answer in component form.

    b.  Sketch the vectors **u**, **v**, and **u** × **v**.

183.  $\mathbf{u} = \langle 2, 0, 0 \rangle$,  $\mathbf{v} = \langle 2, 2, 0 \rangle$

184.  $\mathbf{u} = \langle 3, 2, -1 \rangle$,  $\mathbf{v} = \langle 1, 1, 0 \rangle$

185.  $\mathbf{u} = 2\mathbf{i} + 3\mathbf{j}$,  $\mathbf{v} = \mathbf{j} + 2\mathbf{k}$

186.  $\mathbf{u} = 2\mathbf{j} + 3\mathbf{k}$,  $\mathbf{v} = 3\mathbf{i} + \mathbf{k}$

187.  Simplify $(\mathbf{i} \times \mathbf{i} - 2\mathbf{i} \times \mathbf{j} - 4\mathbf{i} \times \mathbf{k} + 3\mathbf{j} \times \mathbf{k}) \times \mathbf{i}$.

188.  Simplify $\mathbf{j} \times (\mathbf{k} \times \mathbf{j} + 2\mathbf{j} \times \mathbf{i} - 3\mathbf{j} \times \mathbf{j} + 5\mathbf{i} \times \mathbf{k})$.

In the following exercises, vectors **u** and **v** are given. Find unit vector **w** in the direction of the cross product vector **u** × **v**. Express your answer using standard unit vectors.

189.  $\mathbf{u} = \langle 3, -1, 2 \rangle$,  $\mathbf{v} = \langle -2, 0, 1 \rangle$

190.  $\mathbf{u} = \langle 2, 6, 1 \rangle$,  $\mathbf{v} = \langle 3, 0, 1 \rangle$

191.  $\mathbf{u} = \overrightarrow{AB}$,  $\mathbf{v} = \overrightarrow{AC}$,  where  $A(1, 0, 1)$, $B(1, -1, 3)$, and $C(0, 0, 5)$

192.  $\mathbf{u} = \overrightarrow{OP}$,  $\mathbf{v} = \overrightarrow{PQ}$,  where $P(-1, 1, 0)$ and $Q(0, 2, 1)$

193.  Determine the real number $\alpha$ such that **u** × **v** and **i** are orthogonal, where $\mathbf{u} = 3\mathbf{i} + \mathbf{j} - 5\mathbf{k}$ and $\mathbf{v} = 4\mathbf{i} - 2\mathbf{j} + \alpha\mathbf{k}$.

194.  Show that **u** × **v** and $2\mathbf{i} - 14\mathbf{j} + 2\mathbf{k}$ cannot be orthogonal for any $\alpha$ real number, where $\mathbf{u} = \mathbf{i} + 7\mathbf{j} - \mathbf{k}$ and $\mathbf{v} = \alpha\mathbf{i} + 5\mathbf{j} + \mathbf{k}$.

195.  Show that **u** × **v** is orthogonal to **u** + **v** and **u** − **v**, where **u** and **v** are nonzero vectors.

196.  Show that **v** × **u** is orthogonal to $(\mathbf{u} \cdot \mathbf{v})(\mathbf{u} + \mathbf{v}) + \mathbf{u}$, where **u** and **v** are nonzero vectors.

197.  Calculate the determinant $\begin{vmatrix} \mathbf{i} & \mathbf{j} & \mathbf{k} \\ 1 & -1 & 7 \\ 2 & 0 & 3 \end{vmatrix}$.

198.  Calculate the determinant $\begin{vmatrix} \mathbf{i} & \mathbf{j} & \mathbf{k} \\ 0 & 3 & -4 \\ 1 & 6 & -1 \end{vmatrix}$.

For the following exercises, the vectors **u** and **v** are given. Use determinant notation to find vector **w** orthogonal to vectors **u** and **v**.

199.  $\mathbf{u} = \langle -1, 0, e^t \rangle$,  $\mathbf{v} = \langle 1, e^{-t}, 0 \rangle$,  where $t$ is a real number

200.  $\mathbf{u} = \langle 1, 0, x \rangle$,  $\mathbf{v} = \langle \frac{2}{x}, 1, 0 \rangle$,  where $x$ is a nonzero real number

201.  Find vector $(\mathbf{a} - 2\mathbf{b}) \times \mathbf{c}$,  where $\mathbf{a} = \begin{vmatrix} \mathbf{i} & \mathbf{j} & \mathbf{k} \\ 2 & -1 & 5 \\ 0 & 1 & 8 \end{vmatrix}$, $\mathbf{b} = \begin{vmatrix} \mathbf{i} & \mathbf{j} & \mathbf{k} \\ 0 & 1 & 1 \\ 2 & -1 & -2 \end{vmatrix}$, and $\mathbf{c} = \mathbf{i} + \mathbf{j} + \mathbf{k}$.

202.  Find vector $\mathbf{c} \times (\mathbf{a} + 3\mathbf{b})$,  where $\mathbf{a} = \begin{vmatrix} \mathbf{i} & \mathbf{j} & \mathbf{k} \\ 5 & 0 & 9 \\ 0 & 1 & 0 \end{vmatrix}$, $\mathbf{b} = \begin{vmatrix} \mathbf{i} & \mathbf{j} & \mathbf{k} \\ 0 & -1 & 1 \\ 7 & 1 & -1 \end{vmatrix}$, and $\mathbf{c} = \mathbf{i} - \mathbf{k}$.

203.  **[T]** Use the cross product **u** × **v** to find the acute angle between vectors **u** and **v**, where $\mathbf{u} = \mathbf{i} + 2\mathbf{j}$ and $\mathbf{v} = \mathbf{i} + \mathbf{k}$. Express the answer in degrees rounded to the nearest integer.

204.  **[T]** Use the cross product **u** × **v** to find the obtuse angle between vectors **u** and **v**, where $\mathbf{u} = -\mathbf{i} + 3\mathbf{j} + \mathbf{k}$ and $\mathbf{v} = \mathbf{i} - 2\mathbf{j}$. Express the answer in degrees rounded to the nearest integer.

205.  Use the sine and cosine of the angle between two nonzero vectors **u** and **v** to prove Lagrange's identity: $\|\mathbf{u} \times \mathbf{v}\|^2 = \|\mathbf{u}\|^2 \|\mathbf{v}\|^2 - (\mathbf{u} \cdot \mathbf{v})^2$.

206.  Verify Lagrange's identity $\|\mathbf{u} \times \mathbf{v}\|^2 = \|\mathbf{u}\|^2 \|\mathbf{v}\|^2 - (\mathbf{u} \cdot \mathbf{v})^2$ for vectors $\mathbf{u} = -\mathbf{i} + \mathbf{j} - 2\mathbf{k}$ and $\mathbf{v} = 2\mathbf{i} - \mathbf{j}$.

207. Nonzero vectors $\mathbf{u}$ and $\mathbf{v}$ are called *collinear* if there exists a nonzero scalar $\alpha$ such that $\mathbf{v} = \alpha\mathbf{u}$. Show that $\mathbf{u}$ and $\mathbf{v}$ are collinear if and only if $\mathbf{u} \times \mathbf{v} = \mathbf{0}$.

208. Nonzero vectors $\mathbf{u}$ and $\mathbf{v}$ are called *collinear* if there exists a nonzero scalar $\alpha$ such that $\mathbf{v} = \alpha\mathbf{u}$. Show that vectors $\overrightarrow{AB}$ and $\overrightarrow{AC}$ are collinear, where $A(4, 1, 0)$, $B(6, 5, -2)$, and $C(5, 3, -1)$.

209. Find the area of the parallelogram with adjacent sides $\mathbf{u} = \langle 3, 2, 0 \rangle$ and $\mathbf{v} = \langle 0, 2, 1 \rangle$.

210. Find the area of the parallelogram with adjacent sides $\mathbf{u} = \mathbf{i} + \mathbf{j}$ and $\mathbf{v} = \mathbf{i} + \mathbf{k}$.

211. Consider points $A(3, -1, 2)$, $B(2, 1, 5)$, and $C(1, -2, -2)$.
   a. Find the area of parallelogram $ABCD$ with adjacent sides $\overrightarrow{AB}$ and $\overrightarrow{AC}$.
   b. Find the area of triangle $ABC$.
   c. Find the distance from point $A$ to line $BC$.

212. Consider points $A(2, -3, 4)$, $B(0, 1, 2)$, and $C(-1, 2, 0)$.
   a. Find the area of parallelogram $ABCD$ with adjacent sides $\overrightarrow{AB}$ and $\overrightarrow{AC}$.
   b. Find the area of triangle $ABC$.
   c. Find the distance from point $B$ to line $AC$.

In the following exercises, vectors $\mathbf{u}$, $\mathbf{v}$, and $\mathbf{w}$ are given.
   a. Find the triple scalar product $\mathbf{u} \cdot (\mathbf{v} \times \mathbf{w})$.
   b. Find the volume of the parallelepiped with the adjacent edges $\mathbf{u}$, $\mathbf{v}$, and $\mathbf{w}$.

213. $\mathbf{u} = \mathbf{i} + \mathbf{j}$, $\mathbf{v} = \mathbf{j} + \mathbf{k}$, and $\mathbf{w} = \mathbf{i} + \mathbf{k}$

214. $\mathbf{u} = \langle -3, 5, -1 \rangle$, $\mathbf{v} = \langle 0, 2, -2 \rangle$, and $\mathbf{w} = \langle 3, 1, 1 \rangle$

215. Calculate the triple scalar products $\mathbf{v} \cdot (\mathbf{u} \times \mathbf{w})$ and $\mathbf{w} \cdot (\mathbf{u} \times \mathbf{v})$, where $\mathbf{u} = \langle 1, 1, 1 \rangle$, $\mathbf{v} = \langle 7, 6, 9 \rangle$, and $\mathbf{w} = \langle 4, 2, 7 \rangle$.

216. Calculate the triple scalar products $\mathbf{w} \cdot (\mathbf{v} \times \mathbf{u})$ and $\mathbf{u} \cdot (\mathbf{w} \times \mathbf{v})$, where $\mathbf{u} = \langle 4, 2, -1 \rangle$, $\mathbf{v} = \langle 2, 5, -3 \rangle$, and $\mathbf{w} = \langle 9, 5, -10 \rangle$.

217. Find vectors $\mathbf{a}$, $\mathbf{b}$, and $\mathbf{c}$ with a triple scalar product given by the determinant $\begin{vmatrix} 1 & 2 & 3 \\ 0 & 2 & 5 \\ 8 & 9 & 2 \end{vmatrix}$. Determine their triple scalar product.

218. The triple scalar product of vectors $\mathbf{a}$, $\mathbf{b}$, and $\mathbf{c}$ is given by the determinant $\begin{vmatrix} 0 & -2 & 1 \\ 0 & 1 & 4 \\ 1 & -3 & 7 \end{vmatrix}$. Find vector $\mathbf{a} - \mathbf{b} + \mathbf{c}$.

219. Consider the parallelepiped with edges $OA$, $OB$, and $OC$, where $A(2, 1, 0)$, $B(1, 2, 0)$, and $C(0, 1, \alpha)$.
   a. Find the real number $\alpha > 0$ such that the volume of the parallelepiped is $3$ units$^3$.
   b. For $\alpha = 1$, find the height $h$ from vertex $C$ of the parallelepiped. Sketch the parallelepiped.

220. Consider points $A(\alpha, 0, 0)$, $B(0, \beta, 0)$, and $C(0, 0, \gamma)$, with $\alpha$, $\beta$, and $\gamma$ positive real numbers.
   a. Determine the volume of the parallelepiped with adjacent sides $\overrightarrow{OA}$, $\overrightarrow{OB}$, and $\overrightarrow{OC}$.
   b. Find the volume of the tetrahedron with vertices $O$, $A$, $B$, and $C$. (*Hint*: The volume of the tetrahedron is $1/6$ of the volume of the parallelepiped.)
   c. Find the distance from the origin to the plane determined by $A$, $B$, and $C$. Sketch the parallelepiped and tetrahedron.

221. Let $\mathbf{u}$, $\mathbf{v}$, and $\mathbf{w}$ be three-dimensional vectors and $c$ be a real number. Prove the following properties of the cross product.
   a. $\mathbf{u} \times \mathbf{u} = 0$
   b. $\mathbf{u} \times (\mathbf{v} + \mathbf{w}) = (\mathbf{u} \times \mathbf{v}) + (\mathbf{u} \times \mathbf{w})$
   c. $c(\mathbf{u} \times \mathbf{v}) = (c\mathbf{u}) \times \mathbf{v} = \mathbf{u} \times (c\mathbf{v})$
   d. $\mathbf{u} \cdot (\mathbf{u} \times \mathbf{v}) = \mathbf{0}$

222. Show that vectors $\mathbf{u} = \langle 1, 0, -8 \rangle$, $\mathbf{v} = \langle 0, 1, 6 \rangle$, and $\mathbf{w} = \langle -1, 9, 3 \rangle$ satisfy the following properties of the cross product.
   a. $\mathbf{u} \times \mathbf{u} = 0$
   b. $\mathbf{u} \times (\mathbf{v} + \mathbf{w}) = (\mathbf{u} \times \mathbf{v}) + (\mathbf{u} \times \mathbf{w})$
   c. $c(\mathbf{u} \times \mathbf{v}) = (c\mathbf{u}) \times \mathbf{v} = \mathbf{u} \times (c\mathbf{v})$
   d. $\mathbf{u} \cdot (\mathbf{u} \times \mathbf{v}) = \mathbf{0}$

**223.** Nonzero vectors **u**, **v**, and **w** are said to be *linearly dependent* if one of the vectors is a linear combination of the other two. For instance, there exist two nonzero real numbers $\alpha$ and $\beta$ such that $\mathbf{w} = \alpha\mathbf{u} + \beta\mathbf{v}$. Otherwise, the vectors are called *linearly independent*. Show that **u**, **v**, and **w** are coplanar if and only if they are linear dependent.

**224.** Consider vectors $\mathbf{u} = \langle\, 1, 4, -7\,\rangle$, $\mathbf{v} = \langle\, 2, -1, 4\,\rangle$, $\mathbf{w} = \langle\, 0, -9, 18\,\rangle$, and $\mathbf{p} = \langle\, 0, -9, 17\,\rangle$.

    a. Show that **u**, **v**, and **w** are coplanar by using their triple scalar product

    b. Show that **u**, **v**, and **w** are coplanar, using the definition that there exist two nonzero real numbers $\alpha$ and $\beta$ such that $\mathbf{w} = \alpha\mathbf{u} + \beta\mathbf{v}$.

    c. Show that **u**, **v**, and **p** are linearly independent—that is, none of the vectors is a linear combination of the other two.

**225.** Consider points $A(0, 0, 2)$, $B(1, 0, 2)$, $C(1, 1, 2)$, and $D(0, 1, 2)$. Are vectors $\overrightarrow{AB}$, $\overrightarrow{AC}$, and $\overrightarrow{AD}$ linearly dependent (that is, one of the vectors is a linear combination of the other two)?

**226.** Show that vectors $\mathbf{i} + \mathbf{j}$, $\mathbf{i} - \mathbf{j}$, and $\mathbf{i} + \mathbf{j} + \mathbf{k}$ are linearly independent—that is, there exist two nonzero real numbers $\alpha$ and $\beta$ such that $\mathbf{i} + \mathbf{j} + \mathbf{k} = \alpha(\mathbf{i} + \mathbf{j}) + \beta(\mathbf{i} - \mathbf{j})$.

**227.** Let $\mathbf{u} = \langle\, u_1, u_2\,\rangle$ and $\mathbf{v} = \langle\, v_1, v_2\,\rangle$ be two-dimensional vectors. The cross product of vectors **u** and **v** is not defined. However, if the vectors are regarded as the three-dimensional vectors $\tilde{\mathbf{u}} = \langle\, u_1, u_2, 0\,\rangle$ and $\tilde{\mathbf{v}} = \langle\, v_1, v_2, 0\,\rangle$, respectively, then, in this case, we can define the cross product of $\tilde{\mathbf{u}}$ and $\tilde{\mathbf{v}}$. In particular, in determinant notation, the cross product of $\tilde{\mathbf{u}}$ and $\tilde{\mathbf{v}}$ is given by

$$\tilde{\mathbf{u}} \times \tilde{\mathbf{v}} = \begin{vmatrix} \mathbf{i} & \mathbf{j} & \mathbf{k} \\ u_1 & u_2 & 0 \\ v_1 & v_2 & 0 \end{vmatrix}.$$

Use this result to compute $(\mathbf{i}\cos\theta + \mathbf{j}\sin\theta) \times (\mathbf{i}\sin\theta - \mathbf{j}\cos\theta)$, where $\theta$ is a real number.

**228.** Consider points $P(2, 1)$, $Q(4, 2)$, and $R(1, 2)$.

    a. Find the area of triangle $P$, $Q$, and $R$.

    b. Determine the distance from point $R$ to the line passing through $P$ and $Q$.

**229.** Determine a vector of magnitude 10 perpendicular to the plane passing through the x-axis and point $P(1, 2, 4)$.

**230.** Determine a unit vector perpendicular to the plane passing through the z-axis and point $A(3, 1, -2)$.

**231.** Consider **u** and **v** two three-dimensional vectors. If the magnitude of the cross product vector $\mathbf{u} \times \mathbf{v}$ is $k$ times larger than the magnitude of vector **u**, show that the magnitude of **v** is greater than or equal to $k$, where $k$ is a natural number.

**232.** **[T]** Assume that the magnitudes of two nonzero vectors **u** and **v** are known. The function $f(\theta) = \|\mathbf{u}\|\ \|\mathbf{v}\| \sin\theta$ defines the magnitude of the cross product vector $\mathbf{u} \times \mathbf{v}$, where $\theta \in [0, \pi]$ is the angle between **u** and **v**.

    a. Graph the function $f$.

    b. Find the absolute minimum and maximum of function $f$. Interpret the results.

    c. If $\|\mathbf{u}\| = 5$ and $\|\mathbf{v}\| = 2$, find the angle between **u** and **v** if the magnitude of their cross product vector is equal to 9.

**233.** Find all vectors $\mathbf{w} = \langle\, w_1, w_2, w_3\,\rangle$ that satisfy the equation $\langle\, 1, 1, 1\,\rangle \times \mathbf{w} = \langle\, -1, -1, 2\,\rangle$.

**234.** Solve the equation $\mathbf{w} \times \langle\, 1, 0, -1\,\rangle = \langle\, 3, 0, 3\,\rangle$, where $\mathbf{w} = \langle\, w_1, w_2, w_3\,\rangle$ is a nonzero vector with a magnitude of 3.

**235.** **[T]** A mechanic uses a 12-in. wrench to turn a bolt. The wrench makes a $30°$ angle with the horizontal. If the mechanic applies a vertical force of 10 lb on the wrench handle, what is the magnitude of the torque at point $P$ (see the following figure)? Express the answer in foot-pounds rounded to two decimal places.

**236.** **[T]** A boy applies the brakes on a bicycle by applying a downward force of 20 lb on the pedal when the 6-in. crank makes a 40° angle with the horizontal (see the following figure). Find the torque at point $P$. Express your answer in foot-pounds rounded to two decimal places.

**237.** **[T]** Find the magnitude of the force that needs to be applied to the end of a 20-cm wrench located on the positive direction of the $y$-axis if the force is applied in the direction $\langle 0, 1, -2 \rangle$ and it produces a 100 N·m torque to the bolt located at the origin.

**238.** **[T]** What is the magnitude of the force required to be applied to the end of a 1-ft wrench at an angle of 35° to produce a torque of 20 N·m?

**239.** **[T]** The force vector $\mathbf{F}$ acting on a proton with an electric charge of $1.6 \times 10^{-19}$ C (in coulombs) moving in a magnetic field $\mathbf{B}$ where the velocity vector $\mathbf{v}$ is given by $\mathbf{F} = 1.6 \times 10^{-19}(\mathbf{v} \times \mathbf{B})$ (here, $\mathbf{v}$ is expressed in meters per second, $\mathbf{B}$ is in tesla [T], and $\mathbf{F}$ is in newtons [N]). Find the force that acts on a proton that moves in the $xy$-plane at velocity $\mathbf{v} = 10^5\mathbf{i} + 10^5\mathbf{j}$ (in meters per second) in a magnetic field given by $\mathbf{B} = 0.3\mathbf{j}$.

**240.** **[T]** The force vector $\mathbf{F}$ acting on a proton with an electric charge of $1.6 \times 10^{-19}$ C moving in a magnetic field $\mathbf{B}$ where the velocity vector $\mathbf{v}$ is given by $\mathbf{F} = 1.6 \times 10^{-19}(\mathbf{v} \times \mathbf{B})$ (here, $\mathbf{v}$ is expressed in meters per second, $\mathbf{B}$ in T, and $\mathbf{F}$ in N). If the magnitude of force $\mathbf{F}$ acting on a proton is $5.9 \times 10^{-17}$ N and the proton is moving at the speed of 300 m/sec in magnetic field $\mathbf{B}$ of magnitude 2.4 T, find the angle between velocity vector $\mathbf{v}$ of the proton and magnetic field $\mathbf{B}$. Express the answer in degrees rounded to the nearest integer.

**241.** **[T]** Consider $\mathbf{r}(t) = \langle \cos t, \sin t, 2t \rangle$ the position vector of a particle at time $t \in [0, 30]$, where the components of $\mathbf{r}$ are expressed in centimeters and time in seconds. Let $\overrightarrow{OP}$ be the position vector of the particle after 1 sec.

a. Determine unit vector $\mathbf{B}(t)$ (called the *binormal unit vector*) that has the direction of cross product vector $\mathbf{v}(t) \times \mathbf{a}(t)$, where $\mathbf{v}(t)$ and $\mathbf{a}(t)$ are the instantaneous velocity vector and, respectively, the acceleration vector of the particle after $t$ seconds.

b. Use a CAS to visualize vectors $\mathbf{v}(1)$, $\mathbf{a}(1)$, and $\mathbf{B}(1)$ as vectors starting at point $P$ along with the path of the particle.

**242.** A solar panel is mounted on the roof of a house. The panel may be regarded as positioned at the points of coordinates (in meters) $A(8, 0, 0)$, $B(8, 18, 0)$, $C(0, 18, 8)$, and $D(0, 0, 8)$ (see the following figure).

a. Find vector $\mathbf{n} = \overrightarrow{AB} \times \overrightarrow{AD}$ perpendicular to the surface of the solar panels. Express the answer using standard unit vectors.

b. Assume unit vector $\mathbf{s} = \frac{1}{\sqrt{3}}\mathbf{i} + \frac{1}{\sqrt{3}}\mathbf{j} + \frac{1}{\sqrt{3}}\mathbf{k}$ points toward the Sun at a particular time of the day and the flow of solar energy is $\mathbf{F} = 900\mathbf{s}$ (in watts per square meter [W/m$^2$]). Find the predicted amount of electrical power the panel can produce, which is given by the dot product of vectors $\mathbf{F}$ and $\mathbf{n}$ (expressed in watts).

c. Determine the angle of elevation of the Sun above the solar panel. Express the answer in degrees rounded to the nearest whole number. (*Hint*: The angle between vectors $\mathbf{n}$ and $\mathbf{s}$ and the angle of elevation are complementary.)

# 2.5 | Equations of Lines and Planes in Space

## Learning Objectives

**2.5.1** Write the vector, parametric, and symmetric of a line through a given point in a given direction, and a line through two given points.

**2.5.2** Find the distance from a point to a given line.

**2.5.3** Write the vector and scalar equations of a plane through a given point with a given normal.

**2.5.4** Find the distance from a point to a given plane.

**2.5.5** Find the angle between two planes.

By now, we are familiar with writing equations that describe a line in two dimensions. To write an equation for a line, we must know two points on the line, or we must know the direction of the line and at least one point through which the line passes. In two dimensions, we use the concept of slope to describe the orientation, or direction, of a line. In three dimensions, we describe the direction of a line using a vector parallel to the line. In this section, we examine how to use equations to describe lines and planes in space.

## Equations for a Line in Space

Let's first explore what it means for two vectors to be parallel. Recall that parallel vectors must have the same or opposite directions. If two nonzero vectors, $\mathbf{u}$ and $\mathbf{v}$, are parallel, we claim there must be a scalar, $k$, such that $\mathbf{u} = k\mathbf{v}$. If $\mathbf{u}$ and $\mathbf{v}$ have the same direction, simply choose $k = \dfrac{\|\mathbf{u}\|}{\|\mathbf{v}\|}$. If $\mathbf{u}$ and $\mathbf{v}$ have opposite directions, choose $k = -\dfrac{\|\mathbf{u}\|}{\|\mathbf{v}\|}$.

Note that the converse holds as well. If $\mathbf{u} = k\mathbf{v}$ for some scalar $k$, then either $\mathbf{u}$ and $\mathbf{v}$ have the same direction $(k > 0)$ or opposite directions $(k < 0)$, so $\mathbf{u}$ and $\mathbf{v}$ are parallel. Therefore, two nonzero vectors $\mathbf{u}$ and $\mathbf{v}$ are parallel if and only if $\mathbf{u} = k\mathbf{v}$ for some scalar $k$. By convention, the zero vector $\mathbf{0}$ is considered to be parallel to all vectors.

As in two dimensions, we can describe a line in space using a point on the line and the direction of the line, or a parallel vector, which we call the **direction vector** (**Figure 2.63**). Let $L$ be a line in space passing through point $P(x_0, y_0, z_0)$. Let $\mathbf{v} = \langle a, b, c \rangle$ be a vector parallel to $L$. Then, for any point on line $Q(x, y, z)$, we know that $\vec{PQ}$ is parallel to $\mathbf{v}$. Thus, as we just discussed, there is a scalar, $t$, such that $\vec{PQ} = t\mathbf{v}$, which gives

$$\vec{PQ} = t\mathbf{v} \tag{2.11}$$
$$\langle x - x_0, y - y_0, z - z_0 \rangle = t \langle a, b, c \rangle$$
$$\langle x - x_0, y - y_0, z - z_0 \rangle = \langle ta, tb, tc \rangle.$$

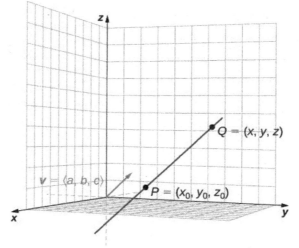

**Figure 2.63** Vector $\mathbf{v}$ is the direction vector for $\vec{PQ}$.

Using vector operations, we can rewrite Equation 2.11 as

$$\langle x - x_0, y - y_0, z - z_0 \rangle = \langle ta, tb, tc \rangle$$
$$\langle x, y, z \rangle - \langle x_0, y_0, z_0 \rangle = t \langle a, b, c \rangle$$
$$\langle x, y, z \rangle = \langle x_0, y_0, z_0 \rangle + t \langle a, b, c \rangle.$$

Setting $\mathbf{r} = \langle x, y, z \rangle$ and $\mathbf{r}_0 = \langle x_0, y_0, z_0 \rangle$, we now have the **vector equation of a line**:

$$\mathbf{r} = \mathbf{r}_0 + t\mathbf{v}. \tag{2.12}$$

Equating components, Equation 2.11 shows that the following equations are simultaneously true: $x - x_0 = ta$, $y - y_0 = tb$, and $z - z_0 = tc$. If we solve each of these equations for the component variables $x$, $y$, and $z$, we get a set of equations in which each variable is defined in terms of the parameter $t$ and that, together, describe the line. This set of three equations forms a set of **parametric equations of a line**:

$$x = x_0 + ta \quad y = y_0 + tb \quad z = z_0 + tc.$$

If we solve each of the equations for $t$ assuming $a$, $b$, and $c$ are nonzero, we get a different description of the same line:

$$\frac{x - x_0}{a} = t \quad \frac{y - y_0}{b} = t \quad \frac{z - z_0}{c} = t.$$

Because each expression equals $t$, they all have the same value. We can set them equal to each other to create **symmetric equations of a line**:

$$\frac{x - x_0}{a} = \frac{y - y_0}{b} = \frac{z - z_0}{c}.$$

We summarize the results in the following theorem.

### Theorem 2.11: Parametric and Symmetric Equations of a Line

A line $L$ parallel to vector $\mathbf{v} = \langle a, b, c \rangle$ and passing through point $P(x_0, y_0, z_0)$ can be described by the following parametric equations:

$$x = x_0 + ta, \ y = y_0 + tb, \ \text{and} \ z = z_0 + tc. \tag{2.13}$$

If the constants $a$, $b$, and $c$ are all nonzero, then $L$ can be described by the symmetric equation of the line:

$$\frac{x - x_0}{a} = \frac{y - y_0}{b} = \frac{z - z_0}{c}. \tag{2.14}$$

The parametric equations of a line are not unique. Using a different parallel vector or a different point on the line leads to a different, equivalent representation. Each set of parametric equations leads to a related set of symmetric equations, so it follows that a symmetric equation of a line is not unique either.

## Example 2.45

### Equations of a Line in Space

Find parametric and symmetric equations of the line passing through points $(1, 4, -2)$ and $(-3, 5, 0)$.

### Solution

First, identify a vector parallel to the line:

$$\mathbf{v} = \langle -3 - 1, 5 - 4, 0 - (-2) \rangle = \langle -4, 1, 2 \rangle.$$

Use either of the given points on the line to complete the parametric equations:

$$x = 1 - 4t, \ y = 4 + t, \ \text{and } z = -2 + 2t.$$

Solve each equation for $t$ to create the symmetric equation of the line:

$$\frac{x-1}{-4} = y - 4 = \frac{z+2}{2}.$$

 **2.43** Find parametric and symmetric equations of the line passing through points $(1, -3, 2)$ and $(5, -2, 8)$.

Sometimes we don't want the equation of a whole line, just a line segment. In this case, we limit the values of our parameter $t$. For example, let $P(x_0, y_0, z_0)$ and $Q(x_1, y_1, z_1)$ be points on a line, and let $\mathbf{p} = \langle x_0, y_0, z_0 \rangle$ and $\mathbf{q} = \langle x_1, y_1, z_1 \rangle$ be the associated position vectors. In addition, let $\mathbf{r} = \langle x, y, z \rangle$. We want to find a vector equation for the line segment between $P$ and $Q$. Using $P$ as our known point on the line, and $\overrightarrow{PQ} = \langle x_1 - x_0, y_1 - y_0, z_1 - z_0 \rangle$ as the direction vector equation, Equation 2.12 gives

$$\mathbf{r} = \mathbf{p} + t\left(\overrightarrow{PQ}\right).$$

Using properties of vectors, then

$$
\begin{aligned}
\mathbf{r} &= \mathbf{p} + t\left(\overrightarrow{PQ}\right) \\
&= \langle x_0, y_0, z_0 \rangle + t\langle x_1 - x_0, y_1 - y_0, z_1 - z_0 \rangle \\
&= \langle x_0, y_0, z_0 \rangle + t(\langle x_1, y_1, z_1 \rangle - \langle x_0, y_0, z_0 \rangle) \\
&= \langle x_0, y_0, z_0 \rangle + t\langle x_1, y_1, z_1 \rangle - t\langle x_0, y_0, z_0 \rangle \\
&= (1 - t)\langle x_0, y_0, z_0 \rangle + t\langle x_1, y_1, z_1 \rangle \\
&= (1 - t)\mathbf{p} + t\mathbf{q}.
\end{aligned}
$$

Thus, the vector equation of the line passing through $P$ and $Q$ is

$$\mathbf{r} = (1 - t)\mathbf{p} + t\mathbf{q}.$$

Remember that we didn't want the equation of the whole line, just the line segment between $P$ and $Q$. Notice that when $t = 0$, we have $\mathbf{r} = \mathbf{p}$, and when $t = 1$, we have $\mathbf{r} = \mathbf{q}$. Therefore, the vector equation of the line segment between $P$ and $Q$ is

$$\mathbf{r} = (1 - t)\mathbf{p} + t\mathbf{q}, \ 0 \le t \le 1. \tag{2.15}$$

Going back to Equation 2.12, we can also find parametric equations for this line segment. We have

$$
\begin{aligned}
\mathbf{r} &= \mathbf{p} + t\left(\overrightarrow{PQ}\right) \\
\langle x, y, z \rangle &= \langle x_0, y_0, z_0 \rangle + t\langle x_1 - x_0, y_1 - y_0, z_1 - z_0 \rangle \\
&= \langle x_0 + t(x_1 - x_0), y_0 + t(y_1 - y_0), z_0 + t(z_1 - z_0) \rangle.
\end{aligned}
$$

Then, the parametric equations are

$$x = x_0 + t(x_1 - x_0), \ y = y_0 + t(y_1 - y_0), \ z = z_0 + t(z_1 - z_0), \ 0 \le t \le 1. \tag{2.16}$$

## Example 2.46

### Parametric Equations of a Line Segment

Find parametric equations of the line segment between the points $P(2, 1, 4)$ and $Q(3, -1, 3)$.

**Solution**

By Equation 2.16, we have

$$x = x_0 + t(x_1 - x_0),\ y = y_0 + t(y_1 - y_0),\ z = z_0 + t(z_1 - z_0),\ 0 \le t \le 1.$$

Working with each component separately, we get

$$\begin{aligned}
x &= x_0 + t(x_1 - x_0) \\
&= 2 + t(3 - 2) \\
&= 2 + t, \\
y &= y_0 + t(y_1 - y_0) \\
&= 1 + t(-1 - 1) \\
&= 1 - 2t,
\end{aligned}$$

and

$$\begin{aligned}
z &= z_0 + t(z_1 - z_0) \\
&= 4 + t(3 - 4) \\
&= 4 - t.
\end{aligned}$$

Therefore, the parametric equations for the line segment are

$$x = 2 + t,\ y = 1 - 2t,\ z = 4 - t,\ 0 \le t \le 1.$$

 **2.44** Find parametric equations of the line segment between points $P(-1, 3, 6)$ and $Q(-8, 2, 4)$.

## Distance between a Point and a Line

We already know how to calculate the distance between two points in space. We now expand this definition to describe the distance between a point and a line in space. Several real-world contexts exist when it is important to be able to calculate these distances. When building a home, for example, builders must consider "setback" requirements, when structures or fixtures have to be a certain distance from the property line. Air travel offers another example. Airlines are concerned about the distances between populated areas and proposed flight paths.

Let $L$ be a line in the plane and let $M$ be any point not on the line. Then, we define distance $d$ from $M$ to $L$ as the length of line segment $\overline{MP}$, where $P$ is a point on $L$ such that $\overline{MP}$ is perpendicular to $L$ (Figure 2.64).

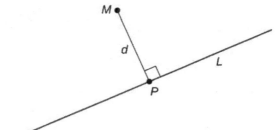

**Figure 2.64** The distance from point $M$ to line $L$ is the length of $\overrightarrow{MP}$.

When we're looking for the distance between a line and a point in space, Figure 2.64 still applies. We still define the distance as the length of the perpendicular line segment connecting the point to the line. In space, however, there is no clear way to know which point on the line creates such a perpendicular line segment, so we select an arbitrary point on the line and use properties of vectors to calculate the distance. Therefore, let $P$ be an arbitrary point on line $L$ and let $\mathbf{v}$ be a direction vector for $L$ (Figure 2.65).

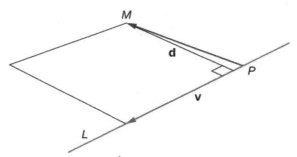

**Figure 2.65** Vectors $\overrightarrow{PM}$ and $\mathbf{v}$ form two sides of a parallelogram with base $\parallel \mathbf{v} \parallel$ and height $d$, which is the distance between a line and a point in space.

By **Area of a Parallelogram**, vectors $\overrightarrow{PM}$ and $\mathbf{v}$ form two sides of a parallelogram with area $\parallel \overrightarrow{PM} \times \mathbf{v} \parallel$. Using a formula from geometry, the area of this parallelogram can also be calculated as the product of its base and height:

$$\parallel \overrightarrow{PM} \times \mathbf{v} \parallel \;=\; \parallel \mathbf{v} \parallel d.$$

We can use this formula to find a general formula for the distance between a line in space and any point not on the line.

### Theorem 2.12: Distance from a Point to a Line

Let $L$ be a line in space passing through point $P$ with direction vector $\mathbf{v}$. If $M$ is any point not on $L$, then the distance from $M$ to $L$ is

$$d = \frac{\parallel \overrightarrow{PM} \times \mathbf{v} \parallel}{\parallel \mathbf{v} \parallel}.$$

### Example 2.47

### Calculating the Distance from a Point to a Line

Find the distance between t point $M = (1, 1, 3)$ and line $\frac{x-3}{4} = \frac{y+1}{2} = z - 3$.

### Solution

From the symmetric equations of the line, we know that vector $\mathbf{v} = \langle 4, 2, 1 \rangle$ is a direction vector for the line. Setting the symmetric equations of the line equal to zero, we see that point $P(3, -1, 3)$ lies on the line. Then,

$$\vec{PM} = \langle 1 - 3, 1 - (-1), 3 - 3 \rangle = \langle -2, 2, 0 \rangle.$$

To calculate the distance, we need to find $\vec{PM} \times \mathbf{v}$:

$$\begin{aligned}
\vec{PM} \times \mathbf{v} &= \begin{vmatrix} \mathbf{i} & \mathbf{j} & \mathbf{k} \\ -2 & 2 & 0 \\ 4 & 2 & 1 \end{vmatrix} \\
&= (2 - 0)\mathbf{i} - (-2 - 0)\mathbf{j} + (-4 - 8)\mathbf{k} \\
&= 2\mathbf{i} + 2\mathbf{j} - 12\mathbf{k}.
\end{aligned}$$

Therefore, the distance between the point and the line is (**Figure 2.66**)

$$\begin{aligned}
d &= \frac{\| \vec{PM} \times \mathbf{v} \|}{\| \mathbf{v} \|} \\
&= \frac{\sqrt{2^2 + 2^2 + 12^2}}{\sqrt{4^2 + 2^2 + 1^2}} \\
&= \frac{2\sqrt{38}}{\sqrt{21}}.
\end{aligned}$$

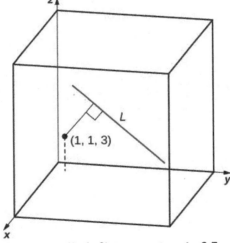

**Figure 2.66** Point $(1, 1, 3)$ is approximately $2.7$ units from the line with symmetric equations $\frac{x-3}{4} = \frac{y+1}{2} = z - 3$.

 **2.45** Find the distance between point $(0, 3, 6)$ and the line with parametric equations $x = 1 - t,\ y = 1 + 2t,\ z = 5 + 3t$.

# Relationships between Lines

Given two lines in the two-dimensional plane, the lines are equal, they are parallel but not equal, or they intersect in a single point. In three dimensions, a fourth case is possible. If two lines in space are not parallel, but do not intersect, then the lines are said to be **skew lines** (Figure 2.67).

**Figure 2.67** In three dimensions, it is possible that two lines do not cross, even when they have different directions.

To classify lines as parallel but not equal, equal, intersecting, or skew, we need to know two things: whether the direction vectors are parallel and whether the lines share a point (Figure 2.68).

Lines Share A Common Point?

|  |  | Yes | No |
|---|---|---|---|
| Direction Vectors Are Parallel? | Yes | Equal | Parallel but not equal |
|  | No | Intersecting | Skew |

**Figure 2.68** Determine the relationship between two lines based on whether their direction vectors are parallel and whether they share a point.

## Example 2.48

### Classifying Lines in Space

For each pair of lines, determine whether the lines are equal, parallel but not equal, skew, or intersecting.

a. $L_1 : x = 2s - 1, \ y = s - 1, \ z = s - 4$

$L_2 : x = t - 3, \ y = 3t + 8, \ z = 5 - 2t$

b. $L_1 : \ x = -y = z$

$L_2 : \dfrac{x - 3}{2} = y = z - 2$

c. $L_1 : x = 6s - 1, \ y = -2s, \ z = 3s + 1$

$L_2 : \dfrac{x - 4}{6} = \dfrac{y + 3}{-2} = \dfrac{z - 1}{3}$

### Solution

a. Line $L_1$ has direction vector $\mathbf{v_1} = \langle \, 2, 1, 1 \, \rangle$; line $L_2$ has direction vector $\mathbf{v_2} = \langle \, 1, 3, -2 \, \rangle$.

Because the direction vectors are not parallel vectors, the lines are either intersecting or skew. To determine whether the lines intersect, we see if there is a point, $(x, y, z)$, that lies on both lines. To find this point, we use the parametric equations to create a system of equalities:

$$2s - 1 = t - 3; \quad s - 1 = 3t + 8; \quad s - 4 = 5 - 2t.$$

By the first equation, $t = 2s + 2$. Substituting into the second equation yields

$$\begin{aligned} s - 1 &= 3(2s + 2) + 8 \\ s - 1 &= 6s + 6 + 8 \\ 5s &= -15 \\ s &= -3. \end{aligned}$$

Substitution into the third equation, however, yields a contradiction:

$$\begin{aligned} s - 4 &= 5 - 2(2s + 2) \\ s - 4 &= 5 - 4s - 4 \\ 5s &= 5 \\ s &= 1. \end{aligned}$$

There is no single point that satisfies the parametric equations for $L_1$ and $L_2$ simultaneously. These lines do not intersect, so they are skew (see the following figure).

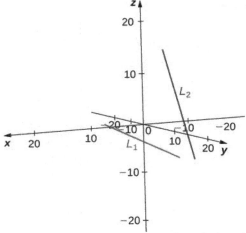

b.  Line $L_1$ has direction vector $\mathbf{v_1} = \langle\, 1, -1, 1\, \rangle$ and passes through the origin, $(0, 0, 0)$. Line $L_2$ has a different direction vector, $\mathbf{v_2} = \langle\, 2, 1, 1\, \rangle$, so these lines are not parallel or equal. Let $r$ represent the parameter for line $L_1$ and let $s$ represent the parameter for $L_2$:

$$\begin{aligned} x &= r & x &= 2s + 3 \\ y &= -r & y &= s \\ z &= r & z &= s + 2. \end{aligned}$$

Solve the system of equations to find $r = 1$ and $s = -1$. If we need to find the point of intersection, we can substitute these parameters into the original equations to get $(1, -1, 1)$ (see the following figure).

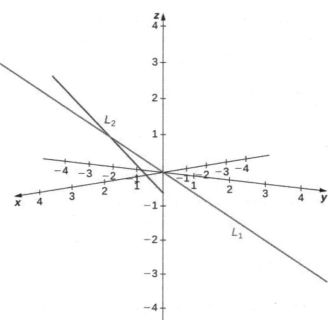

c.  Lines $L_1$ and $L_2$ have equivalent direction vectors: $\mathbf{v} = \langle\, 6, -2, 3 \,\rangle$. These two lines are parallel (see the following figure).

 **2.46**  Describe the relationship between the lines with the following parametric equations:

$$x = 1 - 4t,\ y = 3 + t,\ z = 8 - 6t$$
$$x = 2 + 3s,\ y = 2s,\ z = -1 - 3s.$$

## Equations for a Plane

We know that a line is determined by two points. In other words, for any two distinct points, there is exactly one line that passes through those points, whether in two dimensions or three. Similarly, given any three points that do not all lie on the same line, there is a unique plane that passes through these points. Just as a line is determined by two points, a plane is determined by three.

This may be the simplest way to characterize a plane, but we can use other descriptions as well. For example, given two distinct, intersecting lines, there is exactly one plane containing both lines. A plane is also determined by a line and any point that does not lie on the line. These characterizations arise naturally from the idea that a plane is determined by three points. Perhaps the most surprising characterization of a plane is actually the most useful.

Imagine a pair of orthogonal vectors that share an initial point. Visualize grabbing one of the vectors and twisting it. As you twist, the other vector spins around and sweeps out a plane. Here, we describe that concept mathematically. Let $\mathbf{n} = \langle a, b, c \rangle$ be a vector and $P = (x_0, y_0, z_0)$ be a point. Then the set of all points $Q = (x, y, z)$ such that $\overrightarrow{PQ}$ is orthogonal to $\mathbf{n}$ forms a plane (Figure 2.69). We say that $\mathbf{n}$ is a **normal vector**, or perpendicular to the plane. Remember, the dot product of orthogonal vectors is zero. This fact generates the **vector equation of a plane**: $\mathbf{n} \cdot \overrightarrow{PQ} = 0$. Rewriting this equation provides additional ways to describe the plane:

$$\mathbf{n} \cdot \overrightarrow{PQ} = 0$$
$$\langle a, b, c \rangle \cdot \langle x - x_0, y - y_0, z - z_0 \rangle = 0$$
$$a(x - x_0) + b(y - y_0) + c(z - z_0) = 0.$$

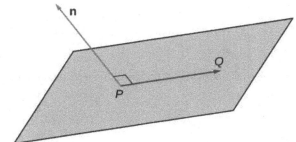

**Figure 2.69** Given a point $P$ and vector $\mathbf{n}$, the set of all points $Q$ with $\overrightarrow{PQ}$ orthogonal to $\mathbf{n}$ forms a plane.

---

**Definition**

Given a point $P$ and vector $\mathbf{n}$, the set of all points $Q$ satisfying the equation $\mathbf{n} \cdot \overrightarrow{PQ} = 0$ forms a plane. The equation

$$\mathbf{n} \cdot \overrightarrow{PQ} = 0 \tag{2.17}$$

is known as the vector equation of a plane.

The **scalar equation of a plane** containing point $P = (x_0, y_0, z_0)$ with normal vector $\mathbf{n} = \langle a, b, c \rangle$ is

$$a(x - x_0) + b(y - y_0) + c(z - z_0) = 0. \tag{2.18}$$

This equation can be expressed as $ax + by + cz + d = 0$, where $d = -ax_0 - by_0 - cz_0$. This form of the equation is sometimes called the **general form of the equation of a plane**.

---

As described earlier in this section, any three points that do not all lie on the same line determine a plane. Given three such points, we can find an equation for the plane containing these points.

## Example 2.49

### Writing an Equation of a Plane Given Three Points in the Plane

Write an equation for the plane containing points $P = (1, 1, -2)$, $Q = (0, 2, 1)$, and $R = (-1, -1, 0)$ in both standard and general forms.

**Solution**

To write an equation for a plane, we must find a normal vector for the plane. We start by identifying two vectors in the plane:

$$\vec{PQ} = \langle 0 - 1, 2 - 1, 1 - (-2) \rangle = \langle -1, 1, 3 \rangle$$
$$\vec{QR} = \langle -1 - 0, -1 - 2, 0 - 1 \rangle = \langle -1, -3, -1 \rangle.$$

The cross product $\vec{PQ} \times \vec{QR}$ is orthogonal to both $\vec{PQ}$ and $\vec{QR}$, so it is normal to the plane that contains these two vectors:

$$
\begin{aligned}
\mathbf{n} &= \vec{PQ} \times \vec{QR} \\
&= \begin{vmatrix} \mathbf{i} & \mathbf{j} & \mathbf{k} \\ -1 & 1 & 3 \\ -1 & -3 & -1 \end{vmatrix} \\
&= (-1 + 9)\mathbf{i} - (1 + 3)\mathbf{j} + (3 + 1)\mathbf{k} \\
&= 8\mathbf{i} - 4\mathbf{j} + 4\mathbf{k}.
\end{aligned}
$$

Thus, $\mathbf{n} = \langle 8, -4, 4 \rangle$, and we can choose any of the three given points to write an equation of the plane:

$$
\begin{aligned}
8(x - 1) - 4(y - 1) + 4(z + 2) &= 0 \\
8x - 4y + 4z + 4 &= 0.
\end{aligned}
$$

The scalar equations of a plane vary depending on the normal vector and point chosen.

## Example 2.50

### Writing an Equation for a Plane Given a Point and a Line

Find an equation of the plane that passes through point $(1, 4, 3)$ and contains the line given by $x = \dfrac{y - 1}{2} = z + 1$.

**Solution**

Symmetric equations describe the line that passes through point $(0, 1, -1)$ parallel to vector $\mathbf{v}_1 = \langle 1, 2, 1 \rangle$ (see the following figure). Use this point and the given point, $(1, 4, 3)$, to identify a second vector parallel to the plane:

$$\mathbf{v}_2 = \langle 1 - 0, 4 - 1, 3 - (-1) \rangle = \langle 1, 3, 4 \rangle.$$

Use the cross product of these vectors to identify a normal vector for the plane:

$$
\begin{aligned}
\mathbf{n} &= \mathbf{v}_1 \times \mathbf{v}_2 \\
&= \begin{vmatrix} \mathbf{i} & \mathbf{j} & \mathbf{k} \\ 1 & 2 & 1 \\ 1 & 3 & 4 \end{vmatrix} \\
&= (8 - 3)\mathbf{i} - (4 - 1)\mathbf{j} + (3 - 2)\mathbf{k} \\
&= 5\mathbf{i} - 3\mathbf{j} + \mathbf{k}.
\end{aligned}
$$

The scalar equations for the plane are $5x - 3(y - 1) + (z + 1) = 0$ and $5x - 3y + z + 4 = 0$.

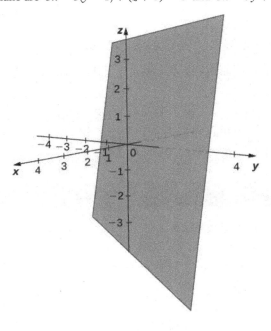

**2.47** Find an equation of the plane containing the lines $L_1$ and $L_2$:

$$L_1 : x = -y = z$$
$$L_2 : \frac{x - 3}{2} = y = z - 2.$$

Now that we can write an equation for a plane, we can use the equation to find the distance $d$ between a point $P$ and the plane. It is defined as the shortest possible distance from $P$ to a point on the plane.

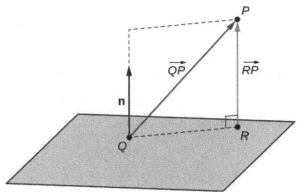

**Figure 2.70** We want to find the shortest distance from point $P$ to the plane. Let point $R$ be the point in the plane such that, for any other point in the plane $Q$, $\| \overrightarrow{RP} \| < \| \overrightarrow{QP} \|$.

Just as we find the two-dimensional distance between a point and a line by calculating the length of a line segment perpendicular to the line, we find the three-dimensional distance between a point and a plane by calculating the length of a line segment perpendicular to the plane. Let $R$ bet the point in the plane such that $\overrightarrow{RP}$ is orthogonal to the plane, and let

$Q$ be an arbitrary point in the plane. Then the projection of vector $\vec{QP}$ onto the normal vector describes vector $\vec{RP}$, as shown in **Figure 2.70**.

---

**Theorem 2.13: The Distance between a Plane and a Point**

Suppose a plane with normal vector $\mathbf{n}$ passes through point $Q$. The distance $d$ from the plane to a point $P$ not in the plane is given by

$$d = \| \operatorname{proj}_\mathbf{n} \vec{QP} \| = \left| \operatorname{comp}_\mathbf{n} \vec{QP} \right| = \frac{\left| \vec{QP} \cdot \mathbf{n} \right|}{\| \mathbf{n} \|}. \tag{2.19}$$

---

## Example 2.51

### Distance between a Point and a Plane

Find the distance between point $P = (3, 1, 2)$ and the plane given by $x - 2y + z = 5$ (see the following figure).

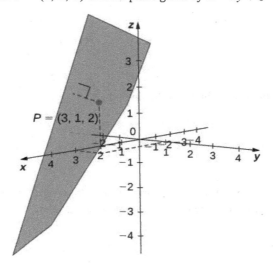

### Solution

The coefficients of the plane's equation provide a normal vector for the plane: $\mathbf{n} = \langle 1, -2, 1 \rangle$. To find vector $\vec{QP}$, we need a point in the plane. Any point will work, so set $y = z = 0$ to see that point $Q = (5, 0, 0)$ lies in the plane. Find the component form of the vector from $Q$ to $P$:

$$\vec{QP} = \langle 3 - 5, 1 - 0, 2 - 0 \rangle = \langle -2, 1, 2 \rangle.$$

Apply the distance formula from **Equation 2.19**:

$$d = \frac{\left|\vec{QP} \cdot \mathbf{n}\right|}{\|\mathbf{n}\|}$$

$$= \frac{|\langle -2, 1, 2 \rangle \cdot \langle 1, -2, 1 \rangle|}{\sqrt{1^2 + (-2)^2 + 1^2}}$$

$$= \frac{|-2 - 2 + 2|}{\sqrt{6}}$$

$$= \frac{2}{\sqrt{6}}.$$

 **2.48** Find the distance between point $P = (5, -1, 0)$ and the plane given by $4x + 2y - z = 3$.

## Parallel and Intersecting Planes

We have discussed the various possible relationships between two lines in two dimensions and three dimensions. When we describe the relationship between two planes in space, we have only two possibilities: the two distinct planes are parallel or they intersect. When two planes are parallel, their normal vectors are parallel. When two planes intersect, the intersection is a line (**Figure 2.71**).

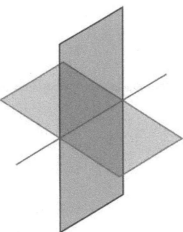

**Figure 2.71** The intersection of two nonparallel planes is always a line.

We can use the equations of the two planes to find parametric equations for the line of intersection.

## Example 2.52

### Finding the Line of Intersection for Two Planes

Find parametric and symmetric equations for the line formed by the intersection of the planes given by $x + y + z = 0$ and $2x - y + z = 0$ (see the following figure).

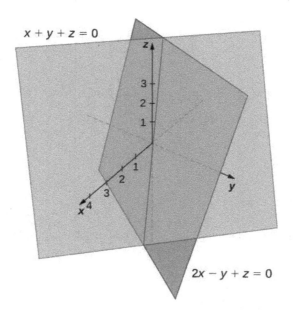

## Solution

Note that the two planes have nonparallel normals, so the planes intersect. Further, the origin satisfies each equation, so we know the line of intersection passes through the origin. Add the plane equations so we can eliminate the one of the variables, in this case, $y$:

$$\begin{array}{rrrrr} x & + & y & + z & = 0 \\ 2x & - & y & + z & = 0 \\ \hline 3x & & & + 2z & = 0. \end{array}$$

This gives us $x = -\frac{2}{3}z$. We substitute this value into the first equation to express $y$ in terms of $z$:

$$\begin{aligned} x + y + z &= 0 \\ -\tfrac{2}{3}z + y + z &= 0 \\ y + \tfrac{1}{3}z &= 0 \\ y &= -\tfrac{1}{3}z. \end{aligned}$$

We now have the first two variables, $x$ and $y$, in terms of the third variable, $z$. Now we define $z$ in terms of $t$. To eliminate the need for fractions, we choose to define the parameter $t$ as $t = -\frac{1}{3}z$. Then, $z = -3t$.

Substituting the parametric representation of $z$ back into the other two equations, we see that the parametric equations for the line of intersection are $x = 2t$, $y = t$, $z = -3t$. The symmetric equations for the line are $\frac{x}{2} = y = \frac{z}{-3}$.

 **2.49** Find parametric equations for the line formed by the intersection of planes $x + y - z = 3$ and $3x - y + 3z = 5$.

In addition to finding the equation of the line of intersection between two planes, we may need to find the angle formed by the intersection of two planes. For example, builders constructing a house need to know the angle where different sections of the roof meet to know whether the roof will look good and drain properly. We can use normal vectors to calculate the angle between the two planes. We can do this because the angle between the normal vectors is the same as the angle between the planes. **Figure 2.72** shows why this is true.

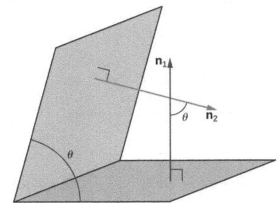

**Figure 2.72** The angle between two planes has the same measure as the angle between the normal vectors for the planes.

We can find the measure of the angle $\theta$ between two intersecting planes by first finding the cosine of the angle, using the following equation:

$$\cos \theta = \frac{|\mathbf{n}_1 \cdot \mathbf{n}_2|}{\|\mathbf{n}_1\| \ \|\mathbf{n}_2\|}.$$

We can then use the angle to determine whether two planes are parallel or orthogonal or if they intersect at some other angle.

## Example 2.53

### Finding the Angle between Two Planes

Determine whether each pair of planes is parallel, orthogonal, or neither. If the planes are intersecting, but not orthogonal, find the measure of the angle between them. Give the answer in radians and round to two decimal places.

    a.  $x + 2y - z = 8$ and $2x + 4y - 2z = 10$

    b.  $2x - 3y + 2z = 3$ and $6x + 2y - 3z = 1$

    c.  $x + y + z = 4$ and $x - 3y + 5z = 1$

### Solution

    a.  The normal vectors for these planes are $\mathbf{n}_1 = \langle 1, 2, -1 \rangle$ and $\mathbf{n}_2 = \langle 2, 4, -2 \rangle$. These two vectors are scalar multiples of each other. The normal vectors are parallel, so the planes are parallel.

    b.  The normal vectors for these planes are $\mathbf{n}_1 = \langle 2, -3, 2 \rangle$ and $\mathbf{n}_2 = \langle 6, 2, -3 \rangle$. Taking the dot product of these vectors, we have

$$\mathbf{n}_1 \cdot \mathbf{n}_2 = \langle 2, -3, 2 \rangle \cdot \langle 6, 2, -3 \rangle = 2(6) - 3(2) + 2(-3) = 0.$$

       The normal vectors are orthogonal, so the corresponding planes are orthogonal as well.

    c.  The normal vectors for these planes are $\mathbf{n}_1 = \langle 1, 1, 1 \rangle$ and $\mathbf{n}_2 = \langle 1, -3, 5 \rangle$:

$$\begin{aligned}
\cos \theta &= \frac{|\mathbf{n}_1 \cdot \mathbf{n}_2|}{\| \mathbf{n}_1 \| \ \| \mathbf{n}_2 \|} \\
&= \frac{|\langle 1, 1, 1 \rangle \cdot \langle 1, -3, 5 \rangle|}{\sqrt{1^2 + 1^2 + 1^2}\sqrt{1^2 + (-3)^2 + 5^2}} \\
&= \frac{3}{\sqrt{105}}.
\end{aligned}$$

The angle between the two planes is $1.27$ rad, or approximately $73°$.

 **2.50** Find the measure of the angle between planes $x + y - z = 3$ and $3x - y + 3z = 5$. Give the answer in radians and round to two decimal places.

When we find that two planes are parallel, we may need to find the distance between them. To find this distance, we simply select a point in one of the planes. The distance from this point to the other plane is the distance between the planes.

Previously, we introduced the formula for calculating this distance in **Equation 2.19**:

$$d = \frac{\overrightarrow{QP} \cdot \mathbf{n}}{\| \mathbf{n} \|},$$

where $Q$ is a point on the plane, $P$ is a point not on the plane, and $\mathbf{n}$ is the normal vector that passes through point $Q$. Consider the distance from point $(x_0, y_0, z_0)$ to plane $ax + by + cz + k = 0$. Let $(x_1, y_1, z_1)$ be any point in the plane. Substituting into the formula yields

$$\begin{aligned}
d &= \frac{|a(x_0 - x_1) + b(y_0 - y_1) + c(z_0 - z_1)|}{\sqrt{a^2 + b^2 + c^2}} \\
&= \frac{|ax_0 + by_0 + cz_0 + k|}{\sqrt{a^2 + b^2 + c^2}}.
\end{aligned}$$

We state this result formally in the following theorem.

**Theorem 2.14: Distance from a Point to a Plane**

Let $P(x_0, y_0, z_0)$ be a point. The distance from $P$ to plane $ax + by + cz + k = 0$ is given by

$$d = \frac{|ax_0 + by_0 + cz_0 + k|}{\sqrt{a^2 + b^2 + c^2}}.$$

## Example 2.54

### Finding the Distance between Parallel Planes

Find the distance between the two parallel planes given by $2x + y - z = 2$ and $2x + y - z = 8$.

### Solution

Point $(1, 0, 0)$ lies in the first plane. The desired distance, then, is

$$
\begin{aligned}
d &= \frac{|ax_0 + by_0 + cz_0 + k|}{\sqrt{a^2 + b^2 + c^2}} \\
&= \frac{|2(1) + 1(0) + (-1)(0) + (-8)|}{\sqrt{2^2 + 1^2 + (-1)^2}} \\
&= \frac{6}{\sqrt{6}} = \sqrt{6}.
\end{aligned}
$$

 **2.51** Find the distance between parallel planes $5x - 2y + z = 6$ and $5x - 2y + z = -3$.

# Student PROJECT

## Distance between Two Skew Lines

**Figure 2.73** Industrial pipe installations often feature pipes running in different directions. How can we find the distance between two skew pipes?

Finding the distance from a point to a line or from a line to a plane seems like a pretty abstract procedure. But, if the lines represent pipes in a chemical plant or tubes in an oil refinery or roads at an intersection of highways, confirming that the distance between them meets specifications can be both important and awkward to measure. One way is to model the two pipes as lines, using the techniques in this chapter, and then calculate the distance between them. The calculation involves forming vectors along the directions of the lines and using both the cross product and the dot product.

The symmetric forms of two lines, $L_1$ and $L_2$, are

$$L_1 : \frac{x - x_1}{a_1} = \frac{y - y_1}{b_1} = \frac{z - z_1}{c_1}$$
$$L_2 : \frac{x - x_2}{a_2} = \frac{y - y_2}{b_2} = \frac{z - z_2}{c_2}.$$

You are to develop a formula for the distance $d$ between these two lines, in terms of the values $a_1$, $b_1$, $c_1$; $a_2$, $b_2$, $c_2$; $x_1$, $y_1$, $z_1$; and $x_2$, $y_2$, $z_2$. The distance between two lines is usually taken to mean the minimum distance, so this is the length of a line segment or the length of a vector that is perpendicular to both lines and intersects both lines.

1.  First, write down two vectors, $\mathbf{v}_1$ and $\mathbf{v}_2$, that lie along $L_1$ and $L_2$, respectively.

2.  Find the cross product of these two vectors and call it $\mathbf{N}$. This vector is perpendicular to $\mathbf{v}_1$ and $\mathbf{v}_2$, and

hence is perpendicular to both lines.

3. From vector $\mathbf{N}$, form a unit vector $\mathbf{n}$ in the same direction.

4. Use symmetric equations to find a convenient vector $\mathbf{v}_{12}$ that lies between any two points, one on each line. Again, this can be done directly from the symmetric equations.

5. The dot product of two vectors is the magnitude of the projection of one vector onto the other—that is, $\mathbf{A} \cdot \mathbf{B} = \parallel \mathbf{A} \parallel \parallel \mathbf{B} \parallel \cos \theta$, where $\theta$ is the angle between the vectors. Using the dot product, find the projection of vector $\mathbf{v}_{12}$ found in step 4 onto unit vector $\mathbf{n}$ found in step 3. This projection is perpendicular to both lines, and hence its length must be the perpendicular distance $d$ between them. Note that the value of $d$ may be negative, depending on your choice of vector $\mathbf{v}_{12}$ or the order of the cross product, so use absolute value signs around the numerator.

6. Check that your formula gives the correct distance of $|-25|/\sqrt{198} \approx 1.78$ between the following two lines:

$$L_1 : \frac{x-5}{2} = \frac{y-3}{4} = \frac{z-1}{3}$$
$$L_2 : \frac{x-6}{3} = \frac{y-1}{5} = \frac{z}{7}.$$

7. Is your general expression valid when the lines are parallel? If not, why not? (*Hint:* What do you know about the value of the cross product of two parallel vectors? Where would that result show up in your expression for $d$?)

8. Demonstrate that your expression for the distance is zero when the lines intersect. Recall that two lines intersect if they are not parallel and they are in the same plane. Hence, consider the direction of $\mathbf{n}$ and $\mathbf{v}_{12}$. What is the result of their dot product?

9. Consider the following application. Engineers at a refinery have determined they need to install support struts between many of the gas pipes to reduce damaging vibrations. To minimize cost, they plan to install these struts at the closest points between adjacent skewed pipes. Because they have detailed schematics of the structure, they are able to determine the correct lengths of the struts needed, and hence manufacture and distribute them to the installation crews without spending valuable time making measurements.
The rectangular frame structure has the dimensions $4.0 \times 15.0 \times 10.0$ m (height, width, and depth). One sector has a pipe entering the lower corner of the standard frame unit and exiting at the diametrically opposed corner (the one farthest away at the top); call this $L_1$. A second pipe enters and exits at the two different opposite lower corners; call this $L_2$ (Figure 2.74).

**Figure 2.74** Two pipes cross through a standard frame unit.

Write down the vectors along the lines representing those pipes, find the cross product between them from which to create the unit vector $\mathbf{n}$, define a vector that spans two points on each line, and finally determine the minimum distance between the lines. (Take the origin to be at the lower corner of the first pipe.) Similarly, you may also develop the symmetric equations for each line and substitute directly into your formula.

# 2.5 EXERCISES

In the following exercises, points $P$ and $Q$ are given. Let $L$ be the line passing through points $P$ and $Q$.

a. Find the vector equation of line $L$.

b. Find parametric equations of line $L$.

c. Find symmetric equations of line $L$.

d. Find parametric equations of the line segment determined by $P$ and $Q$.

243. $P(-3, 5, 9)$, $Q(4, -7, 2)$

244. $P(4, 0, 5)$, $Q(2, 3, 1)$

245. $P(-1, 0, 5)$, $Q(4, 0, 3)$

246. $P(7, -2, 6)$, $Q(-3, 0, 6)$

For the following exercises, point $P$ and vector $\mathbf{v}$ are given. Let $L$ be the line passing through point $P$ with direction $\mathbf{v}$.

a. Find parametric equations of line $L$.

b. Find symmetric equations of line $L$.

c. Find the intersection of the line with the $xy$-plane.

247. $P(1, -2, 3)$, $\mathbf{v} = \langle 1, 2, 3 \rangle$

248. $P(3, 1, 5)$, $\mathbf{v} = \langle 1, 1, 1 \rangle$

249. $P(3, 1, 5)$, $\mathbf{v} = \vec{QR}$, where $Q(2, 2, 3)$ and $R(3, 2, 3)$

250. $P(2, 3, 0)$, $\mathbf{v} = \vec{QR}$, where $Q(0, 4, 5)$ and $R(0, 4, 6)$

For the following exercises, line $L$ is given.

a. Find point $P$ that belongs to the line and direction vector $\mathbf{v}$ of the line. Express $\mathbf{v}$ in component form.

b. Find the distance from the origin to line $L$.

251. $x = 1 + t$, $y = 3 + t$, $z = 5 + 4t$, $t \in \mathbb{R}$

252. $-x = y + 1$, $z = 2$

253. Find the distance between point $A(-3, 1, 1)$ and the line of symmetric equations $x = -y = -z$.

254. Find the distance between point $A(4, 2, 5)$ and the line of parametric equations $x = -1 - t$, $y = -t$, $z = 2$, $t \in \mathbb{R}$.

For the following exercises, lines $L_1$ and $L_2$ are given.

a. Verify whether lines $L_1$ and $L_2$ are parallel.

b. If the lines $L_1$ and $L_2$ are parallel, then find the distance between them.

255. $L_1 : x = 1 + t$, $y = t$, $z = 2 + t$, $t \in \mathbb{R}$, $L_2 : x - 3 = y - 1 = z - 3$

256. $L_1 : x = 2$, $y = 1$, $z = t$, $L_2 : x = 1$, $y = 1$, $z = 2 - 3t$, $t \in \mathbb{R}$

257. Show that the line passing through points $P(3, 1, 0)$ and $Q(1, 4, -3)$ is perpendicular to the line with equation $x = 3t$, $y = 3 + 8t$, $z = -7 + 6t$, $t \in \mathbb{R}$.

258. Are the lines of equations $x = -2 + 2t$, $y = -6$, $z = 2 + 6t$ and $x = -1 + t$, $y = 1 + t$, $z = t$, $t \in \mathbb{R}$, perpendicular to each other?

259. Find the point of intersection of the lines of equations $x = -2y = 3z$ and $x = -5 - t$, $y = -1 + t$, $z = t - 11$, $t \in \mathbb{R}$.

260. Find the intersection point of the $x$-axis with the line of parametric equations $x = 10 + t$, $y = 2 - 2t$, $z = -3 + 3t$, $t \in \mathbb{R}$.

For the following exercises, lines $L_1$ and $L_2$ are given. Determine whether the lines are equal, parallel but not equal, skew, or intersecting.

261. $L_1 : x = y - 1 = -z$ and $L_2 : x - 2 = -y = \frac{z}{2}$

262. $L_1 : x = 2t$, $y = 0$, $z = 3$, $t \in \mathbb{R}$ and $L_2 : x = 0$, $y = 8 + s$, $z = 7 + s$, $s \in \mathbb{R}$

263. $L_1 : x = -1 + 2t$, $y = 1 + 3t$, $z = 7t$, $t \in \mathbb{R}$ and $L_2 : x - 1 = \frac{2}{3}(y - 4) = \frac{2}{7}z - 2$

264. $L_1 : 3x = y + 1 = 2z$ and $L_2 : x = 6 + 2t$, $y = 17 + 6t$, $z = 9 + 3t$, $t \in \mathbb{R}$

265.  Consider line $L$ of symmetric equations $x - 2 = -y = \frac{z}{2}$ and point $A(1, 1, 1)$.

   a.  Find parametric equations for a line parallel to $L$ that passes through point $A$.

   b.  Find symmetric equations of a line skew to $L$ and that passes through point $A$.

   c.  Find symmetric equations of a line that intersects $L$ and passes through point $A$.

266.  Consider line $L$ of parametric equations $x = t, \; y = 2t, \; z = 3, \quad t \in \mathbb{R}$ .

   a.  Find parametric equations for a line parallel to $L$ that passes through the origin.

   b.  Find parametric equations of a line skew to $L$ that passes through the origin.

   c.  Find symmetric equations of a line that intersects $L$ and passes through the origin.

For the following exercises, point $P$ and vector $\mathbf{n}$ are given.

   a.  Find the scalar equation of the plane that passes through $P$ and has normal vector $\mathbf{n}$.

   b.  Find the general form of the equation of the plane that passes through $P$ and has normal vector $\mathbf{n}$.

267.  $P(0, 0, 0), \quad \mathbf{n} = 3\mathbf{i} - 2\mathbf{j} + 4\mathbf{k}$

268.  $P(3, 2, 2), \quad \mathbf{n} = 2\mathbf{i} + 3\mathbf{j} - \mathbf{k}$

269.  $P(1, 2, 3), \quad \mathbf{n} = \langle 1, 2, 3 \rangle$

270.  $P(0, 0, 0), \quad \mathbf{n} = \langle -3, 2, -1 \rangle$

For the following exercises, the equation of a plane is given.

   a.  Find normal vector $\mathbf{n}$ to the plane. Express $\mathbf{n}$ using standard unit vectors.

   b.  Find the intersections of the plane with the axes of coordinates.

   c.  Sketch the plane.

271.  **[T]** $4x + 5y + 10z - 20 = 0$

272.  $3x + 4y - 12 = 0$

273.  $3x - 2y + 4z = 0$

274.  $x + z = 0$

275.  Given point $P(1, 2, 3)$ and vector $\mathbf{n} = \mathbf{i} + \mathbf{j}$, find point $Q$ on the $x$-axis such that $\overrightarrow{PQ}$ and $\mathbf{n}$ are orthogonal.

276.  Show there is no plane perpendicular to $\mathbf{n} = \mathbf{i} + \mathbf{j}$ that passes through points $P(1, 2, 3)$ and $Q(2, 3, 4)$.

277.  Find parametric equations of the line passing through point $P(-2, 1, 3)$ that is perpendicular to the plane of equation $2x - 3y + z = 7$.

278.  Find symmetric equations of the line passing through point $P(2, 5, 4)$ that is perpendicular to the plane of equation $2x + 3y - 5z = 0$.

279.  Show that line $\frac{x-1}{2} = \frac{y+1}{3} = \frac{z-2}{4}$ is parallel to plane $x - 2y + z = 6$.

280.  Find the real number $\alpha$ such that the line of parametric equations $x = t, \; y = 2 - t, \; z = 3 + t$, $t \in \mathbb{R}$ is parallel to the plane of equation $\alpha x + 5y + z - 10 = 0$.

For the following exercises, points $P$, $Q$, and $R$ are given.

   a.  Find the general equation of the plane passing through $P$, $Q$, and $R$.

   b.  Write the vector equation $\mathbf{n} \cdot \overrightarrow{PS} = 0$ of the plane at a., where $S(x, y, z)$ is an arbitrary point of the plane.

   c.  Find parametric equations of the line passing through the origin that is perpendicular to the plane passing through $P$, $Q$, and $R$.

281.  $P(1, 1, 1), \; Q(2, 4, 3), \;$ and $R(-1, -2, -1)$

282.  $P(-2, 1, 4), \; Q(3, 1, 3), \;$ and $R(-2, 1, 0)$

283.  Consider the planes of equations $x + y + z = 1$ and $x + z = 0$.

   a.  Show that the planes intersect.

   b.  Find symmetric equations of the line passing through point $P(1, 4, 6)$ that is parallel to the line of intersection of the planes.

284. Consider the planes of equations $-y + z - 2 = 0$ and $x - y = 0$.

    a. Show that the planes intersect.

    b. Find parametric equations of the line passing through point $P(-8, 0, 2)$ that is parallel to the line of intersection of the planes.

285. Find the scalar equation of the plane that passes through point $P(-1, 2, 1)$ and is perpendicular to the line of intersection of planes $x + y - z - 2 = 0$ and $2x - y + 3z - 1 = 0$.

286. Find the general equation of the plane that passes through the origin and is perpendicular to the line of intersection of planes $-x + y + 2 = 0$ and $z - 3 = 0$.

287. Determine whether the line of parametric equations $x = 1 + 2t$, $y = -2t$, $z = 2 + t$, $t \in \mathbb{R}$ intersects the plane with equation $3x + 4y + 6z - 7 = 0$. If it does intersect, find the point of intersection.

288. Determine whether the line of parametric equations $x = 5$, $y = 4 - t$, $z = 2t$, $t \in \mathbb{R}$ intersects the plane with equation $2x - y + z = 5$. If it does intersect, find the point of intersection.

289. Find the distance from point $P(1, 5, -4)$ to the plane of equation $3x - y + 2z - 6 = 0$.

290. Find the distance from point $P(1, -2, 3)$ to the plane of equation $(x - 3) + 2(y + 1) - 4z = 0$.

For the following exercises, the equations of two planes are given.

    a. Determine whether the planes are parallel, orthogonal, or neither.

    b. If the planes are neither parallel nor orthogonal, then find the measure of the angle between the planes. Express the answer in degrees rounded to the nearest integer.

291. [T] $x + y + z = 0$, $\quad 2x - y + z - 7 = 0$

292. $5x - 3y + z = 4$, $\quad x + 4y + 7z = 1$

293. $x - 5y - z = 1$, $\quad 5x - 25y - 5z = -3$

294. [T] $x - 3y + 6z = 4$, $\quad 5x + y - z = 4$

295. Show that the lines of equations $x = t$, $y = 1 + t$, $z = 2 + t$, $t \in \mathbb{R}$, and $\dfrac{x}{2} = \dfrac{y - 1}{3} = z - 3$ are skew, and find the distance between them.

296. Show that the lines of equations $x = -1 + t$, $y = -2 + t$, $z = 3t$, $t \in \mathbb{R}$, and $x = 5 + s$, $y = -8 + 2s$, $z = 7s$, $s \in \mathbb{R}$ are skew, and find the distance between them.

297. Consider point $C(-3, 2, 4)$ and the plane of equation $2x + 4y - 3z = 8$.

    a. Find the radius of the sphere with center $C$ tangent to the given plane.

    b. Find point $P$ of tangency.

298. Consider the plane of equation $x - y - z - 8 = 0$.

    a. Find the equation of the sphere with center $C$ at the origin that is tangent to the given plane.

    b. Find parametric equations of the line passing through the origin and the point of tangency.

299. Two children are playing with a ball. The girl throws the ball to the boy. The ball travels in the air, curves $3$ ft to the right, and falls $5$ ft away from the girl (see the following figure). If the plane that contains the trajectory of the ball is perpendicular to the ground, find its equation.

300. [T] John allocates $d$ dollars to consume monthly three goods of prices $a$, $b$, and $c$. In this context, the budget equation is defined as $ax + by + cz = d$, where $x \geq 0$, $y \geq 0$, and $z \geq 0$ represent the number of items bought from each of the goods. The budget set is given by $\{(x, y, z) | ax + by + cz \leq d, x \geq 0, y \geq 0, z \geq 0\}$, and the budget plane is the part of the plane of equation $ax + by + cz = d$ for which $x \geq 0$, $y \geq 0$, and $z \geq 0$. Consider $a = \$8$, $b = \$5$, $c = \$10$, and $d = \$500$.

    a. Use a CAS to graph the budget set and budget plane.

    b. For $z = 25$, find the new budget equation and graph the budget set in the same system of coordinates.

301. **[T]** Consider $\mathbf{r}(t) = \langle \sin t, \cos t, 2t \rangle$ the position vector of a particle at time $t \in [0, 3]$, where the components of $\mathbf{r}$ are expressed in centimeters and time is measured in seconds. Let $\overrightarrow{OP}$ be the position vector of the particle after 1 sec.

   a. Determine the velocity vector $\mathbf{v}(1)$ of the particle after 1 sec.

   b. Find the scalar equation of the plane that is perpendicular to $\mathbf{v}(1)$ and passes through point $P$.

      This plane is called the *normal plane* to the path of the particle at point $P$.

   c. Use a CAS to visualize the path of the particle along with the velocity vector and normal plane at point $P$.

302. **[T]** A solar panel is mounted on the roof of a house. The panel may be regarded as positioned at the points of coordinates (in meters) $A(8, 0, 0)$, $B(8, 18, 0)$, $C(0, 18, 8)$, and $D(0, 0, 8)$ (see the following figure).

   a. Find the general form of the equation of the plane that contains the solar panel by using points $A$, $B$, and $C$, and show that its normal vector is equivalent to $\overrightarrow{AB} \times \overrightarrow{AD}$.

   b. Find parametric equations of line $L_1$ that passes through the center of the solar panel and has direction vector $\mathbf{s} = \frac{1}{\sqrt{3}}\mathbf{i} + \frac{1}{\sqrt{3}}\mathbf{j} + \frac{1}{\sqrt{3}}\mathbf{k}$, which points toward the position of the Sun at a particular time of day.

   c. Find symmetric equations of line $L_2$ that passes through the center of the solar panel and is perpendicular to it.

   d. Determine the angle of elevation of the Sun above the solar panel by using the angle between lines $L_1$ and $L_2$.

# 2.6 | Quadric Surfaces

| Learning Objectives |
| --- |
| 2.6.1 Identify a cylinder as a type of three-dimensional surface. |
| 2.6.2 Recognize the main features of ellipsoids, paraboloids, and hyperboloids. |
| 2.6.3 Use traces to draw the intersections of quadric surfaces with the coordinate planes. |

We have been exploring vectors and vector operations in three-dimensional space, and we have developed equations to describe lines, planes, and spheres. In this section, we use our knowledge of planes and spheres, which are examples of three-dimensional figures called *surfaces*, to explore a variety of other surfaces that can be graphed in a three-dimensional coordinate system.

## Identifying Cylinders

The first surface we'll examine is the cylinder. Although most people immediately think of a hollow pipe or a soda straw when they hear the word *cylinder*, here we use the broad mathematical meaning of the term. As we have seen, cylindrical surfaces don't have to be circular. A rectangular heating duct is a cylinder, as is a rolled-up yoga mat, the cross-section of which is a spiral shape.

In the two-dimensional coordinate plane, the equation $x^2 + y^2 = 9$ describes a circle centered at the origin with radius 3.

In three-dimensional space, this same equation represents a surface. Imagine copies of a circle stacked on top of each other centered on the $z$-axis (**Figure 2.75**), forming a hollow tube. We can then construct a cylinder from the set of lines parallel to the $z$-axis passing through circle $x^2 + y^2 = 9$ in the $xy$-plane, as shown in the figure. In this way, any curve in one of the coordinate planes can be extended to become a surface.

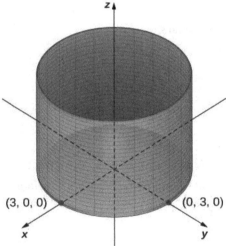

**Figure 2.75** In three-dimensional space, the graph of equation $x^2 + y^2 = 9$ is a cylinder with radius 3 centered on the $z$-axis. It continues indefinitely in the positive and negative directions.

| Definition |
| --- |
| A set of lines parallel to a given line passing through a given curve is known as a cylindrical surface, or **cylinder**. The parallel lines are called **rulings**. |

From this definition, we can see that we still have a cylinder in three-dimensional space, even if the curve is not a circle. Any curve can form a cylinder, and the rulings that compose the cylinder may be parallel to any given line (**Figure 2.76**).

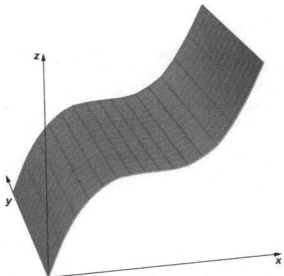

**Figure 2.76** In three-dimensional space, the graph of equation $z = x^3$ is a cylinder, or a cylindrical surface with rulings parallel to the $y$-axis.

## Example 2.55

### Graphing Cylindrical Surfaces

Sketch the graphs of the following cylindrical surfaces.

a.  $x^2 + z^2 = 25$

b.  $z = 2x^2 - y$

c.  $y = \sin x$

### Solution

a.  The variable $y$ can take on any value without limit. Therefore, the lines ruling this surface are parallel to the $y$-axis. The intersection of this surface with the $xz$-plane forms a circle centered at the origin with radius $5$ (see the following figure).

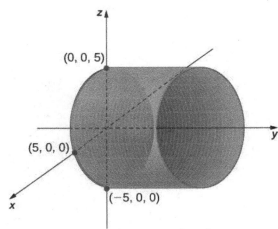

**Figure 2.77** The graph of equation $x^2 + z^2 = 25$ is a cylinder with radius $5$ centered on the $y$-axis.

b. In this case, the equation contains all three variables — $x$, $y$, and $z$ — so none of the variables can vary arbitrarily. The easiest way to visualize this surface is to use a computer graphing utility (see the following figure).

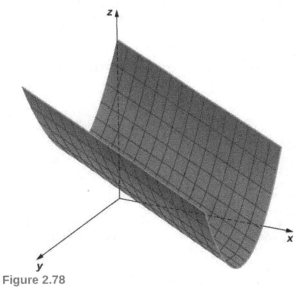

**Figure 2.78**

c. In this equation, the variable $z$ can take on any value without limit. Therefore, the lines composing this surface are parallel to the $z$-axis. The intersection of this surface with the $yz$-plane outlines curve $y = \sin x$ (see the following figure).

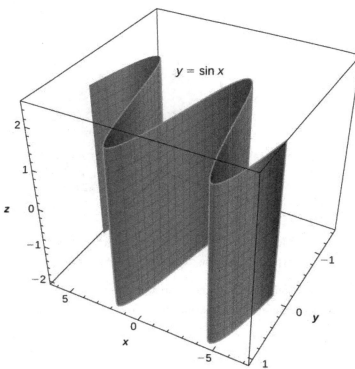

**Figure 2.79** The graph of equation $y = \sin x$ is formed by a set of lines parallel to the $z$-axis passing through curve $y = \sin x$ in the $xy$-plane.

 **2.52** Sketch or use a graphing tool to view the graph of the cylindrical surface defined by equation $z = y^2$.

When sketching surfaces, we have seen that it is useful to sketch the intersection of the surface with a plane parallel to one of the coordinate planes. These curves are called traces. We can see them in the plot of the cylinder in **Figure 2.80**.

**Definition**

The **traces** of a surface are the cross-sections created when the surface intersects a plane parallel to one of the coordinate planes.

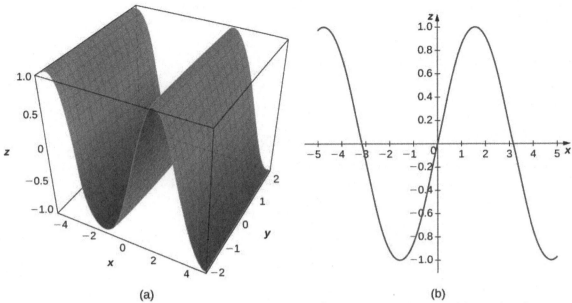

**Figure 2.80** (a) This is one view of the graph of equation $z = \sin x$. (b) To find the trace of the graph in the $xz$-plane, set $y = 0$. The trace is simply a two-dimensional sine wave.

Traces are useful in sketching cylindrical surfaces. For a cylinder in three dimensions, though, only one set of traces is useful. Notice, in **Figure 2.80**, that the trace of the graph of $z = \sin x$ in the $xz$-plane is useful in constructing the graph. The trace in the $xy$-plane, though, is just a series of parallel lines, and the trace in the $yz$-plane is simply one line.

Cylindrical surfaces are formed by a set of parallel lines. Not all surfaces in three dimensions are constructed so simply, however. We now explore more complex surfaces, and traces are an important tool in this investigation.

## Quadric Surfaces

We have learned about surfaces in three dimensions described by first-order equations; these are planes. Some other common types of surfaces can be described by second-order equations. We can view these surfaces as three-dimensional extensions of the conic sections we discussed earlier: the ellipse, the parabola, and the hyperbola. We call these graphs quadric surfaces.

---
**Definition**

**Quadric surfaces** are the graphs of equations that can be expressed in the form

$$Ax^2 + By^2 + Cz^2 + Dxy + Exz + Fyz + Gx + Hy + Jz + K = 0.$$

---

When a quadric surface intersects a coordinate plane, the trace is a conic section.

An **ellipsoid** is a surface described by an equation of the form $\frac{x^2}{a^2} + \frac{y^2}{b^2} + \frac{z^2}{c^2} = 1$. Set $x = 0$ to see the trace of the ellipsoid in the $yz$-plane. To see the traces in the $y$- and $xz$-planes, set $z = 0$ and $y = 0$, respectively. Notice that, if $a = b$, the trace in the $xy$-plane is a circle. Similarly, if $a = c$, the trace in the $xz$-plane is a circle and, if $b = c$, then the trace in the $yz$-plane is a circle. A sphere, then, is an ellipsoid with $a = b = c$.

**Example 2.56**

## Sketching an Ellipsoid

Sketch the ellipsoid $\dfrac{x^2}{2^2} + \dfrac{y^2}{3^2} + \dfrac{z^2}{5^2} = 1$.

### Solution

Start by sketching the traces. To find the trace in the $xy$-plane, set $z = 0$: $\dfrac{x^2}{2^2} + \dfrac{y^2}{3^2} = 1$ (see **Figure 2.81**). To find the other traces, first set $y = 0$ and then set $x = 0$.

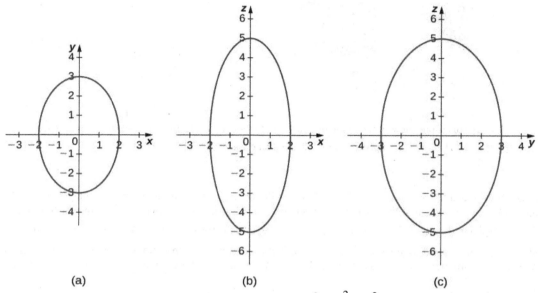

**Figure 2.81** (a) This graph represents the trace of equation $\dfrac{x^2}{2^2} + \dfrac{y^2}{3^2} + \dfrac{z^2}{5^2} = 1$ in the $xy$-plane, when we set $z = 0$. (b) When we set $y = 0$, we get the trace of the ellipsoid in the $xz$-plane, which is an ellipse. (c) When we set $x = 0$, we get the trace of the ellipsoid in the $yz$-plane, which is also an ellipse.

Now that we know what traces of this solid look like, we can sketch the surface in three dimensions (**Figure 2.82**).

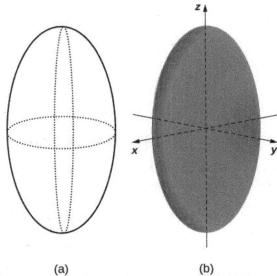

**(a)**                    **(b)**

Figure 2.82   (a) The traces provide a framework for the surface. (b) The center of this ellipsoid is the origin.

The trace of an ellipsoid is an ellipse in each of the coordinate planes. However, this does not have to be the case for all quadric surfaces. Many quadric surfaces have traces that are different kinds of conic sections, and this is usually indicated by the name of the surface. For example, if a surface can be described by an equation of the form $\frac{x^2}{a^2} + \frac{y^2}{b^2} = \frac{z}{c}$, then we call that surface an **elliptic paraboloid**. The trace in the $xy$-plane is an ellipse, but the traces in the $xz$-plane and $yz$-plane are parabolas (Figure 2.83). Other elliptic paraboloids can have other orientations simply by interchanging the variables to give us a different variable in the linear term of the equation $\frac{x^2}{a^2} + \frac{z^2}{c^2} = \frac{y}{b}$ or $\frac{y^2}{b^2} + \frac{z^2}{c^2} = \frac{x}{a}$.

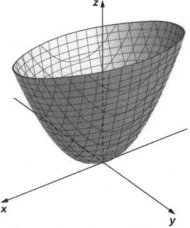

Figure 2.83   This quadric surface is called an *elliptic paraboloid.*

Example 2.57

**Identifying Traces of Quadric Surfaces**

Describe the traces of the elliptic paraboloid $x^2 + \dfrac{y^2}{2^2} = \dfrac{z}{5}$.

**Solution**

To find the trace in the $xy$-plane, set $z = 0$: $x^2 + \dfrac{y^2}{2^2} = 0$. The trace in the plane $z = 0$ is simply one point, the origin. Since a single point does not tell us what the shape is, we can move up the $z$-axis to an arbitrary plane to find the shape of other traces of the figure.

The trace in plane $z = 5$ is the graph of equation $x^2 + \dfrac{y^2}{2^2} = 1$, which is an ellipse. In the $xz$-plane, the equation becomes $z = 5x^2$. The trace is a parabola in this plane and in any plane with the equation $y = b$.

In planes parallel to the $yz$-plane, the traces are also parabolas, as we can see in the following figure.

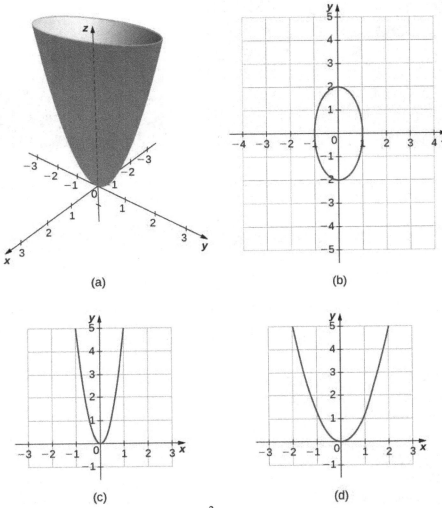

Figure 2.84  (a) The paraboloid $x^2 + \dfrac{y^2}{2^2} = \dfrac{z}{5}$. (b) The trace in plane $z = 5$. (c) The

trace in the $xz$-plane. (d) The trace in the $yz$-plane.

**2.53** A hyperboloid of one sheet is any surface that can be described with an equation of the form $\dfrac{x^2}{a^2} + \dfrac{y^2}{b^2} - \dfrac{z^2}{c^2} = 1$. Describe the traces of the hyperboloid of one sheet given by equation $\dfrac{x^2}{3^2} + \dfrac{y^2}{2^2} - \dfrac{z^2}{5^2} = 1$.

Hyperboloids of one sheet have some fascinating properties. For example, they can be constructed using straight lines, such as in the sculpture in **Figure 2.85**(a). In fact, cooling towers for nuclear power plants are often constructed in the shape of a hyperboloid. The builders are able to use straight steel beams in the construction, which makes the towers very strong while using relatively little material (**Figure 2.85**(b)).

Figure 2.85 (a) A sculpture in the shape of a hyperboloid can be constructed of straight lines. (b) Cooling towers for nuclear power plants are often built in the shape of a hyperboloid.

## Example 2.58

### Chapter Opener: Finding the Focus of a Parabolic Reflector

Energy hitting the surface of a parabolic reflector is concentrated at the focal point of the reflector (Figure 2.86). If the surface of a parabolic reflector is described by equation $\frac{x^2}{100} + \frac{y^2}{100} = \frac{z}{4},$ where is the focal point of the reflector?

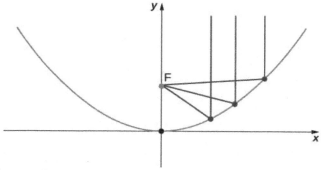

Figure 2.86 Energy reflects off of the parabolic reflector and is collected at the focal point. (credit: modification of CGP Grey, Wikimedia Commons)

### Solution

Since $z$ is the first-power variable, the axis of the reflector corresponds to the $z$-axis. The coefficients of $x^2$ and $y^2$ are equal, so the cross-section of the paraboloid perpendicular to the $z$-axis is a circle. We can consider a trace in the $xz$-plane or the $yz$-plane; the result is the same. Setting $y = 0,$ the trace is a parabola opening up along the $z$-axis, with standard equation $x^2 = 4pz,$ where $p$ is the focal length of the parabola. In this case, this equation becomes $x^2 = 100 \cdot \frac{z}{4} = 4pz$ or $25 = 4p.$ So $p$ is $6.25$ m, which tells us that the focus of the paraboloid is $6.25$ m up the axis from the vertex. Because the vertex of this surface is the origin, the focal point is $(0, 0, 6.25).$

Seventeen standard quadric surfaces can be derived from the general equation

$$Ax^2 + By^2 + Cz^2 + Dxy + Exz + Fyz + Gx + Hy + Jz + K = 0.$$

The following figures summarizes the most important ones.

### Characteristics of Common Quadric Surfaces

**Ellipsoid**

$$\frac{x^2}{a^2} + \frac{y^2}{b^2} + \frac{z^2}{c^2} = 1$$

*Traces*
In plane $z = p$: an ellipse
In plane $y = q$: an ellipse
In plane $x = r$: an ellipse

If $a = b = c$, then this surface is a sphere.

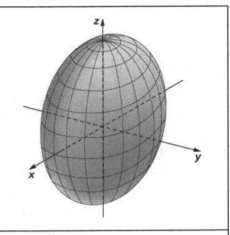

**Hyperboloid of One Sheet**

$$\frac{x^2}{a^2} + \frac{y^2}{b^2} - \frac{z^2}{c^2} = 1$$

*Traces*
In plane $z = p$: an ellipse
In plane $y = q$: a hyperbola
In plane $x = r$: a hyperbola

In the equation for this surface, two of the variables have positive coefficients and one has a negative coefficient. The axis of the surface corresponds to the variable with the negative coefficient.

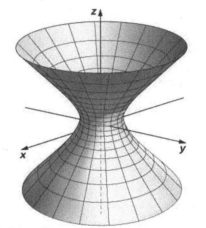

**Hyperboloid of Two Sheets**

$$\frac{z^2}{c^2} - \frac{x^2}{a^2} - \frac{y^2}{b^2} = 1$$

*Traces*
In plane $z = p$: an ellipse or the empty set (no trace)
In plane $y = q$: a hyperbola
In plane $x = r$: a hyperbola

In the equation for this surface, two of the variables have negative coefficients and one has a positive coefficient. The axis of the surface corresponds to the variable with a positive coefficient. The surface does not intersect the coordinate plane perpendicular to the axis.

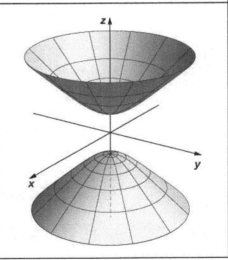

**Figure 2.87** Characteristics of Common Quadratic Surfaces: Ellipsoid, **Hyperboloid of One Sheet, Hyperboloid of Two Sheets**.

## Characteristics of Common Quadric Surfaces

### Elliptic Cone

$$\frac{x^2}{a^2} + \frac{y^2}{b^2} - \frac{z^2}{c^2} = 0$$

*Traces*
In plane $z = p$: an ellipse
In plane $y = q$: a hyperbola
In plane $x = r$: a hyperbola
In the $xz$ – plane: a pair of lines that intersect at the origin
In the $yz$ – plane: a pair of lines that intersect at the origin

The axis of the surface corresponds to the variable with a negative coefficient. The traces in the coordinate planes parallel to the axis are intersecting lines.

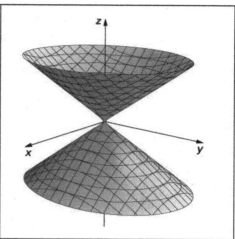

### Elliptic Paraboloid

$$z = \frac{x^2}{a^2} + \frac{y^2}{b^2}$$

*Traces*
In plane $z = p$: an ellipse
In plane $y = q$: a parabola
In plane $x = r$: a parabola

The axis of the surface corresponds to the linear variable.

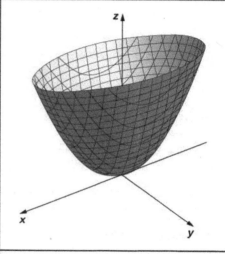

### Hyperbolic Paraboloid

$$z = \frac{x^2}{a^2} - \frac{y^2}{b^2}$$

*Traces*
In plane $z = p$: a hyperbola
In plane $y = q$: a parabola
In plane $x = r$: a parabola

The axis of the surface corresponds to the linear variable.

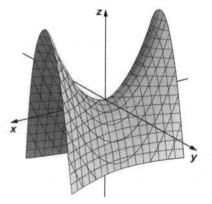

**Figure 2.88** Characteristics of Common Quadratic Surfaces: **Elliptic Cone**, **Elliptic Paraboloid**, Hyperbolic Paraboloid.

### Example 2.59

### Identifying Equations of Quadric Surfaces

Identify the surfaces represented by the given equations.

a. $16x^2 + 9y^2 + 16z^2 = 144$

b. $9x^2 - 18x + 4y^2 + 16y - 36z + 25 = 0$

**Solution**

a. The $x, y,$ and $z$ terms are all squared, and are all positive, so this is probably an ellipsoid. However, let's put the equation into the standard form for an ellipsoid just to be sure. We have

$$16x^2 + 9y^2 + 16z^2 = 144.$$

Dividing through by 144 gives

$$\frac{x^2}{9} + \frac{y^2}{16} + \frac{z^2}{9} = 1.$$

So, this is, in fact, an ellipsoid, centered at the origin.

b. We first notice that the $z$ term is raised only to the first power, so this is either an elliptic paraboloid or a hyperbolic paraboloid. We also note there are $x$ terms and $y$ terms that are not squared, so this quadric surface is not centered at the origin. We need to complete the square to put this equation in one of the standard forms. We have

$$
\begin{aligned}
9x^2 - 18x + 4y^2 + 16y - 36z + 25 &= 0 \\
9x^2 - 18x + 4y^2 + 16y + 25 &= 36z \\
9(x^2 - 2x) + 4(y^2 + 4y) + 25 &= 36z \\
9(x^2 - 2x + 1 - 1) + 4(y^2 + 4y + 4 - 4) + 25 &= 36z \\
9(x - 1)^2 - 9 + 4(y + 2)^2 - 16 + 25 &= 36z \\
9(x - 1)^2 + 4(y + 2)^2 &= 36z \\
\frac{(x - 1)^2}{4} + \frac{(y - 2)^2}{9} &= z.
\end{aligned}
$$

This is an elliptic paraboloid centered at $(1, 2, 0)$.

 **2.54** Identify the surface represented by equation $9x^2 + y^2 - z^2 + 2z - 10 = 0$.

# 2.6 EXERCISES

For the following exercises, sketch and describe the cylindrical surface of the given equation.

303. **[T]** $x^2 + z^2 = 1$

304. **[T]** $x^2 + y^2 = 9$

305. **[T]** $z = \cos\left(\frac{\pi}{2} + x\right)$

306. **[T]** $z = e^x$

307. **[T]** $z = 9 - y^2$

308. **[T]** $z = \ln(x)$

For the following exercises, the graph of a quadric surface is given.

   a. Specify the name of the quadric surface.

   b. Determine the axis of symmetry of the quadric surface.

309.

310.

311.

312.

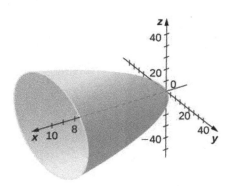

For the following exercises, match the given quadric surface with its corresponding equation in standard form.

   a. $\dfrac{x^2}{4} + \dfrac{y^2}{9} - \dfrac{z^2}{12} = 1$

b. $\dfrac{x^2}{4} - \dfrac{y^2}{9} - \dfrac{z^2}{12} = 1$

c. $\dfrac{x^2}{4} + \dfrac{y^2}{9} + \dfrac{z^2}{12} = 1$

d. $z^2 = 4x^2 + 3y^2$

e. $z = 4x^2 - y^2$

f. $4x^2 + y^2 - z^2 = 0$

313. Hyperboloid of two sheets

314. Ellipsoid

315. Elliptic paraboloid

316. Hyperbolic paraboloid

317. Hyperboloid of one sheet

318. Elliptic cone

For the following exercises, rewrite the given equation of the quadric surface in standard form. Identify the surface.

319. $-x^2 + 36y^2 + 36z^2 = 9$

320. $-4x^2 + 25y^2 + z^2 = 100$

321. $-3x^2 + 5y^2 - z^2 = 10$

322. $3x^2 - y^2 - 6z^2 = 18$

323. $5y = x^2 - z^2$

324. $8x^2 - 5y^2 - 10z = 0$

325. $x^2 + 5y^2 + 3z^2 - 15 = 0$

326. $63x^2 + 7y^2 + 9z^2 - 63 = 0$

327. $x^2 + 5y^2 - 8z^2 = 0$

328. $5x^2 - 4y^2 + 20z^2 = 0$

329. $6x = 3y^2 + 2z^2$

330. $49y = x^2 + 7z^2$

For the following exercises, find the trace of the given quadric surface in the specified plane of coordinates and sketch it.

331. **[T]** $x^2 + z^2 + 4y = 0,\ z = 0$

332. **[T]** $x^2 + z^2 + 4y = 0,\ x = 0$

333. **[T]** $-4x^2 + 25y^2 + z^2 = 100,\ x = 0$

334. **[T]** $-4x^2 + 25y^2 + z^2 = 100,\ y = 0$

335. **[T]** $x^2 + \dfrac{y^2}{4} + \dfrac{z^2}{100} = 1,\ x = 0$

336. **[T]** $x^2 - y - z^2 = 1,\ y = 0$

337. Use the graph of the given quadric surface to answer the questions.

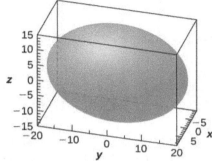

a. Specify the name of the quadric surface.
b. Which of the equations—$16x^2 + 9y^2 + 36z^2 = 3600,\ 9x^2 + 36y^2 + 16z^2 = 3600$, or $36x^2 + 9y^2 + 16z^2 = 3600$—corresponds to the graph?
c. Use b. to write the equation of the quadric surface in standard form.

338. Use the graph of the given quadric surface to answer the questions.

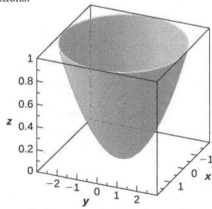

a. Specify the name of the quadric surface.
b. Which of the equations—$36z = 9x^2 + y^2,\ 9x^2 + 4y^2 = 36z$, or $-36z = -81x^2 + 4y^2$—corresponds to the graph above?
c. Use b. to write the equation of the quadric surface in standard form.

For the following exercises, the equation of a quadric surface is given.

    a.  Use the method of completing the square to write the equation in standard form.

    b.  Identify the surface.

339.  $x^2 + 2z^2 + 6x - 8z + 1 = 0$

340.  $4x^2 - y^2 + z^2 - 8x + 2y + 2z + 3 = 0$

341.  $x^2 + 4y^2 - 4z^2 - 6x - 16y - 16z + 5 = 0$

342.  $x^2 + z^2 - 4y + 4 = 0$

343.  $x^2 + \dfrac{y^2}{4} - \dfrac{z^2}{3} + 6x + 9 = 0$

344.  $x^2 - y^2 + z^2 - 12z + 2x + 37 = 0$

345.  Write the standard form of the equation of the ellipsoid centered at the origin that passes through points $A(2, 0, 0)$, $B(0, 0, 1)$,  and $C\left(\frac{1}{2}, \sqrt{11}, \frac{1}{2}\right)$.

346.  Write the standard form of the equation of the ellipsoid centered at point $P(1, 1, 0)$ that passes through points $A(6, 1, 0)$, $B(4, 2, 0)$ and $C(1, 2, 1)$.

347.  Determine the intersection points of elliptic cone $x^2 - y^2 - z^2 = 0$ with the line of symmetric equations $\dfrac{x-1}{2} = \dfrac{y+1}{3} = z$.

348.  Determine the intersection points of parabolic hyperboloid $z = 3x^2 - 2y^2$ with the line of parametric equations $x = 3t$, $y = 2t$, $z = 19t$,  where $t \in \mathbb{R}$.

349.  Find the equation of the quadric surface with points $P(x, y, z)$ that are equidistant from point $Q(0, -1, 0)$ and plane of equation $y = 1$. Identify the surface.

350.  Find the equation of the quadric surface with points $P(x, y, z)$ that are equidistant from point $Q(0, 2, 0)$ and plane of equation $y = -2$. Identify the surface.

351.  If the surface of a parabolic reflector is described by equation $400z = x^2 + y^2$,  find the focal point of the reflector.

352.  Consider the parabolic reflector described by equation $z = 20x^2 + 20y^2$. Find its focal point.

353.  Show that quadric surface $x^2 + y^2 + z^2 + 2xy + 2xz + 2yz + x + y + z = 0$ reduces to two parallel planes.

354.  Show that quadric surface $x^2 + y^2 + z^2 - 2xy - 2xz + 2yz - 1 = 0$ reduces to two parallel planes passing.

355.  **[T]** The intersection between cylinder $(x - 1)^2 + y^2 = 1$ and sphere $x^2 + y^2 + z^2 = 4$ is called a *Viviani curve*.

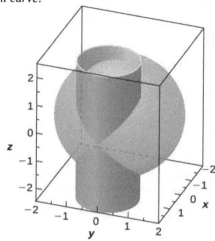

    a.  Solve the system consisting of the equations of the surfaces to find the equation of the intersection curve. (*Hint:* Find $x$ and $y$ in terms of $z$.)

    b.  Use a computer algebra system (CAS) to visualize the intersection curve on sphere $x^2 + y^2 + z^2 = 4$.

356.  Hyperboloid of one sheet $25x^2 + 25y^2 - z^2 = 25$ and elliptic cone $-25x^2 + 75y^2 + z^2 = 0$ are represented in the following figure along with their intersection curves. Identify the intersection curves and find their equations (*Hint:* Find $y$ from the system consisting of the equations of the surfaces.)

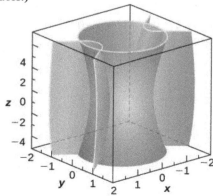

**357.** **[T]** Use a CAS to create the intersection between cylinder $9x^2 + 4y^2 = 18$ and ellipsoid $36x^2 + 16y^2 + 9z^2 = 144,$ and find the equations of the intersection curves.

**358.** **[T]** A spheroid is an ellipsoid with two equal semiaxes. For instance, the equation of a spheroid with the $z$-axis as its axis of symmetry is given by $\frac{x^2}{a^2} + \frac{y^2}{a^2} + \frac{z^2}{c^2} = 1,$ where $a$ and $c$ are positive real numbers. The spheroid is called *oblate* if $c < a,$ and *prolate* for $c > a.$

   a. The eye cornea is approximated as a prolate spheroid with an axis that is the eye, where $a = 8.7$ mm and $c = 9.6$ mm. Write the equation of the spheroid that models the cornea and sketch the surface.

   b. Give two examples of objects with prolate spheroid shapes.

**359.** **[T]** In cartography, Earth is approximated by an oblate spheroid rather than a sphere. The radii at the equator and poles are approximately 3963 mi and 3950 mi, respectively.

   a. Write the equation in standard form of the ellipsoid that represents the shape of Earth. Assume the center of Earth is at the origin and that the trace formed by plane $z = 0$ corresponds to the equator.

   b. Sketch the graph.

   c. Find the equation of the intersection curve of the surface with plane $z = 1000$ that is parallel to the $xy$-plane. The intersection curve is called a *parallel*.

   d. Find the equation of the intersection curve of the surface with plane $x + y = 0$ that passes through the $z$-axis. The intersection curve is called a *meridian*.

**360.** **[T]** A set of buzzing stunt magnets (or "rattlesnake eggs") includes two sparkling, polished, superstrong spheroid-shaped magnets well-known for children's entertainment. Each magnet is 1.625 in. long and 0.5 in. wide at the middle. While tossing them into the air, they create a buzzing sound as they attract each other.

   a. Write the equation of the prolate spheroid centered at the origin that describes the shape of one of the magnets.

   b. Write the equations of the prolate spheroids that model the shape of the buzzing stunt magnets. Use a CAS to create the graphs.

**361.** **[T]** A heart-shaped surface is given by equation $\left(x^2 + \frac{9}{4}y^2 + z^2 - 1\right)^3 - x^2 z^3 - \frac{9}{80}y^2 z^3 = 0.$

   a. Use a CAS to graph the surface that models this shape.

   b. Determine and sketch the trace of the heart-shaped surface on the $xz$-plane.

**362.** **[T]** The ring torus symmetric about the $z$-axis is a special type of surface in topology and its equation is given by $\left(x^2 + y^2 + z^2 + R^2 - r^2\right)^2 = 4R^2\left(x^2 + y^2\right),$ where $R > r > 0.$ The numbers $R$ and $r$ are called are the major and minor radii, respectively, of the surface. The following figure shows a ring torus for which $R = 2$ and $r = 1.$

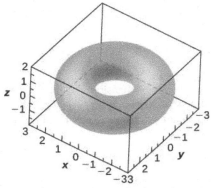

   a. Write the equation of the ring torus with $R = 2$ and $r = 1,$ and use a CAS to graph the surface. Compare the graph with the figure given.

   b. Determine the equation and sketch the trace of the ring torus from a. on the $xy$-plane.

   c. Give two examples of objects with ring torus shapes.

# 2.7 | Cylindrical and Spherical Coordinates

## Learning Objectives

2.7.1 Convert from cylindrical to rectangular coordinates.
2.7.2 Convert from rectangular to cylindrical coordinates.
2.7.3 Convert from spherical to rectangular coordinates.
2.7.4 Convert from rectangular to spherical coordinates.

The Cartesian coordinate system provides a straightforward way to describe the location of points in space. Some surfaces, however, can be difficult to model with equations based on the Cartesian system. This is a familiar problem; recall that in two dimensions, polar coordinates often provide a useful alternative system for describing the location of a point in the plane, particularly in cases involving circles. In this section, we look at two different ways of describing the location of points in space, both of them based on extensions of polar coordinates. As the name suggests, cylindrical coordinates are useful for dealing with problems involving cylinders, such as calculating the volume of a round water tank or the amount of oil flowing through a pipe. Similarly, spherical coordinates are useful for dealing with problems involving spheres, such as finding the volume of domed structures.

## Cylindrical Coordinates

When we expanded the traditional Cartesian coordinate system from two dimensions to three, we simply added a new axis to model the third dimension. Starting with polar coordinates, we can follow this same process to create a new three-dimensional coordinate system, called the cylindrical coordinate system. In this way, cylindrical coordinates provide a natural extension of polar coordinates to three dimensions.

### Definition

In the **cylindrical coordinate system**, a point in space (Figure 2.89) is represented by the ordered triple $(r, \theta, z)$, where

- $(r, \theta)$ are the polar coordinates of the point's projection in the $xy$-plane

- $z$ is the usual $z$-coordinate in the Cartesian coordinate system

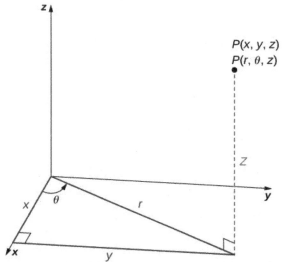

**Figure 2.89** The right triangle lies in the $xy$-plane. The length of the hypotenuse is $r$ and $\theta$ is the measure of the angle formed by the positive $x$-axis and the hypotenuse. The $z$-coordinate describes the location of the point above or below the $xy$-plane.

In the $xy$-plane, the right triangle shown in **Figure 2.89** provides the key to transformation between cylindrical and Cartesian, or rectangular, coordinates.

---

### Theorem 2.15: Conversion between Cylindrical and Cartesian Coordinates

The rectangular coordinates $(x, y, z)$ and the cylindrical coordinates $(r, \theta, z)$ of a point are related as follows:

$$
\begin{aligned}
x &= r\cos\theta \\
y &= r\sin\theta \\
z &= z
\end{aligned}
$$
These equations are used to convert from cylindrical coordinates to rectangular coordinates.

and

$$
\begin{aligned}
r^2 &= x^2 + y^2 \\
\tan\theta &= \frac{y}{x} \\
z &= z
\end{aligned}
$$
These equations are used to convert from rectangular coordinates to cylindrical coordinates.

---

As when we discussed conversion from rectangular coordinates to polar coordinates in two dimensions, it should be noted that the equation $\tan\theta = \frac{y}{x}$ has an infinite number of solutions. However, if we restrict $\theta$ to values between $0$ and $2\pi$, then we can find a unique solution based on the quadrant of the $xy$-plane in which original point $(x, y, z)$ is located. Note that if $x = 0$, then the value of $\theta$ is either $\frac{\pi}{2}$, $\frac{3\pi}{2}$, or $0$, depending on the value of $y$.

Notice that these equations are derived from properties of right triangles. To make this easy to see, consider point $P$ in the $xy$-plane with rectangular coordinates $(x, y, 0)$ and with cylindrical coordinates $(r, \theta, 0)$, as shown in the following figure.

**Figure 2.90** The Pythagorean theorem provides equation $r^2 = x^2 + y^2$. Right-triangle relationships tell us that $x = r\cos\theta$, $y = r\sin\theta$, and $\tan\theta = y/x$.

Let's consider the differences between rectangular and cylindrical coordinates by looking at the surfaces generated when each of the coordinates is held constant. If $c$ is a constant, then in rectangular coordinates, surfaces of the form $x = c$, $y = c$, or $z = c$ are all planes. Planes of these forms are parallel to the $yz$-plane, the $xz$-plane, and the $xy$-plane, respectively. When we convert to cylindrical coordinates, the $z$-coordinate does not change. Therefore, in cylindrical coordinates, surfaces of the form $z = c$ are planes parallel to the $xy$-plane. Now, let's think about surfaces of the form $r = c$. The points on these surfaces are at a fixed distance from the $z$-axis. In other words, these surfaces are vertical circular cylinders. Last, what about $\theta = c$? The points on a surface of the form $\theta = c$ are at a fixed angle from the $x$-axis, which gives us a half-plane that starts at the $z$-axis (**Figure 2.91** and **Figure 2.92**).

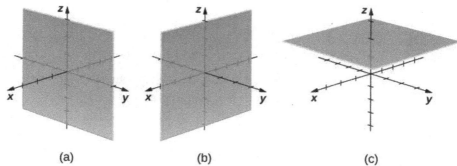

(a)   (b)   (c)

**Figure 2.91** In rectangular coordinates, (a) surfaces of the form $x = c$ are planes parallel to the $yz$-plane, (b) surfaces of the form $y = c$ are planes parallel to the $xz$-plane, and (c) surfaces of the form $z = c$ are planes parallel to the $xy$-plane.

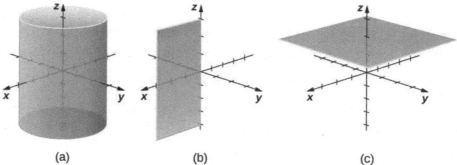

(a)   (b)   (c)

**Figure 2.92** In cylindrical coordinates, (a) surfaces of the form $r = c$ are vertical cylinders of radius $r$, (b) surfaces of the form $\theta = c$ are half-planes at angle $\theta$ from the $x$-axis, and (c) surfaces of the form $z = c$ are planes parallel to the $xy$-plane.

## Example 2.60

### Converting from Cylindrical to Rectangular Coordinates

Plot the point with cylindrical coordinates $\left(4, \frac{2\pi}{3}, -2\right)$ and express its location in rectangular coordinates.

### Solution

Conversion from cylindrical to rectangular coordinates requires a simple application of the equations listed in **Conversion between Cylindrical and Cartesian Coordinates**:

$$x = r\cos\theta = 4\cos\frac{2\pi}{3} = -2$$
$$y = r\sin\theta = 4\sin\frac{2\pi}{3} = 2\sqrt{3}$$
$$z = -2.$$

The point with cylindrical coordinates $\left(4, \frac{2\pi}{3}, -2\right)$ has rectangular coordinates $\left(-2, 2\sqrt{3}, -2\right)$ (see the following figure).

**Figure 2.93** The projection of the point in the *xy*-plane is 4 units from the origin. The line from the origin to the point's projection forms an angle of $\frac{2\pi}{3}$ with the positive *x*-axis. The point lies 2 units below the *xy*-plane.

 **2.55**   Point $R$ has cylindrical coordinates $\left(5, \frac{\pi}{6}, 4\right)$. Plot $R$ and describe its location in space using rectangular, or Cartesian, coordinates.

If this process seems familiar, it is with good reason. This is exactly the same process that we followed in **Introduction to Parametric Equations and Polar Coordinates** to convert from polar coordinates to two-dimensional rectangular coordinates.

## Example 2.61

## Converting from Rectangular to Cylindrical Coordinates

Convert the rectangular coordinates $(1, -3, 5)$ to cylindrical coordinates.

### Solution

Use the second set of equations from Conversion between Cylindrical and Cartesian Coordinates to translate from rectangular to cylindrical coordinates:

$$r^2 = x^2 + y^2$$
$$r = \pm\sqrt{1^2 + (-3)^2} = \pm\sqrt{10}.$$

We choose the positive square root, so $r = \sqrt{10}$. Now, we apply the formula to find $\theta$. In this case, $y$ is negative and $x$ is positive, which means we must select the value of $\theta$ between $\frac{3\pi}{2}$ and $2\pi$:

$$\tan \theta = \frac{y}{x} = \frac{-3}{1}$$
$$\theta = \arctan(-3) \approx 5.03 \text{ rad}.$$

In this case, the $z$-coordinates are the same in both rectangular and cylindrical coordinates:

$$z = 5.$$

The point with rectangular coordinates $(1, -3, 5)$ has cylindrical coordinates approximately equal to $(\sqrt{10}, 5.03, 5)$.

 **2.56** Convert point $(-8, 8, -7)$ from Cartesian coordinates to cylindrical coordinates.

The use of cylindrical coordinates is common in fields such as physics. Physicists studying electrical charges and the capacitors used to store these charges have discovered that these systems sometimes have a cylindrical symmetry. These systems have complicated modeling equations in the Cartesian coordinate system, which make them difficult to describe and analyze. The equations can often be expressed in more simple terms using cylindrical coordinates. For example, the cylinder described by equation $x^2 + y^2 = 25$ in the Cartesian system can be represented by cylindrical equation $r = 5$.

### Example 2.62

#### Identifying Surfaces in the Cylindrical Coordinate System

Describe the surfaces with the given cylindrical equations.

  a.  $\theta = \frac{\pi}{4}$

  b.  $r^2 + z^2 = 9$

  c.  $z = r$

### Solution

a.  When the angle $\theta$ is held constant while $r$ and $z$ are allowed to vary, the result is a half-plane (see the following figure).

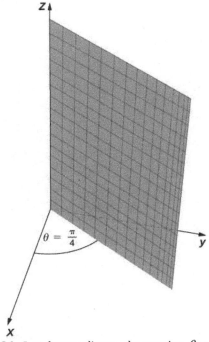

**Figure 2.94** In polar coordinates, the equation $\theta = \pi/4$ describes the ray extending diagonally through the first quadrant. In three dimensions, this same equation describes a half-plane.

b.  Substitute $r^2 = x^2 + y^2$ into equation $r^2 + z^2 = 9$ to express the rectangular form of the equation: $x^2 + y^2 + z^2 = 9$. This equation describes a sphere centered at the origin with radius 3 (see the following figure).

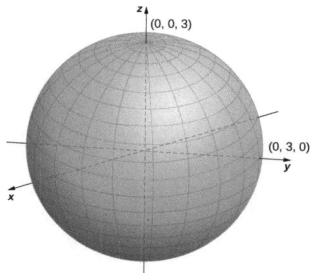

**Figure 2.95** The sphere centered at the origin with radius 3 can be described by the cylindrical equation $r^2 + z^2 = 9$.

c.  To describe the surface defined by equation $z = r$, is it useful to examine traces parallel to the $xy$-plane. For example, the trace in plane $z = 1$ is circle $r = 1$, the trace in plane $z = 3$ is circle $r = 3$, and so on. Each trace is a circle. As the value of $z$ increases, the radius of the circle also increases. The resulting surface is a cone (see the following figure).

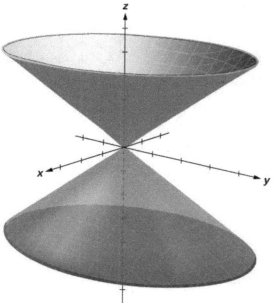

**Figure 2.96** The traces in planes parallel to the $xy$-plane are circles. The radius of the circles increases as $z$ increases.

**2.57** Describe the surface with cylindrical equation $r = 6$.

## Spherical Coordinates

In the Cartesian coordinate system, the location of a point in space is described using an ordered triple in which each coordinate represents a distance. In the cylindrical coordinate system, location of a point in space is described using two distances ($r$ and $z$) and an angle measure ($\theta$). In the spherical coordinate system, we again use an ordered triple to describe the location of a point in space. In this case, the triple describes one distance and two angles. Spherical coordinates make it simple to describe a sphere, just as cylindrical coordinates make it easy to describe a cylinder. Grid lines for spherical coordinates are based on angle measures, like those for polar coordinates.

---

**Definition**

In the **spherical coordinate system**, a point $P$ in space (**Figure 2.97**) is represented by the ordered triple ($\rho, \theta, \varphi$) where

- $\rho$ (the Greek letter rho) is the distance between $P$ and the origin ($\rho \neq 0$);

- $\theta$ is the same angle used to describe the location in cylindrical coordinates;

- $\varphi$ (the Greek letter phi) is the angle formed by the positive $z$-axis and line segment $\overline{OP}$, where $O$ is the origin and $0 \leq \varphi \leq \pi$.

---

**Figure 2.97** The relationship among spherical, rectangular, and cylindrical coordinates.

By convention, the origin is represented as $(0, 0, 0)$ in spherical coordinates.

---

**Theorem 2.16: Converting among Spherical, Cylindrical, and Rectangular Coordinates**

Rectangular coordinates $(x, y, z)$ and spherical coordinates $(\rho, \theta, \varphi)$ of a point are related as follows:

$$
\begin{aligned}
x &= \rho \sin \varphi \cos \theta \\
y &= \rho \sin \varphi \sin \theta \\
z &= \rho \cos \varphi
\end{aligned}
$$

These equations are used to convert from spherical coordinates to rectangular coordinates.

and

$$
\begin{aligned}
\rho^2 &= x^2 + y^2 + z^2 \\
\tan \theta &= \frac{y}{x}
\end{aligned}
$$

These equations are used to convert from rectangular coordinates to spherical

$$
\varphi = \arccos\left(\frac{z}{\sqrt{x^2 + y^2 + z^2}}\right).
$$

coordinates.

If a point has cylindrical coordinates $(r, \theta, z)$, then these equations define the relationship between cylindrical and spherical coordinates.

$$
\begin{aligned}
r &= \rho \sin \varphi \\
\theta &= \theta \\
z &= \rho \cos \varphi
\end{aligned}
$$

These equations are used to convert from spherical coordinates to cylindrical coordinates.

and

$$
\begin{aligned}
\rho &= \sqrt{r^2 + z^2} \\
\theta &= \theta
\end{aligned}
$$

These equations are used to convert from cylindrical coordinates to spherical

$$
\varphi = \arccos\left(\frac{z}{\sqrt{r^2 + z^2}}\right)
$$

coordinates.

The formulas to convert from spherical coordinates to rectangular coordinates may seem complex, but they are straightforward applications of trigonometry. Looking at **Figure 2.98**, it is easy to see that $r = \rho \sin \varphi$. Then, looking at the triangle in the $xy$-plane with $r$ as its hypotenuse, we have $x = r \cos \theta = \rho \sin \varphi \cos \theta$. The derivation of the formula for $y$ is similar. **Figure 2.96** also shows that $\rho^2 = r^2 + z^2 = x^2 + y^2 + z^2$ and $z = \rho \cos \varphi$. Solving this last equation for $\varphi$ and then substituting $\rho = \sqrt{r^2 + z^2}$ (from the first equation) yields $\varphi = \arccos\left(\frac{z}{\sqrt{r^2 + z^2}}\right)$. Also, note that, as before, we must be careful when using the formula $\tan \theta = \frac{y}{x}$ to choose the correct value of $\theta$.

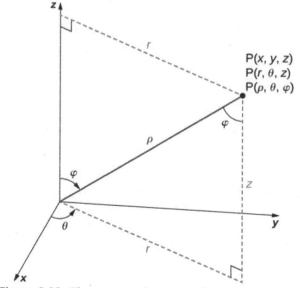

**Figure 2.98** The equations that convert from one system to another are derived from right-triangle relationships.

As we did with cylindrical coordinates, let's consider the surfaces that are generated when each of the coordinates is held constant. Let $c$ be a constant, and consider surfaces of the form $\rho = c$. Points on these surfaces are at a fixed distance from the origin and form a sphere. The coordinate $\theta$ in the spherical coordinate system is the same as in the cylindrical coordinate system, so surfaces of the form $\theta = c$ are half-planes, as before. Last, consider surfaces of the form $\varphi = 0$. The points on these surfaces are at a fixed angle from the $z$-axis and form a half-cone (**Figure 2.99**).

(a)                               (b)                               (c)

**Figure 2.99** In spherical coordinates, surfaces of the form $\rho = c$ are spheres of radius $\rho$ (a), surfaces of the form $\theta = c$ are half-planes at an angle $\theta$ from the $x$-axis (b), and surfaces of the form $\phi = c$ are half-cones at an angle $\phi$ from the $z$-axis (c).

## Example 2.63

### Converting from Spherical Coordinates

Plot the point with spherical coordinates $\left(8, \frac{\pi}{3}, \frac{\pi}{6}\right)$ and express its location in both rectangular and cylindrical coordinates.

### Solution

Use the equations in **Converting among Spherical, Cylindrical, and Rectangular Coordinates** to translate between spherical and cylindrical coordinates (**Figure 2.100**):

$$x = \rho \sin \varphi \cos \theta = 8 \sin\left(\frac{\pi}{6}\right)\cos\left(\frac{\pi}{3}\right) = 8\left(\frac{1}{2}\right)\frac{1}{2} = 2$$

$$y = \rho \sin \varphi \sin \theta = 8 \sin\left(\frac{\pi}{6}\right)\sin\left(\frac{\pi}{3}\right) = 8\left(\frac{1}{2}\right)\frac{\sqrt{3}}{2} = 2\sqrt{3}$$

$$z = \rho \cos \varphi = 8 \cos\left(\frac{\pi}{6}\right) = 8\left(\frac{\sqrt{3}}{2}\right) = 4\sqrt{3}.$$

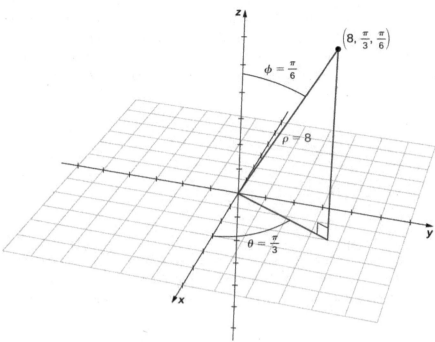

**Figure 2.100** The projection of the point in the $xy$-plane is $4$ units from the origin. The line from the origin to the point's projection forms an angle of $\pi/3$ with the positive $x$-axis. The point lies $4\sqrt{3}$ units above the $xy$-plane.

The point with spherical coordinates $\left(8, \frac{\pi}{3}, \frac{\pi}{6}\right)$ has rectangular coordinates $\left(2, 2\sqrt{3}, 4\sqrt{3}\right)$.

Finding the values in cylindrical coordinates is equally straightforward:

$$
\begin{aligned}
r &= \rho \sin \varphi = 8 \sin \frac{\pi}{6} = 4 \\
\theta &= \theta \\
z &= \rho \cos \varphi = 8 \cos \frac{\pi}{6} = 4\sqrt{3}.
\end{aligned}
$$

Thus, cylindrical coordinates for the point are $\left(4, \frac{\pi}{3}, 4\sqrt{3}\right)$.

 **2.58** Plot the point with spherical coordinates $\left(2, -\frac{5\pi}{6}, \frac{\pi}{6}\right)$ and describe its location in both rectangular and cylindrical coordinates.

## Example 2.64

### Converting from Rectangular Coordinates

Convert the rectangular coordinates $\left(-1, 1, \sqrt{6}\right)$ to both spherical and cylindrical coordinates.

## Solution

Start by converting from rectangular to spherical coordinates:

$$\rho^2 = x^2 + y^2 + z^2 = (-1)^2 + 1^2 + (\sqrt{6})^2 = 8 \qquad \tan\theta = \frac{1}{-1}$$

$$\rho = 2\sqrt{2} \qquad\qquad\qquad\qquad\qquad\qquad \theta = \arctan(-1) = \frac{3\pi}{4}.$$

Because $(x, y) = (-1, 1)$, then the correct choice for $\theta$ is $\frac{3\pi}{4}$.

There are actually two ways to identify $\varphi$. We can use the equation $\varphi = \arccos\left(\frac{z}{\sqrt{x^2 + y^2 + z^2}}\right)$. A more simple

approach, however, is to use equation $z = \rho\cos\varphi$. We know that $z = \sqrt{6}$ and $\rho = 2\sqrt{2}$, so

$$\sqrt{6} = 2\sqrt{2}\cos\varphi, \ \text{ so } \cos\varphi = \frac{\sqrt{6}}{2\sqrt{2}} = \frac{\sqrt{3}}{2}$$

and therefore $\varphi = \frac{\pi}{6}$. The spherical coordinates of the point are $\left(2\sqrt{2}, \frac{3\pi}{4}, \frac{\pi}{6}\right)$.

To find the cylindrical coordinates for the point, we need only find $r$:

$$r = \rho\sin\varphi = 2\sqrt{2}\sin\left(\frac{\pi}{6}\right) = \sqrt{2}.$$

The cylindrical coordinates for the point are $\left(\sqrt{2}, \frac{3\pi}{4}, \sqrt{6}\right)$.

## Example 2.65

### Identifying Surfaces in the Spherical Coordinate System

Describe the surfaces with the given spherical equations.

a. $\theta = \frac{\pi}{3}$

b. $\varphi = \frac{5\pi}{6}$

c. $\rho = 6$

d. $\rho = \sin\theta\sin\varphi$

## Solution

a. The variable $\theta$ represents the measure of the same angle in both the cylindrical and spherical coordinate systems. Points with coordinates $\left(\rho, \frac{\pi}{3}, \varphi\right)$ lie on the plane that forms angle $\theta = \frac{\pi}{3}$ with the positive $x$-axis. Because $\rho > 0$, the surface described by equation $\theta = \frac{\pi}{3}$ is the half-plane shown in **Figure 2.101**.

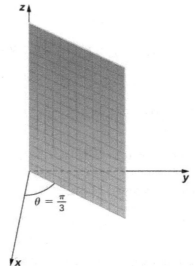

**Figure 2.101** The surface described by equation $\theta = \frac{\pi}{3}$ is a half-plane.

b.   Equation $\varphi = \frac{5\pi}{6}$ describes all points in the spherical coordinate system that lie on a line from the origin forming an angle measuring $\frac{5\pi}{6}$ rad with the positive $z$-axis. These points form a half-cone (**Figure 2.102**). Because there is only one value for $\varphi$ that is measured from the positive $z$-axis, we do not get the full cone (with two pieces).

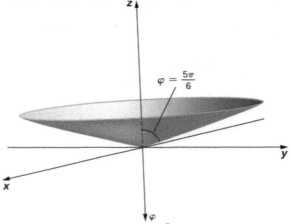

**Figure 2.102** The equation $\varphi = \frac{5\pi}{6}$ describes a cone.

To find the equation in rectangular coordinates, use equation $\varphi = \arccos\left(\dfrac{z}{\sqrt{x^2 + y^2 + z^2}}\right)$.

$$\frac{5\pi}{6} = \arccos\left(\frac{z}{\sqrt{x^2 + y^2 + z^2}}\right)$$

$$\cos\frac{5\pi}{6} = \frac{z}{\sqrt{x^2 + y^2 + z^2}}$$

$$-\frac{\sqrt{3}}{2} = \frac{z}{\sqrt{x^2 + y^2 + z^2}}$$

$$\frac{3}{4} = \frac{z^2}{x^2 + y^2 + z^2}$$

$$\frac{3x^2}{4} + \frac{3y^2}{4} + \frac{3z^2}{4} = z^2$$

$$\frac{3x^2}{4} + \frac{3y^2}{4} - \frac{z^2}{4} = 0.$$

This is the equation of a cone centered on the $z$-axis.

c.  Equation $\rho = 6$ describes the set of all points $6$ units away from the origin—a sphere with radius $6$ (**Figure 2.103**).

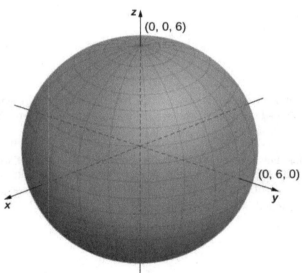

**Figure 2.103**  Equation $\rho = 6$ describes a sphere with radius 6.

d.  To identify this surface, convert the equation from spherical to rectangular coordinates, using equations $y = \rho \sin\varphi \sin\theta$ and $\rho^2 = x^2 + y^2 + z^2$:

$$\rho = \sin\theta \sin\varphi$$
$$\rho^2 = \rho\sin\theta\sin\varphi \qquad \text{Multiply both sides of the equation by } \rho.$$
$$x^2 + y^2 + z^2 = y \qquad \text{Substitute rectangular variables using the equations above.}$$
$$x^2 + y^2 - y + z^2 = 0 \qquad \text{Subtract } y \text{ from both sides of the equation.}$$
$$x^2 + y^2 - y + \tfrac{1}{4} + z^2 = \tfrac{1}{4} \qquad \text{Complete the square.}$$
$$x^2 + \left(y - \tfrac{1}{2}\right)^2 + z^2 = \tfrac{1}{4}. \qquad \text{Rewrite the middle terms as a perfect square.}$$

The equation describes a sphere centered at point $\left(0, \tfrac{1}{2}, 0\right)$ with radius $\tfrac{1}{2}$.

 **2.59** Describe the surfaces defined by the following equations.

    a.  $\rho = 13$

    b.  $\theta = \dfrac{2\pi}{3}$

    c.  $\varphi = \dfrac{\pi}{4}$

Spherical coordinates are useful in analyzing systems that have some degree of symmetry about a point, such as the volume of the space inside a domed stadium or wind speeds in a planet's atmosphere. A sphere that has Cartesian equation $x^2 + y^2 + z^2 = c^2$ has the simple equation $\rho = c$ in spherical coordinates.

In geography, latitude and longitude are used to describe locations on Earth's surface, as shown in **Figure 2.104**. Although the shape of Earth is not a perfect sphere, we use spherical coordinates to communicate the locations of points on Earth. Let's assume Earth has the shape of a sphere with radius 4000 mi. We express angle measures in degrees rather than radians because latitude and longitude are measured in degrees.

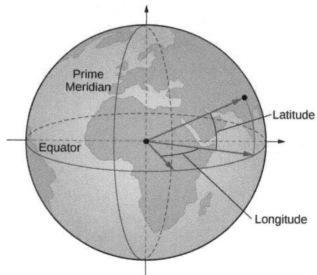

**Figure 2.104** In the latitude–longitude system, angles describe the location of a point on Earth relative to the equator and the prime meridian.

Let the center of Earth be the center of the sphere, with the ray from the center through the North Pole representing the positive *z*-axis. The prime meridian represents the trace of the surface as it intersects the *xz*-plane. The equator is the trace of the sphere intersecting the *xy*-plane.

### Example 2.66

#### Converting Latitude and Longitude to Spherical Coordinates

The latitude of Columbus, Ohio, is $40°$ N and the longitude is $83°$ W, which means that Columbus is $40°$ north of the equator. Imagine a ray from the center of Earth through Columbus and a ray from the center of Earth through the equator directly south of Columbus. The measure of the angle formed by the rays is $40°$. In the same way, measuring from the prime meridian, Columbus lies $83°$ to the west. Express the location of Columbus in spherical coordinates.

#### Solution

The radius of Earth is $4000$ mi, so $\rho = 4000$. The intersection of the prime meridian and the equator lies on the positive *x*-axis. Movement to the west is then described with negative angle measures, which shows that $\theta = -83°$, Because Columbus lies $40°$ north of the equator, it lies $50°$ south of the North Pole, so $\varphi = 50°$.

In spherical coordinates, Columbus lies at point $(4000, -83°, 50°)$.

 **2.60**  Sydney, Australia is at $34°$S and $151°$E. Express Sydney's location in spherical coordinates.

Cylindrical and spherical coordinates give us the flexibility to select a coordinate system appropriate to the problem at hand. A thoughtful choice of coordinate system can make a problem much easier to solve, whereas a poor choice can lead to unnecessarily complex calculations. In the following example, we examine several different problems and discuss how to select the best coordinate system for each one.

### Example 2.67

#### Choosing the Best Coordinate System

In each of the following situations, we determine which coordinate system is most appropriate and describe how we would orient the coordinate axes. There could be more than one right answer for how the axes should be oriented, but we select an orientation that makes sense in the context of the problem. *Note:* There is not enough information to set up or solve these problems; we simply select the coordinate system (**Figure 2.105**).

    a.   Find the center of gravity of a bowling ball.

    b.   Determine the velocity of a submarine subjected to an ocean current.

    c.   Calculate the pressure in a conical water tank.

    d.   Find the volume of oil flowing through a pipeline.

    e.   Determine the amount of leather required to make a football.

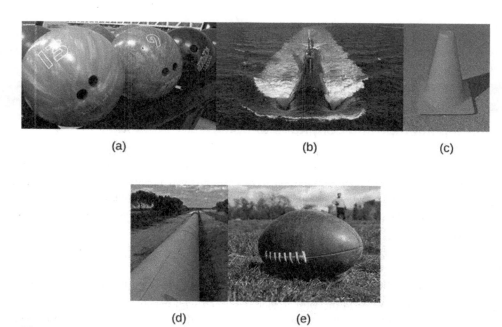

**Figure 2.105** (credit: (a) modification of work by scl hua, Wikimedia, (b) modification of work by DVIDSHUB, Flickr, (c) modification of work by Michael Malak, Wikimedia, (d) modification of work by Sean Mack, Wikimedia, (e) modification of work by Elvert Barnes, Flickr)

## Solution

a. Clearly, a bowling ball is a sphere, so spherical coordinates would probably work best here. The origin should be located at the physical center of the ball. There is no obvious choice for how the $x$-, $y$- and $z$-axes should be oriented. Bowling balls normally have a weight block in the center. One possible choice is to align the $z$-axis with the axis of symmetry of the weight block.

b. A submarine generally moves in a straight line. There is no rotational or spherical symmetry that applies in this situation, so rectangular coordinates are a good choice. The $z$-axis should probably point upward. The $x$- and $y$-axes could be aligned to point east and north, respectively. The origin should be some convenient physical location, such as the starting position of the submarine or the location of a particular port.

c. A cone has several kinds of symmetry. In cylindrical coordinates, a cone can be represented by equation $z = kr$, where $k$ is a constant. In spherical coordinates, we have seen that surfaces of the form $\varphi = c$ are half-cones. Last, in rectangular coordinates, elliptic cones are quadric surfaces and can be represented by equations of the form $z^2 = \dfrac{x^2}{a^2} + \dfrac{y^2}{b^2}$. In this case, we could choose any of the three. However, the equation for the surface is more complicated in rectangular coordinates than in the other two systems, so we might want to avoid that choice. In addition, we are talking about a water tank, and the depth of the water might come into play at some point in our calculations, so it might be nice to have a component that represents height and depth directly. Based on this reasoning, cylindrical coordinates might be the best choice. Choose the $z$-axis to align with the axis of the cone. The orientation of the other two axes is arbitrary. The origin should be the bottom point of the cone.

d. A pipeline is a cylinder, so cylindrical coordinates would be best the best choice. In this case, however, we would likely choose to orient our $z$-axis with the center axis of the pipeline. The $x$-axis could be chosen to point straight downward or to some other logical direction. The origin should be chosen based on the problem statement. Note that this puts the $z$-axis in a horizontal orientation, which is a little different from what we usually do. It may make sense to choose an unusual orientation for the axes if it makes sense for the problem.

e. A football has rotational symmetry about a central axis, so cylindrical coordinates would work best. The $z$-axis should align with the axis of the ball. The origin could be the center of the ball or perhaps one of the ends. The position of the $x$-axis is arbitrary.

 **2.61** Which coordinate system is most appropriate for creating a star map, as viewed from Earth (see the following figure)?

How should we orient the coordinate axes?

## 2.7 EXERCISES

Use the following figure as an aid in identifying the relationship between the rectangular, cylindrical, and spherical coordinate systems.

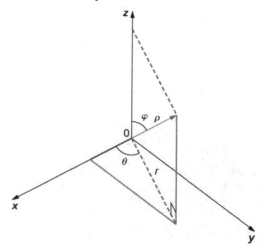

For the following exercises, the cylindrical coordinates $(r, \theta, z)$ of a point are given. Find the rectangular coordinates $(x, y, z)$ of the point.

363. $\left(4, \frac{\pi}{6}, 3\right)$

364. $\left(3, \frac{\pi}{3}, 5\right)$

365. $\left(4, \frac{7\pi}{6}, 3\right)$

366. $(2, \pi, -4)$

For the following exercises, the rectangular coordinates $(x, y, z)$ of a point are given. Find the cylindrical coordinates $(r, \theta, z)$ of the point.

367. $(1, \sqrt{3}, 2)$

368. $(1, 1, 5)$

369. $(3, -3, 7)$

370. $(-2\sqrt{2}, 2\sqrt{2}, 4)$

For the following exercises, the equation of a surface in cylindrical coordinates is given.

Find the equation of the surface in rectangular coordinates. Identify and graph the surface.

371. **[T]** $r = 4$

372. **[T]** $z = r^2 \cos^2 \theta$

373. **[T]** $r^2 \cos(2\theta) + z^2 + 1 = 0$

374. **[T]** $r = 3 \sin \theta$

375. **[T]** $r = 2 \cos \theta$

376. **[T]** $r^2 + z^2 = 5$

377. **[T]** $r = 2 \sec \theta$

378. **[T]** $r = 3 \csc \theta$

For the following exercises, the equation of a surface in rectangular coordinates is given. Find the equation of the surface in cylindrical coordinates.

379. $z = 3$

380. $x = 6$

381. $x^2 + y^2 + z^2 = 9$

382. $y = 2x^2$

383. $x^2 + y^2 - 16x = 0$

384. $x^2 + y^2 - 3\sqrt{x^2 + y^2} + 2 = 0$

For the following exercises, the spherical coordinates $(\rho, \theta, \varphi)$ of a point are given. Find the rectangular coordinates $(x, y, z)$ of the point.

385. $(3, 0, \pi)$

386. $\left(1, \frac{\pi}{6}, \frac{\pi}{6}\right)$

387. $\left(12, -\frac{\pi}{4}, \frac{\pi}{4}\right)$

388. $\left(3, \frac{\pi}{4}, \frac{\pi}{6}\right)$

For the following exercises, the rectangular coordinates $(x, y, z)$ of a point are given. Find the spherical coordinates $(\rho, \theta, \varphi)$ of the point. Express the measure of the angles in degrees rounded to the nearest integer.

389. $(4, 0, 0)$

390.  $(-1, 2, 1)$

391.  $(0, 3, 0)$

392.  $\left(-2, 2\sqrt{3}, 4\right)$

For the following exercises, the equation of a surface in spherical coordinates is given. Find the equation of the surface in rectangular coordinates. Identify and graph the surface.

393.  **[T]** $\rho = 3$

394.  **[T]** $\varphi = \frac{\pi}{3}$

395.  **[T]** $\rho = 2\cos\varphi$

396.  **[T]** $\rho = 4\csc\varphi$

397.  **[T]** $\varphi = \frac{\pi}{2}$

398.  **[T]** $\rho = 6\csc\varphi\sec\theta$

For the following exercises, the equation of a surface in rectangular coordinates is given. Find the equation of the surface in spherical coordinates. Identify the surface.

399.  $x^2 + y^2 - 3z^2 = 0, \quad z \neq 0$

400.  $x^2 + y^2 + z^2 - 4z = 0$

401.  $z = 6$

402.  $x^2 + y^2 = 9$

For the following exercises, the cylindrical coordinates of a point are given. Find its associated spherical coordinates, with the measure of the angle $\varphi$ in radians rounded to four decimal places.

403.  **[T]** $\left(1, \frac{\pi}{4}, 3\right)$

404.  **[T]** $(5, \pi, 12)$

405.  $\left(3, \frac{\pi}{2}, 3\right)$

406.  $\left(3, -\frac{\pi}{6}, 3\right)$

For the following exercises, the spherical coordinates of a point are given. Find its associated cylindrical coordinates.

407.  $\left(2, -\frac{\pi}{4}, \frac{\pi}{2}\right)$

408.  $\left(4, \frac{\pi}{4}, \frac{\pi}{6}\right)$

409.  $\left(8, \frac{\pi}{3}, \frac{\pi}{2}\right)$

410.  $\left(9, -\frac{\pi}{6}, \frac{\pi}{3}\right)$

For the following exercises, find the most suitable system of coordinates to describe the solids.

411.  The solid situated in the first octant with a vertex at the origin and enclosed by a cube of edge length $a$, where $a > 0$

412.  A spherical shell determined by the region between two concentric spheres centered at the origin, of radii of $a$ and $b$, respectively, where $b > a > 0$

413.  A solid inside sphere $x^2 + y^2 + z^2 = 9$ and outside cylinder $\left(x - \frac{3}{2}\right)^2 + y^2 = \frac{9}{4}$

414.  A cylindrical shell of height $10$ determined by the region between two cylinders with the same center, parallel rulings, and radii of $2$ and $5$, respectively

415.  **[T]** Use a CAS to graph in cylindrical coordinates the region between elliptic paraboloid $z = x^2 + y^2$ and cone $x^2 + y^2 - z^2 = 0$.

416.  **[T]** Use a CAS to graph in spherical coordinates the "ice cream-cone region" situated above the $xy$-plane between sphere $x^2 + y^2 + z^2 = 4$ and elliptical cone $x^2 + y^2 - z^2 = 0$.

417. Washington, DC, is located at $39°$ N and $77°$ W (see the following figure). Assume the radius of Earth is 4000 mi. Express the location of Washington, DC, in spherical coordinates.

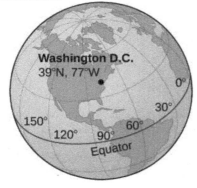

418. San Francisco is located at $37.78°N$ and $122.42°W$. Assume the radius of Earth is 4000 mi. Express the location of San Francisco in spherical coordinates.

419. Find the latitude and longitude of Rio de Janeiro if its spherical coordinates are $(4000, -43.17°, 102.91°)$.

420. Find the latitude and longitude of Berlin if its spherical coordinates are $(4000, 13.38°, 37.48°)$.

421. **[T]** Consider the torus of equation $\left(x^2 + y^2 + z^2 + R^2 - r^2\right)^2 = 4R^2\left(x^2 + y^2\right),$ where $R \geq r > 0.$

    a. Write the equation of the torus in spherical coordinates.

    b. If $R = r,$ the surface is called a *horn torus*. Show that the equation of a horn torus in spherical coordinates is $\rho = 2R \sin \varphi.$

    c. Use a CAS to graph the horn torus with $R = r = 2$ in spherical coordinates.

422. **[T]** The "bumpy sphere" with an equation in spherical coordinates is $\rho = a + b \cos(m\theta)\sin(n\varphi),$ with $\theta \in [0, 2\pi]$ and $\varphi \in [0, \pi],$ where $a$ and $b$ are positive numbers and $m$ and $n$ are positive integers, may be used in applied mathematics to model tumor growth.

    a. Show that the "bumpy sphere" is contained inside a sphere of equation $\rho = a + b.$ Find the values of $\theta$ and $\varphi$ at which the two surfaces intersect.

    b. Use a CAS to graph the surface for $a = 14,$ $b = 2,$ $m = 4,$ and $n = 6$ along with sphere $\rho = a + b.$

    c. Find the equation of the intersection curve of the surface at b. with the cone $\varphi = \frac{\pi}{12}.$ Graph the intersection curve in the plane of intersection.

# CHAPTER 2 REVIEW

## KEY TERMS

**component** a scalar that describes either the vertical or horizontal direction of a vector

**coordinate plane** a plane containing two of the three coordinate axes in the three-dimensional coordinate system, named by the axes it contains: the $xy$-plane, $xz$-plane, or the $yz$-plane

**cross product** $\mathbf{u} \times \mathbf{v} = (u_2 v_3 - u_3 v_2)\mathbf{i} - (u_1 v_3 - u_3 v_1)\mathbf{j} + (u_1 v_2 - u_2 v_1)\mathbf{k}$, where $\mathbf{u} = \langle u_1, u_2, u_3 \rangle$ and $\mathbf{v} = \langle v_1, v_2, v_3 \rangle$

**cylinder** a set of lines parallel to a given line passing through a given curve

**cylindrical coordinate system** a way to describe a location in space with an ordered triple $(r, \theta, z)$, where $(r, \theta)$ represents the polar coordinates of the point's projection in the $xy$-plane, and $z$ represents the point's projection onto the $z$-axis

**determinant** a real number associated with a square matrix

**direction angles** the angles formed by a nonzero vector and the coordinate axes

**direction cosines** the cosines of the angles formed by a nonzero vector and the coordinate axes

**direction vector** a vector parallel to a line that is used to describe the direction, or orientation, of the line in space

**dot product or scalar product** $\mathbf{u} \cdot \mathbf{v} = u_1 v_1 + u_2 v_2 + u_3 v_3$ where $\mathbf{u} = \langle u_1, u_2, u_3 \rangle$ and $\mathbf{v} = \langle v_1, v_2, v_3 \rangle$

**ellipsoid** a three-dimensional surface described by an equation of the form $\frac{x^2}{a^2} + \frac{y^2}{b^2} + \frac{z^2}{c^2} = 1$; all traces of this surface are ellipses

**elliptic cone** a three-dimensional surface described by an equation of the form $\frac{x^2}{a^2} + \frac{y^2}{b^2} - \frac{z^2}{c^2} = 0$; traces of this surface include ellipses and intersecting lines

**elliptic paraboloid** a three-dimensional surface described by an equation of the form $z = \frac{x^2}{a^2} + \frac{y^2}{b^2}$; traces of this surface include ellipses and parabolas

**equivalent vectors** vectors that have the same magnitude and the same direction

**general form of the equation of a plane** an equation in the form $ax + by + cz + d = 0$, where $\mathbf{n} = \langle a, b, c \rangle$ is a normal vector of the plane, $P = (x_0, y_0, z_0)$ is a point on the plane, and $d = -ax_0 - by_0 - cz_0$

**hyperboloid of one sheet** a three-dimensional surface described by an equation of the form $\frac{x^2}{a^2} + \frac{y^2}{b^2} - \frac{z^2}{c^2} = 1$; traces of this surface include ellipses and hyperbolas

**hyperboloid of two sheets** a three-dimensional surface described by an equation of the form $\frac{z^2}{c^2} - \frac{x^2}{a^2} - \frac{y^2}{b^2} = 1$; traces of this surface include ellipses and hyperbolas

**initial point** the starting point of a vector

**magnitude** the length of a vector

**normal vector** a vector perpendicular to a plane

**normalization** using scalar multiplication to find a unit vector with a given direction

**octants** the eight regions of space created by the coordinate planes

**orthogonal vectors** vectors that form a right angle when placed in standard position

**parallelepiped** a three-dimensional prism with six faces that are parallelograms

**parallelogram method** a method for finding the sum of two vectors; position the vectors so they share the same initial point; the vectors then form two adjacent sides of a parallelogram; the sum of the vectors is the diagonal of that parallelogram

**parametric equations of a line** the set of equations $x = x_0 + ta$, $y = y_0 + tb$, and $z = z_0 + tc$ describing the line with direction vector $\mathbf{v} = \langle a, b, c \rangle$ passing through point $(x_0, y_0, z_0)$

**quadric surfaces** surfaces in three dimensions having the property that the traces of the surface are conic sections (ellipses, hyperbolas, and parabolas)

**right-hand rule** a common way to define the orientation of the three-dimensional coordinate system; when the right hand is curved around the $z$-axis in such a way that the fingers curl from the positive $x$-axis to the positive $y$-axis, the thumb points in the direction of the positive $z$-axis

**rulings** parallel lines that make up a cylindrical surface

**scalar** a real number

**scalar equation of a plane** the equation $a(x - x_0) + b(y - y_0) + c(z - z_0) = 0$ used to describe a plane containing point $P = (x_0, y_0, z_0)$ with normal vector $\mathbf{n} = \langle a, b, c \rangle$ or its alternate form $ax + by + cz + d = 0$, where $d = -ax_0 - by_0 - cz_0$

**scalar multiplication** a vector operation that defines the product of a scalar and a vector

**scalar projection** the magnitude of the vector projection of a vector

**skew lines** two lines that are not parallel but do not intersect

**sphere** the set of all points equidistant from a given point known as the *center*

**spherical coordinate system** a way to describe a location in space with an ordered triple $(\rho, \theta, \varphi)$, where $\rho$ is the distance between $P$ and the origin $(\rho \neq 0)$, $\theta$ is the same angle used to describe the location in cylindrical coordinates, and $\varphi$ is the angle formed by the positive $z$-axis and line segment $\overline{OP}$, where $O$ is the origin and $0 \le \varphi \le \pi$

**standard equation of a sphere** $(x - a)^2 + (y - b)^2 + (z - c)^2 = r^2$ describes a sphere with center $(a, b, c)$ and radius $r$

**standard unit vectors** unit vectors along the coordinate axes: $\mathbf{i} = \langle 1, 0 \rangle$, $\mathbf{j} = \langle 0, 1 \rangle$

**standard-position vector** a vector with initial point $(0, 0)$

**symmetric equations of a line** the equations $\frac{x - x_0}{a} = \frac{y - y_0}{b} = \frac{z - z_0}{c}$ describing the line with direction vector $\mathbf{v} = \langle a, b, c \rangle$ passing through point $(x_0, y_0, z_0)$

**terminal point** the endpoint of a vector

**three-dimensional rectangular coordinate system** a coordinate system defined by three lines that intersect at right angles; every point in space is described by an ordered triple $(x, y, z)$ that plots its location relative to the defining axes

**torque** the effect of a force that causes an object to rotate

**trace** the intersection of a three-dimensional surface with a coordinate plane

**triangle inequality** the length of any side of a triangle is less than the sum of the lengths of the other two sides

**triangle method** a method for finding the sum of two vectors; position the vectors so the terminal point of one vector is the initial point of the other; these vectors then form two sides of a triangle; the sum of the vectors is the vector that forms the third side; the initial point of the sum is the initial point of the first vector; the terminal point of the sum is the terminal point of the second vector

**triple scalar product** the dot product of a vector with the cross product of two other vectors: $\mathbf{u} \cdot (\mathbf{v} \times \mathbf{w})$

**unit vector** a vector with margnitude 1

**vector** a mathematical object that has both magnitude and direction

**vector addition** a vector operation that defines the sum of two vectors

**vector difference** the vector difference $\mathbf{v} - \mathbf{w}$ is defined as $\mathbf{v} + (-\mathbf{w}) = \mathbf{v} + (-1)\mathbf{w}$

**vector equation of a line** the equation $\mathbf{r} = \mathbf{r}_0 + t\mathbf{v}$ used to describe a line with direction vector $\mathbf{v} = \langle a, b, c \rangle$ passing through point $P = (x_0, y_0, z_0)$, where $\mathbf{r}_0 = \langle x_0, y_0, z_0 \rangle$, is the position vector of point $P$

**vector equation of a plane** the equation $\mathbf{n} \cdot \vec{PQ} = 0$, where $P$ is a given point in the plane, $Q$ is any point in the plane, and $\mathbf{n}$ is a normal vector of the plane

**vector product** the cross product of two vectors

**vector projection** the component of a vector that follows a given direction

**vector sum** the sum of two vectors, $\mathbf{v}$ and $\mathbf{w}$, can be constructed graphically by placing the initial point of $\mathbf{w}$ at the terminal point of $\mathbf{v}$; then the vector sum $\mathbf{v} + \mathbf{w}$ is the vector with an initial point that coincides with the initial point of $\mathbf{v}$, and with a terminal point that coincides with the terminal point of $\mathbf{w}$

**work done by a force** work is generally thought of as the amount of energy it takes to move an object; if we represent an applied force by a vector $\mathbf{F}$ and the displacement of an object by a vector $\mathbf{s}$, then the work done by the force is the dot product of $\mathbf{F}$ and $\mathbf{s}$.

**zero vector** the vector with both initial point and terminal point $(0, 0)$

## KEY EQUATIONS

- **Distance between two points in space:**
$$d = \sqrt{(x_2 - x_1)^2 + (y_2 - y_1)^2 + (z_2 - z_1)^2}$$

- **Sphere with center $(a, b, c)$ and radius $r$:**
$$(x - a)^2 + (y - b)^2 + (z - c)^2 = r^2$$

- **Dot product of u and v**
$$\mathbf{u} \cdot \mathbf{v} = u_1 v_1 + u_2 v_2 + u_3 v_3$$
$$= \|\mathbf{u}\| \ \|\mathbf{v}\| \cos \theta$$

- **Cosine of the angle formed by u and v**
$$\cos \theta = \frac{\mathbf{u} \cdot \mathbf{v}}{\|\mathbf{u}\| \ \|\mathbf{v}\|}$$

- **Vector projection of v onto u**
$$\text{proj}_{\mathbf{u}} \mathbf{v} = \frac{\mathbf{u} \cdot \mathbf{v}}{\|\mathbf{u}\|^2} \mathbf{u}$$

- **Scalar projection of v onto u**
$$\text{comp}_{\mathbf{u}} \mathbf{v} = \frac{\mathbf{u} \cdot \mathbf{v}}{\|\mathbf{u}\|}$$

- **Work done by a force F to move an object through displacement vector $\vec{PQ}$**
$$W = \mathbf{F} \cdot \vec{PQ} = \|\mathbf{F}\| \ \|\vec{PQ}\| \cos \theta$$

- **The cross product of two vectors in terms of the unit vectors**

$$\mathbf{u} \times \mathbf{v} = (u_2 v_3 - u_3 v_2)\mathbf{i} - (u_1 v_3 - u_3 v_1)\mathbf{j} + (u_1 v_2 - u_2 v_1)\mathbf{k}$$

- **Vector Equation of a Line**
  $$\mathbf{r} = \mathbf{r}_0 + t\mathbf{v}$$

- **Parametric Equations of a Line**
  $$x = x_0 + ta, \quad y = y_0 + tb, \quad \text{and} \quad z = z_0 + tc$$

- **Symmetric Equations of a Line**
  $$\frac{x - x_0}{a} = \frac{y - y_0}{b} = \frac{z - z_0}{c}$$

- **Vector Equation of a Plane**
  $$\mathbf{n} \cdot \vec{PQ} = 0$$

- **Scalar Equation of a Plane**
  $$a(x - x_0) + b(y - y_0) + c(z - z_0) = 0$$

- **Distance between a Plane and a Point**
  $$d = \| \operatorname{proj}_{\mathbf{n}} \vec{QP} \| = \left| \operatorname{comp}_{\mathbf{n}} \vec{QP} \right| = \frac{\left| \vec{QP} \cdot \mathbf{n} \right|}{\| \mathbf{n} \|}$$

# KEY CONCEPTS

## 2.1 Vectors in the Plane

- Vectors are used to represent quantities that have both magnitude and direction.

- We can add vectors by using the parallelogram method or the triangle method to find the sum. We can multiply a vector by a scalar to change its length or give it the opposite direction.

- Subtraction of vectors is defined in terms of adding the negative of the vector.

- A vector is written in component form as $\mathbf{v} = \langle x, y \rangle$.

- The magnitude of a vector is a scalar: $\| \mathbf{v} \| = \sqrt{x^2 + y^2}$.

- A unit vector $\mathbf{u}$ has magnitude $1$ and can be found by dividing a vector by its magnitude: $\mathbf{u} = \frac{1}{\| \mathbf{v} \|}\mathbf{v}$. The standard unit vectors are $\mathbf{i} = \langle 1, 0 \rangle$ and $\mathbf{j} = \langle 0, 1 \rangle$. A vector $\mathbf{v} = \langle x, y \rangle$ can be expressed in terms of the standard unit vectors as $\mathbf{v} = x\mathbf{i} + y\mathbf{j}$.

- Vectors are often used in physics and engineering to represent forces and velocities, among other quantities.

## 2.2 Vectors in Three Dimensions

- The three-dimensional coordinate system is built around a set of three axes that intersect at right angles at a single point, the origin. Ordered triples $(x, y, z)$ are used to describe the location of a point in space.

- The distance $d$ between points $(x_1, y_1, z_1)$ and $(x_2, y_2, z_2)$ is given by the formula
  $$d = \sqrt{(x_2 - x_1)^2 + (y_2 - y_1)^2 + (z_2 - z_1)^2}.$$

- In three dimensions, the equations $x = a$, $y = b$, and $z = c$ describe planes that are parallel to the coordinate planes.

- The standard equation of a sphere with center $(a, b, c)$ and radius $r$ is
  $$(x - a)^2 + (y - b)^2 + (z - c)^2 = r^2.$$

- In three dimensions, as in two, vectors are commonly expressed in component form, $\mathbf{v} = \langle x, y, z \rangle$, or in terms of the standard unit vectors, $x\mathbf{i} + y\mathbf{j} + z\mathbf{k}$.

- Properties of vectors in space are a natural extension of the properties for vectors in a plane. Let $\mathbf{v} = \langle x_1, y_1, z_1 \rangle$ and $\mathbf{w} = \langle x_2, y_2, z_2 \rangle$ be vectors, and let $k$ be a scalar.

  - **Scalar multiplication:** $k\mathbf{v} = \langle kx_1, ky_1, kz_1 \rangle$

  - **Vector addition:** $\mathbf{v} + \mathbf{w} = \langle x_1, y_1, z_1 \rangle + \langle x_2, y_2, z_2 \rangle = \langle x_1 + x_2, y_1 + y_2, z_1 + z_2 \rangle$

  - **Vector subtraction:** $\mathbf{v} - \mathbf{w} = \langle x_1, y_1, z_1 \rangle - \langle x_2, y_2, z_2 \rangle = \langle x_1 - x_2, y_1 - y_2, z_1 - z_2 \rangle$

  - **Vector magnitude:** $\| \mathbf{v} \| = \sqrt{x_1^2 + y_1^2 + z_1^2}$

  - **Unit vector in the direction of v:** $\dfrac{\mathbf{v}}{\| \mathbf{v} \|} = \dfrac{1}{\| \mathbf{v} \|} \langle x_1, y_1, z_1 \rangle = \langle \dfrac{x_1}{\| \mathbf{v} \|}, \dfrac{y_1}{\| \mathbf{v} \|}, \dfrac{z_1}{\| \mathbf{v} \|} \rangle$, $\mathbf{v} \neq \mathbf{0}$

## 2.3 The Dot Product

- The dot product, or scalar product, of two vectors $\mathbf{u} = \langle u_1, u_2, u_3 \rangle$ and $\mathbf{v} = \langle v_1, v_2, v_3 \rangle$ is $\mathbf{u} \cdot \mathbf{v} = u_1 v_1 + u_2 v_2 + u_3 v_3$.

- The dot product satisfies the following properties:

  - $\mathbf{u} \cdot \mathbf{v} = \mathbf{v} \cdot \mathbf{u}$

  - $\mathbf{u} \cdot (\mathbf{v} + \mathbf{w}) = \mathbf{u} \cdot \mathbf{v} + \mathbf{u} \cdot \mathbf{w}$

  - $c(\mathbf{u} \cdot \mathbf{v}) = (c\mathbf{u}) \cdot \mathbf{v} = \mathbf{u} \cdot (c\mathbf{v})$

  - $\mathbf{v} \cdot \mathbf{v} = \| \mathbf{v} \|^2$

- The dot product of two vectors can be expressed, alternatively, as $\mathbf{u} \cdot \mathbf{v} = \| \mathbf{u} \| \, \| \mathbf{v} \| \cos \theta$. This form of the dot product is useful for finding the measure of the angle formed by two vectors.

- Vectors $\mathbf{u}$ and $\mathbf{v}$ are orthogonal if $\mathbf{u} \cdot \mathbf{v} = 0$.

- The angles formed by a nonzero vector and the coordinate axes are called the *direction angles* for the vector. The cosines of these angles are known as the *direction cosines*.

- The vector projection of $\mathbf{v}$ onto $\mathbf{u}$ is the vector $\operatorname{proj}_\mathbf{u} \mathbf{v} = \dfrac{\mathbf{u} \cdot \mathbf{v}}{\| \mathbf{u} \|^2} \mathbf{u}$. The magnitude of this vector is known as the *scalar projection* of $\mathbf{v}$ onto $\mathbf{u}$, given by $\operatorname{comp}_\mathbf{u} \mathbf{v} = \dfrac{\mathbf{u} \cdot \mathbf{v}}{\| \mathbf{u} \|}$.

- Work is done when a force is applied to an object, causing displacement. When the force is represented by the vector $\mathbf{F}$ and the displacement is represented by the vector $\mathbf{s}$, then the work done $W$ is given by the formula $W \doteq \mathbf{F} \cdot s = \| \mathbf{F} \| \, \| \mathbf{s} \| \cos \theta$.

## 2.4 The Cross Product

- The cross product $\mathbf{u} \times \mathbf{v}$ of two vectors $\mathbf{u} = \langle u_1, u_2, u_3 \rangle$ and $\mathbf{v} = \langle v_1, v_2, v_3 \rangle$ is a vector orthogonal to both $\mathbf{u}$ and $\mathbf{v}$. Its length is given by $\| \mathbf{u} \times \mathbf{v} \| = \| \mathbf{u} \| \cdot \| \mathbf{v} \| \cdot \sin \theta$, where $\theta$ is the angle between $\mathbf{u}$ and $\mathbf{v}$. Its direction is given by the right-hand rule.

- The algebraic formula for calculating the cross product of two vectors, $\mathbf{u} = \langle u_1, u_2, u_3 \rangle$ and $\mathbf{v} = \langle v_1, v_2, v_3 \rangle$, is $\mathbf{u} \times \mathbf{v} = (u_2 v_3 - u_3 v_2)\mathbf{i} - (u_1 v_3 - u_3 v_1)\mathbf{j} + (u_1 v_2 - u_2 v_1)\mathbf{k}$.

- The cross product satisfies the following properties for vectors $\mathbf{u}$, $\mathbf{v}$, and $\mathbf{w}$, and scalar $c$:

    ◦ $\mathbf{u} \times \mathbf{v} = -(\mathbf{v} \times \mathbf{u})$

    ◦ $\mathbf{u} \times (\mathbf{v} + \mathbf{w}) = \mathbf{u} \times \mathbf{v} + \mathbf{u} \times \mathbf{w}$

    ◦ $c(\mathbf{u} \times \mathbf{v}) = (c\mathbf{u}) \times \mathbf{v} = \mathbf{u} \times (c\mathbf{v})$

    ◦ $\mathbf{u} \times \mathbf{0} = \mathbf{0} \times \mathbf{u} = \mathbf{0}$

    ◦ $\mathbf{v} \times \mathbf{v} = \mathbf{0}$

    ◦ $\mathbf{u} \cdot (\mathbf{v} \times \mathbf{w}) = (\mathbf{u} \times \mathbf{v}) \cdot \mathbf{w}$

- The cross product of vectors $\mathbf{u} = \langle u_1, u_2, u_3 \rangle$ and $\mathbf{v} = \langle v_1, v_2, v_3 \rangle$ is the determinant $\begin{vmatrix} \mathbf{i} & \mathbf{j} & \mathbf{k} \\ u_1 & u_2 & u_3 \\ v_1 & v_2 & v_3 \end{vmatrix}$.

- If vectors $\mathbf{u}$ and $\mathbf{v}$ form adjacent sides of a parallelogram, then the area of the parallelogram is given by $\| \mathbf{u} \times \mathbf{v} \|$.

- The triple scalar product of vectors $\mathbf{u}$, $\mathbf{v}$, and $\mathbf{w}$ is $\mathbf{u} \cdot (\mathbf{v} \times \mathbf{w})$.

- The volume of a parallelepiped with adjacent edges given by vectors $\mathbf{u}$, $\mathbf{v}$, and $\mathbf{w}$ is $V = |\mathbf{u} \cdot (\mathbf{v} \times \mathbf{w})|$.

- If the triple scalar product of vectors $\mathbf{u}$, $\mathbf{v}$, and $\mathbf{w}$ is zero, then the vectors are coplanar. The converse is also true: If the vectors are coplanar, then their triple scalar product is zero.

- The cross product can be used to identify a vector orthogonal to two given vectors or to a plane.

- Torque $\tau$ measures the tendency of a force to produce rotation about an axis of rotation. If force $\mathbf{F}$ is acting at a distance $\mathbf{r}$ from the axis, then torque is equal to the cross product of $\mathbf{r}$ and $\mathbf{F}$: $\tau = \mathbf{r} \times \mathbf{F}$.

## 2.5 Equations of Lines and Planes in Space

- In three dimensions, the direction of a line is described by a direction vector. The vector equation of a line with direction vector $\mathbf{v} = \langle a, b, c \rangle$ passing through point $P = (x_0, y_0, z_0)$ is $\mathbf{r} = \mathbf{r}_0 + t\mathbf{v}$, where $\mathbf{r}_0 = \langle x_0, y_0, z_0 \rangle$ is the position vector of point $P$. This equation can be rewritten to form the parametric equations of the line: $x = x_0 + ta$, $y = y_0 + tb$, and $z = z_0 + tc$. The line can also be described with the symmetric equations $\frac{x - x_0}{a} = \frac{y - y_0}{b} = \frac{z - z_0}{c}$.

- Let $L$ be a line in space passing through point $P$ with direction vector $\mathbf{v}$. If $Q$ is any point not on $L$, then the distance from $Q$ to $L$ is $d = \frac{\| \overrightarrow{PQ} \times \mathbf{v} \|}{\| \mathbf{v} \|}$.

- In three dimensions, two lines may be parallel but not equal, equal, intersecting, or skew.

- Given a point $P$ and vector $\mathbf{n}$, the set of all points $Q$ satisfying equation $\mathbf{n} \cdot \overrightarrow{PQ} = 0$ forms a plane. Equation $\mathbf{n} \cdot \overrightarrow{PQ} = 0$ is known as the *vector equation of a plane*.

- The scalar equation of a plane containing point $P = (x_0, y_0, z_0)$ with normal vector $\mathbf{n} = \langle a, b, c \rangle$ is $a(x - x_0) + b(y - y_0) + c(z - z_0) = 0$. This equation can be expressed as $ax + by + cz + d = 0$, where $d = -ax_0 - by_0 - cz_0$. This form of the equation is sometimes called the *general form of the equation of a plane*.

- Suppose a plane with normal vector $\mathbf{n}$ passes through point $Q$. The distance $D$ from the plane to point $P$ not in the plane is given by

$$D = \| \text{proj}_{\mathbf{n}} \overrightarrow{QP} \| = \left| \text{comp}_{\mathbf{n}} \overrightarrow{QP} \right| = \frac{\left| \overrightarrow{QP} \cdot \mathbf{n} \right|}{\| \mathbf{n} \|}.$$

- The normal vectors of parallel planes are parallel. When two planes intersect, they form a line.
- The measure of the angle $\theta$ between two intersecting planes can be found using the equation: $\cos \theta = \frac{|\mathbf{n}_1 \cdot \mathbf{n}_2|}{\| \mathbf{n}_1 \| \ \| \mathbf{n}_2 \|}$, where $\mathbf{n}_1$ and $\mathbf{n}_2$ are normal vectors to the planes.
- The distance $D$ from point $(x_0, y_0, z_0)$ to plane $ax + by + cz + d = 0$ is given by

$$D = \frac{|a(x_0 - x_1) + b(y_0 - y_1) + c(z_0 - z_1)|}{\sqrt{a^2 + b^2 + c^2}} = \frac{|ax_0 + by_0 + cz_0 + d|}{\sqrt{a^2 + b^2 + c^2}}.$$

## 2.6 Quadric Surfaces

- A set of lines parallel to a given line passing through a given curve is called a *cylinder*, or a *cylindrical surface*. The parallel lines are called *rulings*.
- The intersection of a three-dimensional surface and a plane is called a *trace*. To find the trace in the $xy$-, $yz$-, or $xz$-planes, set $z = 0$, $x = 0$, or $y = 0$, respectively.
- Quadric surfaces are three-dimensional surfaces with traces composed of conic sections. Every quadric surface can be expressed with an equation of the form $Ax^2 + By^2 + Cz^2 + Dxy + Exz + Fyz + Gx + Hy + Jz + K = 0.$
- To sketch the graph of a quadric surface, start by sketching the traces to understand the framework of the surface.
- Important quadric surfaces are summarized in Figure 2.87 and Figure 2.88.

## 2.7 Cylindrical and Spherical Coordinates

- In the cylindrical coordinate system, a point in space is represented by the ordered triple $(r, \theta, z)$, where $(r, \theta)$ represents the polar coordinates of the point's projection in the $xy$-plane and $z$ represents the point's projection onto the $z$-axis.
- To convert a point from cylindrical coordinates to Cartesian coordinates, use equations $x = r \cos \theta$, $y = r \sin \theta$, and $z = z$.
- To convert a point from Cartesian coordinates to cylindrical coordinates, use equations $r^2 = x^2 + y^2$, $\tan \theta = \frac{y}{x}$, and $z = z$.
- In the spherical coordinate system, a point $P$ in space is represented by the ordered triple $(\rho, \theta, \varphi)$, where $\rho$ is the distance between $P$ and the origin $(\rho \neq 0)$, $\theta$ is the same angle used to describe the location in cylindrical coordinates, and $\varphi$ is the angle formed by the positive $z$-axis and line segment $\overline{OP}$, where $O$ is the origin and $0 \leq \varphi \leq \pi$.
- To convert a point from spherical coordinates to Cartesian coordinates, use equations $x = \rho \sin \varphi \cos \theta$, $y = \rho \sin \varphi \sin \theta$, and $z = \rho \cos \varphi$.
- To convert a point from Cartesian coordinates to spherical coordinates, use equations $\rho^2 = x^2 + y^2 + z^2$, $\tan \theta = \frac{y}{x}$, and $\varphi = \arccos\left( \frac{z}{\sqrt{x^2 + y^2 + z^2}} \right)$.
- To convert a point from spherical coordinates to cylindrical coordinates, use equations $r = \rho \sin \varphi$, $\theta = \theta$, and $z = \rho \cos \varphi$.

- To convert a point from cylindrical coordinates to spherical coordinates, use equations $\rho = \sqrt{r^2 + z^2}, \quad \theta = \theta,$ and $\varphi = \arccos\left(\dfrac{z}{\sqrt{r^2 + z^2}}\right).$

# CHAPTER 2 REVIEW EXERCISES

For the following exercises, determine whether the statement is *true or false*. Justify the answer with a proof or a counterexample.

**423.** For vectors $\mathbf{a}$ and $\mathbf{b}$ and any given scalar $c$, $c(\mathbf{a} \cdot \mathbf{b}) = (c\mathbf{a}) \cdot \mathbf{b}$.

**424.** For vectors $\mathbf{a}$ and $\mathbf{b}$ and any given scalar $c$, $c(\mathbf{a} \times \mathbf{b}) = (c\mathbf{a}) \times \mathbf{b}$.

**425.** The symmetric equation for the line of intersection between two planes $x + y + z = 2$ and $x + 2y - 4z = 5$ is given by $-\dfrac{x-1}{6} = \dfrac{y-1}{5} = z$.

**426.** If $\mathbf{a} \cdot \mathbf{b} = 0$, then $\mathbf{a}$ is perpendicular to $\mathbf{b}$.

For the following exercises, use the given vectors to find the quantities.

**427.** $\mathbf{a} = 9\mathbf{i} - 2\mathbf{j},\ \mathbf{b} = -3\mathbf{i} + \mathbf{j}$
  a. $3\mathbf{a} + \mathbf{b}$
  b. $|\mathbf{a}|$
  c. $\mathbf{a} \times |\mathbf{b} \times |\mathbf{a}$
  d. $\mathbf{b} \times |\mathbf{a}$

**428.** $\mathbf{a} = 2\mathbf{i} + \mathbf{j} - 9\mathbf{k},\ \mathbf{b} = -\mathbf{i} + 2\mathbf{k},\ \mathbf{c} = 4\mathbf{i} - 2\mathbf{j} + \mathbf{k}$
  a. $2\mathbf{a} - \mathbf{b}$
  b. $|\mathbf{b} \times \mathbf{c}|$
  c. $\mathbf{b} \times |\mathbf{b} \times \mathbf{c}|$
  d. $\mathbf{c} \times |\mathbf{b} \times \mathbf{a}|$
  e. $\text{proj}_{\mathbf{a}} \mathbf{b}$

**429.** Find the values of $a$ such that vectors $\langle 2, 4, a \rangle$ and $\langle 0, -1, a \rangle$ are orthogonal.

For the following exercises, find the unit vectors.

**430.** Find the unit vector that has the same direction as vector $\mathbf{v}$ that begins at $(0, -3)$ and ends at $(4, 10)$.

**431.** Find the unit vector that has the same direction as vector $\mathbf{v}$ that begins at $(1, 4, 10)$ and ends at $(3, 0, 4)$.

For the following exercises, find the area or volume of the given shapes.

**432.** The parallelogram spanned by vectors $\mathbf{a} = \langle 1, 13 \rangle$ and $\mathbf{b} = \langle 3, 21 \rangle$

**433.** The parallelepiped formed by $\mathbf{a} = \langle 1, 4, 1 \rangle$ and $\mathbf{b} = \langle 3, 6, 2 \rangle$, and $\mathbf{c} = \langle -2, 1, -5 \rangle$

For the following exercises, find the vector and parametric equations of the line with the given properties.

**434.** The line that passes through point $(2, -3, 7)$ that is parallel to vector $\langle 1, 3, -2 \rangle$

**435.** The line that passes through points $(1, 3, 5)$ and $(-2, 6, -3)$

For the following exercises, find the equation of the plane with the given properties.

**436.** The plane that passes through point $(4, 7, -1)$ and has normal vector $\mathbf{n} = \langle 3, 4, 2 \rangle$

**437.** The plane that passes through points $(0, 1, 5)$, $(2, -1, 6)$, and $(3, 2, 5)$.

For the following exercises, find the traces for the surfaces in planes $x = k,\ y = k,\ \text{and}\ z = k$. Then, describe and draw the surfaces.

**438.** $9x^2 + 4y^2 - 16y + 36z^2 = 20$

**439.** $x^2 = y^2 + z^2$

For the following exercises, write the given equation in cylindrical coordinates and spherical coordinates.

**440.** $x^2 + y^2 + z^2 = 144$

**441.** $z = x^2 + y^2 - 1$

For the following exercises, convert the given equations from cylindrical or spherical coordinates to rectangular coordinates. Identify the given surface.

**442.** $\rho^2 \left( \sin^2(\varphi) - \cos^2(\varphi) \right) = 1$

**443.** $r^2 - 2r\cos(\theta) + z^2 = 1$

For the following exercises, consider a small boat crossing a river.

**444.** If the boat velocity is $5$ km/h due north in still water and the water has a current of $2$ km/h due west (see the following figure), what is the velocity of the boat relative to shore? What is the angle $\theta$ that the boat is actually traveling?

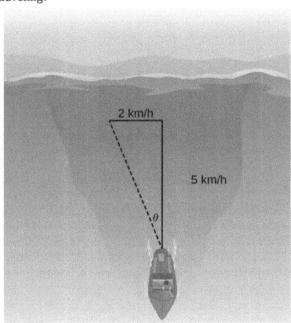

**445.** When the boat reaches the shore, two ropes are thrown to people to help pull the boat ashore. One rope is at an angle of $25°$ and the other is at $35°$. If the boat must be pulled straight and at a force of $500$N, find the magnitude of force for each rope (see the following figure).

**446.** An airplane is flying in the direction of $52°$ east of north with a speed of 450 mph. A strong wind has a bearing $33°$ east of north with a speed of 50 mph. What is the resultant ground speed and bearing of the airplane?

**447.** Calculate the work done by moving a particle from position $(1, 2, 0)$ to $(8, 4, 5)$ along a straight line with a force $\mathbf{F} = 2\mathbf{i} + 3\mathbf{j} - \mathbf{k}$.

The following problems consider your unsuccessful attempt to take the tire off your car using a wrench to loosen the bolts. Assume the wrench is $0.3$ m long and you are able to apply a 200-N force.

**448.** Because your tire is flat, you are only able to apply your force at a $60°$ angle. What is the torque at the center of the bolt? Assume this force is not enough to loosen the bolt.

**449.** Someone lends you a tire jack and you are now able to apply a 200-N force at an $80°$ angle. Is your resulting torque going to be more or less? What is the new resulting torque at the center of the bolt? Assume this force is not enough to loosen the bolt.

# 3 | VECTOR-VALUED FUNCTIONS

**Figure 3.1** Halley's Comet appeared in view of Earth in 1986 and will appear again in 2061.

## Chapter Outline

**3.1** Vector-Valued Functions and Space Curves

**3.2** Calculus of Vector-Valued Functions

**3.3** Arc Length and Curvature

**3.4** Motion in Space

## Introduction

In 1705, using Sir Isaac Newton's new laws of motion, the astronomer Edmond Halley made a prediction. He stated that comets that had appeared in 1531, 1607, and 1682 were actually the same comet and that it would reappear in 1758. Halley was proved to be correct, although he did not live to see it. However, the comet was later named in his honor.

Halley's Comet follows an elliptical path through the solar system, with the Sun appearing at one focus of the ellipse. This motion is predicted by Johannes Kepler's first law of planetary motion, which we mentioned briefly in the **Introduction to Parametric Equations and Polar Coordinates**. In **Example 3.15**, we show how to use Kepler's third law of planetary motion along with the calculus of vector-valued functions to find the average distance of Halley's Comet from the Sun.

Vector-valued functions provide a useful method for studying various curves both in the plane and in three-dimensional space. We can apply this concept to calculate the velocity, acceleration, arc length, and curvature of an object's trajectory. In this chapter, we examine these methods and show how they are used.

# 3.1 | Vector-Valued Functions and Space Curves

## Learning Objectives

3.1.1 Write the general equation of a vector-valued function in component form and unit-vector form.

3.1.2 Recognize parametric equations for a space curve.

3.1.3 Describe the shape of a helix and write its equation.

3.1.4 Define the limit of a vector-valued function.

Our study of vector-valued functions combines ideas from our earlier examination of single-variable calculus with our description of vectors in three dimensions from the preceding chapter. In this section we extend concepts from earlier chapters and also examine new ideas concerning curves in three-dimensional space. These definitions and theorems support the presentation of material in the rest of this chapter and also in the remaining chapters of the text.

## Definition of a Vector-Valued Function

Our first step in studying the calculus of vector-valued functions is to define what exactly a vector-valued function is. We can then look at graphs of vector-valued functions and see how they define curves in both two and three dimensions.

### Definition

A **vector-valued function** is a function of the form

$$\mathbf{r}(t) = f(t)\mathbf{i} + g(t)\mathbf{j} \quad \text{or} \quad \mathbf{r}(t) = f(t)\mathbf{i} + g(t)\mathbf{j} + h(t)\mathbf{k}, \tag{3.1}$$

where the **component functions** $f$, $g$, and $h$, are real-valued functions of the parameter $t$. Vector-valued functions are also written in the form

$$\mathbf{r}(t) = \langle\, f(t), g(t) \,\rangle \quad \text{or} \quad \mathbf{r}(t) = \langle\, f(t), g(t), h(t) \,\rangle. \tag{3.2}$$

In both cases, the first form of the function defines a two-dimensional vector-valued function; the second form describes a three-dimensional vector-valued function.

The parameter $t$ can lie between two real numbers: $a \le t \le b$. Another possibility is that the value of $t$ might take on all real numbers. Last, the component functions themselves may have domain restrictions that enforce restrictions on the value of $t$. We often use $t$ as a parameter because $t$ can represent time.

## Example 3.1

### Evaluating Vector-Valued Functions and Determining Domains

For each of the following vector-valued functions, evaluate $\mathbf{r}(0)$, $\mathbf{r}\left(\frac{\pi}{2}\right)$, and $\mathbf{r}\left(\frac{2\pi}{3}\right)$. Do any of these functions have domain restrictions?

a.   $\mathbf{r}(t) = 4\cos t\,\mathbf{i} + 3\sin t\,\mathbf{j}$

b.   $\mathbf{r}(t) = 3\tan t\,\mathbf{i} + 4\sec t\,\mathbf{j} + 5t\,\mathbf{k}$

### Solution

a.   To calculate each of the function values, substitute the appropriate value of $t$ into the function:

$$\mathbf{r}(0) = 4\cos(0)\mathbf{i} + 3\sin(0)\mathbf{j}$$
$$= 4\mathbf{i} + 0\mathbf{j} = 4\mathbf{i}$$
$$\mathbf{r}\left(\frac{\pi}{2}\right) = 4\cos\left(\frac{\pi}{2}\right)\mathbf{i} + 3\sin\left(\frac{\pi}{2}\right)\mathbf{j}$$
$$= 0\mathbf{i} + 3\mathbf{j} = 3\mathbf{j}$$
$$\mathbf{r}\left(\frac{2\pi}{3}\right) = 4\cos\left(\frac{2\pi}{3}\right)\mathbf{i} + 3\sin\left(\frac{2\pi}{3}\right)\mathbf{j}$$
$$= 4\left(-\frac{1}{2}\right)\mathbf{i} + 3\left(\frac{\sqrt{3}}{2}\right)\mathbf{j} = -2\mathbf{i} + \frac{3\sqrt{3}}{2}\mathbf{j}.$$

To determine whether this function has any domain restrictions, consider the component functions separately. The first component function is $f(t) = 4\cos t$ and the second component function is $g(t) = 3\sin t$. Neither of these functions has a domain restriction, so the domain of $\mathbf{r}(t) = 4\cos t\mathbf{i} + 3\sin t\mathbf{j}$ is all real numbers.

b. To calculate each of the function values, substitute the appropriate value of $t$ into the function:

$$\mathbf{r}(0) = 3\tan(0)\mathbf{i} + 4\sec(0)\mathbf{j} + 5(0)\mathbf{k}$$
$$= 0\mathbf{i} + 4\mathbf{j} + 0\mathbf{k} = 4\mathbf{j}$$
$$\mathbf{r}\left(\frac{\pi}{2}\right) = 3\tan\left(\frac{\pi}{2}\right)\mathbf{i} + 4\sec\left(\frac{\pi}{2}\right)\mathbf{j} + 5\left(\frac{\pi}{2}\right)\mathbf{k}, \text{ which does not exist}$$
$$\mathbf{r}\left(\frac{2\pi}{3}\right) = 3\tan\left(\frac{2\pi}{3}\right)\mathbf{i} + 4\sec\left(\frac{2\pi}{3}\right)\mathbf{j} + 5\left(\frac{2\pi}{3}\right)\mathbf{k}$$
$$= 3\left(-\sqrt{3}\right)\mathbf{i} + 4(-2)\mathbf{j} + \frac{10\pi}{3}\mathbf{k}$$
$$= -3\sqrt{3}\mathbf{i} - 8\mathbf{j} + \frac{10\pi}{3}\mathbf{k}.$$

To determine whether this function has any domain restrictions, consider the component functions separately. The first component function is $f(t) = 3\tan t$, the second component function is $g(t) = 4\sec t$, and the third component function is $h(t) = 5t$. The first two functions are not defined for odd multiples of $\pi/2$, so the function is not defined for odd multiples of $\pi/2$. Therefore,

$$\text{dom}(\mathbf{r}(t)) = \left\{ t \middle| t \neq \frac{(2n + 1)\pi}{2} \right\}, \quad \text{where } n \text{ is any integer.}$$

 **3.1**  For the vector-valued function $\mathbf{r}(t) = \left(t^2 - 3t\right)\mathbf{i} + (4t + 1)\mathbf{j}$,  evaluate $\mathbf{r}(0)$, $\mathbf{r}(1)$, and $\mathbf{r}(-4)$. Does this function have any domain restrictions?

**Example 3.1** illustrates an important concept. The domain of a vector-valued function consists of real numbers. The domain can be all real numbers or a subset of the real numbers. The range of a vector-valued function consists of vectors. Each real number in the domain of a vector-valued function is mapped to either a two- or a three-dimensional vector.

## Graphing Vector-Valued Functions

Recall that a plane vector consists of two quantities: direction and magnitude. Given any point in the plane (the *initial point*), if we move in a specific direction for a specific distance, we arrive at a second point. This represents the *terminal point* of the vector. We calculate the components of the vector by subtracting the coordinates of the initial point from the coordinates of the terminal point.

A vector is considered to be in *standard position* if the initial point is located at the origin. When graphing a vector-valued function, we typically graph the vectors in the domain of the function in standard position, because doing so guarantees the uniqueness of the graph. This convention applies to the graphs of three-dimensional vector-valued functions as well. The graph of a vector-valued function of the form $\mathbf{r}(t) = f(t)\mathbf{i} + g(t)\mathbf{j}$ consists of the set of all $(t,\ \mathbf{r}(t))$, and the path it traces is called a **plane curve**. The graph of a vector-valued function of the form $\mathbf{r}(t) = f(t)\mathbf{i} + g(t)\mathbf{j} + h(t)\mathbf{k}$ consists of the set of all $(t,\ \mathbf{r}(t))$, and the path it traces is called a **space curve**. Any representation of a plane curve or space curve using a vector-valued function is called a **vector parameterization** of the curve.

## Example 3.2

### Graphing a Vector-Valued Function

Create a graph of each of the following vector-valued functions:

a.  The plane curve represented by $\mathbf{r}(t) = 4\cos t\,\mathbf{i} + 3\sin t\,\mathbf{j},\quad 0 \le t \le 2\pi$

b.  The plane curve represented by $\mathbf{r}(t) = 4\cos t^3\,\mathbf{i} + 3\sin t^3\,\mathbf{j},\quad 0 \le t \le 2\pi$

c.  The space curve represented by $\mathbf{r}(t) = \cos t\,\mathbf{i} + \sin t\,\mathbf{j} + t\,\mathbf{k},\quad 0 \le t \le 4\pi$

### Solution

a.  As with any graph, we start with a table of values. We then graph each of the vectors in the second column of the table in standard position and connect the terminal points of each vector to form a curve (**Figure 3.2**). This curve turns out to be an ellipse centered at the origin.

| $t$ | $\mathbf{r}(t)$ | $t$ | $\mathbf{r}(t)$ |
|---|---|---|---|
| $0$ | $4\mathbf{i}$ | $\pi$ | $-4\mathbf{i}$ |
| $\dfrac{\pi}{4}$ | $2\sqrt{2}\mathbf{i} + \dfrac{3\sqrt{2}}{2}\mathbf{j}$ | $\dfrac{5\pi}{4}$ | $-2\sqrt{2}\mathbf{i} - \dfrac{3\sqrt{2}}{2}\mathbf{j}$ |
| $\dfrac{\pi}{2}$ | $3\mathbf{j}$ | $\dfrac{3\pi}{2}$ | $-3\mathbf{j}$ |
| $\dfrac{3\pi}{4}$ | $-2\sqrt{2}\mathbf{i} + \dfrac{3\sqrt{2}}{2}\mathbf{j}$ | $\dfrac{7\pi}{4}$ | $2\sqrt{2}\mathbf{i} - \dfrac{3\sqrt{2}}{2}\mathbf{j}$ |
| $2\pi$ | $4\mathbf{i}$ | | |

**Table 3.1**
Table of Values for $\mathbf{r}(t) = 4\cos t\,\mathbf{i} + 3\sin t\,\mathbf{j},\quad 0 \le t \le 2\pi$

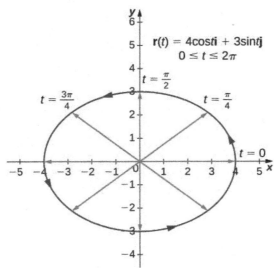

**Figure 3.2** The graph of the first vector-valued function is an ellipse.

b. The table of values for $\mathbf{r}(t) = 4\cos t\,\mathbf{i} + 3\sin t\,\mathbf{j}, \quad 0 \le t \le 2\pi$ is as follows:

| $t$ | $\mathbf{r}(t)$ | $t$ | $\mathbf{r}(t)$ |
|---|---|---|---|
| 0 | $4\mathbf{i}$ | $\pi$ | $-4\mathbf{i}$ |
| $\frac{\pi}{4}$ | $2\sqrt{2}\mathbf{i} + \frac{3\sqrt{2}}{2}\mathbf{j}$ | $\frac{5\pi}{4}$ | $-2\sqrt{2}\mathbf{i} - \frac{3\sqrt{2}}{2}\mathbf{j}$ |
| $\frac{\pi}{2}$ | $3\mathbf{j}$ | $\frac{3\pi}{2}$ | $-3\mathbf{j}$ |
| $\frac{3\pi}{4}$ | $-2\sqrt{2}\mathbf{i} + \frac{3\sqrt{2}}{2}\mathbf{j}$ | $\frac{7\pi}{4}$ | $2\sqrt{2}\mathbf{i} - \frac{3\sqrt{2}}{2}\mathbf{j}$ |
| $2\pi$ | $4\mathbf{i}$ | | |

**Table 3.2**
Table of Values for $\mathbf{r}(t) = 4\cos t\,\mathbf{i} + 3\sin t\,\mathbf{j}, \quad 0 \le t \le 2\pi$

The graph of this curve is also an ellipse centered at the origin.

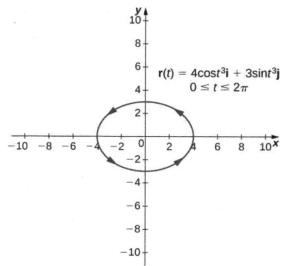

**Figure 3.3** The graph of the second vector-valued function is also an ellipse.

c.   We go through the same procedure for a three-dimensional vector function.

| $t$ | $\mathbf{r}(t)$ | $t$ | $\mathbf{r}(t)$ |
|---|---|---|---|
| $0$ | $4\mathbf{i}$ | $\pi$ | $-4\mathbf{j} + \pi\mathbf{k}$ |
| $\frac{\pi}{4}$ | $2\sqrt{2}\mathbf{i} + 2\sqrt{2}\mathbf{j} + \frac{\pi}{4}\mathbf{k}$ | $\frac{5\pi}{4}$ | $-2\sqrt{2}\mathbf{i} - 2\sqrt{2}\mathbf{j} + \frac{5\pi}{4}\mathbf{k}$ |
| $\frac{\pi}{2}$ | $4\mathbf{j} + \frac{\pi}{2}\mathbf{k}$ | $\frac{3\pi}{2}$ | $-4\mathbf{j} + \frac{3\pi}{2}\mathbf{k}$ |
| $\frac{3\pi}{4}$ | $-2\sqrt{2}\mathbf{i} + 2\sqrt{2}\mathbf{j} + \frac{3\pi}{4}\mathbf{k}$ | $\frac{7\pi}{4}$ | $2\sqrt{2}\mathbf{i} - 2\sqrt{2}\mathbf{j} + \frac{7\pi}{4}\mathbf{k}$ |
| $2\pi$ | $4\mathbf{i} + 2\pi\mathbf{k}$ | | |

**Table 3.3**
Table of Values for $\mathbf{r}(t) = \cos t\,\mathbf{i} + \sin t\,\mathbf{j} + t\mathbf{k}, \quad 0 \le t \le 4\pi$

The values then repeat themselves, except for the fact that the coefficient of k is always increasing (**Figure 3.4**). This curve is called a **helix**. Notice that if the **k** component is eliminated, then the function becomes $\mathbf{r}(t) = \cos t\,\mathbf{i} + \sin t\,\mathbf{j}$, which is a unit circle centered at the origin.

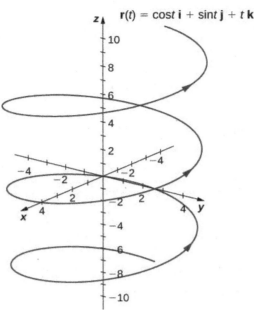

Figure 3.4  The graph of the third vector-valued function is a helix.

You may notice that the graphs in parts a. and b. are identical. This happens because the function describing curve b is a so-called **reparameterization** of the function describing curve a. In fact, any curve has an infinite number of reparameterizations; for example, we can replace $t$ with $2t$ in any of the three previous curves without changing the shape of the curve. The interval over which $t$ is defined may change, but that is all. We return to this idea later in this chapter when we study arc-length parameterization.

As mentioned, the name of the shape of the curve of the graph in Example 3.2c. is a **helix** (Figure 3.4). The curve resembles a spring, with a circular cross-section looking down along the z-axis. It is possible for a helix to be elliptical in cross-section as well. For example, the vector-valued function $\mathbf{r}(t) = 4\cos t\,\mathbf{i} + 3\sin t\,\mathbf{j} + t\,\mathbf{k}$ describes an elliptical helix. The projection of this helix into the $x$, $y$-plane is an ellipse. Last, the arrows in the graph of this helix indicate the orientation of the curve as $t$ progresses from 0 to $4\pi$.

 **3.2**  Create a graph of the vector-valued function $\mathbf{r}(t) = \left(t^2 - 1\right)\mathbf{i} + (2t - 3)\mathbf{j}, \quad 0 \le t \le 3$.

At this point, you may notice a similarity between vector-valued functions and parameterized curves. Indeed, given a vector-valued function $\mathbf{r}(t) = f(t)\mathbf{i} + g(t)\mathbf{j}$, we can define $x = f(t)$ and $y = g(t)$. If a restriction exists on the values of $t$ (for example, $t$ is restricted to the interval $[a, b]$ for some constants $a < b$), then this restriction is enforced on the parameter. The graph of the parameterized function would then agree with the graph of the vector-valued function, except that the vector-valued graph would represent vectors rather than points. Since we can parameterize a curve defined by a function $y = f(x)$, it is also possible to represent an arbitrary plane curve by a vector-valued function.

## Limits and Continuity of a Vector-Valued Function

We now take a look at the **limit of a vector-valued function**. This is important to understand to study the calculus of vector-valued functions.

**Definition**

A vector-valued function **r** approaches the limit **L** as $t$ approaches $a$, written

$$\lim_{t \to a} \mathbf{r}(t) = \mathbf{L},$$

provided

$$\lim_{t \to a} \| \mathbf{r}(t) - \mathbf{L} \| = 0.$$

This is a rigorous definition of the limit of a vector-valued function. In practice, we use the following theorem:

**Theorem 3.1: Limit of a Vector-Valued Function**

Let $f$, $g$, and $h$ be functions of $t$. Then the limit of the vector-valued function $\mathbf{r}(t) = f(t)\mathbf{i} + g(t)\mathbf{j}$ as $t$ approaches $a$ is given by

$$\lim_{t \to a} \mathbf{r}(t) = \left[ \lim_{t \to a} f(t) \right] \mathbf{i} + \left[ \lim_{t \to a} g(t) \right] \mathbf{j}, \tag{3.3}$$

provided the limits $\lim_{t \to a} f(t)$ and $\lim_{t \to a} g(t)$ exist. Similarly, the limit of the vector-valued function $\mathbf{r}(t) = f(t)\mathbf{i} + g(t)\mathbf{j} + h(t)\mathbf{k}$ as $t$ approaches $a$ is given by

$$\lim_{t \to a} \mathbf{r}(t) = \left[ \lim_{t \to a} f(t) \right] \mathbf{i} + \left[ \lim_{t \to a} g(t) \right] \mathbf{j} + \left[ \lim_{t \to a} h(t) \right] \mathbf{k}, \tag{3.4}$$

provided the limits $\lim_{t \to a} f(t)$, $\lim_{t \to a} g(t)$ and $\lim_{t \to a} h(t)$ exist.

In the following example, we show how to calculate the limit of a vector-valued function.

## Example 3.3

### Evaluating the Limit of a Vector-Valued Function

For each of the following vector-valued functions, calculate $\lim_{t \to 3} \mathbf{r}(t)$ for

a.  $\mathbf{r}(t) = \left( t^2 - 3t + 4 \right)\mathbf{i} + (4t + 3)\mathbf{j}$

b.  $\mathbf{r}(t) = \dfrac{2t - 4}{t + 1}\mathbf{i} + \dfrac{t}{t^2 + 1}\mathbf{j} + (4t - 3)\mathbf{k}$

**Solution**

a.  Use **Equation 3.3** and substitute the value $t = 3$ into the two component expressions:

$$\begin{aligned}
\lim_{t \to 3} \mathbf{r}(t) &= \lim_{t \to 3} \left[ \left( t^2 - 3t + 4 \right)\mathbf{i} + (4t + 3)\mathbf{j} \right] \\
&= \left[ \lim_{t \to 3} \left( t^2 - 3t + 4 \right) \right] \mathbf{i} + \left[ \lim_{t \to 3} (4t + 3) \right] \mathbf{j} \\
&= 4\mathbf{i} + 15\mathbf{j}.
\end{aligned}$$

b.  Use **Equation 3.4** and substitute the value $t = 3$ into the three component expressions:

$$\lim_{t \to 3} \mathbf{r}(t) = \lim_{t \to 3} \left( \frac{2t-4}{t+1}\mathbf{i} + \frac{t}{t^2+1}\mathbf{j} + (4t-3)\mathbf{k} \right)$$

$$= \left[ \lim_{t \to 3} \left( \frac{2t-4}{t+1} \right) \right] \mathbf{i} + \left[ \lim_{t \to 3} \left( \frac{t}{t^2+1} \right) \right] \mathbf{j} + \left[ \lim_{t \to 3} (4t-3) \right] \mathbf{k}$$

$$= \frac{1}{2}\mathbf{i} + \frac{3}{10}\mathbf{j} + 9\mathbf{k}.$$

**3.3** Calculate $\lim_{t \to -2} \mathbf{r}(t)$ for the function $\mathbf{r}(t) = \sqrt{t^2 - 3t - 1}\,\mathbf{i} + (4t+3)\mathbf{j} + \sin\frac{(t+1)\pi}{2}\mathbf{k}$.

Now that we know how to calculate the limit of a vector-valued function, we can define continuity at a point for such a function.

**Definition**

Let $f$, $g$, and $h$ be functions of $t$. Then, the vector-valued function $\mathbf{r}(t) = f(t)\mathbf{i} + g(t)\mathbf{j}$ is continuous at point $t = a$ if the following three conditions hold:

1. $\mathbf{r}(a)$ exists

2. $\lim_{t \to a} \mathbf{r}(t)$ exists

3. $\lim_{t \to a} \mathbf{r}(t) = \mathbf{r}(a)$

Similarly, the vector-valued function $\mathbf{r}(t) = f(t)\mathbf{i} + g(t)\mathbf{j} + h(t)\mathbf{k}$ is continuous at point $t = a$ if the following three conditions hold:

1. $\mathbf{r}(a)$ exists

2. $\lim_{t \to a} \mathbf{r}(t)$ exists

3. $\lim_{t \to a} \mathbf{r}(t) = \mathbf{r}(a)$

# 3.1 EXERCISES

1. Give the component functions $x = f(t)$ and $y = g(t)$ for the vector-valued function $\mathbf{r}(t) = 3\sec t\,\mathbf{i} + 2\tan t\,\mathbf{j}$.

2. Given $\mathbf{r}(t) = 3\sec t\,\mathbf{i} + 2\tan t\,\mathbf{j}$, find the following values (if possible).

    a. $\mathbf{r}\left(\dfrac{\pi}{4}\right)$

    b. $\mathbf{r}(\pi)$

    c. $\mathbf{r}\left(\dfrac{\pi}{2}\right)$

3. Sketch the curve of the vector-valued function $\mathbf{r}(t) = 3\sec t\,\mathbf{i} + 2\tan t\,\mathbf{j}$ and give the orientation of the curve. Sketch asymptotes as a guide to the graph.

4. Evaluate $\lim\limits_{t \to 0} \left\langle e^t\,\mathbf{i} + \dfrac{\sin t}{t}\,\mathbf{j} + e^{-t}\,\mathbf{k} \right\rangle$.

5. Given the vector-valued function $\mathbf{r}(t) = \langle \cos t,\ \sin t \rangle$, find the following values:

    a. $\lim\limits_{t \to \frac{\pi}{4}} \mathbf{r}(t)$

    b. $\mathbf{r}\left(\dfrac{\pi}{3}\right)$

    c. Is $\mathbf{r}(t)$ continuous at $t = \dfrac{\pi}{3}$?

    d. Graph $\mathbf{r}(t)$.

6. Given the vector-valued function $\mathbf{r}(t) = \langle t,\ t^2 + 1 \rangle$, find the following values:

    a. $\lim\limits_{t \to -3} \mathbf{r}(t)$

    b. $\mathbf{r}(-3)$

    c. Is $\mathbf{r}(t)$ continuous at $x = -3$?

    d. $\mathbf{r}(t + 2) - \mathbf{r}(t)$

7. Let $\mathbf{r}(t) = e^t\,\mathbf{i} + \sin t\,\mathbf{j} + \ln t\,\mathbf{k}$. Find the following values:

    a. $\mathbf{r}\left(\dfrac{\pi}{4}\right)$

    b. $\lim\limits_{t \to \pi/4} \mathbf{r}(t)$

    c. Is $\mathbf{r}(t)$ continuous at $t = t = \dfrac{\pi}{4}$?

Find the limit of the following vector-valued functions at the indicated value of $t$.

8. $\lim\limits_{t \to 4} \left\langle \sqrt{t - 3},\ \dfrac{\sqrt{t} - 2}{t - 4},\ \tan\left(\dfrac{\pi}{t}\right) \right\rangle$

9. $\lim\limits_{t \to \pi/2} \mathbf{r}(t)$ for $\mathbf{r}(t) = e^t\,\mathbf{i} + \sin t\,\mathbf{j} + \ln t\,\mathbf{k}$

10. $\lim\limits_{t \to \infty} \left\langle e^{-2t},\ \dfrac{2t + 3}{3t - 1},\ \arctan(2t) \right\rangle$

11. $\lim\limits_{t \to e^2} \left\langle t\ln(t),\ \dfrac{\ln t}{t^2},\ \sqrt{\ln\left(t^2\right)} \right\rangle$

12. $\lim\limits_{t \to \pi/6} \left\langle \cos^2 t,\ \sin^2 t,\ 1 \right\rangle$

13. $\lim\limits_{t \to \infty} \mathbf{r}(t)$ for $\mathbf{r}(t) = 2e^{-t}\,\mathbf{i} + e^{-t}\,\mathbf{j} + \ln(t - 1)\,\mathbf{k}$

14. Describe the curve defined by the vector-valued function $\mathbf{r}(t) = (1 + t)\,\mathbf{i} + (2 + 5t)\,\mathbf{j} + (-1 + 6t)\,\mathbf{k}$.

Find the domain of the vector-valued functions.

15. Domain: $\mathbf{r}(t) = \langle t^2,\ \tan t,\ \ln t \rangle$

16. Domain: $\mathbf{r}(t) = \left\langle t^2,\ \sqrt{t - 3},\ \dfrac{3}{2t + 1} \right\rangle$

17. Domain: $\mathbf{r}(t) = \left\langle \csc(t),\ \dfrac{1}{\sqrt{t - 3}},\ \ln(t - 2) \right\rangle$

Let $\mathbf{r}(t) = \langle \cos t,\ t,\ \sin t \rangle$ and use it to answer the following questions.

18. For what values of $t$ is $\mathbf{r}(t)$ continuous?

19. Sketch the graph of $\mathbf{r}(t)$.

20. Find the domain of $\mathbf{r}(t) = 2e^{-t}\,\mathbf{i} + e^{-t}\,\mathbf{j} + \ln(t - 1)\,\mathbf{k}$.

21. For what values of $t$ is $\mathbf{r}(t) = 2e^{-t}\,\mathbf{i} + e^{-t}\,\mathbf{j} + \ln(t - 1)\,\mathbf{k}$ continuous?

Eliminate the parameter $t$, write the equation in Cartesian coordinates, then sketch the graphs of the vector-valued functions.

22. $\mathbf{r}(t) = 2t\,\mathbf{i} + t^2\,\mathbf{j}$ (*Hint*: Let $x = 2t$ and $y = t^2$. Solve the first equation for $x$ in terms of $t$ and substitute this result into the second equation.)

23. $\mathbf{r}(t) = t^3\,\mathbf{i} + 2t\,\mathbf{j}$

24. $\mathbf{r}(t) = 2(\sinh t)\,\mathbf{i} + 2(\cosh t)\,\mathbf{j},\ t > 0$

25. $\mathbf{r}(t) = 3(\cos t)\,\mathbf{i} + 3(\sin t)\,\mathbf{j}$

26. $\mathbf{r}(t) = \langle 3\sin t,\ 3\cos t \rangle$

Use a graphing utility to sketch each of the following vector-valued functions:

27. **[T]** $\mathbf{r}(t) = 2\cos t^2\,\mathbf{i} + (2 - \sqrt{t})\mathbf{j}$

28. **[T]** $\mathbf{r}(t) = \langle\, e^{\cos(3t)},\, e^{-\sin(t)}\,\rangle$

29. **[T]** $\mathbf{r}(t) = \langle\, 2 - \sin(2t),\, 3 + 2\cos t\,\rangle$

30. $4x^2 + 9y^2 = 36$; clockwise and counterclockwise

31. $\mathbf{r}(t) = \langle\, t,\, t^2\,\rangle$; from left to right

32. The line through $P$ and $Q$ where $P$ is $(1,\ 4,\ -2)$ and $Q$ is $(3,\ 9,\ 6)$

Consider the curve described by the vector-valued function $\mathbf{r}(t) = (50e^{-t}\cos t)\mathbf{i} + (50e^{-t}\sin t)\mathbf{j} + (5 - 5e^{-t})\mathbf{k}$.

33. What is the initial point of the path corresponding to $\mathbf{r}(0)$?

34. What is $\displaystyle\lim_{t \to \infty} \mathbf{r}(t)$?

35. **[T]** Use technology to sketch the curve.

36. Eliminate the parameter $t$ to show that $z = 5 - \dfrac{r}{10}$ where $r^2 = x^2 + y^2$.

37. **[T]** Let $r(t) = \cos t\,\mathbf{i} + \sin t\,\mathbf{j} + 0.3\sin(2t)\mathbf{k}$. Use technology to graph the curve (called the *roller-coaster curve*) over the interval $[0,\ 2\pi)$. Choose at least two views to determine the peaks and valleys.

38. **[T]** Use the result of the preceding problem to construct an equation of a roller coaster with a steep drop from the peak and steep incline from the "valley." Then, use technology to graph the equation.

39. Use the results of the preceding two problems to construct an equation of a path of a roller coaster with more than two turning points (peaks and valleys).

40.
   a. Graph the curve
   $r(t) = (4 + \cos(18t))\cos(t)\mathbf{i} + (4 + \cos(18t)\sin(t))\mathbf{j} + 0.3\sin(18t)\mathbf{k}$
   using two viewing angles of your choice to see the overall shape of the curve.
   b. Does the curve resemble a "slinky"?
   c. What changes to the equation should be made to increase the number of coils of the slinky?

# 3.2 | Calculus of Vector-Valued Functions

## Learning Objectives

**3.2.1** Write an expression for the derivative of a vector-valued function.

**3.2.2** Find the tangent vector at a point for a given position vector.

**3.2.3** Find the unit tangent vector at a point for a given position vector and explain its significance.

**3.2.4** Calculate the definite integral of a vector-valued function.

To study the calculus of vector-valued functions, we follow a similar path to the one we took in studying real-valued functions. First, we define the derivative, then we examine applications of the derivative, then we move on to defining integrals. However, we will find some interesting new ideas along the way as a result of the vector nature of these functions and the properties of space curves.

## Derivatives of Vector-Valued Functions

Now that we have seen what a vector-valued function is and how to take its limit, the next step is to learn how to differentiate a vector-valued function. The definition of the derivative of a vector-valued function is nearly identical to the definition of a real-valued function of one variable. However, because the range of a vector-valued function consists of vectors, the same is true for the range of the derivative of a vector-valued function.

### Definition

The **derivative of a vector-valued function** $\mathbf{r}(t)$ is

$$\mathbf{r}'(t) = \lim_{\Delta t \to 0} \frac{\mathbf{r}(t + \Delta t) - \mathbf{r}(t)}{\Delta t}, \tag{3.5}$$

provided the limit exists. If $\mathbf{r}'(t)$ exists, then $\mathbf{r}$ is differentiable at $t$. If $\mathbf{r}'(t)$ exists for all $t$ in an open interval $(a, b)$, then $\mathbf{r}$ is differentiable over the interval $(a, b)$. For the function to be differentiable over the closed interval $[a, b]$, the following two limits must exist as well:

$$\mathbf{r}'(a) = \lim_{\Delta t \to 0^+} \frac{\mathbf{r}(a + \Delta t) - \mathbf{r}(a)}{\Delta t} \text{ and } \mathbf{r}'(b) = \lim_{\Delta t \to 0^-} \frac{\mathbf{r}(b + \Delta t) - \mathbf{r}(b)}{\Delta t}.$$

Many of the rules for calculating derivatives of real-valued functions can be applied to calculating the derivatives of vector-valued functions as well. Recall that the derivative of a real-valued function can be interpreted as the slope of a tangent line or the instantaneous rate of change of the function. The derivative of a vector-valued function can be understood to be an instantaneous rate of change as well; for example, when the function represents the position of an object at a given point in time, the derivative represents its velocity at that same point in time.

We now demonstrate taking the derivative of a vector-valued function.

## Example 3.4

### Finding the Derivative of a Vector-Valued Function

Use the definition to calculate the derivative of the function

$$\mathbf{r}(t) = (3t + 4)\mathbf{i} + \left(t^2 - 4t + 3\right)\mathbf{j}.$$

### Solution

Let's use **Equation 3.5**:

$$\begin{aligned}
\mathbf{r}'(t) &= \lim_{\Delta t \to 0} \frac{\mathbf{r}(t + \Delta t) - \mathbf{r}(t)}{\Delta t} \\
&= \lim_{\Delta t \to 0} \frac{\left[(3(t + \Delta t) + 4)\mathbf{i} + \left((t + \Delta t)^2 - 4(t + \Delta t) + 3\right)\mathbf{j}\right] - \left[(3t + 4)\mathbf{i} + \left(t^2 - 4t + 3\right)\mathbf{j}\right]}{\Delta t} \\
&= \lim_{\Delta t \to 0} \frac{(3t + 3\Delta t + 4)\mathbf{i} - (3t + 4)\mathbf{i} + \left(t^2 + 2t\Delta t + (\Delta t)^2 - 4t - 4\Delta t + 3\right)\mathbf{j} - \left(t^2 - 4t + 3\right)\mathbf{j}}{\Delta t} \\
&= \lim_{\Delta t \to 0} \frac{(3\Delta t)\mathbf{i} + \left(2t\Delta t + (\Delta t)^2 - 4\Delta t\right)\mathbf{j}}{\Delta t} \\
&= \lim_{\Delta t \to 0} (3\mathbf{i} + (2t + \Delta t - 4)\mathbf{j}) \\
&= 3\mathbf{i} + (2t - 4)\mathbf{j}.
\end{aligned}$$

 **3.4**   Use the definition to calculate the derivative of the function $\mathbf{r}(t) = \left(2t^2 + 3\right)\mathbf{i} + (5t - 6)\mathbf{j}$.

Notice that in the calculations in **Example 3.4**, we could also obtain the answer by first calculating the derivative of each component function, then putting these derivatives back into the vector-valued function. This is always true for calculating the derivative of a vector-valued function, whether it is in two or three dimensions. We state this in the following theorem. The proof of this theorem follows directly from the definitions of the limit of a vector-valued function and the derivative of a vector-valued function.

---

### Theorem 3.2: Differentiation of Vector-Valued Functions

Let $f$, $g$, and $h$ be differentiable functions of $t$.

   i.   If $\mathbf{r}(t) = f(t)\mathbf{i} + g(t)\mathbf{j}$,   then $\mathbf{r}'(t) = f'(t)\mathbf{i} + g'(t)\mathbf{j}$.

   ii.   If $\mathbf{r}(t) = f(t)\mathbf{i} + g(t)\mathbf{j} + h(t)\mathbf{k}$,   then $\mathbf{r}'(t) = f'(t)\mathbf{i} + g'(t)\mathbf{j} + h'(t)\mathbf{k}$.

---

## Example 3.5

### Calculating the Derivative of Vector-Valued Functions

Use **Differentiation of Vector-Valued Functions** to calculate the derivative of each of the following functions.

   a.   $\mathbf{r}(t) = (6t + 8)\mathbf{i} + \left(4t^2 + 2t - 3\right)\mathbf{j}$

   b.   $\mathbf{r}(t) = 3\cos t\,\mathbf{i} + 4\sin t\,\mathbf{j}$

   c.   $\mathbf{r}(t) = e^t \sin t\,\mathbf{i} + e^t \cos t\,\mathbf{j} - e^{2t}\,\mathbf{k}$

### Solution

We use **Differentiation of Vector-Valued Functions** and what we know about differentiating functions of one variable.

a. The first component of $\mathbf{r}(t) = (6t + 8)\mathbf{i} + \left(4t^2 + 2t - 3\right)\mathbf{j}$ is $f(t) = 6t + 8$. The second component is $g(t) = 4t^2 + 2t - 3$. We have $f'(t) = 6$ and $g'(t) = 8t + 2$, so the theorem gives $\mathbf{r}'(t) = 6\mathbf{i} + (8t + 2)\mathbf{j}$.

b. The first component is $f(t) = 3\cos t$ and the second component is $g(t) = 4\sin t$. We have $f'(t) = -3\sin t$ and $g'(t) = 4\cos t$, so we obtain $\mathbf{r}'(t) = -3\sin t\,\mathbf{i} + 4\cos t\,\mathbf{j}$.

c. The first component of $\mathbf{r}(t) = e^t\sin t\,\mathbf{i} + e^t\cos t\,\mathbf{j} - e^{2t}\mathbf{k}$ is $f(t) = e^t\sin t$, the second component is $g(t) = e^t\cos t$, and the third component is $h(t) = -e^{2t}$. We have $f'(t) = e^t(\sin t + \cos t)$, $g'(t) = e^t(\cos t - \sin t)$, and $h'(t) = -2e^{2t}$, so the theorem gives $\mathbf{r}'(t) = e^t(\sin t + \cos t)\mathbf{i} + e^t(\cos t - \sin t)\mathbf{j} - 2e^{2t}\mathbf{k}$.

 **3.5** Calculate the derivative of the function

$$\mathbf{r}(t) = (t\ln t)\mathbf{i} + \left(5e^t\right)\mathbf{j} + (\cos t - \sin t)\mathbf{k}.$$

We can extend to vector-valued functions the properties of the derivative that we presented in the **Introduction to Derivatives (http://cnx.org/content/m53494/latest/)** . In particular, the constant multiple rule, the sum and difference rules, the product rule, and the chain rule all extend to vector-valued functions. However, in the case of the product rule, there are actually three extensions: (1) for a real-valued function multiplied by a vector-valued function, (2) for the dot product of two vector-valued functions, and (3) for the cross product of two vector-valued functions.

---

**Theorem 3.3: Properties of the Derivative of Vector-Valued Functions**

Let $\mathbf{r}$ and $\mathbf{u}$ be differentiable vector-valued functions of $t$, let $f$ be a differentiable real-valued function of $t$, and let $c$ be a scalar.

|     |     |     |     |
|-----|-----|-----|-----|
| i. | $\frac{d}{dt}[c\mathbf{r}(t)]$ | $= c\mathbf{r}'(t)$ | Scalar multiple |
| ii. | $\frac{d}{dt}[\mathbf{r}(t) \pm \mathbf{u}(t)]$ | $= \mathbf{r}'(t) \pm \mathbf{u}'(t)$ | Sum and difference |
| iii. | $\frac{d}{dt}[f(t)\mathbf{u}(t)]$ | $= f'(t)\mathbf{u}(t) + f(t)\mathbf{u}'(t)$ | Scalar product |
| iv. | $\frac{d}{dt}[\mathbf{r}(t) \cdot \mathbf{u}(t)]$ | $= \mathbf{r}'(t) \cdot \mathbf{u}(t) + \mathbf{r}(t) \cdot \mathbf{u}'(t)$ | Dot product |
| v. | $\frac{d}{dt}[\mathbf{r}(t) \times \mathbf{u}(t)]$ | $= \mathbf{r}'(t) \times \mathbf{u}(t) + \mathbf{r}(t) \times \mathbf{u}'(t)$ | Cross product |
| vi. | $\frac{d}{dt}[\mathbf{r}(f(t))]$ | $= \mathbf{r}'(f(t)) \cdot f'(t)$ | Chain rule |
| vii. | If $\mathbf{r}(t) \cdot \mathbf{r}(t)$ | $= c$, then $\mathbf{r}(t) \cdot \mathbf{r}'(t) = 0$. | |

---

**Proof**

The proofs of the first two properties follow directly from the definition of the derivative of a vector-valued function. The third property can be derived from the first two properties, along with the product rule from the **Introduction to Derivatives (http://cnx.org/content/m53494/latest/)** . Let $\mathbf{u}(t) = g(t)\mathbf{i} + h(t)\mathbf{j}$. Then

$$\frac{d}{dt}[f(t)\mathbf{u}(t)] = \frac{d}{dt}[f(t)(g(t)\mathbf{i} + h(t)\mathbf{j})]$$

$$= \frac{d}{dt}[f(t)g(t)\mathbf{i} + f(t)h(t)\mathbf{j}]$$

$$= \frac{d}{dt}[f(t)g(t)]\mathbf{i} + \frac{d}{dt}[f(t)h(t)]\mathbf{j}$$

$$= (f'(t)g(t) + f(t)g'(t))\mathbf{i} + (f'(t)h(t) + f(t)h'(t))\mathbf{j}$$

$$= f'(t)\mathbf{u}(t) + f(t)\mathbf{u}'(t).$$

To prove property iv. let $\mathbf{r}(t) = f_1(t)\mathbf{i} + g_1(t)\mathbf{j}$ and $\mathbf{u}(t) = f_2(t)\mathbf{i} + g_2(t)\mathbf{j}$. Then

$$\frac{d}{dt}[\mathbf{r}(t) \cdot \mathbf{u}(t)] = \frac{d}{dt}[f_1(t)f_2(t) + g_1(t)g_2(t)]$$

$$= f_1'(t)f_2(t) + f_1(t)f_2'(t) + g_1'(t)g_2(t) + g_1(t)g_2'(t)$$

$$= f_1'(t)f_2(t) + g_1'(t)g_2(t) + f_1(t)f_2'(t) + g_1(t)g_2'(t)$$

$$= (f_1'\mathbf{i} + g_1'\mathbf{j}) \cdot (f_2\mathbf{i} + g_2\mathbf{j}) + (f_1\mathbf{i} + g_1\mathbf{j}) \cdot (f_2'\mathbf{i} + g_2'\mathbf{j})$$

$$= \mathbf{r}'(t) \cdot \mathbf{u}(t) + \mathbf{r}(t) \cdot \mathbf{u}'(t).$$

The proof of property v. is similar to that of property iv. Property vi. can be proved using the chain rule. Last, property vii. follows from property iv:

$$\frac{d}{dt}[\mathbf{r}(t) \cdot \mathbf{r}(t)] = \frac{d}{dt}[c]$$

$$\mathbf{r}'(t) \cdot \mathbf{r}(t) + \mathbf{r}(t) \cdot \mathbf{r}'(t) = 0$$

$$2\mathbf{r}(t) \cdot \mathbf{r}'(t) = 0$$

$$\mathbf{r}(t) \cdot \mathbf{r}'(t) = 0.$$

□

Now for some examples using these properties.

## Example 3.6

### Using the Properties of Derivatives of Vector-Valued Functions

Given the vector-valued functions

$$\mathbf{r}(t) = (6t + 8)\mathbf{i} + \left(4t^2 + 2t - 3\right)\mathbf{j} + 5t\mathbf{k}$$

and

$$\mathbf{u}(t) = \left(t^2 - 3\right)\mathbf{i} + (2t + 4)\mathbf{j} + \left(t^3 - 3t\right)\mathbf{k},$$

calculate each of the following derivatives using the properties of the derivative of vector-valued functions.

a.   $\frac{d}{dt}[\mathbf{r}(t) \cdot \mathbf{u}(t)]$

b.   $\frac{d}{dt}[\mathbf{u}(t) \times \mathbf{u}'(t)]$

### Solution

a.   We have $\mathbf{r}'(t) = 6\mathbf{i} + (8t + 2)\mathbf{j} + 5\mathbf{k}$ and $\mathbf{u}'(t) = 2t\mathbf{i} + 2\mathbf{j} + \left(3t^2 - 3\right)\mathbf{k}$. Therefore, according to property iv.:

$$\frac{d}{dt}[\mathbf{r}(t) \cdot \mathbf{u}(t)] = \mathbf{r}'(t) \cdot \mathbf{u}(t) + \mathbf{r}(t) \cdot \mathbf{u}'(t)$$

$$= (6\mathbf{i} + (8t + 2)\mathbf{j} + 5\mathbf{k}) \cdot \left( (t^2 - 3)\mathbf{i} + (2t + 4)\mathbf{j} + (t^3 - 3t)\mathbf{k} \right)$$

$$+ \left( (6t + 8)\mathbf{i} + (4t^2 + 2t - 3)\mathbf{j} + 5t\mathbf{k} \right) \cdot (2t\mathbf{i} + 2\mathbf{j} + (3t^2 - 3)\mathbf{k})$$

$$= 6(t^2 - 3) + (8t + 2)(2t + 4) + 5(t^3 - 3t)$$

$$+ 2t(6t + 8) + 2(4t^2 + 2t - 3) + 5t(3t^2 - 3)$$

$$= 20t^3 + 42t^2 + 26t - 16.$$

b.  First, we need to adapt property v. for this problem:

$$\frac{d}{dt}[\mathbf{u}(t) \times \mathbf{u}'(t)] = \mathbf{u}'(t) \times \mathbf{u}'(t) + \mathbf{u}(t) \times \mathbf{u}''(t).$$

Recall that the cross product of any vector with itself is zero. Furthermore, $\mathbf{u}''(t)$ represents the second derivative of $\mathbf{u}(t)$:

$$\mathbf{u}''(t) = \frac{d}{dt}[\mathbf{u}'(t)] = \frac{d}{dt}\left[2t\mathbf{i} + 2\mathbf{j} + (3t^2 - 3)\mathbf{k}\right] = 2\mathbf{i} + 6t\mathbf{k}.$$

Therefore,

$$\frac{d}{dt}[\mathbf{u}(t) \times \mathbf{u}'(t)] = \mathbf{0} + \left( (t^2 - 3)\mathbf{i} + (2t + 4)\mathbf{j} + (t^3 - 3t)\mathbf{k} \right) \times (2\mathbf{i} + 6t\mathbf{k})$$

$$= \begin{vmatrix} \mathbf{i} & \mathbf{j} & \mathbf{k} \\ t^2 - 3 & 2t + 4 & t^3 - 3t \\ 2 & 0 & 6t \end{vmatrix}$$

$$= 6t(2t + 4)\mathbf{i} - \left( 6t(t^2 - 3) - 2(t^3 - 3t) \right)\mathbf{j} - 2(2t + 4)\mathbf{k}$$

$$= (12t^2 + 24t)\mathbf{i} + (12t - 4t^3)\mathbf{j} - (4t + 8)\mathbf{k}.$$

 **3.6**  Given the vector-valued functions $\mathbf{r}(t) = \cos t\mathbf{i} + \sin t\mathbf{j} - e^{2t}\mathbf{k}$ and $\mathbf{u}(t) = t\mathbf{i} + \sin t\mathbf{j} + \cos t\mathbf{k}$, calculate $\frac{d}{dt}[\mathbf{r}(t) \cdot \mathbf{r}'(t)]$ and $\frac{d}{dt}[\mathbf{u}(t) \times \mathbf{r}(t)]$.

## Tangent Vectors and Unit Tangent Vectors

Recall from the **Introduction to Derivatives (http://cnx.org/content/m53494/latest/)** that the derivative at a point can be interpreted as the slope of the tangent line to the graph at that point. In the case of a vector-valued function, the derivative provides a tangent vector to the curve represented by the function. Consider the vector-valued function $\mathbf{r}(t) = \cos t\mathbf{i} + \sin t\mathbf{j}$. The derivative of this function is $\mathbf{r}'(t) = -\sin t\mathbf{i} + \cos t\mathbf{j}$. If we substitute the value $t = \pi/6$ into both functions we get

$$\mathbf{r}\left(\frac{\pi}{6}\right) = \frac{\sqrt{3}}{2}\mathbf{i} + \frac{1}{2}\mathbf{j} \quad \text{and} \quad \mathbf{r}'\left(\frac{\pi}{6}\right) = -\frac{1}{2}\mathbf{i} + \frac{\sqrt{3}}{2}\mathbf{j}.$$

The graph of this function appears in **Figure 3.5**, along with the vectors $\mathbf{r}\left(\frac{\pi}{6}\right)$ and $\mathbf{r}'\left(\frac{\pi}{6}\right)$.

**Figure 3.5** The tangent line at a point is calculated from the derivative of the vector-valued function $\mathbf{r}(t)$.

Notice that the vector $\mathbf{r}'\!\left(\dfrac{\pi}{6}\right)$ is tangent to the circle at the point corresponding to $t = \pi/6$. This is an example of a **tangent vector** to the plane curve defined by $\mathbf{r}(t) = \cos t\,\mathbf{i} + \sin t\,\mathbf{j}$.

---

**Definition**

Let C be a curve defined by a vector-valued function $\mathbf{r}$, and assume that $\mathbf{r}'(t)$ exists when $t = t_0$. A tangent vector $\mathbf{v}$ at $t = t_0$ is any vector such that, when the tail of the vector is placed at point $\mathbf{r}(t_0)$ on the graph, vector $\mathbf{v}$ is tangent to curve C. Vector $\mathbf{r}'(t_0)$ is an example of a tangent vector at point $t = t_0$. Furthermore, assume that $\mathbf{r}'(t) \neq \mathbf{0}$. The **principal unit tangent vector** at $t$ is defined to be

$$\mathbf{T}(t) = \frac{\mathbf{r}'(t)}{\|\mathbf{r}'(t)\|}, \tag{3.6}$$

provided $\|\mathbf{r}'(t)\| \neq 0$.

---

The unit tangent vector is exactly what it sounds like: a unit vector that is tangent to the curve. To calculate a unit tangent vector, first find the derivative $\mathbf{r}'(t)$. Second, calculate the magnitude of the derivative. The third step is to divide the derivative by its magnitude.

## Example 3.7

### Finding a Unit Tangent Vector

Find the unit tangent vector for each of the following vector-valued functions:

    a.  $\mathbf{r}(t) = \cos t\,\mathbf{i} + \sin t\,\mathbf{j}$

    b.  $\mathbf{u}(t) = \left(3t^2 + 2t\right)\mathbf{i} + \left(2 - 4t^3\right)\mathbf{j} + (6t + 5)\mathbf{k}$

**Solution**

    a.

First step: $\mathbf{r}'(t) = -\sin t \mathbf{i} + \cos t \mathbf{j}$

Second step: $\|\mathbf{r}'(t)\| = \sqrt{(-\sin t)^2 + (\cos t)^2} = 1$

Third step: $\mathbf{T}(t) = \dfrac{\mathbf{r}'(t)}{\|\mathbf{r}'(t)\|} = \dfrac{-\sin t \mathbf{i} + \cos t \mathbf{j}}{1} = -\sin t \mathbf{i} + \cos t \mathbf{j}$

b.

First step: $\mathbf{u}'(t) = (6t + 2)\mathbf{i} - 12t^2 \mathbf{j} + 6\mathbf{k}$

Second step: $\|\mathbf{u}'(t)\| = \sqrt{(6t+2)^2 + \left(-12t^2\right)^2 + 6^2}$

$= \sqrt{144t^4 + 36t^2 + 24t + 40}$

$= 2\sqrt{36t^4 + 9t^2 + 6t + 10}$

Third step: $\mathbf{T}(t) = \dfrac{\mathbf{u}'(t)}{\|\mathbf{u}'(t)\|} = \dfrac{(6t + 2)\mathbf{i} - 12t^2 \mathbf{j} + 6\mathbf{k}}{2\sqrt{36t^4 + 9t^2 + 6t + 10}}$

$= \dfrac{3t + 1}{\sqrt{36t^4 + 9t^2 + 6t + 10}}\mathbf{i} - \dfrac{6t^2}{\sqrt{36t^4 + 9t^2 + 6t + 10}}\mathbf{j} + \dfrac{3}{\sqrt{36t^4 + 9t^2 + 6t + 10}}\mathbf{k}$

 **3.7** Find the unit tangent vector for the vector-valued function

$$\mathbf{r}(t) = \left(t^2 - 3\right)\mathbf{i} + (2t + 1)\mathbf{j} + (t - 2)\mathbf{k}.$$

# Integrals of Vector-Valued Functions

We introduced antiderivatives of real-valued functions in **Antiderivatives (http://cnx.org/content/m53621/latest/)** and definite integrals of real-valued functions in **The Definite Integral (http://cnx.org/content/m53631/latest/)** . Each of these concepts can be extended to vector-valued functions. Also, just as we can calculate the derivative of a vector-valued function by differentiating the component functions separately, we can calculate the antiderivative in the same manner. Furthermore, the Fundamental Theorem of Calculus applies to vector-valued functions as well.

The antiderivative of a vector-valued function appears in applications. For example, if a vector-valued function represents the velocity of an object at time $t$, then its antiderivative represents position. Or, if the function represents the acceleration of the object at a given time, then the antiderivative represents its velocity.

**Definition**

Let $f$, $g$, and $h$ be integrable real-valued functions over the closed interval $[a, b]$.

1. The **indefinite integral of a vector-valued function** $\mathbf{r}(t) = f(t)\mathbf{i} + g(t)\mathbf{j}$ is

$$\int [f(t)\mathbf{i} + g(t)\mathbf{j}]dt = \left[\int f(t)dt\right]\mathbf{i} + \left[\int g(t)dt\right]\mathbf{j}. \tag{3.7}$$

The **definite integral of a vector-valued function** is

$$\int_a^b [f(t)\mathbf{i} + g(t)\mathbf{j}]dt = \left[\int_a^b f(t)dt\right]\mathbf{i} + \left[\int_a^b g(t)dt\right]\mathbf{j}. \tag{3.8}$$

2. The indefinite integral of a vector-valued function $\mathbf{r}(t) = f(t)\mathbf{i} + g(t)\mathbf{j} + h(t)\mathbf{k}$ is

$$\int [f(t)\mathbf{i} + g(t)\mathbf{j} + h(t)\mathbf{k}]dt = \left[\int f(t)dt\right]\mathbf{i} + \left[\int g(t)dt\right]\mathbf{j} + \left[\int h(t)dt\right]\mathbf{k}. \tag{3.9}$$

The definite integral of the vector-valued function is

$$\int_a^b [f(t)\mathbf{i} + g(t)\mathbf{j} + h(t)\mathbf{k}]dt = \left[\int_a^b f(t)dt\right]\mathbf{i} + \left[\int_a^b g(t)dt\right]\mathbf{j} + \left[\int_a^b h(t)dt\right]\mathbf{k}. \qquad (3.10)$$

Since the indefinite integral of a vector-valued function involves indefinite integrals of the component functions, each of these component integrals contains an integration constant. They can all be different. For example, in the two-dimensional case, we can have

$$\int f(t)dt = F(t) + C_1 \text{ and } \int g(t)dt = G(t) + C_2,$$

where $F$ and $G$ are antiderivatives of $f$ and $g$, respectively. Then

$$\begin{aligned}
\int [f(t)\mathbf{i} + g(t)\mathbf{j}]dt &= \left[\int f(t)dt\right]\mathbf{i} + \left[\int g(t)dt\right]\mathbf{j} \\
&= (F(t) + C_1)\mathbf{i} + (G(t) + C_2)\mathbf{j} \\
&= F(t)\mathbf{i} + G(t)\mathbf{j} + C_1\,\mathbf{i} + C_2\,\mathbf{j} \\
&= F(t)\mathbf{i} + G(t)\mathbf{j} + \mathbf{C},
\end{aligned}$$

where $\mathbf{C} = C_1\,\mathbf{i} + C_2\,\mathbf{j}$. Therefore, the integration constant becomes a constant vector.

## Example 3.8

### Integrating Vector-Valued Functions

Calculate each of the following integrals:

a. $\int \left[(3t^2 + 2t)\mathbf{i} + (3t - 6)\mathbf{j} + (6t^3 + 5t^2 - 4)\mathbf{k}\right]dt$

b. $\int \left[\langle t, t^2, t^3 \rangle \times \langle t^3, t^2, t \rangle\right]dt$

c. $\int_0^{\pi/3} \left[\sin 2t\,\mathbf{i} + \tan t\,\mathbf{j} + e^{-2t}\,\mathbf{k}\right]dt$

### Solution

a. We use the first part of the definition of the integral of a space curve:

$$\begin{aligned}
\int &\left[(3t^2 + 2t)\mathbf{i} + (3t - 6)\mathbf{j} + (6t^3 + 5t^2 - 4)\mathbf{k}\right]dt \\
&= \left[\int 3t^2 + 2t\,dt\right]\mathbf{i} + \left[\int 3t - 6dt\right]\mathbf{j} + \left[\int 6t^3 + 5t^2 - 4dt\right]\mathbf{k} \\
&= (t^3 + t^2)\mathbf{i} + \left(\tfrac{3}{2}t^2 - 6t\right)\mathbf{j} + \left(\tfrac{3}{2}t^4 + \tfrac{5}{3}t^3 - 4t\right)\mathbf{k} + \mathbf{C}.
\end{aligned}$$

b. First calculate $\langle t, t^2, t^3 \rangle \times \langle t^3, t^2, t \rangle$:

$$\begin{aligned}
\langle t, t^2, t^3 \rangle \times \langle t^3, t^2, t \rangle &= \begin{vmatrix} \mathbf{i} & \mathbf{j} & \mathbf{k} \\ t & t^2 & t^3 \\ t^3 & t^2 & t \end{vmatrix} \\
&= (t^2(t) - t^3(t^2))\mathbf{i} - (t^2 - t^3(t^3))\mathbf{j} + (t(t^2) - t^2(t^3))\mathbf{k} \\
&= (t^3 - t^5)\mathbf{i} + (t^6 - t^2)\mathbf{j} + (t^3 - t^5)\mathbf{k}.
\end{aligned}$$

Next, substitute this back into the integral and integrate:

$$\int \Big[ \langle t, t^2, t^3 \rangle \times \langle t^3, t^2, t \rangle \Big] dt = \int \big(t^3 - t^5\big)\mathbf{i} + \big(t^6 - t^2\big)\mathbf{j} + \big(t^3 - t^5\big)\mathbf{k}\, dt$$

$$= \Big(\frac{t^4}{4} - \frac{t^6}{6}\Big)\mathbf{i} + \Big(\frac{t^7}{7} - \frac{t^3}{3}\Big)\mathbf{j} + \Big(\frac{t^4}{4} - \frac{t^6}{6}\Big)\mathbf{k} + \mathbf{C}.$$

c.  Use the second part of the definition of the integral of a space curve:

$$\int_0^{\pi/3} \Big[ \sin 2t\, \mathbf{i} + \tan t\, \mathbf{j} + e^{-2t}\, \mathbf{k} \Big] dt$$

$$= \Big[ \int_0^{\pi/3} \sin 2t\, dt \Big] \mathbf{i} + \Big[ \int_0^{\pi/3} \tan t\, dt \Big] \mathbf{j} + \Big[ \int_0^{\pi/3} e^{-2t}\, dt \Big] \mathbf{k}$$

$$= \Big( -\frac{1}{2}\cos 2t \Big)\Big|_0^{\pi/3}\, \mathbf{i} - (\ln(\cos t))\big|_0^{\pi/3}\, \mathbf{j} - \Big( \frac{1}{2}e^{-2t} \Big)\Big|_0^{\pi/3}\, \mathbf{k}$$

$$= \Big( -\frac{1}{2}\cos \frac{2\pi}{3} + \frac{1}{2}\cos 0 \Big)\mathbf{i} - \Big( \ln\Big(\cos\frac{\pi}{3}\Big) - \ln(\cos 0) \Big)\mathbf{j} - \Big( \frac{1}{2}e^{-2\pi/3} - \frac{1}{2}e^{-2(0)} \Big)\mathbf{k}$$

$$= \Big( \frac{1}{4} + \frac{1}{2} \Big)\mathbf{i} - (-\ln 2)\, \mathbf{j} - \Big( \frac{1}{2}e^{-2\pi/3} - \frac{1}{2} \Big)\mathbf{k}$$

$$= \frac{3}{4}\mathbf{i} + (\ln 2)\, \mathbf{j} + \Big( \frac{1}{2} - \frac{1}{2}e^{-2\pi/3} \Big)\mathbf{k}.$$

 **3.8**  Calculate the following integral:

$$\int_1^3 \Big[ (2t + 4)\mathbf{i} + \big(3t^2 - 4t\big)\mathbf{j} \Big] dt.$$

# 3.2 EXERCISES

Compute the derivatives of the vector-valued functions.

41. $\mathbf{r}(t) = t^3\mathbf{i} + 3t^2\mathbf{j} + \frac{t^3}{6}\mathbf{k}$

42. $\mathbf{r}(t) = \sin(t)\mathbf{i} + \cos(t)\mathbf{j} + e^t\mathbf{k}$

43. $\mathbf{r}(t) = e^{-t}\mathbf{i} + \sin(3t)\mathbf{j} + 10\sqrt{t}\mathbf{k}$. A sketch of the graph is shown here. Notice the varying periodic nature of the graph.

44. $\mathbf{r}(t) = e^t\mathbf{i} + 2e^t\mathbf{j} + \mathbf{k}$

45. $\mathbf{r}(t) = \mathbf{i} + \mathbf{j} + \mathbf{k}$

46. $\mathbf{r}(t) = te^t\mathbf{i} + t\ln(t)\mathbf{j} + \sin(3t)\mathbf{k}$

47. $\mathbf{r}(t) = \frac{1}{t+1}\mathbf{i} + \arctan(t)\mathbf{j} + \ln t^3\mathbf{k}$

48. $\mathbf{r}(t) = \tan(2t)\mathbf{i} + \sec(2t)\mathbf{j} + \sin^2(t)\mathbf{k}$

49. $\mathbf{r}(t) = 3\mathbf{i} + 4\sin(3t)\mathbf{j} + t\cos(t)\mathbf{k}$

50. $\mathbf{r}(t) = t^2\mathbf{i} + te^{-2t}\mathbf{j} - 5e^{-4t}\mathbf{k}$

For the following problems, find a tangent vector at the indicated value of $t$.

51. $\mathbf{r}(t) = t\mathbf{i} + \sin(2t)\mathbf{j} + \cos(3t)\mathbf{k}; t = \frac{\pi}{3}$

52. $\mathbf{r}(t) = 3t^3\mathbf{i} + 2t^2\mathbf{j} + \frac{1}{t}\mathbf{k}; t = 1$

53. $\mathbf{r}(t) = 3e^t\mathbf{i} + 2e^{-3t}\mathbf{j} + 4e^{2t}\mathbf{k}; \ t = \ln(2)$

54. $\mathbf{r}(t) = \cos(2t)\mathbf{i} + 2\sin t\mathbf{j} + t^2\mathbf{k}; t = \frac{\pi}{2}$

Find the unit tangent vector for the following parameterized curves.

55. $\mathbf{r}(t) = 6\mathbf{i} + \cos(3t)\mathbf{j} + 3\sin(4t)\mathbf{k}, \ \ 0 \le t < 2\pi$

56. $\mathbf{r}(t) = \cos t\mathbf{i} + \sin t\mathbf{j} + \sin t\mathbf{k}, \ \ \ 0 \le t < 2\pi$. Two views of this curve are presented here:

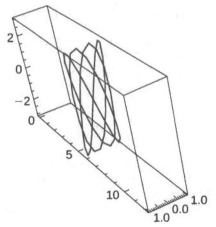

57. $\mathbf{r}(t) = 3\cos(4t)\mathbf{i} + 3\sin(4t)\mathbf{j} + 5t\mathbf{k}, 1 \le t \le 2$

58. $\mathbf{r}(t) = t\mathbf{i} + 3t\mathbf{j} + t^2\mathbf{k}$

Let $\mathbf{r}(t) = t\mathbf{i} + t^2\mathbf{j} - t^4\mathbf{k}$ and $s(t) = \sin(t)\mathbf{i} + e^t\mathbf{j} + \cos(t)\mathbf{k}$. Here is the graph of the function:

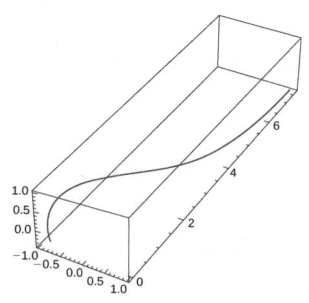

Find the following.

59. $\dfrac{d}{dt}\left[r\left(t^2\right)\right]$

60. $\dfrac{d}{dt}\left[t^2 \cdot s(t)\right]$

61. $\dfrac{d}{dt}\left[r(t) \cdot s(t)\right]$

62. Compute the first, second, and third derivatives of $\mathbf{r}(t) = 3t\mathbf{i} + 6\ln(t)\mathbf{j} + 5e^{-3t}\,\mathbf{k}$.

63. Find $\mathbf{r}'(t) \cdot \mathbf{r}''(t)$ for $\mathbf{r}(t) = -3t^5\,\mathbf{i} + 5t\mathbf{j} + 2t^2\,\mathbf{k}$.

64. The acceleration function, initial velocity, and initial position of a particle are
$\mathbf{a}(t) = -5\cos t\,\mathbf{i} - 5\sin t\,\mathbf{j}$, $\mathbf{v}(0) = 9\mathbf{i} + 2\mathbf{j}$, and $\mathbf{r}(0) = 5\mathbf{i}$.
Find $\mathbf{v}(t)$ and $\mathbf{r}(t)$.

65. The position vector of a particle is
$\mathbf{r}(t) = 5\sec(2t)\mathbf{i} - 4\tan(t)\mathbf{j} + 7t^2\,\mathbf{k}$.

    a. Graph the position function and display a view of the graph that illustrates the asymptotic behavior of the function.
    b. Find the velocity as $t$ approaches but is not equal to $\pi/4$ (if it exists).

66. Find the velocity and the speed of a particle with the position function $\mathbf{r}(t) = \left(\dfrac{2t-1}{2t+1}\right)\mathbf{i} + \ln(1 - 4t^2)\mathbf{j}$. The speed of a particle is the magnitude of the velocity and is represented by $\|r'(t)\|$.

A particle moves on a circular path of radius $b$ according to the function $\mathbf{r}(t) = b\cos(\omega t)\mathbf{i} + b\sin(\omega t)\mathbf{j}$, where $\omega$ is the angular velocity, $d\theta/dt$.

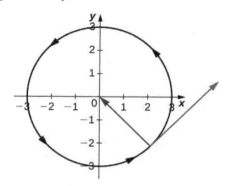

67. Find the velocity function and show that $\mathbf{v}(t)$ is always orthogonal to $\mathbf{r}(t)$.

68. Show that the speed of the particle is proportional to the angular velocity.

69. Evaluate $\dfrac{d}{dt}[\mathbf{u}(t) \times \mathbf{u}'(t)]$ given $\mathbf{u}(t) = t^2\,\mathbf{i} - 2t\mathbf{j} + \mathbf{k}$.

70. Find the antiderivative of $\mathbf{r}'(t) = \cos(2t)\mathbf{i} - 2\sin t\,\mathbf{j} + \dfrac{1}{1+t^2}\mathbf{k}$ that satisfies the initial condition $\mathbf{r}(0) = 3\mathbf{i} - 2\mathbf{j} + \mathbf{k}$.

71. Evaluate $\displaystyle\int_0^3 \|t\mathbf{i} + t^2\,\mathbf{j}\|\,dt$.

72. An object starts from rest at point $P(1, 2, 0)$ and moves with an acceleration of $\mathbf{a}(t) = \mathbf{j} + 2\mathbf{k}$, where $\|\mathbf{a}(t)\|$ is measured in feet per second per second. Find the location of the object after $t = 2$ sec.

73. Show that if the speed of a particle traveling along a curve represented by a vector-valued function is constant, then the velocity function is always perpendicular to the acceleration function.

74. Given $\mathbf{r}(t) = t\mathbf{i} + 3t\mathbf{j} + t^2\,\mathbf{k}$ and $\mathbf{u}(t) = 4t\mathbf{i} + t^2\,\mathbf{j} + t^3\,\mathbf{k}$, find $\dfrac{d}{dt}(\mathbf{r}(t) \times \mathbf{u}(t))$.

75. Given $\mathbf{r}(t) = \langle\, t + \cos t,\ t - \sin t \,\rangle$, find the velocity and the speed at any time.

76. Find the velocity vector for the function $\mathbf{r}(t) = \langle\, e^t,\ e^{-t},\ 0 \,\rangle$.

77. Find the equation of the tangent line to the curve $\mathbf{r}(t) = \langle\, e^t,\ e^{-t},\ 0 \,\rangle$ at $t = 0$.

**78.** Describe and sketch the curve represented by the vector-valued function $\mathbf{r}(t) = \langle\, 6t, 6t - t^2 \,\rangle$.

**79.** Locate the highest point on the curve $\mathbf{r}(t) = \langle\, 6t, 6t - t^2 \,\rangle$ and give the value of the function at this point.

The position vector for a particle is $\mathbf{r}(t) = t\mathbf{i} + t^2\,\mathbf{j} + t^3\,\mathbf{k}$. The graph is shown here:

**80.** Find the velocity vector at any time.

**81.** Find the speed of the particle at time $t = 2$ sec.

**82.** Find the acceleration at time $t = 2$ sec.

A particle travels along the path of a helix with the equation $\mathbf{r}(t) = \cos(t)\mathbf{i} + \sin(t)\mathbf{j} + t\mathbf{k}$. See the graph presented here:

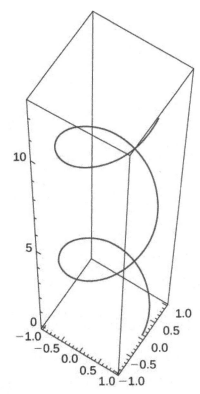

Find the following:

**83.** Velocity of the particle at any time

**84.** Speed of the particle at any time

**85.** Acceleration of the particle at any time

**86.** Find the unit tangent vector for the helix.

A particle travels along the path of an ellipse with the equation $\mathbf{r}(t) = \cos t\,\mathbf{i} + 2\sin t\,\mathbf{j} + 0\mathbf{k}$. Find the following:

**87.** Velocity of the particle

**88.** Speed of the particle at $t = \frac{\pi}{4}$

**89.** Acceleration of the particle at $t = \frac{\pi}{4}$

Given the vector-valued function $\mathbf{r}(t) = \langle\, \tan t, \sec t, 0 \,\rangle$ (graph is shown here), find the following:

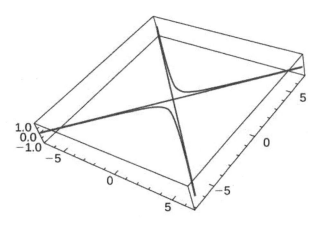

90. Velocity

91. Speed

92. Acceleration

93. Find the minimum speed of a particle traveling along the curve $\mathbf{r}(t) = \langle\, t + \cos t,\ t - \sin t\,\rangle \quad t \in [0,\, 2\pi)$.

Given $\qquad \mathbf{r}(t) = t\mathbf{i} + 2\sin t\,\mathbf{j} + 2\cos t\,\mathbf{k} \qquad$ and $\mathbf{u}(t) = \frac{1}{t}\mathbf{i} + 2\sin t\,\mathbf{j} + 2\cos t\,\mathbf{k}$, find the following:

94. $\mathbf{r}(t) \times \mathbf{u}(t)$

95. $\frac{d}{dt}(\mathbf{r}(t) \times \mathbf{u}(t))$

96. Now, use the product rule for the derivative of the cross product of two vectors and show this result is the same as the answer for the preceding problem.

Find the unit tangent vector $\mathbf{T}(t)$ for the following vector-valued functions.

97. $\mathbf{r}(t) = \langle\, t,\ \frac{1}{t}\,\rangle$. The graph is shown here:

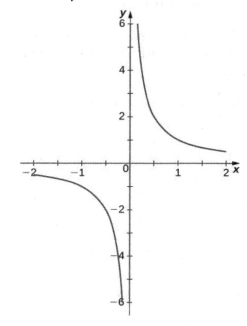

98. $\mathbf{r}(t) = \langle\, t\cos t,\ t\sin t\,\rangle$

99. $\mathbf{r}(t) = \langle\, t + 1,\ 2t + 1,\ 2t + 2\,\rangle$

Evaluate the following integrals:

100. $\int \left( e^t\,\mathbf{i} + \sin t\,\mathbf{j} + \frac{1}{2t - 1}\mathbf{k} \right) dt$

101. $\int_0^1 \mathbf{r}(t)\,dt, \quad \text{where } \mathbf{r}(t) = \langle\, \sqrt[3]{t},\ \frac{1}{t + 1},\ e^{-t}\,\rangle$

# 3.3 | Arc Length and Curvature

## Learning Objectives

3.3.1 Determine the length of a particle's path in space by using the arc-length function.

3.3.2 Explain the meaning of the curvature of a curve in space and state its formula.

3.3.3 Describe the meaning of the normal and binormal vectors of a curve in space.

In this section, we study formulas related to curves in both two and three dimensions, and see how they are related to various properties of the same curve. For example, suppose a vector-valued function describes the motion of a particle in space. We would like to determine how far the particle has traveled over a given time interval, which can be described by the arc length of the path it follows. Or, suppose that the vector-valued function describes a road we are building and we want to determine how sharply the road curves at a given point. This is described by the curvature of the function at that point. We explore each of these concepts in this section.

## Arc Length for Vector Functions

We have seen how a vector-valued function describes a curve in either two or three dimensions. Recall **Alternative Formulas for Curvature**, which states that the formula for the arc length of a curve defined by the parametric functions $x = x(t)$, $y = y(t)$, $t_1 \leq t \leq t_2$ is given by

$$s = \int_{t_1}^{t_2} \sqrt{(x'(t))^2 + (y'(t))^2}\, dt.$$

In a similar fashion, if we define a smooth curve using a vector-valued function $\mathbf{r}(t) = f(t)\,\mathbf{i} + g(t)\,\mathbf{j}$, where $a \leq t \leq b$, the arc length is given by the formula

$$s = \int_{a}^{b} \sqrt{(f'(t))^2 + (g'(t))^2}\, dt.$$

In three dimensions, if the vector-valued function is described by $\mathbf{r}(t) = f(t)\,\mathbf{i} + g(t)\,\mathbf{j} + h(t)\,\mathbf{k}$ over the same interval $a \leq t \leq b$, the arc length is given by

$$s = \int_{a}^{b} \sqrt{(f'(t))^2 + (g'(t))^2 + (h'(t))^2}\, dt.$$

### Theorem 3.4: Arc-Length Formulas

i. *Plane curve*: Given a smooth curve $C$ defined by the function $\mathbf{r}(t) = f(t)\,\mathbf{i} + g(t)\,\mathbf{j}$, where $t$ lies within the interval $[a, b]$, the arc length of $C$ over the interval is

$$s = \int_{a}^{b} \sqrt{[f'(t)]^2 + [g'(t)]^2}\, dt = \int_{a}^{b} \| \mathbf{r}'(t) \| \, dt. \tag{3.11}$$

ii. *Space curve*: Given a smooth curve $C$ defined by the function $\mathbf{r}(t) = f(t)\,\mathbf{i} + g(t)\,\mathbf{j} + h(t)\,\mathbf{k}$, where $t$ lies within the interval $[a, b]$, the arc length of $C$ over the interval is

$$s = \int_{a}^{b} \sqrt{[f'(t)]^2 + [g'(t)]^2 + [h'(t)]^2}\, dt = \int_{a}^{b} \| \mathbf{r}'(t) \| \, dt. \tag{3.12}$$

The two formulas are very similar; they differ only in the fact that a space curve has three component functions instead of two. Note that the formulas are defined for smooth curves: curves where the vector-valued function $\mathbf{r}(t)$ is differentiable with a non-zero derivative. The smoothness condition guarantees that the curve has no cusps (or corners) that could make the formula problematic.

## Example 3.9

### Finding the Arc Length

Calculate the arc length for each of the following vector-valued functions:

a.  $\mathbf{r}(t) = (3t - 2)\mathbf{i} + (4t + 5)\mathbf{j}$, $1 \le t \le 5$

b.  $\mathbf{r}(t) = \langle t\cos t, \, t\sin t, \, 2t \rangle$, $0 \le t \le 2\pi$

### Solution

a.  Using Equation 3.11, $\mathbf{r}'(t) = 3\mathbf{i} + 4\mathbf{j}$,  so

$$
\begin{aligned}
s &= \int_a^b \| \mathbf{r}'(t) \| \; dt \\
&= \int_a^5 \sqrt{3^2 + 4^2}\, dt \\
&= \int_1^5 5 \, dt = 5t\big|_1^5 = 20.
\end{aligned}
$$

b.  Using Equation 3.12, $\mathbf{r}'(t) = \langle \cos t - t\sin t, \, \sin t + t\cos t, \, 2 \rangle$,  so

$$
\begin{aligned}
s &= \int_a^b \| \mathbf{r}'(t) \| \; dt \\
&= \int_0^{2\pi} \sqrt{(\cos t - t\sin t)^2 + (\sin t + t\cos t)^2 + 2^2}\, dt \\
&= \int_0^{2\pi} \sqrt{\left(\cos^2 t - 2t\sin t\cos t + t^2\sin^2 t\right) + \left(\sin^2 t + 2t\sin t\cos t + t^2\cos^2 t\right) + 4}\, dt \\
&= \int_0^{2\pi} \sqrt{\cos^2 t + \sin^2 t + t^2\left(\cos^2 t + \sin^2 t\right) + 4}\, dt \\
&= \int_0^{2\pi} \sqrt{t^2 + 5}\, dt.
\end{aligned}
$$

Here we can use a table integration formula

$$
\int \sqrt{u^2 + a^2}\, du = \frac{u}{2}\sqrt{u^2 + a^2} + \frac{a^2}{2}\ln\left|u + \sqrt{u^2 + a^2}\right| + C,
$$

so we obtain

$$
\begin{aligned}
\int_0^{2\pi} \sqrt{t^2 + 5}\, dt &= \frac{1}{2}\left(t\sqrt{t^2 + 5} + 5\ln\left|t + \sqrt{t^2 + 5}\right|\right)\Big|_0^{2\pi} \\
&= \frac{1}{2}\left(2\pi\sqrt{4\pi^2 + 5} + 5\ln\left(2\pi + \sqrt{4\pi^2 + 5}\right)\right) - \frac{5}{2}\ln\sqrt{5} \\
&\approx 25.343.
\end{aligned}
$$

  **3.9**  Calculate the arc length of the parameterized curve

$$
\mathbf{r}(t) = \langle 2t^2 + 1, \, 2t^2 - 1, \, t^3 \rangle, \; 0 \le t \le 3.
$$

We now return to the helix introduced earlier in this chapter. A vector-valued function that describes a helix can be written in the form

$$\mathbf{r}(t) = R\cos\left(\frac{2\pi Nt}{h}\right)\mathbf{i} + R\sin\left(\frac{2\pi Nt}{h}\right)\mathbf{j} + t\,\mathbf{k}, \ \ 0 \le t \le h,$$

where $R$ represents the radius of the helix, $h$ represents the height (distance between two consecutive turns), and the helix completes $N$ turns. Let's derive a formula for the arc length of this helix using Equation 3.12. First of all,

$$\mathbf{r}'(t) = -\frac{2\pi NR}{h}\sin\left(\frac{2\pi Nt}{h}\right)\mathbf{i} + \frac{2\pi NR}{h}\cos\left(\frac{2\pi Nt}{h}\right)\mathbf{j} + \mathbf{k}.$$

Therefore,

$$\begin{aligned}
s &= \int_a^b \|\mathbf{r}'(t)\|\ dt \\
&= \int_0^h \sqrt{\left(-\frac{2\pi NR}{h}\sin\left(\frac{2\pi Nt}{h}\right)\right)^2 + \left(\frac{2\pi NR}{h}\cos\left(\frac{2\pi Nt}{h}\right)\right)^2 + 1^2}\,dt \\
&= \int_0^h \sqrt{\frac{4\pi^2 N^2 R^2}{h^2}\left(\sin^2\left(\frac{2\pi Nt}{h}\right) + \cos^2\left(\frac{2\pi Nt}{h}\right)\right) + 1}\,dt \\
&= \int_0^h \sqrt{\frac{4\pi^2 N^2 R^2}{h^2} + 1}\,dt \\
&= \left[ t\sqrt{\frac{4\pi^2 N^2 R^2}{h^2} + 1}\ \right]_0^h \\
&= h\sqrt{\frac{4\pi^2 N^2 R^2 + h^2}{h^2}} \\
&= \sqrt{4\pi^2 N^2 R^2 + h^2}.
\end{aligned}$$

This gives a formula for the length of a wire needed to form a helix with $N$ turns that has radius $R$ and height $h$.

## Arc-Length Parameterization

We now have a formula for the arc length of a curve defined by a vector-valued function. Let's take this one step further and examine what an **arc-length function** is.

If a vector-valued function represents the position of a particle in space as a function of time, then the arc-length function measures how far that particle travels as a function of time. The formula for the arc-length function follows directly from the formula for arc length:

$$s(t) = \int_a^t \sqrt{(f'(u))^2 + (g'(u))^2 + (h'(u))^2}\,du. \tag{3.13}$$

If the curve is in two dimensions, then only two terms appear under the square root inside the integral. The reason for using the independent variable $u$ is to distinguish between time and the variable of integration. Since $s(t)$ measures distance traveled as a function of time, $s'(t)$ measures the speed of the particle at any given time. Since we have a formula for $s(t)$ in Equation 3.13, we can differentiate both sides of the equation:

$$\begin{aligned}
s'(t) &= \frac{d}{dt}\left[\int_a^t \sqrt{(f'(u))^2 + (g'(u))^2 + (h'(u))^2}\,du\right] \\
&= \frac{d}{dt}\left[\int_a^t \|\mathbf{r}'(u)\|\ du\right] \\
&= \|\mathbf{r}'(t)\|.
\end{aligned}$$

If we assume that $\mathbf{r}(t)$ defines a smooth curve, then the arc length is always increasing, so $s'(t) > 0$ for $t > a$. Last, if $\mathbf{r}(t)$ is a curve on which $\|\mathbf{r}'(t)\| = 1$ for all $t$, then

$$s(t) = \int_a^t \|\mathbf{r}'(u)\|\ du = \int_a^t 1\,du = t - a,$$

which means that $t$ represents the arc length as long as $a = 0$.

### Theorem 3.5: Arc-Length Function

Let $\mathbf{r}(t)$ describe a smooth curve for $t \geq a$. Then the arc-length function is given by

$$s(t) = \int_a^t \| \mathbf{r}'(u) \| \, du. \tag{3.14}$$

Furthermore, $\frac{ds}{dt} = \| \mathbf{r}'(t) \| > 0$. If $\| \mathbf{r}'(t) \| = 1$ for all $t \geq a$, then the parameter $t$ represents the arc length from the starting point at $t = a$.

A useful application of this theorem is to find an alternative parameterization of a given curve, called an **arc-length parameterization**. Recall that any vector-valued function can be reparameterized via a change of variables. For example, if we have a function $\mathbf{r}(t) = \langle 3\cos t, 3\sin t \rangle$, $0 \leq t \leq 2\pi$ that parameterizes a circle of radius 3, we can change the parameter from $t$ to $4t$, obtaining a new parameterization $\mathbf{r}(t) = \langle 3\cos 4t, 3\sin 4t \rangle$. The new parameterization still defines a circle of radius 3, but now we need only use the values $0 \leq t \leq \pi/2$ to traverse the circle once.

Suppose that we find the arc-length function $s(t)$ and are able to solve this function for $t$ as a function of $s$. We can then reparameterize the original function $\mathbf{r}(t)$ by substituting the expression for $t$ back into $\mathbf{r}(t)$. The vector-valued function is now written in terms of the parameter $s$. Since the variable $s$ represents the arc length, we call this an *arc-length parameterization* of the original function $\mathbf{r}(t)$. One advantage of finding the arc-length parameterization is that the distance traveled along the curve starting from $s = 0$ is now equal to the parameter $s$. The arc-length parameterization also appears in the context of curvature (which we examine later in this section) and line integrals, which we study in the **Introduction to Vector Calculus**.

## Example 3.10

### Finding an Arc-Length Parameterization

Find the arc-length parameterization for each of the following curves:

    a.  $\mathbf{r}(t) = 4\cos t \, \mathbf{i} + 4\sin t \, \mathbf{j}$, $t \geq 0$

    b.  $\mathbf{r}(t) = \langle t + 3, \ 2t - 4, \ 2t \rangle$, $t \geq 3$

### Solution

    a.  First we find the arc-length function using **Equation 3.14**:

$$\begin{aligned}
s(t) &= \int_a^t \| \mathbf{r}'(u) \| \, du \\
&= \int_0^t \| \langle -4\sin u, 4\cos u \rangle \| \, du \\
&= \int_0^t \sqrt{(-4\sin u)^2 + (4\cos u)^2} \, du \\
&= \int_0^t \sqrt{16\sin^2 u + 16\cos^2 u} \, du \\
&= \int_0^t 4 \, du = 4t,
\end{aligned}$$

        which gives the relationship between the arc length $s$ and the parameter $t$ as $s = 4t$; so, $t = s/4$. Next we replace the variable $t$ in the original function $\mathbf{r}(t) = 4\cos t\,\mathbf{i} + 4\sin t\,\mathbf{j}$ with the expression $s/4$ to obtain

$$\mathbf{r}(s) = 4\cos\left(\tfrac{s}{4}\right)\mathbf{i} + 4\sin\left(\tfrac{s}{4}\right)\mathbf{j}.$$

This is the arc-length parameterization of $\mathbf{r}(t)$. Since the original restriction on $t$ was given by $t \geq 0$, the restriction on $s$ becomes $s/4 \geq 0$, or $s \geq 0$.

b.  The arc-length function is given by **Equation 3.14**:

$$
\begin{aligned}
s(t) &= \int_a^t \| \mathbf{r}'(u) \| \ du \\
&= \int_3^t \| \langle 1, 2, 2 \rangle \| \ du \\
&= \int_3^t \sqrt{1^2 + 2^2 + 2^2} \ du \\
&= \int_3^t 3 \ du \\
&= 3t - 9.
\end{aligned}
$$

Therefore, the relationship between the arc length $s$ and the parameter $t$ is $s = 3t - 9$, so $t = \tfrac{s}{3} + 3$.
Substituting this into the original function $\mathbf{r}(t) = \langle t+3, \ 2t-4, \ 2t \rangle$ yields

$$\mathbf{r}(s) = \left\langle \left(\tfrac{s}{3}+3\right)+3, \ 2\left(\tfrac{s}{3}+3\right)-4, \ 2\left(\tfrac{s}{3}+3\right) \right\rangle = \left\langle \tfrac{s}{3}+6, \ \tfrac{2s}{3}+2, \ \tfrac{2s}{3}+6 \right\rangle.$$

This is an arc-length parameterization of $\mathbf{r}(t)$. The original restriction on the parameter $t$ was $t \geq 3$, so the restriction on $s$ is $(s/3)+3 \geq 3$, or $s \geq 0$.

**3.10**   Find the arc-length function for the helix

$$\mathbf{r}(t) = \langle 3\cos t, \ 3\sin t, \ 4t \rangle, \ t \geq 0.$$

Then, use the relationship between the arc length and the parameter $t$ to find an arc-length parameterization of $\mathbf{r}(t)$.

## Curvature

An important topic related to arc length is curvature. The concept of curvature provides a way to measure how sharply a smooth curve turns. A circle has constant curvature. The smaller the radius of the circle, the greater the curvature.

Think of driving down a road. Suppose the road lies on an arc of a large circle. In this case you would barely have to turn the wheel to stay on the road. Now suppose the radius is smaller. In this case you would need to turn more sharply to stay on the road. In the case of a curve other than a circle, it is often useful first to inscribe a circle to the curve at a given point so that it is tangent to the curve at that point and "hugs" the curve as closely as possible in a neighborhood of the point (**Figure 3.6**). The curvature of the graph at that point is then defined to be the same as the curvature of the inscribed circle.

**Figure 3.6** The graph represents the curvature of a function $y = f(x)$. The sharper the turn in the graph, the greater the curvature, and the smaller the radius of the inscribed circle.

### Definition

Let $C$ be a smooth curve in the plane or in space given by $\mathbf{r}(s)$, where $s$ is the arc-length parameter. The **curvature** $\kappa$ at $s$ is

$$\kappa = \left\| \frac{d\mathbf{T}}{ds} \right\| = \| \mathbf{T}'(s) \| .$$

> Visit this website (http://www.openstaxcollege.org/l/20_spacecurve) for more information about the curvature of a space curve.

The formula in the definition of curvature is not very useful in terms of calculation. In particular, recall that $\mathbf{T}(t)$ represents the unit tangent vector to a given vector-valued function $\mathbf{r}(t)$, and the formula for $\mathbf{T}(t)$ is $\mathbf{T}(t) = \dfrac{\mathbf{r}'(t)}{\| \mathbf{r}'(t) \|}$. To use the formula for curvature, it is first necessary to express $\mathbf{r}(t)$ in terms of the arc-length parameter $s$, then find the unit tangent vector $\mathbf{T}(s)$ for the function $\mathbf{r}(s)$, then take the derivative of $\mathbf{T}(s)$ with respect to $s$. This is a tedious process. Fortunately, there are equivalent formulas for curvature.

### Theorem 3.6: Alternative Formulas for Curvature

If $C$ is a smooth curve given by $\mathbf{r}(t)$, then the curvature $\kappa$ of $C$ at $t$ is given by

$$\kappa = \frac{\| \mathbf{T}'(t) \|}{\| \mathbf{r}'(t) \|}. \tag{3.15}$$

If $C$ is a three-dimensional curve, then the curvature can be given by the formula

$$\kappa = \frac{\| \mathbf{r}'(t) \times \mathbf{r}''(t) \|}{\| \mathbf{r}'(t) \|^3}. \tag{3.16}$$

If $C$ is the graph of a function $y = f(x)$ and both $y'$ and $y''$ exist, then the curvature $\kappa$ at point $(x, y)$ is given by

$$\kappa = \frac{|y''|}{\left[ 1 + (y')^2 \right]^{3/2}}. \tag{3.17}$$

### Proof

The first formula follows directly from the chain rule:

$$\frac{d\mathbf{T}}{dt} = \frac{d\mathbf{T}}{ds} \frac{ds}{dt},$$

where $s$ is the arc length along the curve $C$. Dividing both sides by $ds/dt$, and taking the magnitude of both sides gives

$$\left\| \frac{d\mathbf{T}}{ds} \right\| = \left\| \frac{\mathbf{T}'(t)}{\frac{ds}{dt}} \right\|.$$

Since $ds/dt = \|\mathbf{r}'(t)\|$, this gives the formula for the curvature $\kappa$ of a curve $C$ in terms of any parameterization of $C$:

$$\kappa = \frac{\|\mathbf{T}'(t)\|}{\|\mathbf{r}'(t)\|}.$$

In the case of a three-dimensional curve, we start with the formulas $\mathbf{T}(t) = (\mathbf{r}'(t))/\|\mathbf{r}'(t)\|$ and $ds/dt = \|\mathbf{r}'(t)\|$. Therefore, $\mathbf{r}'(t) = (ds/dt)\mathbf{T}(t)$. We can take the derivative of this function using the scalar product formula:

$$\mathbf{r}''(t) = \frac{d^2 s}{dt^2}\mathbf{T}(t) + \frac{ds}{dt}\mathbf{T}'(t).$$

Using these last two equations we get

$$\begin{aligned}
\mathbf{r}'(t) \times \mathbf{r}''(t) &= \frac{ds}{dt}\mathbf{T}(t) \times \left( \frac{d^2 s}{dt^2}\mathbf{T}(t) + \frac{ds}{dt}\mathbf{T}'(t) \right) \\
&= \frac{ds}{dt}\frac{d^2 s}{dt^2}\mathbf{T}(t) \times \mathbf{T}(t) + \left(\frac{ds}{dt}\right)^2 \mathbf{T}(t) \times \mathbf{T}'(t).
\end{aligned}$$

Since $\mathbf{T}(t) \times \mathbf{T}(t) = \mathbf{0}$, this reduces to

$$\mathbf{r}'(t) \times \mathbf{r}''(t) = \left(\frac{ds}{dt}\right)^2 \mathbf{T}(t) \times \mathbf{T}'(t).$$

Since $\mathbf{T}'$ is parallel to $\mathbf{N}$, and $\mathbf{T}$ is orthogonal to $\mathbf{N}$, it follows that $\mathbf{T}$ and $\mathbf{T}'$ are orthogonal. This means that $\|\mathbf{T} \times \mathbf{T}'\| = \|\mathbf{T}\| \|\mathbf{T}'\| \sin(\pi/2) = \|\mathbf{T}'\|$, so

$$\mathbf{r}'(t) \times \mathbf{r}''(t) = \left(\frac{ds}{dt}\right)^2 \|\mathbf{T}'(t)\|.$$

Now we solve this equation for $\|\mathbf{T}'(t)\|$ and use the fact that $ds/dt = \|\mathbf{r}'(t)\|$:

$$\|\mathbf{T}'(t)\| = \frac{\|\mathbf{r}'(t) \times \mathbf{r}''(t)\|}{\|\mathbf{r}'(t)\|^2}.$$

Then, we divide both sides by $\|\mathbf{r}'(t)\|$. This gives

$$\kappa = \frac{\|\mathbf{T}'(t)\|}{\|\mathbf{r}'(t)\|} = \frac{\|\mathbf{r}'(t) \times \mathbf{r}''(t)\|}{\|\mathbf{r}'(t)\|^3}.$$

This proves Equation 3.16. To prove Equation 3.17, we start with the assumption that curve $C$ is defined by the function $y = f(x)$. Then, we can define $\mathbf{r}(t) = x\mathbf{i} + f(x)\mathbf{j} + 0\mathbf{k}$. Using the previous formula for curvature:

$$\begin{aligned}
\mathbf{r}'(t) &= \mathbf{i} + f'(x)\mathbf{j} \\
\mathbf{r}''(t) &= f''(x)\mathbf{j} \\
\mathbf{r}'(t) \times \mathbf{r}''(t) &= \begin{vmatrix} \mathbf{i} & \mathbf{j} & \mathbf{k} \\ 1 & f'(x) & 0 \\ 0 & f''(x) & 0 \end{vmatrix} = f''(x)\mathbf{k}.
\end{aligned}$$

Therefore,

$$\kappa = \frac{\|\mathbf{r}'(t) \times \mathbf{r}''(t)\|}{\|\mathbf{r}'(t)\|^3} = \frac{|f''(x)|}{\left(1 + [(f'(x))^2]\right)^{3/2}}.$$

$\square$

## Example 3.11

### Finding Curvature

Find the curvature for each of the following curves at the given point:

a.   $\mathbf{r}(t) = 4\cos t\,\mathbf{i} + 4\sin t\,\mathbf{j} + 3t\,\mathbf{k},\ t = \frac{4\pi}{3}$

b.   $f(x) = \sqrt{4x - x^2},\ x = 2$

### Solution

a.   This function describes a helix.

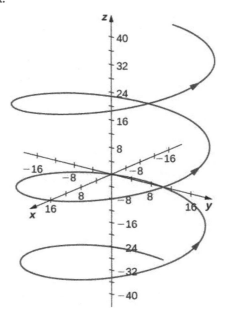

The curvature of the helix at $t = (4\pi)/3$ can be found by using **Equation 3.15**. First, calculate $\mathbf{T}(t)$:

$$
\begin{aligned}
\mathbf{T}(t) &= \frac{\mathbf{r}'(t)}{\|\,\mathbf{r}'(t)\,\|} \\[2mm]
&= \frac{\langle\, -4\sin t,\ 4\cos t,\ 3\,\rangle}{\sqrt{(-4\sin t)^2 + (4\cos t)^2 + 3^2}} \\[2mm]
&= \langle\, -\tfrac{4}{5}\sin t,\ \tfrac{4}{5}\cos t,\ \tfrac{3}{5}\,\rangle.
\end{aligned}
$$

Next, calculate $\mathbf{T}'(t)$:

$$
\mathbf{T}'(t) = \langle\, -\tfrac{4}{5}\cos t,\ -\tfrac{4}{5}\sin t,\ 0\,\rangle.
$$

Last, apply **Equation 3.15**:

$$\kappa = \frac{\|\mathbf{T}'(t)\|}{\|\mathbf{r}'(t)\|} = \frac{\|\left\langle -\frac{4}{5}\cos t, \ -\frac{4}{5}\sin t, \ 0 \right\rangle\|}{\|\left\langle -4\sin t, \ 4\cos t, \ 3 \right\rangle\|}$$

$$= \frac{\sqrt{\left(-\frac{4}{5}\cos t\right)^2 + \left(-\frac{4}{5}\sin t\right)^2 + 0^2}}{\sqrt{(-4\sin t)^2 + (4\cos t)^2 + 3^2}}$$

$$= \frac{4/5}{5} = \frac{4}{25}.$$

The curvature of this helix is constant at all points on the helix.

b.   This function describes a semicircle.

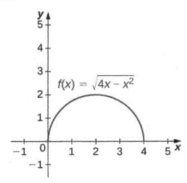

$f(x) = \sqrt{4x - x^2}$

To find the curvature of this graph, we must use **Equation 3.16**. First, we calculate $y'$ and $y''$:

$$y = \sqrt{4x - x^2} = \left(4x - x^2\right)^{1/2}$$

$$y' = \frac{1}{2}\left(4x - x^2\right)^{-1/2}(4 - 2x) = (2 - x)\left(4x - x^2\right)^{-1/2}$$

$$y'' = -\left(4x - x^2\right)^{-1/2} + (2 - x)\left(-\frac{1}{2}\right)\left(4x - x^2\right)^{-3/2}(4 - 2x)$$

$$= -\frac{4x - x^2}{\left(4x - x^2\right)^{3/2}} - \frac{(2 - x)^2}{\left(4x - x^2\right)^{3/2}}$$

$$= \frac{x^2 - 4x - \left(4 - 4x + x^2\right)}{\left(4x - x^2\right)^{3/2}}$$

$$= -\frac{4}{\left(4x - x^2\right)^{3/2}}.$$

Then, we apply **Equation 3.17**:

$$\kappa = \frac{|y''|}{\left[1 + (y')^2\right]^{3/2}}$$

$$= \frac{\left|-\dfrac{4}{\left(4x - x^2\right)^{3/2}}\right|}{\left[1 + \left((2 - x)\left(4x - x^2\right)^{-1/2}\right)^2\right]^{3/2}} = \frac{\left|\dfrac{4}{\left(4x - x^2\right)^{3/2}}\right|}{\left[1 + \dfrac{(2 - x)^2}{4x - x^2}\right]^{3/2}}$$

$$= \frac{\left|\dfrac{4}{\left(4x - x^2\right)^{3/2}}\right|}{\left[\dfrac{4x - x^2 + x^2 - 4x + 4}{4x - x^2}\right]^{3/2}} = \left|\frac{4}{\left(4x - x^2\right)^{3/2}}\right| \cdot \frac{\left(4x - x^2\right)^{3/2}}{8}$$

$$= \frac{1}{2}.$$

The curvature of this circle is equal to the reciprocal of its radius. There is a minor issue with the absolute value in **Equation 3.16**; however, a closer look at the calculation reveals that the denominator is positive for any value of $x$.

 **3.11**   Find the curvature of the curve defined by the function

$$y = 3x^2 - 2x + 4$$

at the point $x = 2$.

## The Normal and Binormal Vectors

We have seen that the derivative $\mathbf{r}'(t)$ of a vector-valued function is a tangent vector to the curve defined by $\mathbf{r}(t)$, and the unit tangent vector $\mathbf{T}(t)$ can be calculated by dividing $\mathbf{r}'(t)$ by its magnitude. When studying motion in three dimensions, two other vectors are useful in describing the motion of a particle along a path in space: the **principal unit normal vector** and the **binormal vector**.

---

### Definition

Let $C$ be a three-dimensional **smooth** curve represented by $\mathbf{r}$ over an open interval $I$. If $\mathbf{T}'(t) \neq \mathbf{0}$, then the principal unit normal vector at $t$ is defined to be

$$\mathbf{N}(t) = \frac{\mathbf{T}'(t)}{\|\mathbf{T}'(t)\|}. \tag{3.18}$$

The binormal vector at $t$ is defined as

$$\mathbf{B}(t) = \mathbf{T}(t) \times \mathbf{N}(t), \tag{3.19}$$

where $\mathbf{T}(t)$ is the unit tangent vector.

---

Note that, by definition, the binormal vector is orthogonal to both the unit tangent vector and the normal vector. Furthermore, $\mathbf{B}(t)$ is always a unit vector. This can be shown using the formula for the magnitude of a cross product

$$\| \mathbf{B}(t) \| \ = \ \| \mathbf{T}(t) \times \mathbf{N}(t) \| \ = \ \| \mathbf{T}(t) \| \ \| \mathbf{N}(t) \| \sin\theta,$$

where $\theta$ is the angle between $\mathbf{T}(t)$ and $\mathbf{N}(t)$. Since $\mathbf{N}(t)$ is the derivative of a unit vector, property (vii) of the derivative of a vector-valued function tells us that $\mathbf{T}(t)$ and $\mathbf{N}(t)$ are orthogonal to each other, so $\theta = \pi/2$. Furthermore, they are both unit vectors, so their magnitude is 1. Therefore, $\| \mathbf{T}(t) \| \ \| \mathbf{N}(t) \| \sin\theta = (1)(1)\sin(\pi/2) = 1$ and $\mathbf{B}(t)$ is a unit vector.

The principal unit normal vector can be challenging to calculate because the unit tangent vector involves a quotient, and this quotient often has a square root in the denominator. In the three-dimensional case, finding the cross product of the unit tangent vector and the unit normal vector can be even more cumbersome. Fortunately, we have alternative formulas for finding these two vectors, and they are presented in Motion in Space.

## Example 3.12

### Finding the Principal Unit Normal Vector and Binormal Vector

For each of the following vector-valued functions, find the principal unit normal vector. Then, if possible, find the binormal vector.

a.  $\mathbf{r}(t) = 4\cos t\,\mathbf{i} - 4\sin t\,\mathbf{j}$

b.  $\mathbf{r}(t) = (6t + 2)\,\mathbf{i} + 5t^2\,\mathbf{j} - 8t\,\mathbf{k}$

### Solution

a.  This function describes a circle.

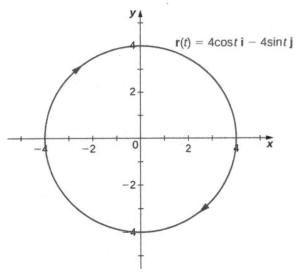

To find the principal unit normal vector, we first must find the unit tangent vector $\mathbf{T}(t)$:

$$\begin{aligned}
\mathbf{T}(t) &= \frac{\mathbf{r}'(t)}{\| \mathbf{r}'(t) \|} \\
&= \frac{-4\sin t\, \mathbf{i} - 4\cos t\, \mathbf{j}}{\sqrt{(-4\sin t)^2 + (-4\cos t)^2}} \\
&= \frac{-4\sin t\, \mathbf{i} - 4\cos t\, \mathbf{j}}{\sqrt{16\sin^2 t + 16\cos^2 t}} \\
&= \frac{-4\sin t\, \mathbf{i} - 4\cos t\, \mathbf{j}}{\sqrt{16\left(\sin^2 t + \cos^2 t\right)}} \\
&= \frac{-4\sin t\, \mathbf{i} - 4\cos t\, \mathbf{j}}{4} \\
&= -\sin t\, \mathbf{i} - \cos t\, \mathbf{j}.
\end{aligned}$$

Next, we use **Equation 3.18**:

$$\begin{aligned}
\mathbf{N}(t) &= \frac{\mathbf{T}'(t)}{\| \mathbf{T}'(t) \|} \\
&= \frac{-\cos t\, \mathbf{i} + \sin t\, \mathbf{j}}{\sqrt{(-\cos t)^2 + (\sin t)^2}} \\
&= \frac{-\cos t\, \mathbf{i} + \sin t\, \mathbf{j}}{\sqrt{\cos^2 t + \sin^2 t}} \\
&= -\cos t\, \mathbf{i} + \sin t\, \mathbf{j}.
\end{aligned}$$

Notice that the unit tangent vector and the principal unit normal vector are orthogonal to each other for all values of $t$:

$$\begin{aligned}
\mathbf{T}(t) \cdot \mathbf{N}(t) &= \langle\, -\sin t,\ -\cos t\,\rangle \cdot \langle\, -\cos t,\ \sin t\,\rangle \\
&= \sin t \cos t - \cos t \sin t \\
&= 0.
\end{aligned}$$

Furthermore, the principal unit normal vector points toward the center of the circle from every point on the circle. Since $\mathbf{r}(t)$ defines a curve in two dimensions, we cannot calculate the binormal vector.

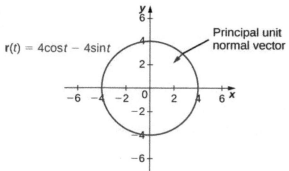

b.  This function looks like this:

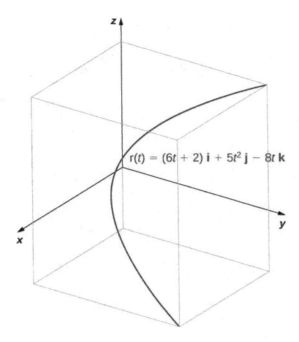

$$\mathbf{r}(t) = (6t + 2)\,\mathbf{i} + 5t^2\,\mathbf{j} - 8t\,\mathbf{k}$$

To find the principal unit normal vector, we first find the unit tangent vector $\mathbf{T}(t)$:

$$
\begin{aligned}
\mathbf{T}(t) &= \frac{\mathbf{r}'(t)}{\|\,\mathbf{r}'(t)\,\|} \\[2mm]
&= \frac{6\,\mathbf{i} + 10t\,\mathbf{j} - 8\,\mathbf{k}}{\sqrt{6^2 + (10t)^2 + (-8)^2}} \\[2mm]
&= \frac{6\,\mathbf{i} + 10t\,\mathbf{j} - 8\,\mathbf{k}}{\sqrt{36 + 100t^2 + 64}} \\[2mm]
&= \frac{6\,\mathbf{i} + 10t\,\mathbf{j} - 8\mathbf{k}}{\sqrt{100(t^2 + 1)}} \\[2mm]
&= \frac{3\,\mathbf{i} - 5t\,\mathbf{j} - 4\mathbf{k}}{5\sqrt{t^2 + 1}} \\[2mm]
&= \tfrac{3}{5}\left(t^2 + 1\right)^{-1/2}\mathbf{i} - t\left(t^2 + 1\right)^{-1/2}\mathbf{j} - \tfrac{4}{5}\left(t^2 + 1\right)^{-1/2}\mathbf{k}.
\end{aligned}
$$

Next, we calculate $\mathbf{T}'(t)$ and $\|\,\mathbf{T}'(t)\,\|$ :

$$\mathbf{T}'(t) = \frac{3}{5}\left(-\frac{1}{2}\right)\left(t^2+1\right)^{-3/2}(2t)\mathbf{i} - \left(\left(t^2+1\right)^{-1/2} - t\left(\frac{1}{2}\right)\left(t^2+1\right)^{-3/2}(2t)\right)\mathbf{j}$$
$$-\frac{4}{5}\left(-\frac{1}{2}\right)\left(t^2+1\right)^{-3/2}(2t)\mathbf{k}$$
$$= -\frac{3t}{5\left(t^2+1\right)^{3/2}}\mathbf{i} - \frac{1}{\left(t^2+1\right)^{3/2}}\mathbf{j} + \frac{4t}{5\left(t^2+1\right)^{3/2}}\mathbf{k}$$

$$\|\mathbf{T}'(t)\| = \sqrt{\left(-\frac{3t}{5\left(t^2+1\right)^{3/2}}\right)^2 + \left(-\frac{1}{\left(t^2+1\right)^{3/2}}\right)^2 + \left(\frac{4t}{5\left(t^2+1\right)^{3/2}}\right)^2}$$
$$= \sqrt{\frac{9t^2}{25\left(t^2+1\right)^3} + \frac{1}{\left(t^2+1\right)^3} + \frac{16t^2}{25\left(t^2+1\right)^3}}$$
$$= \sqrt{\frac{25t^2+25}{25\left(t^2+1\right)^3}}$$
$$= \sqrt{\frac{1}{\left(t^2+1\right)^2}}$$
$$= \frac{1}{t^2+1}.$$

Therefore, according to Equation 3.18:

$$\mathbf{N}(t) = \frac{\mathbf{T}'(t)}{\|\mathbf{T}'(t)\|}$$
$$= \left(-\frac{3t}{5\left(t^2+1\right)^{3/2}}\mathbf{i} - \frac{1}{\left(t^2+1\right)^{3/2}}\mathbf{j} + \frac{4t}{5\left(t^2+1\right)^{3/2}}\mathbf{k}\right)(t^2+1)$$
$$= -\frac{3t}{5\left(t^2+1\right)^{1/2}}\mathbf{i} - \frac{5}{5\left(t^2+1\right)^{1/2}}\mathbf{j} + \frac{4t}{5\left(t^2+1\right)^{1/2}}\mathbf{k}$$
$$= -\frac{3t\,\mathbf{i} + 5\mathbf{j} - 4t\,\mathbf{k}}{5\sqrt{t^2+1}}.$$

Once again, the unit tangent vector and the principal unit normal vector are orthogonal to each other for all values of $t$:

$$\mathbf{T}(t)\cdot\mathbf{N}(t) = \left(\frac{3\,\mathbf{i} - 5t\,\mathbf{j} - 4\mathbf{k}}{5\sqrt{t^2+1}}\right)\cdot\left(-\frac{3t\,\mathbf{i} + 5\mathbf{j} - 4t\,\mathbf{k}}{5\sqrt{t^2+1}}\right)$$
$$= \frac{3(-3t) - 5t(-5) - 4(4t)}{5\sqrt{t^2+1}}$$
$$= \frac{-9t + 25t - 16t}{5\sqrt{t^2+1}}$$
$$= 0.$$

Last, since $\mathbf{r}(t)$ represents a three-dimensional curve, we can calculate the binormal vector using Equation 3.17:

$$\mathbf{B}(t) = \mathbf{T}(t) \times \mathbf{N}(t)$$

$$= \begin{vmatrix} \mathbf{i} & \mathbf{j} & \mathbf{k} \\ \dfrac{3}{5\sqrt{t^2+1}} & -\dfrac{5t}{5\sqrt{t^2+1}} & -\dfrac{4}{5\sqrt{t^2+1}} \\ -\dfrac{3t}{5\sqrt{t^2+1}} & -\dfrac{5}{5\sqrt{t^2+1}} & \dfrac{4t}{5\sqrt{t^2+1}} \end{vmatrix}$$

$$= \left( \left( -\frac{5t}{5\sqrt{t^2+1}} \right)\left( \frac{4t}{5\sqrt{t^2+1}} \right) - \left( -\frac{4}{5\sqrt{t^2+1}} \right)\left( -\frac{5}{5\sqrt{t^2+1}} \right) \right)\mathbf{i}$$

$$\quad - \left( \left( \frac{3}{5\sqrt{t^2+1}} \right)\left( \frac{4t}{5\sqrt{t^2+1}} \right) - \left( -\frac{4}{5\sqrt{t^2+1}} \right)\left( -\frac{3t}{5\sqrt{t^2+1}} \right) \right)\mathbf{j}$$

$$\quad + \left( \left( \frac{3}{5\sqrt{t^2+1}} \right)\left( -\frac{5}{5\sqrt{t^2+1}} \right) - \left( -\frac{5t}{5\sqrt{t^2+1}} \right)\left( -\frac{3t}{5\sqrt{t^2+1}} \right) \right)\mathbf{k}$$

$$= \left( \frac{-20t^2 - 20}{25(t^2+1)} \right)\mathbf{i} + \left( \frac{-15 - 15t^2}{25(t^2+1)} \right)\mathbf{k}$$

$$= -20\left( \frac{t^2+1}{25(t^2+1)} \right)\mathbf{i} - 15\left( \frac{t^2+1}{25(t^2+1)} \right)\mathbf{k}$$

$$= -\frac{4}{5}\mathbf{i} - \frac{3}{5}\mathbf{k}.$$

**3.12** Find the unit normal vector for the vector-valued function $\mathbf{r}(t) = \left(t^2 - 3t\right)\mathbf{i} + (4t+1)\,\mathbf{j}$ and evaluate it at $t = 2$.

For any smooth curve in three dimensions that is defined by a vector-valued function, we now have formulas for the unit tangent vector **T**, the unit normal vector **N**, and the binormal vector **B**. The unit normal vector and the binormal vector form a plane that is perpendicular to the curve at any point on the curve, called the **normal plane**. In addition, these three vectors form a frame of reference in three-dimensional space called the **Frenet frame of reference** (also called the **TNB** frame) (**Figure 3.7**). Lat, the plane determined by the vectors **T** and **N** forms the osculating plane of $C$ at any point $P$ on the curve.

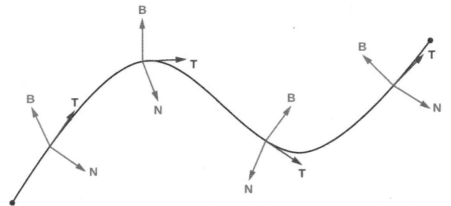

**Figure 3.7** This figure depicts a Frenet frame of reference. At every point $P$ on a three-dimensional curve, the unit tangent, unit normal, and binormal vectors form a three-dimensional frame of reference.

Suppose we form a circle in the osculating plane of $C$ at point $P$ on the curve. Assume that the circle has the same curvature as the curve does at point $P$ and let the circle have radius $r$. Then, the curvature of the circle is given by $1/r$. We call $r$ the **radius of curvature** of the curve, and it is equal to the reciprocal of the curvature. If this circle lies on the concave side of the curve and is tangent to the curve at point $P$, then this circle is called the **osculating circle** of $C$ at $P$, as shown in the following figure.

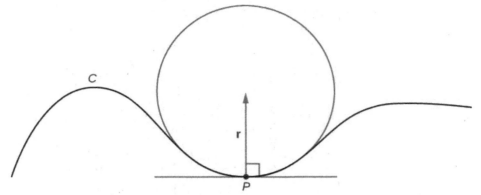

**Figure 3.8** In this osculating circle, the circle is tangent to curve $C$ at point $P$ and shares the same curvature.

 For more information on osculating circles, see this demonstration (http://www.openstaxcollege.org/ l/20_OsculCircle1) on curvature and torsion, this article (http://www.openstaxcollege.org/l/ 20_OsculCircle3) on osculating circles, and this discussion (http://www.openstaxcollege.org/l/ 20_OsculCircle2) of Serret formulas.

To find the equation of an osculating circle in two dimensions, we need find only the center and radius of the circle.

### Example 3.13

#### Finding the Equation of an Osculating Circle

Find the equation of the osculating circle of the helix defined by the function $y = x^3 - 3x + 1$ at $x = 1$.

#### Solution

Figure 3.9 shows the graph of $y = x^3 - 3x + 1$.

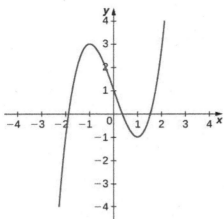

**Figure 3.9** We want to find the osculating circle of this graph at the point where $t = 1$.

First, let's calculate the curvature at $x = 1$:

$$\kappa = \frac{|f''(x)|}{\left(1 + [f'(x)]^2\right)^{3/2}} = \frac{|6x|}{\left(1 + \left[3x^2 - 3\right]^2\right)^{3/2}}.$$

This gives $\kappa = 6$. Therefore, the radius of the osculating circle is given by $R = \frac{1}{\kappa} = \frac{1}{6}$. Next, we then calculate the coordinates of the center of the circle. When $x = 1$, the slope of the tangent line is zero. Therefore, the center of the osculating circle is directly above the point on the graph with coordinates $(1, -1)$. The center is located at $\left(1, -\frac{5}{6}\right)$. The formula for a circle with radius $r$ and center $(h, k)$ is given by $(x - h)^2 + (y - k)^2 = r^2$.

Therefore, the equation of the osculating circle is $(x - 1)^2 + \left(y + \frac{5}{6}\right)^2 = \frac{1}{36}$. The graph and its osculating circle appears in the following graph.

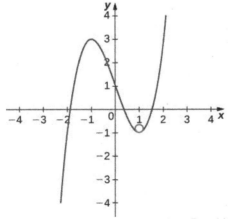

**Figure 3.10** The osculating circle has radius $R = 1/6$.

**3.13** Find the equation of the osculating circle of the curve defined by the vector-valued function $y = 2x^2 - 4x + 5$ at $x = 1$.

# 3.3 EXERCISES

Find the arc length of the curve on the given interval.

102.  $\mathbf{r}(t) = t^2\mathbf{i} + 14t\mathbf{j}, \ 0 \le t \le 7$. This portion of the graph is shown here:

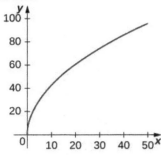

103.  $\mathbf{r}(t) = t^2\mathbf{i} + (2t^2 + 1)\mathbf{j}, \ 1 \le t \le 3$

104.  $\mathbf{r}(t) = \langle 2\sin t, \ 5t, \ 2\cos t \rangle, \ 0 \le t \le \pi$. This portion of the graph is shown here:

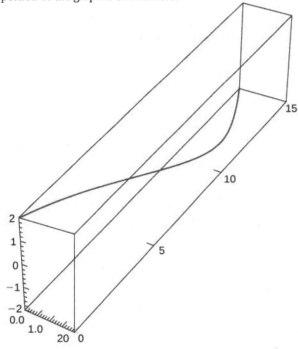

105.  $\mathbf{r}(t) = \langle t^2 + 1, \ 4t^3 + 3 \rangle, \ -1 \le t \le 0$

106.  $\mathbf{r}(t) = \langle e^{-t}\cos t, \ e^{-t}\sin t \rangle$ over the interval $\left[0, \frac{\pi}{2}\right]$. Here is the portion of the graph on the indicated interval:

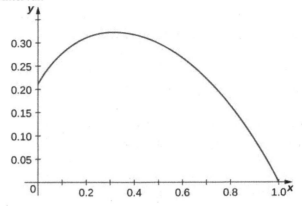

107.  Find the length of one turn of the helix given by $\mathbf{r}(t) = \frac{1}{2}\cos t\mathbf{i} + \frac{1}{2}\sin t\mathbf{j} + \sqrt{\frac{3}{4}}\,t\,\mathbf{k}$.

108.  Find the arc length of the vector-valued function $\mathbf{r}(t) = -t\mathbf{i} + 4t\mathbf{j} + 3t\mathbf{k}$ over $[0, 1]$.

109.  A particle travels in a circle with the equation of motion $\mathbf{r}(t) = 3\cos t\mathbf{i} + 3\sin t\mathbf{j} + 0\mathbf{k}$. Find the distance traveled around the circle by the particle.

110.  Set up an integral to find the circumference of the ellipse with the equation $\mathbf{r}(t) = \cos t\mathbf{i} + 2\sin t\mathbf{j} + 0\mathbf{k}$.

111.  Find the length of the curve $\mathbf{r}(t) = \langle \sqrt{2}t, \ e^t, \ e^{-t} \rangle$ over the interval $0 \le t \le 1$. The graph is shown here:

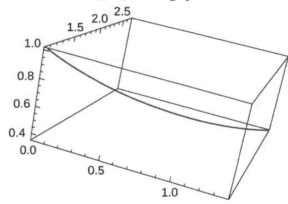

112.  Find the length of the curve $\mathbf{r}(t) = \langle 2\sin t, \ 5t, \ 2\cos t \rangle$ for $t \in [-10, 10]$.

113.  The position function for a particle is $\mathbf{r}(t) = a\cos(\omega t)\mathbf{i} + b\sin(\omega t)\mathbf{j}$. Find the unit tangent vector and the unit normal vector at $t = 0$.

114.    Given   $\mathbf{r}(t) = a\cos(\omega t)\mathbf{i} + b\sin(\omega t)\mathbf{j}$,    find the binormal vector $\mathbf{B}(0)$.

115.    Given   $\mathbf{r}(t) = \langle\, 2e^t,\ e^t\cos t,\ e^t\sin t \,\rangle$,    determine the tangent vector $\mathbf{T}(t)$.

116.    Given   $\mathbf{r}(t) = \langle\, 2e^t,\ e^t\cos t,\ e^t\sin t \,\rangle$,    determine the unit tangent vector $\mathbf{T}(t)$ evaluated at $t = 0$.

117.    Given   $\mathbf{r}(t) = \langle\, 2e^t,\ e^t\cos t,\ e^t\sin t \,\rangle$,    find the unit normal vector $\mathbf{N}(t)$ evaluated at $t = 0$,    $\mathbf{N}(0)$.

118.    Given   $\mathbf{r}(t) = \langle\, 2e^t,\ e^t\cos t,\ e^t\sin t \,\rangle$,    find the unit normal vector evaluated at $t = 0$.

119.    Given   $\mathbf{r}(t) = t\mathbf{i} + t^2\mathbf{j} + t\mathbf{k}$,   find the unit tangent vector $\mathbf{T}(t)$. The graph is shown here:

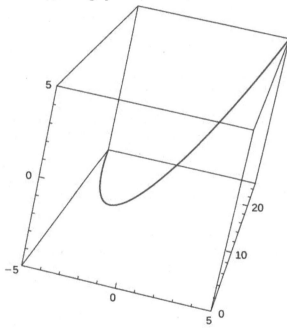

120.    Find the unit tangent vector $\mathbf{T}(t)$ and unit normal vector $\mathbf{N}(t)$ at $t = 0$ for the plane curve $\mathbf{r}(t) = \langle\, t^3 - 4t,\ 5t^2 - 2 \,\rangle$. The graph is shown here:

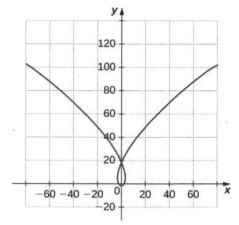

121.    Find the unit tangent vector $\mathbf{T}(t)$ for $\mathbf{r}(t) = 3t\mathbf{i} + 5t^2\mathbf{j} + 2t\mathbf{k}$

122.    Find the principal normal vector to the curve $\mathbf{r}(t) = \langle\, 6\cos t,\ 6\sin t \,\rangle$ at the point determined by $t = \pi/3$.

123.    Find   $\mathbf{T}(t)$   for   the   curve $\mathbf{r}(t) = \left(t^3 - 4t\right)\mathbf{i} + \left(5t^2 - 2\right)\mathbf{j}$.

124.    Find   $\mathbf{N}(t)$   for   the   curve $\mathbf{r}(t) = \left(t^3 - 4t\right)\mathbf{i} + \left(5t^2 - 2\right)\mathbf{j}$.

125.    Find the unit normal vector $\mathbf{N}(t)$ for $\mathbf{r}(t) = \langle\, 2\sin t,\ 5t,\ 2\cos t \,\rangle$.

126.    Find the unit tangent vector $\mathbf{T}(t)$ for $\mathbf{r}(t) = \langle\, 2\sin t,\ 5t,\ 2\cos t \,\rangle$.

127.    Find the arc-length function $s(t)$ for the line segment given by $\mathbf{r}(t) = \langle\, 3 - 3t,\ 4t \,\rangle$. Write $r$ as a parameter of $s$.

128.    Parameterize the helix   $\mathbf{r}(t) = \cos t\mathbf{i} + \sin t\mathbf{j} + t\mathbf{k}$ using the arc-length parameter $s$, from $t = 0$.

129.    Parameterize the curve using the arc-length parameter $s$, at the point at which $t = 0$ for $\mathbf{r}(t) = e^t\sin t\mathbf{i} + e^t\cos t\mathbf{j}$.

130. Find the curvature of the curve $\mathbf{r}(t) = 5\cos t\mathbf{i} + 4\sin t\mathbf{j}$ at $t = \pi/3$. (*Note:* The graph is an ellipse.)

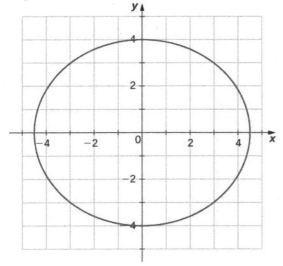

131. Find the $x$-coordinate at which the curvature of the curve $y = 1/x$ is a maximum value.

132. Find the curvature of the curve $\mathbf{r}(t) = 5\cos t\mathbf{i} + 5\sin t\mathbf{j}$. Does the curvature depend upon the parameter $t$?

133. Find the curvature $\kappa$ for the curve $y = x - \frac{1}{4}x^2$ at the point $x = 2$.

134. Find the curvature $\kappa$ for the curve $y = \frac{1}{3}x^3$ at the point $x = 1$.

135. Find the curvature $\kappa$ of the curve $\mathbf{r}(t) = t\mathbf{i} + 6t^2\mathbf{j} + 4t\mathbf{k}$. The graph is shown here:

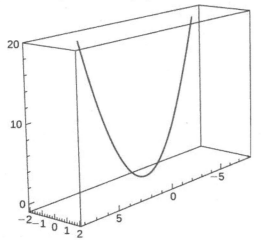

136. Find the curvature of $\mathbf{r}(t) = \langle 2\sin t, 5t, 2\cos t \rangle$.

137. Find the curvature of $\mathbf{r}(t) = \sqrt{2}t\mathbf{i} + e^t\mathbf{j} + e^{-t}\mathbf{k}$ at point $P(0, 1, 1)$.

138. At what point does the curve $y = e^x$ have maximum curvature?

139. What happens to the curvature as $x \to \infty$ for the curve $y = e^x$?

140. Find the point of maximum curvature on the curve $y = \ln x$.

141. Find the equations of the normal plane and the osculating plane of the curve $\mathbf{r}(t) = \langle 2\sin(3t), t, 2\cos(3t) \rangle$ at point $(0, \pi, -2)$.

142. Find equations of the osculating circles of the ellipse $4y^2 + 9x^2 = 36$ at the points $(2, 0)$ and $(0, 3)$.

143. Find the equation for the osculating plane at point $t = \pi/4$ on the curve $\mathbf{r}(t) = \cos(2t)\mathbf{i} + \sin(2t)\mathbf{j} + t$.

144. Find the radius of curvature of $6y = x^3$ at the point $\left(2, \frac{4}{3}\right)$.

145. Find the curvature at each point $(x, y)$ on the hyperbola $\mathbf{r}(t) = \langle a\cosh(t), b\sinh(t) \rangle$.

146. Calculate the curvature of the circular helix $\mathbf{r}(t) = r\sin(t)\mathbf{i} + r\cos(t)\mathbf{j} + t\mathbf{k}$.

147. Find the radius of curvature of $y = \ln(x + 1)$ at point $(2, \ln 3)$.

148. Find the radius of curvature of the hyperbola $xy = 1$ at point $(1, 1)$.

A particle moves along the plane curve C described by $\mathbf{r}(t) = t\mathbf{i} + t^2\mathbf{j}$. Solve the following problems.

149. Find the length of the curve over the interval $[0, 2]$.

150. Find the curvature of the plane curve at $t = 0, 1, 2$.

151. Describe the curvature as $t$ increases from $t = 0$ to $t = 2$.

The surface of a large cup is formed by revolving the graph of the function $y = 0.25x^{1.6}$ from $x = 0$ to $x = 5$ about the $y$-axis (measured in centimeters).

152. **[T]** Use technology to graph the surface.

153. Find the curvature $\kappa$ of the generating curve as a function of $x$.

154. **[T]** Use technology to graph the curvature function.

# 3.4 | Motion in Space

## Learning Objectives

**3.4.1** Describe the velocity and acceleration vectors of a particle moving in space.

**3.4.2** Explain the tangential and normal components of acceleration.

**3.4.3** State Kepler's laws of planetary motion.

We have now seen how to describe curves in the plane and in space, and how to determine their properties, such as arc length and curvature. All of this leads to the main goal of this chapter, which is the description of motion along plane curves and space curves. We now have all the tools we need; in this section, we put these ideas together and look at how to use them.

## Motion Vectors in the Plane and in Space

Our starting point is using vector-valued functions to represent the position of an object as a function of time. All of the following material can be applied either to curves in the plane or to space curves. For example, when we look at the orbit of the planets, the curves defining these orbits all lie in a plane because they are elliptical. However, a particle traveling along a helix moves on a curve in three dimensions.

### Definition

Let $\mathbf{r}(t)$ be a twice-differentiable vector-valued function of the parameter $t$ that represents the position of an object as a function of time. The **velocity vector** $\mathbf{v}(t)$ of the object is given by

$$\text{Velocity} = \mathbf{v}(t) = \mathbf{r}'(t). \tag{3.20}$$

The **acceleration vector** $\mathbf{a}(t)$ is defined to be

$$\text{Acceleration} = \mathbf{a}(t) = \mathbf{v}'(t) = \mathbf{r}''(t). \tag{3.21}$$

The *speed* is defined to be

$$\text{Speed} = v(t) = \|\mathbf{v}(t)\| = \|\mathbf{r}'(t)\| = \frac{ds}{dt}. \tag{3.22}$$

Since $\mathbf{r}(t)$ can be in either two or three dimensions, these vector-valued functions can have either two or three components. In two dimensions, we define $\mathbf{r}(t) = x(t)\mathbf{i} + y(t)\mathbf{j}$ and in three dimensions $\mathbf{r}(t) = x(t)\mathbf{i} + y(t)\mathbf{j} + z(t)\mathbf{k}$. Then the velocity, acceleration, and speed can be written as shown in the following table.

| Quantity | Two Dimensions | Three Dimensions |
|---|---|---|
| Position | $\mathbf{r}(t) = x(t)\mathbf{i} + y(t)\mathbf{j}$ | $\mathbf{r}(t) = x(t)\mathbf{i} + y(t)\mathbf{j} + z(t)\mathbf{k}$ |
| Velocity | $\mathbf{v}(t) = x'(t)\mathbf{i} + y'(t)\mathbf{j}$ | $\mathbf{v}(t) = x'(t)\mathbf{i} + y'(t)\mathbf{j} + z'(t)\mathbf{k}$ |
| Acceleration | $\mathbf{a}(t) = x''(t)\mathbf{i} + y''(t)\mathbf{j}$ | $\mathbf{a}(t) = x''(t)\mathbf{i} + y''(t)\mathbf{j} + z''(t)\mathbf{k}$ |
| Speed | $v(t) = \sqrt{(x'(t))^2 + (y'(t))^2}$ | $v(t) = \sqrt{(x'(t))^2 + (y'(t))^2 + (z'(t))^2}$ |

**Table 3.4** Formulas for Position, Velocity, Acceleration, and Speed

## Example 3.14

### Studying Motion Along a Parabola

A particle moves in a parabolic path defined by the vector-valued function $\mathbf{r}(t) = t^2\mathbf{i} + \sqrt{5 - t^2}\mathbf{j}$, where $t$ measures time in seconds.

    a.  Find the velocity, acceleration, and speed as functions of time.

    b.  Sketch the curve along with the velocity vector at time $t = 1$.

### Solution

    a.  We use **Equation 3.20**, **Equation 3.21**, and **Equation 3.22**:

$$\mathbf{v}(t) \;=\; \mathbf{r}'(t) = 2t\mathbf{i} - \frac{t}{\sqrt{5 - t^2}}\mathbf{j}$$

$$\mathbf{a}(t) \;=\; \mathbf{v}'(t) = 2\mathbf{i} - 5\left(5 - t^2\right)^{-\frac{3}{2}}\mathbf{j}$$

$$v(t) \;=\; \|\mathbf{r}'(t)\|$$

$$= \sqrt{(2t)^2 + \left(-\frac{t}{\sqrt{5 - t^2}}\right)^2}$$

$$= \sqrt{4t^2 + \frac{t^2}{5 - t^2}}$$

$$= \sqrt{\frac{21t^2 - 4t^4}{5 - t^2}}.$$

    b.  The graph of $\mathbf{r}(t) = t^2\mathbf{i} + \sqrt{5 - t^2}\mathbf{j}$ is a portion of a parabola (**Figure 3.11**). The velocity vector at $t = 1$ is

$$\mathbf{v}(1) = \mathbf{r}'(1) = 2(1)\mathbf{i} - \frac{1}{\sqrt{5 - (1)^2}}\mathbf{j} = 2\mathbf{i} - \tfrac{1}{2}\mathbf{j}$$

and the acceleration vector at $t = 1$ is

$$\mathbf{a}(1) = \mathbf{v}'(1) = 2\mathbf{i} - 5\left(5 - (1)^2\right)^{-3/2}\mathbf{j} = 2\mathbf{i} - \tfrac{5}{8}\mathbf{j}.$$

Notice that the velocity vector is tangent to the path, as is always the case.

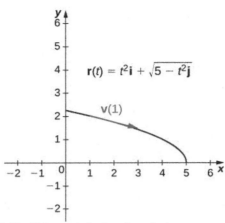

**Figure 3.11** This graph depicts the velocity vector at time $t = 1$ for a particle moving in a parabolic path.

**3.14** A particle moves in a path defined by the vector-valued function $\mathbf{r}(t) = \left(t^2 - 3t\right)\mathbf{i} + (2t - 4)\mathbf{j} + (t + 2)\mathbf{k},$ where $t$ measures time in seconds and where distance is measured in feet. Find the velocity, acceleration, and speed as functions of time.

To gain a better understanding of the velocity and acceleration vectors, imagine you are driving along a curvy road. If you do not turn the steering wheel, you would continue in a straight line and run off the road. The speed at which you are traveling when you run off the road, coupled with the direction, gives a vector representing your velocity, as illustrated in the following figure.

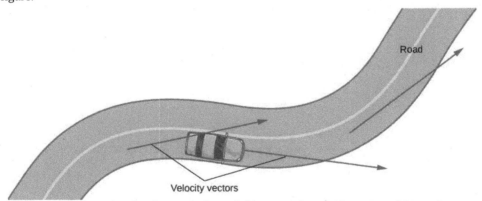

**Figure 3.12** At each point along a road traveled by a car, the velocity vector of the car is tangent to the path traveled by the car.

However, the fact that you must turn the steering wheel to stay on the road indicates that your velocity is always changing (even if your speed is not) because your *direction* is constantly changing to keep you on the road. As you turn to the right, your acceleration vector also points to the right. As you turn to the left, your acceleration vector points to the left. This indicates that your velocity and acceleration vectors are constantly changing, regardless of whether your actual speed varies (**Figure 3.13**).

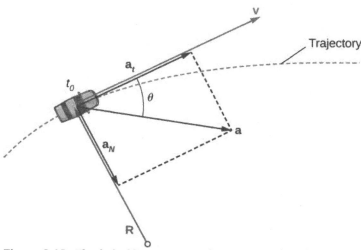

**Figure 3.13** The dashed line represents the trajectory of an object (a car, for example). The acceleration vector points toward the inside of the turn at all times.

## Components of the Acceleration Vector

We can combine some of the concepts discussed in Arc Length and Curvature with the acceleration vector to gain a deeper understanding of how this vector relates to motion in the plane and in space. Recall that the unit tangent vector $\mathbf{T}$ and the unit normal vector $\mathbf{N}$ form an osculating plane at any point $P$ on the curve defined by a vector-valued function $\mathbf{r}(t)$.

The following theorem shows that the acceleration vector $\mathbf{a}(t)$ lies in the osculating plane and can be written as a linear combination of the unit tangent and the unit normal vectors.

---

**Theorem 3.7: The Plane of the Acceleration Vector**

The acceleration vector $\mathbf{a}(t)$ of an object moving along a curve traced out by a twice-differentiable function $\mathbf{r}(t)$ lies in the plane formed by the unit tangent vector $\mathbf{T}(t)$ and the principal unit normal vector $\mathbf{N}(t)$ to $C$. Furthermore,

$$\mathbf{a}(t) = v'(t)\mathbf{T}(t) + [v(t)]^2 \kappa \mathbf{N}(t).$$

Here, $v(t)$ is the speed of the object and $\kappa$ is the curvature of $C$ traced out by $\mathbf{r}(t)$.

---

**Proof**

Because $\mathbf{v}(t) = \mathbf{r}'(t)$ and $\mathbf{T}(t) = \dfrac{\mathbf{r}'(t)}{\|\mathbf{r}'(t)\|}$, we have $\mathbf{v}(t) = \|\mathbf{r}'(t)\|\mathbf{T}(t) = v(t)\mathbf{T}(t)$. Now we differentiate this equation:

$$\mathbf{a}(t) = \mathbf{v}'(t) = \frac{d}{dt}\bigl(v(t)\mathbf{T}(t)\bigr) = v'(t)\mathbf{T}(t) + v(t)\mathbf{T}'(t).$$

Since $\mathbf{N}(t) = \dfrac{\mathbf{T}'(t)}{\|\mathbf{T}'(t)\|}$, we know $\mathbf{T}'(t) = \|\mathbf{T}'(t)\|\mathbf{N}(t)$, so

$$\mathbf{a}(t) = v'(t)\mathbf{T}(t) + v(t)\|\mathbf{T}'(t)\|\mathbf{N}(t).$$

A formula for curvature is $\kappa = \dfrac{\|\mathbf{T}'(t)\|}{\|\mathbf{r}'(t)\|}$, so $\|\mathbf{T}'(t)\| = \kappa\|\mathbf{r}'(t)\| = \kappa v(t)$. This gives

$$\mathbf{a}(t) = v'(t)\mathbf{T}(t) + \kappa(v(t))^2\mathbf{N}(t).$$

☐

The coefficients of $\mathbf{T}(t)$ and $\mathbf{N}(t)$ are referred to as the **tangential component of acceleration** and the **normal component**

**of acceleration**, respectively. We write $a_{\mathbf{T}}$ to denote the tangential component and $a_{\mathbf{N}}$ to denote the normal component.

### Theorem 3.8: Tangential and Normal Components of Acceleration

Let $\mathbf{r}(t)$ be a vector-valued function that denotes the position of an object as a function of time. Then $\mathbf{a}(t) = \mathbf{r}''(t)$ is the acceleration vector. The tangential and normal components of acceleration $a_{\mathbf{T}}$ and $a_{\mathbf{N}}$ are given by the formulas

$$a_{\mathbf{T}} = \mathbf{a} \cdot \mathbf{T} = \frac{\mathbf{v} \cdot \mathbf{a}}{\| \mathbf{v} \|} \qquad (3.23)$$

and

$$a_{\mathbf{N}} = \mathbf{a} \cdot \mathbf{N} = \frac{\| \mathbf{v} \times \mathbf{a} \|}{\| \mathbf{v} \|} = \sqrt{\| \mathbf{a} \|^2 - a_{\mathbf{T}}^2}. \qquad (3.24)$$

These components are related by the formula

$$\mathbf{a}(t) = a_{\mathbf{T}} \mathbf{T}(t) + a_{\mathbf{N}} \mathbf{N}(t). \qquad (3.25)$$

Here $\mathbf{T}(t)$ is the unit tangent vector to the curve defined by $\mathbf{r}(t)$, and $\mathbf{N}(t)$ is the unit normal vector to the curve defined by $\mathbf{r}(t)$.

The normal component of acceleration is also called the *centripetal component of acceleration* or sometimes the *radial component of acceleration*. To understand centripetal acceleration, suppose you are traveling in a car on a circular track at a constant speed. Then, as we saw earlier, the acceleration vector points toward the center of the track at all times. As a rider in the car, you feel a pull toward the *outside* of the track because you are constantly turning. This sensation acts in the opposite direction of centripetal acceleration. The same holds true for noncircular paths. The reason is that your body tends to travel in a straight line and resists the force resulting from acceleration that push it toward the side. Note that at point $B$ in Figure 3.14 the acceleration vector is pointing backward. This is because the car is decelerating as it goes into the curve.

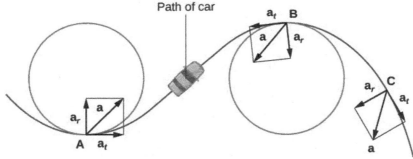

**Figure 3.14** The tangential and normal components of acceleration can be used to describe the acceleration vector.

The tangential and normal unit vectors at any given point on the curve provide a frame of reference at that point. The tangential and normal components of acceleration are the projections of the acceleration vector onto $\mathbf{T}$ and $\mathbf{N}$, respectively.

### Example 3.15

#### Finding Components of Acceleration

A particle moves in a path defined by the vector-valued function $\mathbf{r}(t) = t^2 \mathbf{i} + (2t - 3)\mathbf{j} + (3t^2 - 3t)\mathbf{k}$, where $t$ measures time in seconds and distance is measured in feet.

    a.  Find $a_{\mathbf{T}}$ and $a_{\mathbf{N}}$ as functions of $t$.

b.  Find $a_\mathbf{T}$ and $a_\mathbf{N}$ at time $t = 2$.

### Solution

a.  Let's start with **Equation 3.23**:

$$\begin{aligned}
\mathbf{v}(t) &= \mathbf{r}'(t) = 2t\mathbf{i} + 2\mathbf{j} + (6t - 3)\mathbf{k} \\
\mathbf{a}(t) &= \mathbf{v}'(t) = 2\mathbf{i} + 6\mathbf{k} \\
a_\mathbf{T} &= \frac{\mathbf{v} \cdot \mathbf{a}}{\| \mathbf{v} \|} \\
&= \frac{(2t\mathbf{i} + 2\mathbf{j} + (6t - 3)\mathbf{k}) \cdot (2\mathbf{i} + 6\mathbf{k})}{\| 2t\mathbf{i} + 2\mathbf{j} + (6t - 3)\mathbf{k} \|} \\
&= \frac{4t + 6(6t - 3)}{\sqrt{(2t)^2 + 2^2 + (6t - 3)^2}} \\
&= \frac{40t - 18}{\sqrt{40t^2 - 36t + 13}}.
\end{aligned}$$

Then we apply **Equation 3.24**:

$$\begin{aligned}
a_\mathbf{N} &= \sqrt{\| \mathbf{a} \|^2 - a} \\
&= \sqrt{\| 2\mathbf{i} + 6\mathbf{k} \|^2 - \left( \frac{40t - 18}{\sqrt{40t^2 - 36t + 13}} \right)^2} \\
&= \sqrt{4 + 36 - \frac{(40t - 18)^2}{40t^2 - 36t + 13}} \\
&= \sqrt{\frac{40(40t^2 - 36t + 13) - (1600t^2 - 1440t + 324)}{40t^2 - 36t + 13}} \\
&= \sqrt{\frac{196}{40t^2 - 36t + 13}} \\
&= \frac{14}{\sqrt{40t^2 - 36t + 13}}.
\end{aligned}$$

b.  We must evaluate each of the answers from part a. at $t = 2$:

$$\begin{aligned}
a_\mathbf{T}(2) &= \frac{40(2) - 18}{\sqrt{40(2)^2 - 36(2) + 13}} \\
&= \frac{80 - 18}{\sqrt{160 - 72 + 13}} = \frac{62}{\sqrt{101}} \\
a_\mathbf{N}(2) &= \frac{14}{\sqrt{40(2)^2 - 36(2) + 13}} \\
&= \frac{14}{\sqrt{160 - 72 + 13}} = \frac{14}{\sqrt{101}}.
\end{aligned}$$

The units of acceleration are feet per second squared, as are the units of the normal and tangential components of acceleration.

**3.15** An object moves in a path defined by the vector-valued function $\mathbf{r}(t) = 4t\mathbf{i} + t^2\mathbf{j}$, where $t$ measures time in seconds.

    a. Find $a_{\mathbf{T}}$ and $a_{\mathbf{N}}$ as functions of $t$.

    b. Find $a_{\mathbf{T}}$ and $a_{\mathbf{N}}$ at time $t = -3$.

## Projectile Motion

Now let's look at an application of vector functions. In particular, let's consider the effect of gravity on the motion of an object as it travels through the air, and how it determines the resulting trajectory of that object. In the following, we ignore the effect of air resistance. This situation, with an object moving with an initial velocity but with no forces acting on it other than gravity, is known as **projectile motion**. It describes the motion of objects from golf balls to baseballs, and from arrows to cannonballs.

First we need to choose a coordinate system. If we are standing at the origin of this coordinate system, then we choose the positive y-axis to be up, the negative y-axis to be down, and the positive x-axis to be forward (i.e., away from the thrower of the object). The effect of gravity is in a downward direction, so Newton's second law tells us that the force on the object resulting from gravity is equal to the mass of the object times the acceleration resulting from to gravity, or $F_g = mg$,

where $F_g$ represents the force from gravity and $g$ represents the acceleration resulting from gravity at Earth's surface.

The value of $g$ in the English system of measurement is approximately 32 ft/sec$^2$ and it is approximately 9.8 m/sec$^2$ in the metric system. This is the only force acting on the object. Since gravity acts in a downward direction, we can write the force resulting from gravity in the form $F_g = -mg\,\mathbf{j}$, as shown in the following figure.

**Figure 3.15** An object is falling under the influence of gravity.

 Visit this **website (http://www.openstaxcollege.org/l/20_projectile)** for a video showing projectile motion.

Newton's second law also tells us that $F = m\mathbf{a}$, where $\mathbf{a}$ represents the acceleration vector of the object. This force must be equal to the force of gravity at all times, so we therefore know that

$$
\begin{aligned}
F &= F_g \\
m\mathbf{a} &= -mg\,\mathbf{j} \\
\mathbf{a} &= -g\,\mathbf{j}.
\end{aligned}
$$

Now we use the fact that the acceleration vector is the first derivative of the velocity vector. Therefore, we can rewrite the last equation in the form

$$\mathbf{v}'(t) = -g\,\mathbf{j}.$$

By taking the antiderivative of each side of this equation we obtain

$$\begin{aligned}\mathbf{v}(t) &= \int -g\,\mathbf{j}dt \\ &= -gt\,\mathbf{j} + \mathbf{C}_1\end{aligned}$$

for some constant vector $\mathbf{C}_1$. To determine the value of this vector, we can use the velocity of the object at a fixed time, say at time $t = 0$. We call this velocity the *initial velocity*: $\mathbf{v}(0) = \mathbf{v}_0$. Therefore, $\mathbf{v}(0) = -g(0)\,\mathbf{j} + \mathbf{C}_1 = \mathbf{v}_0$ and $\mathbf{C}_1 = \mathbf{v}_0$. This gives the velocity vector as $\mathbf{v}(t) = -gt\,\mathbf{j} + \mathbf{v}_0$.

Next we use the fact that velocity $\mathbf{v}(t)$ is the derivative of position $\mathbf{s}(t)$. This gives the equation

$$\mathbf{s}'(t) = -gt\,\mathbf{j} + \mathbf{v}_0.$$

Taking the antiderivative of both sides of this equation leads to

$$\begin{aligned}\mathbf{s}(t) &= \int -gt\,\mathbf{j} + \mathbf{v}_0\,dt \\ &= -\tfrac{1}{2}gt^2\,\mathbf{j} + \mathbf{v}_0 t + \mathbf{C}_2,\end{aligned}$$

with another unknown constant vector $\mathbf{C}_2$. To determine the value of $\mathbf{C}_2$, we can use the position of the object at a given time, say at time $t = 0$. We call this position the *initial position*: $\mathbf{s}(0) = \mathbf{s}_0$. Therefore, $\mathbf{s}(0) = -(1/2)g(0)^2\,\mathbf{j} + \mathbf{v}_0(0) + \mathbf{C}_2 = \mathbf{s}_0$ and $\mathbf{C}_2 = \mathbf{s}_0$. This gives the position of the object at any time as

$$\mathbf{s}(t) = -\tfrac{1}{2}gt^2\,\mathbf{j} + \mathbf{v}_0 t + \mathbf{s}_0.$$

Let's take a closer look at the initial velocity and initial position. In particular, suppose the object is thrown upward from the origin at an angle $\theta$ to the horizontal, with initial speed $v_0$. How can we modify the previous result to reflect this scenario?

First, we can assume it is thrown from the origin. If not, then we can move the origin to the point from where it is thrown. Therefore, $\mathbf{s}_0 = \mathbf{0}$, as shown in the following figure.

**Figure 3.16** Projectile motion when the object is thrown upward at an angle $\theta$. The horizontal motion is at constant velocity and the vertical motion is at constant acceleration.

We can rewrite the initial velocity vector in the form $\mathbf{v}_0 = v_0 \cos\theta\,\mathbf{i} + v_0 \sin\theta\,\mathbf{j}$. Then the equation for the position function $\mathbf{s}(t)$ becomes

$$s(t) = -\frac{1}{2}gt^2\,\mathbf{j} + v_0 t\cos\theta\,\mathbf{i} + v_0 t\sin\theta\,\mathbf{j}$$
$$= v_0 t\cos\theta\,\mathbf{i} + v_0 t\sin\theta\,\mathbf{j} - \frac{1}{2}gt^2\,\mathbf{j}$$
$$= v_0 t\cos\theta\,\mathbf{i} + \left(v_0 t\sin\theta - \frac{1}{2}gt^2\right)\mathbf{j}.$$

The coefficient of $\mathbf{i}$ represents the horizontal component of $s(t)$ and is the horizontal distance of the object from the origin at time $t$. The maximum value of the horizontal distance (measured at the same initial and final altitude) is called the range $R$. The coefficient of $\mathbf{j}$ represents the vertical component of $s(t)$ and is the altitude of the object at time $t$. The maximum value of the vertical distance is the height $H$.

## Example 3.16

### Motion of a Cannonball

During an Independence Day celebration, a cannonball is fired from a cannon on a cliff toward the water. The cannon is aimed at an angle of 30° above horizontal and the initial speed of the cannonball is 600 ft/sec. The cliff is 100 ft above the water (**Figure 3.17**).

   a.  Find the maximum height of the cannonball.

   b.  How long will it take for the cannonball to splash into the sea?

   c.  How far out to sea will the cannonball hit the water?

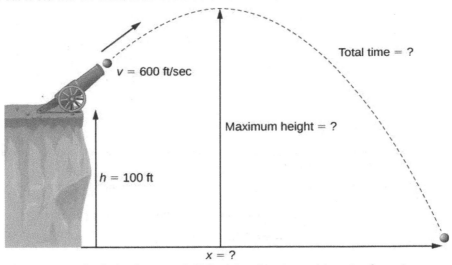

**Figure 3.17** The flight of a cannonball (ignoring air resistance) is projectile motion.

### Solution

We use the equation

$$s(t) = v_0 t\cos\theta\,\mathbf{i} + \left(v_0 t\sin\theta - \frac{1}{2}gt^2\right)\mathbf{j}$$

with $\theta = 30°$, $g = 32$ ft/sec$^2$, and $v_0 = 600$ ft/sec. Then the position equation becomes

$$s(t) = 600t(\cos 30)\mathbf{i} + \left(600t\sin 30 - \frac{1}{2}(32)t^2\right)\mathbf{j}$$
$$= 300t\sqrt{3}\,\mathbf{i} + \left(300t - 16t^2\right)\mathbf{j}.$$

   a.  The cannonball reaches its maximum height when the vertical component of its velocity is zero, because the cannonball is neither rising nor falling at that point. The velocity vector is

$$\mathbf{v}(t) = \mathbf{s}'(t)$$
$$= 300\sqrt{3}\mathbf{i} + (300 - 32t)\mathbf{j}.$$

Therefore, the vertical component of velocity is given by the expression $300 - 32t$. Setting this expression equal to zero and solving for $t$ gives $t = 9.375$ sec. The height of the cannonball at this time is given by the vertical component of the position vector, evaluated at $t = 9.375$.

$$\mathbf{s}(9.375) = 300(9.375)\sqrt{3}\mathbf{i} + \left(300(9.375) - 16(9.375)^2\right)\mathbf{j}$$
$$= 4871.39\mathbf{i} + 1406.25\mathbf{j}$$

Therefore, the maximum height of the cannonball is 1406.39 ft above the cannon, or 1506.39 ft above sea level.

b.  When the cannonball lands in the water, it is 100 ft below the cannon. Therefore, the vertical component of the position vector is equal to $-100$. Setting the vertical component of $\mathbf{s}(t)$ equal to $-100$ and solving, we obtain

$$300t - 16t^2 = -100$$
$$16t^2 - 300t - 100 = 0$$
$$4t^2 - 75t - 25 = 0$$
$$t = \frac{75 \pm \sqrt{(-75)^2 - 4(4)(-25)}}{2(4)}$$
$$= \frac{75 \pm \sqrt{6025}}{8}$$
$$= \frac{75 \pm 5\sqrt{241}}{8}.$$

The positive value of $t$ that solves this equation is approximately 19.08. Therefore, the cannonball hits the water after approximately 19.08 sec.

c.  To find the distance out to sea, we simply substitute the answer from part (b) into $\mathbf{s}(t)$:

$$\mathbf{s}(19.08) = 300(19.08)\sqrt{3}\mathbf{i} + \left(300(19.08) - 16(19.08)^2\right)\mathbf{j}$$
$$= 9914.26\mathbf{i} - 100.7424\mathbf{j}.$$

Therefore, the ball hits the water about 9914.26 ft away from the base of the cliff. Notice that the vertical component of the position vector is very close to $-100$, which tells us that the ball just hit the water.

Note that 9914.26 feet is not the true range of the cannon since the cannonball lands in the ocean at a location below the cannon. The range of the cannon would be determined by finding how far out the cannonball is when its height is 100 ft above the water (the same as the altitude of the cannon).

 **3.16**   An archer fires an arrow at an angle of 40° above the horizontal with an initial speed of 98 m/sec. The height of the archer is 171.5 cm. Find the horizontal distance the arrow travels before it hits the ground.

One final question remains: In general, what is the maximum distance a projectile can travel, given its initial speed? To determine this distance, we assume the projectile is fired from ground level and we wish it to return to ground level. In other words, we want to determine an equation for the range. In this case, the equation of projectile motion is

$$\mathbf{s}(t) = v_0 t\cos\theta\mathbf{i} + \left(v_0 t\sin\theta - \tfrac{1}{2}gt^2\right)\mathbf{j}.$$

Setting the second component equal to zero and solving for $t$ yields

$$v_0 t\sin\theta - \tfrac{1}{2}gt^2 = 0$$

$$t\left(v_0\sin\theta - \tfrac{1}{2}gt\right) = 0.$$

Therefore, either $t = 0$ or $t = \dfrac{2v_0\sin\theta}{g}$. We are interested in the second value of $t$, so we substitute this into $\mathbf{s}(t)$, which gives

$$\mathbf{s}\left(\frac{2v_0\sin\theta}{g}\right) = v_0\left(\frac{2v_0\sin\theta}{g}\right)\cos\theta\mathbf{i} + \left(v_0\left(\frac{2v_0\sin\theta}{g}\right)\sin\theta - \tfrac{1}{2}g\left(\frac{2v_0\sin\theta}{g}\right)^2\right)\mathbf{j}$$

$$= \left(\frac{2v_0^2\sin\theta\cos\theta}{g}\right)\mathbf{i}$$

$$= \frac{v_0^2\sin 2\theta}{g}\mathbf{i}.$$

Thus, the expression for the range of a projectile fired at an angle $\theta$ is

$$R = \frac{v_0^2\sin 2\theta}{g}\mathbf{i}.$$

The only variable in this expression is $\theta$. To maximize the distance traveled, take the derivative of the coefficient of $\mathbf{i}$ with respect to $\theta$ and set it equal to zero:

$$\frac{d}{d\theta}\left(\frac{v_0^2\sin 2\theta}{g}\right) = 0$$

$$\frac{2v_0^2\cos 2\theta}{g} = 0$$

$$\theta = 45°.$$

This value of $\theta$ is the smallest positive value that makes the derivative equal to zero. Therefore, in the absence of air resistance, the best angle to fire a projectile (to maximize the range) is at a $45°$ angle. The distance it travels is given by

$$\mathbf{s}\left(\frac{2v_0\sin 45}{g}\right) = \frac{v_0^2\sin 90}{g}\mathbf{i} = \frac{v_0^2}{g}\mathbf{j}.$$

Therefore, the range for an angle of $45°$ is $v_0^2/g$.

## Kepler's Laws

During the early 1600s, Johannes Kepler was able to use the amazingly accurate data from his mentor Tycho Brahe to formulate his three laws of planetary motion, now known as **Kepler's laws of planetary motion**. These laws also apply to other objects in the solar system in orbit around the Sun, such as comets (e.g., Halley's comet) and asteroids. Variations of these laws apply to satellites in orbit around Earth.

### Theorem 3.9: Kepler's Laws of Planetary Motion

   i.  The path of any planet about the Sun is elliptical in shape, with the center of the Sun located at one focus of the ellipse (the law of ellipses).

   ii.  A line drawn from the center of the Sun to the center of a planet sweeps out equal areas in equal time intervals (the law of equal areas) (Figure 3.18).

iii.    The ratio of the squares of the periods of any two planets is equal to the ratio of the cubes of the lengths of their semimajor orbital axes (the law of harmonies).

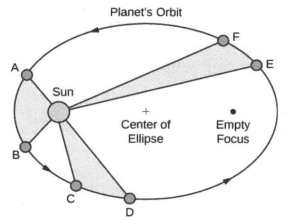

**Figure 3.18** Kepler's first and second laws are pictured here. The Sun is located at a focus of the elliptical orbit of any planet. Furthermore, the shaded areas are all equal, assuming that the amount of time measured as the planet moves is the same for each region.

Kepler's third law is especially useful when using appropriate units. In particular, *1 astronomical unit* is defined to be the average distance from Earth to the Sun, and is now recognized to be 149,597,870,700 m or, approximately 93,000,000 mi. We therefore write 1 A.U. = 93,000,000 mi. Since the time it takes for Earth to orbit the Sun is 1 year, we use Earth years for units of time. Then, substituting 1 year for the period of Earth and 1 A.U. for the average distance to the Sun, Kepler's third law can be written as

$$T_P^2 = D_P^3$$

for any planet in the solar system, where $T_P$ is the period of that planet measured in Earth years and $D_P$ is the average distance from that planet to the Sun measured in astronomical units. Therefore, if we know the average distance from a planet to the Sun (in astronomical units), we can then calculate the length of its year (in Earth years), and vice versa.

Kepler's laws were formulated based on observations from Brahe; however, they were not proved formally until Sir Isaac Newton was able to apply calculus. Furthermore, Newton was able to generalize Kepler's third law to other orbital systems, such as a moon orbiting around a planet. Kepler's original third law only applies to objects orbiting the Sun.

### Proof

Let's now prove Kepler's first law using the calculus of vector-valued functions. First we need a coordinate system. Let's place the Sun at the origin of the coordinate system and let the vector-valued function $\mathbf{r}(t)$ represent the location of a planet as a function of time. Newton proved Kepler's law using his second law of motion and his law of universal gravitation. Newton's second law of motion can be written as $\mathbf{F} = m\mathbf{a}$, where $\mathbf{F}$ represents the net force acting on the planet. His law of universal gravitation can be written in the form $\mathbf{F} = -\dfrac{GmM}{\|\mathbf{r}\|^2} \cdot \dfrac{\mathbf{r}}{\|\mathbf{r}\|}$, which indicates that the force resulting from the gravitational attraction of the Sun points back toward the Sun, and has magnitude $\dfrac{GmM}{\|\mathbf{r}\|^2}$ (Figure 3.19).

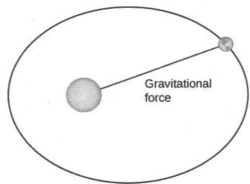

**Figure 3.19** The gravitational force between Earth and the Sun is equal to the mass of the earth times its acceleration.

Setting these two forces equal to each other, and using the fact that $\mathbf{a}(t) = \mathbf{v}'(t)$, we obtain

$$m\mathbf{v}'(t) = -\frac{GmM}{\|\mathbf{r}\|^2} \cdot \frac{\mathbf{r}}{\|\mathbf{r}\|},$$

which can be rewritten as

$$\frac{d\mathbf{v}}{dt} = -\frac{GM}{\|\mathbf{r}\|^3}\mathbf{r}.$$

This equation shows that the vectors $d\mathbf{v}/dt$ and $\mathbf{r}$ are parallel to each other, so $d\mathbf{v}/dt \times \mathbf{r} = \mathbf{0}$. Next, let's differentiate $\mathbf{r} \times \mathbf{v}$ with respect to time:

$$\frac{d}{dt}(\mathbf{r} \times \mathbf{v}) = \frac{d\mathbf{r}}{dt} \times \mathbf{v} + \mathbf{r} \times \frac{d\mathbf{v}}{dt} = \mathbf{v} \times \mathbf{v} + \mathbf{0} = \mathbf{0}.$$

This proves that $\mathbf{r} \times \mathbf{v}$ is a constant vector, which we call $\mathbf{C}$. Since $\mathbf{r}$ and $\mathbf{v}$ are both perpendicular to $\mathbf{C}$ for all values of $t$, they must lie in a plane perpendicular to $\mathbf{C}$. Therefore, the motion of the planet lies in a plane.

Next we calculate the expression $d\mathbf{v}/dt \times \mathbf{C}$:

$$\frac{d\mathbf{v}}{dt} \times \mathbf{C} = -\frac{GM}{\|\mathbf{r}\|^3}\mathbf{r} \times (\mathbf{r} \times \mathbf{v}) = -\frac{GM}{\|\mathbf{r}\|^3}[(\mathbf{r} \cdot \mathbf{v})\mathbf{r} - (\mathbf{r} \cdot \mathbf{r})\mathbf{v}]. \tag{3.26}$$

The last equality in **Equation 3.26** is from the triple cross product formula (**Introduction to Vectors in Space**). We need an expression for $\mathbf{r} \cdot \mathbf{v}$. To calculate this, we differentiate $\mathbf{r} \cdot \mathbf{r}$ with respect to time:

$$\frac{d}{dt}(\mathbf{r} \cdot \mathbf{r}) = \frac{d\mathbf{r}}{dt} \cdot \mathbf{r} + \mathbf{r} \cdot \frac{d\mathbf{r}}{dt} = 2\mathbf{r} \cdot \frac{d\mathbf{r}}{dt} = 2\mathbf{r} \cdot \mathbf{v}. \tag{3.27}$$

Since $\mathbf{r} \cdot \mathbf{r} = \|\mathbf{r}\|^2$, we also have

$$\frac{d}{dt}(\mathbf{r} \cdot \mathbf{r}) = \frac{d}{dt}\|\mathbf{r}\|^2 = 2\|\mathbf{r}\|\frac{d}{dt}\|\mathbf{r}\|. \tag{3.28}$$

Combining **Equation 3.27** and **Equation 3.28**, we get

$$2\mathbf{r} \cdot \mathbf{v} = 2\|\mathbf{r}\|\frac{d}{dt}\|\mathbf{r}\|$$

$$\mathbf{r} \cdot \mathbf{v} = \|\mathbf{r}\|\frac{d}{dt}\|\mathbf{r}\|.$$

Substituting this into **Equation 3.26** gives us

$$\frac{d\mathbf{v}}{dt} \times \mathbf{C} = -\frac{GM}{\|\mathbf{r}\|^3}[(\mathbf{r} \cdot \mathbf{v})\mathbf{r} - (\mathbf{r} \cdot \mathbf{r})\mathbf{v}] \qquad\qquad (3.29)$$

$$= -\frac{GM}{\|\mathbf{r}\|^3}\left[\|\mathbf{r}\|\left(\frac{d}{dt}\|\mathbf{r}\|\right)\mathbf{r} - \|\mathbf{r}\|^2\mathbf{v}\right]$$

$$= -GM\left[\frac{1}{\|\mathbf{r}\|^2}\left(\frac{d}{dt}\|\mathbf{r}\|\right)\mathbf{r} - \frac{1}{\|\mathbf{r}\|}\mathbf{v}\right]$$

$$= GM\left[\frac{\mathbf{v}}{\|\mathbf{r}\|} - \frac{\mathbf{r}}{\|\mathbf{r}\|^2}\left(\frac{d}{dt}\|\mathbf{r}\|\right)\right].$$

However,

$$\frac{d}{dt}\frac{\mathbf{r}}{\|\mathbf{r}\|} = \frac{\frac{d}{dt}(\mathbf{r})\|\mathbf{r}\| - \mathbf{r}\frac{d}{dt}\|\mathbf{r}\|}{\|\mathbf{r}\|^2}$$

$$= \frac{\frac{d\mathbf{r}}{dt}}{\|\mathbf{r}\|} - \frac{\mathbf{r}}{\|\mathbf{r}\|^2}\frac{d}{dt}\|\mathbf{r}\|$$

$$= \frac{\mathbf{v}}{\|\mathbf{r}\|} - \frac{\mathbf{r}}{\|\mathbf{r}\|^2}\frac{d}{dt}\|\mathbf{r}\|.$$

Therefore, Equation 3.29 becomes

$$\frac{d\mathbf{v}}{dt} \times \mathbf{C} = GM\left(\frac{d}{dt}\frac{\mathbf{r}}{\|\mathbf{r}\|}\right).$$

Since $\mathbf{C}$ is a constant vector, we can integrate both sides and obtain

$$\mathbf{v} \times \mathbf{C} = GM\frac{\mathbf{r}}{\|\mathbf{r}\|} + \mathbf{D},$$

where $\mathbf{D}$ is a constant vector. Our goal is to solve for $\|\mathbf{r}\|$. Let's start by calculating $\mathbf{r} \cdot (\mathbf{v} \times \mathbf{C})$:

$$\mathbf{r} \cdot (\mathbf{v} \times \mathbf{C}) = \mathbf{r} \cdot \left(GM\frac{\mathbf{r}}{\|\mathbf{r}\|} + \mathbf{D}\right) = GM\frac{\|\mathbf{r}\|^2}{\|\mathbf{r}\|} + \mathbf{r} \cdot \mathbf{D} = GM\|\mathbf{r}\| + \mathbf{r} \cdot \mathbf{D}.$$

However, $\mathbf{r} \cdot (\mathbf{v} \times \mathbf{C}) = (\mathbf{r} \times \mathbf{v}) \cdot \mathbf{C}$, so

$$(\mathbf{r} \times \mathbf{v}) \cdot \mathbf{C} = GM\|\mathbf{r}\| + \mathbf{r} \cdot \mathbf{D}.$$

Since $\mathbf{r} \times \mathbf{v} = \mathbf{C}$, we have

$$\|\mathbf{C}\|^2 = GM\|\mathbf{r}\| + \mathbf{r} \cdot \mathbf{D}.$$

Note that $\mathbf{r} \cdot \mathbf{D} = \|\mathbf{r}\|\,\|\mathbf{D}\|\cos\theta$, where $\theta$ is the angle between $\mathbf{r}$ and $\mathbf{D}$. Therefore,

$$\|\mathbf{C}\|^2 = GM\|\mathbf{r}\| + \|\mathbf{r}\|\,\|\mathbf{D}\|\cos\theta.$$

Solving for $\|\mathbf{r}\|$,

$$\|\mathbf{r}\| = \frac{\|\mathbf{C}\|^2}{GM + \|\mathbf{D}\|\cos\theta} = \frac{\|\mathbf{C}\|^2}{GM}\left(\frac{1}{1 + e\cos\theta}\right),$$

where $e = \|\mathbf{D}\|/GM$. This is the polar equation of a conic with a focus at the origin, which we set up to be the Sun. It is a hyperbola if $e > 1$, a parabola if $e = 1$, or an ellipse if $e < 1$. Since planets have closed orbits, the only possibility is an ellipse. However, at this point it should be mentioned that hyperbolic comets do exist. These are objects that are merely passing through the solar system at speeds too great to be trapped into orbit around the Sun. As they pass close enough to the Sun, the gravitational field of the Sun deflects the trajectory enough so the path becomes hyperbolic.

$\square$

## Example 3.17

### Using Kepler's Third Law for Nonheliocentric Orbits

Kepler's third law of planetary motion can be modified to the case of one object in orbit around an object other than the Sun, such as the Moon around the Earth. In this case, Kepler's third law becomes

$$P^2 = \frac{4\pi^2 a^3}{G(m + M)}, \qquad\qquad (3.30)$$

where $m$ is the mass of the Moon and $M$ is the mass of Earth, $a$ represents the length of the major axis of the elliptical orbit, and $P$ represents the period.

Given that the mass of the Moon is $7.35 \times 10^{22}$ kg, the mass of Earth is $5.97 \times 10^{24}$ kg, $G = 6.67 \times 10^{-11}$ m /kg $\cdot$ sec$^2$, and the period of the moon is 27.3 days, let's find the length of the major axis of the orbit of the Moon around Earth.

### Solution

It is important to be consistent with units. Since the universal gravitational constant contains seconds in the units, we need to use seconds for the period of the Moon as well:

$$27.3 \text{ days} \times \frac{24 \text{ hr}}{1 \text{ day}} \times \frac{3600 \text{ sec}}{1 \text{ hour}} = 2{,}358{,}720 \text{ sec}.$$

Substitute all the data into **Equation 3.30** and solve for $a$:

$$(2{,}358{,}720 \text{ sec})^2 = \frac{4\pi^2 a^3}{\left(6.67 \times 10^{-11} \frac{\text{m}}{\text{kg} \cdot \text{sec}^2}\right)\left(7.35 \text{ x } 10^{22} \text{ kg} + 5.97 \text{ x } 10^{24} \text{ kg}\right)}$$

$$5.563 \times 10^{12} = \frac{4\pi^2 a^3}{\left(6.67 \times 10^{-11} \text{ m}^3\right)\left(6.04 \text{ x } 10^{24}\right)}$$

$$\left(5.563 \times 10^{12}\right)\left(6.67 \times 10^{-11} \text{ m}^3\right)\left(6.04 \times 10^{24}\right) = 4\pi^2 a^3$$

$$a^3 = \frac{2.241 \times 10^{27}}{4\pi^2} \text{m}^3$$

$$a = 3.84 \times 10^8 \text{ m}$$

$$\approx 384{,}000 \text{ km}.$$

### Analysis

According to solarsystem.nasa.gov, the actual average distance from the Moon to Earth is 384,400 km. This is calculated using reflectors left on the Moon by Apollo astronauts back in the 1960s.

 **3.17**  Titan is the largest moon of Saturn. The mass of Titan is approximately $1.35 \times 10^{23}$ kg. The mass of Saturn is approximately $5.68 \times 10^{26}$ kg. Titan takes approximately 16 days to orbit Saturn. Use this information, along with the universal gravitation constant $G = 6.67 \times 10^{-11}$ m /kg $\cdot$ sec$^2$ to estimate the distance from Titan to Saturn.

## Example 3.18

### Chapter Opener: Halley's Comet

We now return to the chapter opener, which discusses the motion of Halley's comet around the Sun. Kepler's first law states that Halley's comet follows an elliptical path around the Sun, with the Sun as one focus of the ellipse. The period of Halley's comet is approximately 76.1 years, depending on how closely it passes by Jupiter and Saturn as it passes through the outer solar system. Let's use $T = 76.1$ years. What is the average distance of Halley's comet from the Sun?

### Solution

Using the equation $T^2 = D^3$ with $T = 76.1$, we obtain $D^3 = 5791.21$, so $D \approx 17.96$ A.U. This comes out to approximately $1.67 \times 10^9$ mi.

A natural question to ask is: What are the maximum (aphelion) and minimum (perihelion) distances from Halley's Comet to the Sun? The eccentricity of the orbit of Halley's Comet is 0.967 (Source: http://nssdc.gsfc.nasa.gov/planetary/factsheet/cometfact.html). Recall that the formula for the eccentricity of an ellipse is $e = c/a$, where $a$ is the length of the semimajor axis and $c$ is the distance from the center to either focus. Therefore, $0.967 = c/17.96$ and $c \approx 17.37$ A.U. Subtracting this from $a$ gives the perihelion distance $p = a - c = 17.96 - 17.37 = 0.59$ A.U. According to the National Space Science Data Center (Source: http://nssdc.gsfc.nasa.gov/planetary/factsheet/cometfact.html), the perihelion distance for Halley's comet is 0.587 A.U. To calculate the aphelion distance, we add

$$P = a + c = 17.96 + 17.37 = 35.33 \text{ A.U.}$$

This is approximately $3.3 \times 10^9$ mi. The average distance from Pluto to the Sun is 39.5 A.U. (Source: http://www.oarval.org/furthest.htm), so it would appear that Halley's Comet stays just within the orbit of Pluto.

# Student PROJECT

## Navigating a Banked Turn

How fast can a racecar travel through a circular turn without skidding and hitting the wall? The answer could depend on several factors:

- The weight of the car;
- The friction between the tires and the road;
- The radius of the circle;
- The "steepness" of the turn.

In this project we investigate this question for NASCAR racecars at the Bristol Motor Speedway in Tennessee. Before considering this track in particular, we use vector functions to develop the mathematics and physics necessary for answering questions such as this.

A car of mass $m$ moves with constant angular speed $\omega$ around a circular curve of radius $R$ (Figure 3.20). The curve is banked at an angle $\theta$. If the height of the car off the ground is $h$, then the position of the car at time $t$ is given by the function $r(t) = \langle R\cos(\omega t), R\sin(\omega t), h \rangle$.

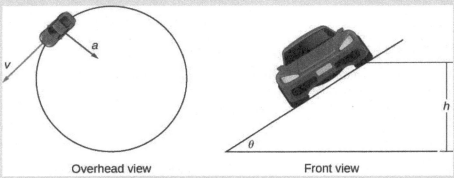

**Figure 3.20**  Views of a race car moving around a track.

1. Find the velocity function $\mathbf{v}(t)$ of the car. Show that $\mathbf{v}$ is tangent to the circular curve. This means that, without a force to keep the car on the curve, the car will shoot off of it.

2. Show that the speed of the car is $\omega R$. Use this to show that $(2\pi 4)/|\mathbf{v}| = (2\pi)/\omega$.

3. Find the acceleration $\mathbf{a}$. Show that this vector points toward the center of the circle and that $|\mathbf{a}| = R\omega^2$.

4. The force required to produce this circular motion is called the *centripetal force*, and it is denoted $\mathbf{F}_{cent}$. This force points toward the center of the circle (not toward the ground). Show that $|\mathbf{F}_{cent}| = (m|\mathbf{v}|^2)/R$.

   As the car moves around the curve, three forces act on it: gravity, the force exerted by the road (this force is perpendicular to the ground), and the friction force (Figure 3.21). Because describing the frictional force generated by the tires and the road is complex, we use a standard approximation for the frictional force. Assume that $\mathbf{f} = \mu\mathbf{N}$ for some positive constant $\mu$. The constant $\mu$ is called the *coefficient of friction*.

**Figure 3.21** The car has three forces acting on it: gravity (denoted by $mg$), the friction force **f**, and the force exerted by the road **N**.

Let $v_{max}$ denote the maximum speed the car can attain through the curve without skidding. In other words, $v_{max}$ is the fastest speed at which the car can navigate the turn. When the car is traveling at this speed, the magnitude of the centripetal force is

$$|\mathbf{F}_{cent}| = \frac{mv_{max}^2}{R}.$$

The next three questions deal with developing a formula that relates the speed $v_{max}$ to the banking angle $\theta$.

5. Show that $\mathbf{N}\cos\theta = mg + \mathbf{f}\sin\theta$. Conclude that $\mathbf{N} = (mg)/(\cos\theta - \mu\sin\theta)$.

6. The centripetal force is the sum of the forces in the horizontal direction, since the centripetal force points toward the center of the circular curve. Show that

$$\mathbf{F}_{cent} = \mathbf{N}\sin\theta + \mathbf{f}\cos\theta.$$

Conclude that

$$\mathbf{F}_{cent} = \frac{\sin\theta + \mu\cos\theta}{\cos\theta - \mu\sin\theta}mg.$$

7. Show that $v_{max}^2 = ((\sin\theta + \mu\cos\theta)/(\cos\theta - \mu\sin\theta))gR$. Conclude that the maximum speed does not actually depend on the mass of the car.

   Now that we have a formula relating the maximum speed of the car and the banking angle, we are in a position to answer the questions like the one posed at the beginning of the project.

   The Bristol Motor Speedway is a NASCAR short track in Bristol, Tennessee. The track has the approximate shape shown in Figure 3.22. Each end of the track is approximately semicircular, so when cars make turns they are traveling along an approximately circular curve. If a car takes the inside track and speeds along the bottom of turn 1, the car travels along a semicircle of radius approximately 211 ft with a banking angle of 24°. If the car decides to take the outside track and speeds along the top of turn 1, then the car travels along a semicircle with a banking angle of 28°. (The track has variable angle banking.)

**Figure 3.22** At the Bristol Motor Speedway, Bristol, Tennessee (a), the turns have an inner radius of about 211 ft and a width of 40 ft (b). (credit: part (a) photo by Raniel Diaz, Flickr)

The coefficient of friction for a normal tire in dry conditions is approximately 0.7. Therefore, we assume the coefficient for a NASCAR tire in dry conditions is approximately 0.98.

Before answering the following questions, note that it is easier to do computations in terms of feet and seconds, and then convert the answers to miles per hour as a final step.

8. In dry conditions, how fast can the car travel through the bottom of the turn without skidding?

9. In dry conditions, how fast can the car travel through the top of the turn without skidding?

10. In wet conditions, the coefficient of friction can become as low as 0.1. If this is the case, how fast can the car travel through the bottom of the turn without skidding?

11. Suppose the measured speed of a car going along the outside edge of the turn is 105 mph. Estimate the coefficient of friction for the car's tires.

# 3.4 EXERCISES

**155.** Given $\mathbf{r}(t) = (3t^2 - 2)\mathbf{i} + (2t - \sin(t))\mathbf{j},$ find the velocity of a particle moving along this curve.

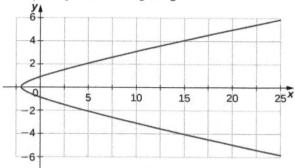

**156.** Given $\mathbf{r}(t) = (3t^2 - 2)\mathbf{i} + (2t - \sin(t))\mathbf{j},$ find the acceleration vector of a particle moving along the curve in the preceding exercise.

Given the following position functions, find the velocity, acceleration, and speed in terms of the parameter $t$.

**157.** $\mathbf{r}(t) = \langle\, 3\cos t,\, 3\sin t,\, t^2 \,\rangle$

**158.** $\mathbf{r}(t) = e^{-t}\mathbf{i} + t^2\mathbf{j} + \tan t\,\mathbf{k}$

**159.** $\mathbf{r}(t) = 2\cos t\,\mathbf{j} + 3\sin t\,\mathbf{k}.$ The graph is shown here:

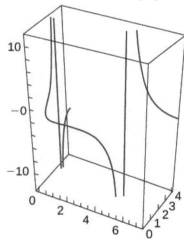

Find the velocity, acceleration, and speed of a particle with the given position function.

**160.** $\mathbf{r}(t) = \langle\, t^2 - 1,\, t \,\rangle$

**161.** $\mathbf{r}(t) = \langle\, e^t,\, e^{-t} \,\rangle$

**162.** $\mathbf{r}(t) = \langle\, \sin t,\, t,\, \cos t \,\rangle$. The graph is shown here:

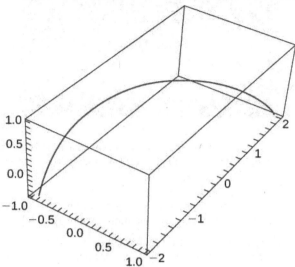

**163.** The position function of an object is given by $\mathbf{r}(t) = \langle\, t^2,\, 5t,\, t^2 - 16t \,\rangle$. At what time is the speed a minimum?

**164.** Let $\mathbf{r}(t) = r\cosh(\omega t)\mathbf{i} + r\sinh(\omega t)\mathbf{j}.$ Find the velocity and acceleration vectors and show that the acceleration is proportional to $\mathbf{r}(t)$.

Consider the motion of a point on the circumference of a rolling circle. As the circle rolls, it generates the cycloid $\mathbf{r}(t) = (\omega t - \sin(\omega t))\mathbf{i} + (1 - \cos(\omega t))\mathbf{j},$ where $\omega$ is the angular velocity of the circle and b is the radius of the circle:

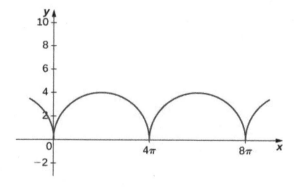

**165.** Find the equations for the velocity, acceleration, and speed of the particle at any time.

A person on a hang glider is spiraling upward as a result of the rapidly rising air on a path having position vector $\mathbf{r}(t) = (3\cos t)\mathbf{i} + (3\sin t)\mathbf{j} + t^2\mathbf{k}.$ The path is similar to that of a helix, although it is not a helix. The graph is shown here:

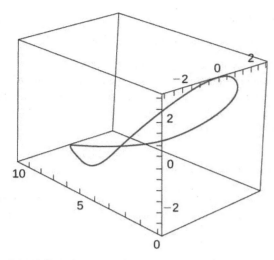

Find the following quantities:

166. The velocity and acceleration vectors

167. The glider's speed at any time

168. The times, if any, at which the glider's acceleration is orthogonal to its velocity

Given that $\mathbf{r}(t) = \langle e^{-5t}\sin t,\ e^{-5t}\cos t,\ 4e^{-5t} \rangle$ is the position vector of a moving particle, find the following quantities:

169. The velocity of the particle

170. The speed of the particle

171. The acceleration of the particle

172. Find the maximum speed of a point on the circumference of an automobile tire of radius 1 ft when the automobile is traveling at 55 mph.

A projectile is shot in the air from ground level with an initial velocity of 500 m/sec at an angle of 60° with the horizontal. The graph is shown here:

173. At what time does the projectile reach maximum height?

174. What is the approximate maximum height of the projectile?

175. At what time is the maximum range of the projectile attained?

176. What is the maximum range?

177. What is the total flight time of the projectile?

A projectile is fired at a height of 1.5 m above the ground with an initial velocity of 100 m/sec and at an angle of 30° above the horizontal. Use this information to answer the following questions:

178. Determine the maximum height of the projectile.

179. Determine the range of the projectile.

180. A golf ball is hit in a horizontal direction off the top edge of a building that is 100 ft tall. How fast must the ball be launched to land 450 ft away?

181. A projectile is fired from ground level at an angle of 8° with the horizontal. The projectile is to have a range of 50 m. Find the minimum velocity necessary to achieve this range.

182. Prove that an object moving in a straight line at a constant speed has an acceleration of zero.

183. The acceleration of an object is given by $\mathbf{a}(t) = t\mathbf{j} + t\mathbf{k}$. The velocity at $t = 1$ sec is $\mathbf{v}(1) = 5\mathbf{j}$ and the position of the object at $t = 1$ sec is $\mathbf{r}(1) = 0\mathbf{i} + 0\mathbf{j} + 0\mathbf{k}$. Find the object's position at any time.

184. Find $\mathbf{r}(t)$ given that $\mathbf{a}(t) = -32\mathbf{j}$, $\mathbf{v}(0) = 600\sqrt{3}\mathbf{i} + 600\mathbf{j}$, and $\mathbf{r}(0) = \mathbf{0}$.

185. Find the tangential and normal components of acceleration for $\mathbf{r}(t) = a\cos(\omega t)\mathbf{i} + b\sin(\omega t)\mathbf{j}$ at $t = 0$.

186. Given $\mathbf{r}(t) = t^2\mathbf{i} + 2t\mathbf{j}$ and $t = 1$, find the tangential and normal components of acceleration.

For each of the following problems, find the tangential and normal components of acceleration.

187.  $\mathbf{r}(t) = \langle e^t \cos t, e^t \sin t, e^t \rangle$. The graph is shown here:

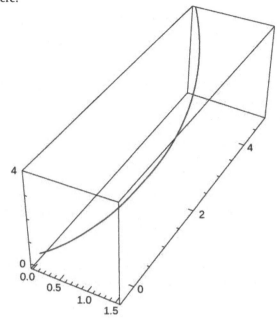

188.  $\mathbf{r}(t) = \langle \cos(2t), \sin(2t), 1 \rangle$

189.  $\mathbf{r}(t) = \langle 2t, t^2, \frac{t^3}{3} \rangle$

190.  $\mathbf{r}(t) = \langle \frac{2}{3}(1 + t)^{3/2}, \frac{2}{3}(1 - t)^{3/2}, \sqrt{2}t \rangle$

191.  $\mathbf{r}(t) = \langle 6t, 3t^2, 2t^3 \rangle$

192.  $\mathbf{r}(t) = t^2 \mathbf{i} + t^2 \mathbf{j} + t^3 \mathbf{k}$

193.  $\mathbf{r}(t) = 3 \cos(2\pi t) \mathbf{i} + 3 \sin(2\pi t) \mathbf{j}$

194.  Find the position vector-valued function $\mathbf{r}(t)$, given that $\mathbf{a}(t) = \mathbf{i} + e^t \mathbf{j}$,  $\mathbf{v}(0) = 2\mathbf{j}$,  and $\mathbf{r}(0) = 2\mathbf{i}$.

195.  The force on a particle is given by $\mathbf{f}(t) = (\cos t)\mathbf{i} + (\sin t)\mathbf{j}$. The particle is located at point $(c, 0)$ at $t = 0$. The initial velocity of the particle is given by $\mathbf{v}(0) = v_0 \mathbf{j}$. Find the path of the particle of mass $\mathbf{m}$. (Recall, $\mathbf{F} = m \cdot \mathbf{a}$.)

196.  An automobile that weighs 2700 lb makes a turn on a flat road while traveling at 56 ft/sec. If the radius of the turn is 70 ft, what is the required frictional force to keep the car from skidding?

197.  Using Kepler's laws, it can be shown that $v_0 = \sqrt{\frac{2GM}{r_0}}$ is the minimum speed needed when $\theta = 0$ so that an object will escape from the pull of a central force resulting from mass $M$. Use this result to find the minimum speed when $\theta = 0$ for a space capsule to escape from the gravitational pull of Earth if the probe is at an altitude of 300 km above Earth's surface.

198.  Find the time in years it takes the dwarf planet Pluto to make one orbit about the Sun given that $a = 39.5$ A.U.

Suppose that the position function for an object in three dimensions is given by the equation $\mathbf{r}(t) = t\cos(t)\mathbf{i} + t\sin(t)\mathbf{j} + 3t\mathbf{k}$.

199.  Show that the particle moves on a circular cone.

200.  Find the angle between the velocity and acceleration vectors when $t = 1.5$.

201.  Find the tangential and normal components of acceleration when $t = 1.5$.

# CHAPTER 3 REVIEW

## KEY TERMS

**acceleration vector** the second derivative of the position vector

**arc-length function** a function $s(t)$ that describes the arc length of curve $C$ as a function of $t$

**arc-length parameterization** a reparameterization of a vector-valued function in which the parameter is equal to the arc length

**binormal vector** a unit vector orthogonal to the unit tangent vector and the unit normal vector

**component functions** the component functions of the vector-valued function $\mathbf{r}(t) = f(t)\mathbf{i} + g(t)\mathbf{j}$ are $f(t)$ and $g(t)$, and the component functions of the vector-valued function $\mathbf{r}(t) = f(t)\mathbf{i} + g(t)\mathbf{j} + h(t)\mathbf{k}$ are $f(t)$, $g(t)$ and $h(t)$

**curvature** the derivative of the unit tangent vector with respect to the arc-length parameter

**definite integral of a vector-valued function** the vector obtained by calculating the definite integral of each of the component functions of a given vector-valued function, then using the results as the components of the resulting function

**derivative of a vector-valued function** the derivative of a vector-valued function $\mathbf{r}(t)$ is
$$\mathbf{r}'(t) = \lim_{\Delta t \to 0} \frac{\mathbf{r}(t + \Delta t) - \mathbf{r}(t)}{\Delta t}, \quad \text{provided the limit exists}$$

**Frenet frame of reference** (TNB frame) a frame of reference in three-dimensional space formed by the unit tangent vector, the unit normal vector, and the binormal vector

**helix** a three-dimensional curve in the shape of a spiral

**indefinite integral of a vector-valued function** a vector-valued function with a derivative that is equal to a given vector-valued function

**Kepler's laws of planetary motion** three laws governing the motion of planets, asteroids, and comets in orbit around the Sun

**limit of a vector-valued function** a vector-valued function $\mathbf{r}(t)$ has a limit $\mathbf{L}$ as $t$ approaches $a$ if $\lim_{t \to a} |\mathbf{r}(t) - \mathbf{L}| = 0$

**normal component of acceleration** the coefficient of the unit normal vector $\mathbf{N}$ when the acceleration vector is written as a linear combination of $\mathbf{T}$ and $\mathbf{N}$

**normal plane** a plane that is perpendicular to a curve at any point on the curve

**osculating circle** a circle that is tangent to a curve $C$ at a point $P$ and that shares the same curvature

**osculating plane** the plane determined by the unit tangent and the unit normal vector

**plane curve** the set of ordered pairs $(f(t), g(t))$ together with their defining parametric equations $x = f(t)$ and $y = g(t)$

**principal unit normal vector** a vector orthogonal to the unit tangent vector, given by the formula $\dfrac{\mathbf{T}'(t)}{\| \mathbf{T}'(t) \|}$

**principal unit tangent vector** a unit vector tangent to a curve $C$

**projectile motion** motion of an object with an initial velocity but no force acting on it other than gravity

**radius of curvature** the reciprocal of the curvature

**reparameterization** an alternative parameterization of a given vector-valued function

**smooth** curves where the vector-valued function $\mathbf{r}(t)$ is differentiable with a non-zero derivative

**space curve** the set of ordered triples $(f(t), g(t), h(t))$ together with their defining parametric equations $x = f(t)$, $y = g(t)$ and $z = h(t)$

**tangent vector** to $\mathbf{r}(t)$ at $t = t_0$ any vector $\mathbf{v}$ such that, when the tail of the vector is placed at point $\mathbf{r}(t_0)$ on the graph, vector $\mathbf{v}$ is tangent to curve $C$

**tangential component of acceleration** the coefficient of the unit tangent vector $\mathbf{T}$ when the acceleration vector is written as a linear combination of $\mathbf{T}$ and $\mathbf{N}$

**vector parameterization** any representation of a plane or space curve using a vector-valued function

**vector-valued function** a function of the form $\mathbf{r}(t) = f(t)\mathbf{i} + g(t)\mathbf{j}$ or $\mathbf{r}(t) = f(t)\mathbf{i} + g(t)\mathbf{j} + h(t)\mathbf{k}$, where the component functions $f$, $g$, and $h$ are real-valued functions of the parameter $t$

**velocity vector** the derivative of the position vector

## KEY EQUATIONS

- **Vector-valued function**
  $$\mathbf{r}(t) = f(t)\mathbf{i} + g(t)\mathbf{j} \text{ or } \mathbf{r}(t) = f(t)\mathbf{i} + g(t)\mathbf{j} + h(t)\mathbf{k}, \text{ or } \mathbf{r}(t) = \langle f(t), g(t) \rangle \text{ or } \mathbf{r}(t) = \langle f(t), g(t), h(t) \rangle$$

- **Limit of a vector-valued function**
  $$\lim_{t \to a} \mathbf{r}(t) = \left[\lim_{t \to a} f(t)\right]\mathbf{i} + \left[\lim_{t \to a} g(t)\right]\mathbf{j} \text{ or } \lim_{t \to a} \mathbf{r}(t) = \left[\lim_{t \to a} f(t)\right]\mathbf{i} + \left[\lim_{t \to a} g(t)\right]\mathbf{j} + \left[\lim_{t \to a} h(t)\right]\mathbf{k}$$

- **Derivative of a vector-valued function**
  $$\mathbf{r}'(t) = \lim_{\Delta t \to 0} \frac{\mathbf{r}(t + \Delta t) - \mathbf{r}(t)}{\Delta t}$$

- **Principal unit tangent vector**
  $$\mathbf{T}(t) = \frac{\mathbf{r}'(t)}{\|\mathbf{r}'(t)\|}$$

- **Indefinite integral of a vector-valued function**
  $$\int [f(t)\mathbf{i} + g(t)\mathbf{j} + h(t)\mathbf{k}]dt = \left[\int f(t)dt\right]\mathbf{i} + \left[\int g(t)dt\right]\mathbf{j} + \left[\int h(t)dt\right]\mathbf{k}$$

- **Definite integral of a vector-valued function**
  $$\int_a^b [f(t)\mathbf{i} + g(t)\mathbf{j} + h(t)\mathbf{k}]dt = \left[\int_a^b f(t)dt\right]\mathbf{i} + \left[\int_a^b g(t)dt\right]\mathbf{j} + \left[\int_a^b h(t)dt\right]\mathbf{k}$$

- **Arc length of space curve**
  $$s = \int_a^b \sqrt{[f'(t)]^2 + [g'(t)]^2 + [h'(t)]^2}\, dt = \int_a^b \|\mathbf{r}'(t)\|\, dt$$

- **Arc-length function**
  $$s(t) = \int_a^t \sqrt{(f'(u))^2 + (g'(u))^2 + (h'(u))^2}\, du \text{ or } s(t) = \int_a^t \|\mathbf{r}'(u)\|\, du$$

- **Curvature**
  $$\kappa = \frac{\|\mathbf{T}'(t)\|}{\|\mathbf{r}'(t)\|} \text{ or } \kappa = \frac{\|\mathbf{r}'(t) \times \mathbf{r}''(t)\|}{\|\mathbf{r}'(t)\|^3} \text{ or } \kappa = \frac{|y''|}{\left[1 + (y')^2\right]^{3/2}}$$

- **Principal unit normal vector**
  $$\mathbf{N}(t) = \frac{\mathbf{T}'(t)}{\|\mathbf{T}'(t)\|}$$

- **Binormal vector**
  $$\mathbf{B}(t) = \mathbf{T}(t) \times \mathbf{N}(t)$$

- **Velocity**

$$\mathbf{v}(t) = \mathbf{r}'(t)$$

- **Acceleration**
  $$\mathbf{a}(t) = \mathbf{v}'(t) = \mathbf{r}''(t)$$

- **Speed**
  $$v(t) = \| \mathbf{v}(t) \| = \| \mathbf{r}'(t) \| = \frac{ds}{dt}$$

- **Tangential component of acceleration**
  $$a_\mathbf{T} = \mathbf{a} \cdot \mathbf{T} = \frac{\mathbf{v} \cdot \mathbf{a}}{\| \mathbf{v} \|}$$

- **Normal component of acceleration**
  $$a_\mathbf{N} = \mathbf{a} \cdot \mathbf{N} = \frac{\| \mathbf{v} \times \mathbf{a} \|}{\| \mathbf{v} \|} = \sqrt{\| \mathbf{a} \|^2 - a^\mathbf{T}}$$

# KEY CONCEPTS

## 3.1 Vector-Valued Functions and Space Curves

- A vector-valued function is a function of the form $\mathbf{r}(t) = f(t)\mathbf{i} + g(t)\mathbf{j}$ or $\mathbf{r}(t) = f(t)\mathbf{i} + g(t)\mathbf{j} + h(t)\mathbf{k}$, where the component functions $f$, $g$, and $h$ are real-valued functions of the parameter $t$.

- The graph of a vector-valued function of the form $\mathbf{r}(t) = f(t)\mathbf{i} + g(t)\mathbf{j}$ is called a *plane curve*. The graph of a vector-valued function of the form $\mathbf{r}(t) = f(t)\mathbf{i} + g(t)\mathbf{j} + h(t)\mathbf{k}$ is called a *space curve*.

- It is possible to represent an arbitrary plane curve by a vector-valued function.

- To calculate the limit of a vector-valued function, calculate the limits of the component functions separately.

## 3.2 Calculus of Vector-Valued Functions

- To calculate the derivative of a vector-valued function, calculate the derivatives of the component functions, then put them back into a new vector-valued function.

- Many of the properties of differentiation from the Introduction to Derivatives (http://cnx.org/content/m53494/latest/) also apply to vector-valued functions.

- The derivative of a vector-valued function $\mathbf{r}(t)$ is also a tangent vector to the curve. The unit tangent vector $\mathbf{T}(t)$ is calculated by dividing the derivative of a vector-valued function by its magnitude.

- The antiderivative of a vector-valued function is found by finding the antiderivatives of the component functions, then putting them back together in a vector-valued function.

- The definite integral of a vector-valued function is found by finding the definite integrals of the component functions, then putting them back together in a vector-valued function.

## 3.3 Arc Length and Curvature

- The arc-length function for a vector-valued function is calculated using the integral formula $s(t) = \int_a^t \| \mathbf{r}'(u) \| \, du$. This formula is valid in both two and three dimensions.

- The curvature of a curve at a point in either two or three dimensions is defined to be the curvature of the inscribed circle at that point. The arc-length parameterization is used in the definition of curvature.

- There are several different formulas for curvature. The curvature of a circle is equal to the reciprocal of its radius.

- The principal unit normal vector at $t$ is defined to be

$$\mathbf{N}(t) = \frac{\mathbf{T}'(t)}{\| \mathbf{T}'(t) \|}.$$

- The binormal vector at $t$ is defined as $\mathbf{B}(t) = \mathbf{T}(t) \times \mathbf{N}(t)$, where $\mathbf{T}(t)$ is the unit tangent vector.

- The Frenet frame of reference is formed by the unit tangent vector, the principal unit normal vector, and the binormal vector.

- The osculating circle is tangent to a curve at a point and has the same curvature as the tangent curve at that point.

## 3.4 Motion in Space

- If $\mathbf{r}(t)$ represents the position of an object at time $t$, then $\mathbf{r}'(t)$ represents the velocity and $\mathbf{r}''(t)$ represents the acceleration of the object at time $t$. The magnitude of the velocity vector is speed.

- The acceleration vector always points toward the concave side of the curve defined by $\mathbf{r}(t)$. The tangential and normal components of acceleration $a_{\mathbf{T}}$ and $a_{\mathbf{N}}$ are the projections of the acceleration vector onto the unit tangent and unit normal vectors to the curve.

- Kepler's three laws of planetary motion describe the motion of objects in orbit around the Sun. His third law can be modified to describe motion of objects in orbit around other celestial objects as well.

- Newton was able to use his law of universal gravitation in conjunction with his second law of motion and calculus to prove Kepler's three laws.

# CHAPTER 3 REVIEW EXERCISES

*True or False?* Justify your answer with a proof or a counterexample.

**202.** A parametric equation that passes through points P and Q can be given by $\mathbf{r}(t) = \langle t^2, 3t+1, t-2 \rangle$, where $P(1, 4, -1)$ and $Q(16, 11, 2)$.

**203.** $\frac{d}{dt}[\mathbf{u}(t) \times \mathbf{u}(t)] = 2\mathbf{u}'(t) \times \mathbf{u}(t)$

**204.** The curvature of a circle of radius $r$ is constant everywhere. Furthermore, the curvature is equal to $1/r$.

**205.** The speed of a particle with a position function $\mathbf{r}(t)$ is $(\mathbf{r}'(t))/(|\mathbf{r}'(t)|)$.

Find the domains of the vector-valued functions.

**206.** $\mathbf{r}(t) = \langle \sin(t), \ln(t), \sqrt{t} \rangle$

**207.** $\mathbf{r}(t) = \langle e^t, \frac{1}{\sqrt{4-t}}, \sec(t) \rangle$

Sketch the curves for the following vector equations. Use a calculator if needed.

**208.** [T] $\mathbf{r}(t) = \langle t^2, t^3 \rangle$

**209.** [T] $\mathbf{r}(t) = \langle \sin(20t)e^{-t}, \cos(20t)e^{-t}, e^{-t} \rangle$

Find a vector function that describes the following curves.

**210.** Intersection of the cylinder $x^2 + y^2 = 4$ with the plane $x + z = 6$

**211.** Intersection of the cone $z = \sqrt{x^2 + y^2}$ and plane $z = y - 4$

Find the derivatives of $\mathbf{u}(t)$, $\mathbf{u}'(t)$, $\mathbf{u}'(t) \times \mathbf{u}(t)$, $\mathbf{u}(t) \times \mathbf{u}'(t)$, and $\mathbf{u}(t) \cdot \mathbf{u}'(t)$. Find the unit tangent vector.

**212.** $\mathbf{u}(t) = \langle e^t, e^{-t} \rangle$

**213.** $\mathbf{u}(t) = \langle t^2, 2t+6, 4t^5 - 12 \rangle$

Evaluate the following integrals.

**214.** $\int (\tan(t)\sec(t)\mathbf{i} - te^{3t}\mathbf{j})dt$

**215.** $\int_1^4 \mathbf{u}(t)dt$, with $\mathbf{u}(t) = \langle \frac{\ln(t)}{t}, \frac{1}{\sqrt{t}}, \sin(\frac{t\pi}{4}) \rangle$

Find the length for the following curves.

**216.** $\mathbf{r}(t) = \langle 3(t), 4\cos(t), 4\sin(t) \rangle$ for $1 \le t \le 4$

**217.** $\mathbf{r}(t) = 2\mathbf{i} + t\mathbf{j} + 3t^2\mathbf{k}$ for $0 \le t \le 1$

Reparameterize the following functions with respect to their arc length measured from $t = 0$ in direction of increasing $t$.

**218.** $\mathbf{r}(t) = 2t\mathbf{i} + (4t - 5)\mathbf{j} + (1 - 3t)\mathbf{k}$

**219.** $\mathbf{r}(t) = \cos(2t)\mathbf{i} + 8t\mathbf{j} - \sin(2t)\mathbf{k}$

Find the curvature for the following vector functions.

**220.** $\mathbf{r}(t) = (2\sin t)\mathbf{i} - 4t\mathbf{j} + (2\cos t)\mathbf{k}$

**221.** $\mathbf{r}(t) = \sqrt{2}e^t\mathbf{i} + \sqrt{2}e^{-t}\mathbf{j} + 2t\mathbf{k}$

**222.** Find the unit tangent vector, the unit normal vector, and the binormal vector for $\mathbf{r}(t) = 2\cos t\mathbf{i} + 3t\mathbf{j} + 2\sin t\mathbf{k}$.

**223.** Find the tangential and normal acceleration components with the position vector $\mathbf{r}(t) = \langle \cos t, \sin t, e^t \rangle$.

**224.** A Ferris wheel car is moving at a constant speed $v$ and has a constant radius $r$. Find the tangential and normal acceleration of the Ferris wheel car.

**225.** The position of a particle is given by $\mathbf{r}(t) = \langle t^2, \ln(t), \sin(\pi t) \rangle$, where $t$ is measured in seconds and $\mathbf{r}$ is measured in meters. Find the velocity, acceleration, and speed functions. What are the position, velocity, speed, and acceleration of the particle at 1 sec?

The following problems consider launching a cannonball out of a cannon. The cannonball is shot out of the cannon with an angle $\theta$ and initial velocity $\mathbf{v}_0$. The only force acting on the cannonball is gravity, so we begin with a constant acceleration $\mathbf{a}(t) = -g\mathbf{j}$.

**226.** Find the velocity vector function $\mathbf{v}(t)$.

**227.** Find the position vector $\mathbf{r}(t)$ and the parametric representation for the position.

**228.** At what angle do you need to fire the cannonball for the horizontal distance to be greatest? What is the total distance it would travel?

# 4 | DIFFERENTIATION OF FUNCTIONS OF SEVERAL VARIABLES

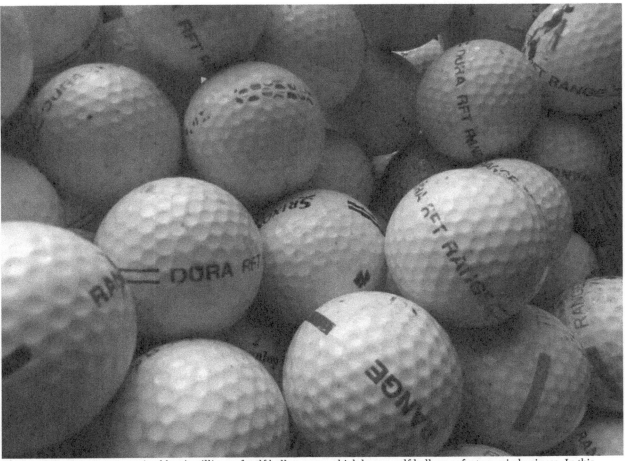

**Figure 4.1** Americans use (and lose) millions of golf balls a year, which keeps golf ball manufacturers in business. In this chapter, we study a profit model and learn methods for calculating optimal production levels for a typical golf ball manufacturing company. (credit: modification of work by oatsy40, Flickr)

## Chapter Outline

# Introduction

In **Introduction to Applications of Derivatives (http://cnx.org/content/m53602/latest/)** , we studied how to determine the maximum and minimum of a function of one variable over a closed interval. This function might represent the temperature over a given time interval, the position of a car as a function of time, or the altitude of a jet plane as it travels from New York to San Francisco. In each of these examples, the function has one independent variable.

Suppose, however, that we have a quantity that depends on more than one variable. For example, temperature can depend on location and the time of day, or a company's profit model might depend on the number of units sold and the amount of money spent on advertising. In this chapter, we look at a company that produces golf balls. We develop a profit model and, under various restrictions, we find that the optimal level of production and advertising dollars spent determines the maximum possible profit. Depending on the nature of the restrictions, both the method of solution and the solution itself changes (see **Example 4.41**).

When dealing with a function of more than one independent variable, several questions naturally arise. For example, how do we calculate limits of functions of more than one variable? The definition of *derivative* we used before involved a limit. Does the new definition of derivative involve limits as well? Do the rules of differentiation apply in this context? Can we find relative extrema of functions using derivatives? All these questions are answered in this chapter.

# 4.1 | Functions of Several Variables

## Learning Objectives

**4.1.1** Recognize a function of two variables and identify its domain and range.

**4.1.2** Sketch a graph of a function of two variables.

**4.1.3** Sketch several traces or level curves of a function of two variables.

**4.1.4** Recognize a function of three or more variables and identify its level surfaces.

Our first step is to explain what a function of more than one variable is, starting with functions of two independent variables. This step includes identifying the domain and range of such functions and learning how to graph them. We also examine ways to relate the graphs of functions in three dimensions to graphs of more familiar planar functions.

## Functions of Two Variables

The definition of a function of two variables is very similar to the definition for a function of one variable. The main difference is that, instead of mapping values of one variable to values of another variable, we map ordered pairs of variables to another variable.

**Definition**

A **function of two variables** $z = f(x, y)$ maps each ordered pair $(x, y)$ in a subset $D$ of the real plane $\mathbb{R}^2$ to a unique real number $z$. The set $D$ is called the *domain* of the function. The *range* of $f$ is the set of all real numbers z that has at least one ordered pair $(x, y) \in D$ such that $f(x, y) = z$ as shown in the following figure.

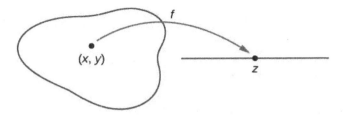

**Domain**                    **Range**

**Figure 4.2** The domain of a function of two variables consists of ordered pairs $(x, y)$.

Determining the domain of a function of two variables involves taking into account any domain restrictions that may exist. Let's take a look.

## Example 4.1

### Domains and Ranges for Functions of Two Variables

Find the domain and range of each of the following functions:

a. $f(x, y) = 3x + 5y + 2$

b. $g(x, y) = \sqrt{9 - x^2 - y^2}$

### Solution

a. This is an example of a linear function in two variables. There are no values or combinations of $x$ and $y$ that cause $f(x, y)$ to be undefined, so the domain of $f$ is $\mathbb{R}^2$. To determine the range, first pick a value for $z$. We need to find a solution to the equation $f(x, y) = z$, or $3x - 5y + 2 = z$. One such solution can be obtained by first setting $y = 0$, which yields the equation $3x + 2 = z$. The solution to this equation is $x = \frac{z - 2}{3}$, which gives the ordered pair $\left(\frac{z-2}{3}, 0\right)$ as a solution to the equation $f(x, y) = z$ for any value of $z$. Therefore, the range of the function is all real numbers, or $\mathbb{R}$.

b. For the function $g(x, y)$ to have a real value, the quantity under the square root must be nonnegative:

$$9 - x^2 - y^2 \geq 0.$$

This inequality can be written in the form

$$x^2 + y^2 \leq 9.$$

Therefore, the domain of $g(x, y)$ is $\{(x, y) \in \mathbb{R}^2 | x^2 + y^2 \leq 9\}$. The graph of this set of points can be described as a disk of radius 3 centered at the origin. The domain includes the boundary circle as shown in the following graph.

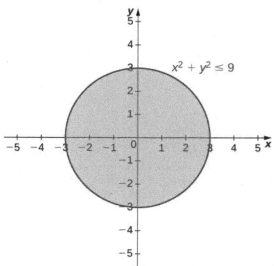

**Figure 4.3** The domain of the function

$g(x, y) = \sqrt{9 - x^2 - y^2}$ is a closed disk of radius 3.

To determine the range of $g(x, y) = \sqrt{9 - x^2 - y^2}$ we start with a point $(x_0, y_0)$ on the boundary of the domain, which is defined by the relation $x^2 + y^2 = 9$. It follows that $x_0^2 + y_0^2 = 9$ and

$$g(x_0, y_0) = \sqrt{9 - x_0^2 - y_0^2} = \sqrt{9 - \left(x_0^2 + y_0^2\right)} = \sqrt{9 - 9} = 0.$$

If $x_0^2 + y_0^2 = 0$ (in other words, $x_0 = y_0 = 0$), then

$$g(x_0, y_0) = \sqrt{9 - x_0^2 - y_0^2} = \sqrt{9 - \left(x_0^2 + y_0^2\right)} = \sqrt{9 - 0} = 3.$$

This is the maximum value of the function. Given any value $c$ between $0$ and $3$, we can find an entire set of points inside the domain of $g$ such that $g(x, y) = c$:

$$\begin{aligned} \sqrt{9 - x^2 - y^2} &= c \\ 9 - x^2 - y^2 &= c^2 \\ x^2 + y^2 &= 9 - c^2. \end{aligned}$$

Since $9 - c^2 > 0$, this describes a circle of radius $\sqrt{9 - c^2}$ centered at the origin. Any point on this circle satisfies the equation $g(x, y) = c$. Therefore, the range of this function can be written in interval notation as $[0, 3]$.

 **4.1** Find the domain and range of the function $f(x, y) = \sqrt{36 - 9x^2 - 9y^2}$.

# Graphing Functions of Two Variables

Suppose we wish to graph the function $z = (x, y)$. This function has two independent variables $(x$ and $y)$ and one dependent variable $(z)$. When graphing a function $y = f(x)$ of one variable, we use the Cartesian plane. We are able to graph any ordered pair $(x, y)$ in the plane, and every point in the plane has an ordered pair $(x, y)$ associated with it. With a function of two variables, each ordered pair $(x, y)$ in the domain of the function is mapped to a real number $z$. Therefore, the graph of the function $f$ consists of ordered triples $(x, y, z)$. The graph of a function $z = (x, y)$ of two variables is called a **surface**.

To understand more completely the concept of plotting a set of ordered triples to obtain a surface in three-dimensional space, imagine the $(x, y)$ coordinate system laying flat. Then, every point in the domain of the function $f$ has a unique $z$-value associated with it. If $z$ is positive, then the graphed point is located above the $xy$-plane, if $z$ is negative, then the graphed point is located below the $xy$-plane. The set of all the graphed points becomes the two-dimensional surface that is the graph of the function $f$.

## Example 4.2

### Graphing Functions of Two Variables

Create a graph of each of the following functions:

   a.   $g(x, y) = \sqrt{9 - x^2 - y^2}$

   b.   $f(x, y) = x^2 + y^2$

### Solution

   a.  In **Example 4.1**, we determined that the domain of $g(x, y) = \sqrt{9 - x^2 - y^2}$ is $\{(x, y) \in \mathbb{R}^2 | x^2 + y^2 \le 9\}$ and the range is $\{z \in \mathbb{R}^2 | 0 \le z \le 3\}$. When $x^2 + y^2 = 9$ we have $g(x, y) = 0$. Therefore any point on the circle of radius $3$ centered at the origin in the $x, y$-plane maps to $z = 0$ in $\mathbb{R}^3$. If $x^2 + y^2 = 8$, then $g(x, y) = 1$, so any point on the circle of radius $2\sqrt{2}$ centered at the origin in the $x, y$-plane maps to $z = 1$ in $\mathbb{R}^3$. As $x^2 + y^2$ gets closer to zero, the value of $z$ approaches 3. When $x^2 + y^2 = 0$, then $g(x, y) = 3$. This is the origin in the $x, y$-plane. If $x^2 + y^2$ is equal to any other value between $0$ and $9$, then $g(x, y)$ equals some other constant between $0$ and $3$. The surface described by this function is a hemisphere centered at the origin with radius $3$ as shown in the following graph.

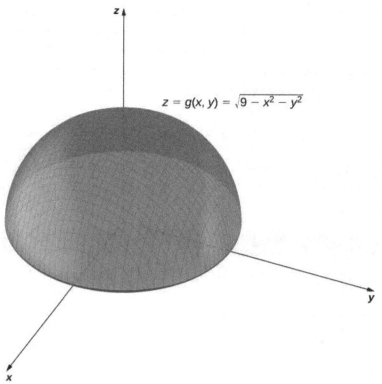

$$z = g(x, y) = \sqrt{9 - x^2 - y^2}$$

**Figure 4.4** Graph of the hemisphere represented by the given function of two variables.

b.  This function also contains the expression $x^2 + y^2$. Setting this expression equal to various values starting at zero, we obtain circles of increasing radius. The minimum value of $f(x, y) = x^2 + y^2$ is zero (attained when $x = y = 0$.). When $x = 0$, the function becomes $z = y^2$, and when $y = 0$, then the function becomes $z = x^2$. These are cross-sections of the graph, and are parabolas. Recall from **Introduction to Vectors in Space** that the name of the graph of $f(x, y) = x^2 + y^2$ is a *paraboloid*. The graph of $f$ appears in the following graph.

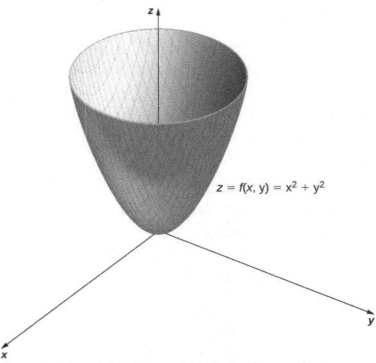

**Figure 4.5** A paraboloid is the graph of the given function of two variables.

## Example 4.3

### Nuts and Bolts

A profit function for a hardware manufacturer is given by

$$f(x, y) = 16 - (x - 3)^2 - (y - 2)^2,$$

where $x$ is the number of nuts sold per month (measured in thousands) and $y$ represents the number of bolts sold per month (measured in thousands). Profit is measured in thousands of dollars. Sketch a graph of this function.

### Solution

This function is a polynomial function in two variables. The domain of $f$ consists of $(x, y)$ coordinate pairs that yield a nonnegative profit:

$$16 - (x - 3)^2 - (y - 2)^2 \geq 0$$
$$(x - 3)^2 + (y - 2)^2 \leq 16.$$

This is a disk of radius $4$ centered at $(3, 2)$. A further restriction is that both $x$ and $y$ must be nonnegative. When $x = 3$ and $y = 2$, $f(x, y) = 16$. Note that it is possible for either value to be a noninteger; for example, it is possible to sell $2.5$ thousand nuts in a month. The domain, therefore, contains thousands of points, so we can consider all points within the disk. For any $z < 16$, we can solve the equation $f(x, y) = 16$:

$$16 - (x - 3)^2 - (y - 2)^2 = z$$
$$(x - 3)^2 + (y - 2)^2 = 16 - z.$$

Since $z < 16$, we know that $16 - z > 0$, so the previous equation describes a circle with radius $\sqrt{16 - z}$ centered at the point $(3, 2)$. Therefore. the range of $f(x, y)$ is $\{z \in \mathbb{R} | z \le 16\}$. The graph of $f(x, y)$ is also a paraboloid, and this paraboloid points downward as shown.

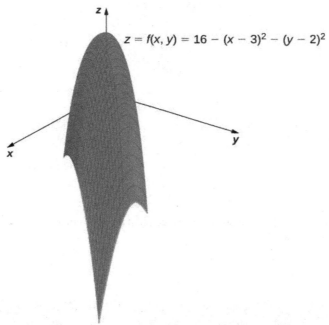

**Figure 4.6** The graph of the given function of two variables is also a paraboloid.

## Level Curves

If hikers walk along rugged trails, they might use a topographical map that shows how steeply the trails change. A topographical map contains curved lines called *contour lines*. Each contour line corresponds to the points on the map that have equal elevation (**Figure 4.7**). A level curve of a function of two variables $f(x, y)$ is completely analogous to a contour line on a topographical map.

(a)    (b)

Figure 4.7  (a) A topographical map of Devil's Tower, Wyoming. Lines that are close together indicate very steep terrain. (b) A perspective photo of Devil's Tower shows just how steep its sides are. Notice the top of the tower has the same shape as the center of the topographical map.

---

### Definition

Given a function $f(x, y)$ and a number $c$ in the range of $f$, a **level curve of a function of two variables** for the value $c$ is defined to be the set of points satisfying the equation $f(x, y) = c$.

---

Returning to the function $g(x, y) = \sqrt{9 - x^2 - y^2}$, we can determine the level curves of this function. The range of $g$ is the closed interval $[0, 3]$. First, we choose any number in this closed interval—say, $c = 2$. The level curve corresponding to $c = 2$ is described by the equation

$$\sqrt{9 - x^2 - y^2} = 2.$$

To simplify, square both sides of this equation:

$$9 - x^2 - y^2 = 4.$$

Now, multiply both sides of the equation by $-1$ and add 9 to each side:

$$x^2 + y^2 = 5.$$

This equation describes a circle centered at the origin with radius $\sqrt{5}$. Using values of $c$ between 0 and 3 yields other circles also centered at the origin. If $c = 3$, then the circle has radius 0, so it consists solely of the origin. Figure 4.8 is a graph of the level curves of this function corresponding to $c = 0, 1, 2,$ and 3. Note that in the previous derivation it may be possible that we introduced extra solutions by squaring both sides. This is not the case here because the range of the square root function is nonnegative.

**Figure 4.8** Level curves of the function $g(x, y) = \sqrt{9 - x^2 - y^2}$, using $c = 0, 1, 2,$ and $3$ ($c = 3$ corresponds to the origin).

A graph of the various level curves of a function is called a **contour map**.

## Example 4.4

### Making a Contour Map

Given the function $f(x, y) = \sqrt{8 + 8x - 4y - 4x^2 - y^2}$, find the level curve corresponding to $c = 0$. Then create a contour map for this function. What are the domain and range of $f$?

### Solution

To find the level curve for $c = 0$, we set $f(x, y) = 0$ and solve. This gives

$$0 = \sqrt{8 + 8x - 4y - 4x^2 - y^2}.$$

We then square both sides and multiply both sides of the equation by $-1$:

$$4x^2 + y^2 - 8x + 4y - 8 = 0.$$

Now, we rearrange the terms, putting the $x$ terms together and the $y$ terms together, and add $8$ to each side:

$$4x^2 - 8x + y^2 + 4y = 8.$$

Next, we group the pairs of terms containing the same variable in parentheses, and factor $4$ from the first pair:

$$4\left(x^2 - 2x\right) + \left(y^2 + 4y\right) = 8.$$

Then we complete the square in each pair of parentheses and add the correct value to the right-hand side:

$$4\left(x^2 - 2x + 1\right) + \left(y^2 + 4y + 4\right) = 8 + 4(1) + 4.$$

Next, we factor the left-hand side and simplify the right-hand side:

$$4(x - 1)^2 + (y + 2)^2 = 16.$$

Last, we divide both sides by $16$:

$$\frac{(x-1)^2}{4} + \frac{(y+2)^2}{16} = 1. \tag{4.1}$$

This equation describes an ellipse centered at $(1, -2)$. The graph of this ellipse appears in the following graph.

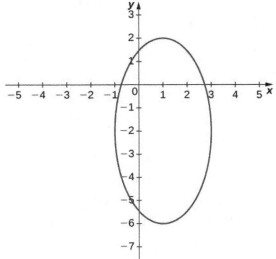

**Figure 4.9** Level curve of the function
$f(x, y) = \sqrt{8 + 8x - 4y - 4x^2 - y^2}$ corresponding to
$c = 0$.

We can repeat the same derivation for values of $c$ less than $4$. Then, **Equation 4.1** becomes

$$\frac{4(x-1)^2}{16 - c^2} + \frac{(y+2)^2}{16 - c^2} = 1$$

for an arbitrary value of $c$. **Figure 4.10** shows a contour map for $f(x, y)$ using the values $c = 0, 1, 2,$ and $3$. When $c = 4$, the level curve is the point $(-1, 2)$.

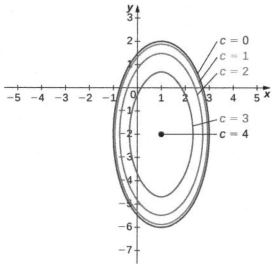

**Figure 4.10** Contour map for the function
$f(x, y) = \sqrt{8 + 8x - 4y - 4x^2 - y^2}$ using the values
$c = 0, 1, 2, 3,$ and $4.$

 **4.2**  Find and graph the level curve of the function $g(x, y) = x^2 + y^2 - 6x + 2y$ corresponding to $c = 15.$

Another useful tool for understanding the **graph of a function of two variables** is called a vertical trace. Level curves are always graphed in the $xy$-plane, but as their name implies, vertical traces are graphed in the $xz$- or $yz$-planes.

---

### Definition

Consider a function $z = f(x, y)$ with domain $D \subseteq \mathbb{R}^2.$ A **vertical trace** of the function can be either the set of points that solves the equation $f(a, y) = z$ for a given constant $x = a$ or $f(x, b) = z$ for a given constant $y = b.$

---

### Example 4.5

#### Finding Vertical Traces

Find vertical traces for the function $f(x, y) = \sin x \cos y$ corresponding to $x = -\frac{\pi}{4}, 0,$ and $\frac{\pi}{4},$ and $y = -\frac{\pi}{4}, 0,$ and $\frac{\pi}{4}.$

#### Solution

First set $x = -\frac{\pi}{4}$ in the equation $z = \sin x \cos y$:

$$z = \sin\left(-\frac{\pi}{4}\right)\cos y = -\frac{\sqrt{2}\cos y}{2} \approx -0.7071 \cos y.$$

This describes a cosine graph in the plane $x = -\frac{\pi}{4}$. The other values of $z$ appear in the following table.

| $c$ | Vertical Trace for $x = c$ |
|---|---|
| $-\frac{\pi}{4}$ | $z = -\frac{\sqrt{2}\cos y}{2}$ |
| $0$ | $z = 0$ |
| $\frac{\pi}{4}$ | $z = \frac{\sqrt{2}\cos y}{2}$ |

Table 4.1
Vertical Traces Parallel to the $xz$-Plane
for the Function $f(x, y) = \sin x \cos y$

In a similar fashion, we can substitute the $y$-values in the equation $f(x, y)$ to obtain the traces in the $yz$-plane, as listed in the following table.

| $d$ | Vertical Trace for $y = d$ |
|---|---|
| $-\frac{\pi}{4}$ | $z = -\frac{\sqrt{2}\sin x}{2}$ |
| $0$ | $z = \sin x$ |
| $\frac{\pi}{4}$ | $z = \frac{\sqrt{2}\sin x}{2}$ |

Table 4.2
Vertical Traces Parallel to the $yz$-Plane
for the Function $f(x, y) = \sin x \cos y$

The three traces in the $xz$-plane are cosine functions; the three traces in the $yz$-plane are sine functions. These curves appear in the intersections of the surface with the planes $x = -\frac{\pi}{4}$, $x = 0$, $x = \frac{\pi}{4}$ and $y = -\frac{\pi}{4}$, $y = 0$, $y = \frac{\pi}{4}$ as shown in the following figure.

$$f(x, y) = \sin x \cos y$$

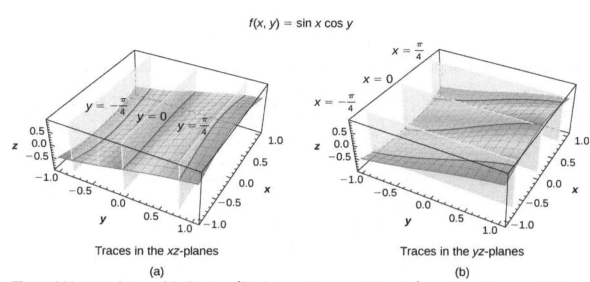

Traces in the *xz*-planes                          Traces in the *yz*-planes

(a)                                                    (b)

**Figure 4.11** Vertical traces of the function $f(x, y)$ are cosine curves in the *xz*-planes (a) and sine curves in the *yz*-planes (b).

 **4.3** Determine the equation of the vertical trace of the function $g(x, y) = -x^2 - y^2 + 2x + 4y - 1$ corresponding to $y = 3$, and describe its graph.

Functions of two variables can produce some striking-looking surfaces. The following figure shows two examples.

$$f(x, y) = x^2 \sin y \qquad\qquad f(x, y) = \sin(e^x) \cos(\ln y)$$

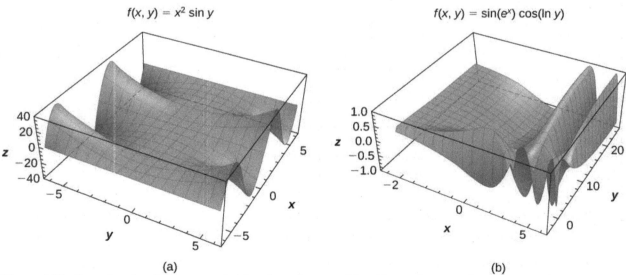

(a)                                                    (b)

**Figure 4.12** Examples of surfaces representing functions of two variables: (a) a combination of a power function and a sine function and (b) a combination of trigonometric, exponential, and logarithmic functions.

## Functions of More Than Two Variables

So far, we have examined only functions of two variables. However, it is useful to take a brief look at functions of more than two variables. Two such examples are

$$f(x, y, z) = x^2 - 2xy + y^2 + 3yz - z^2 + 4x - 2y + 3x - 6 \text{ (a polynomial in three variables)}$$

and

$$g(x, y, t) = \left(x^2 - 4xy + y^2\right)\sin t - (3x + 5y)\cos t.$$

In the first function, $(x, y, z)$ represents a point in space, and the function $f$ maps each point in space to a fourth quantity, such as temperature or wind speed. In the second function, $(x, y)$ can represent a point in the plane, and $t$ can represent time. The function might map a point in the plane to a third quantity (for example, pressure) at a given time $t$. The method for finding the domain of a function of more than two variables is analogous to the method for functions of one or two variables.

## Example 4.6

### Domains for Functions of Three Variables

Find the domain of each of the following functions:

a. $f(x, y, z) = \dfrac{3x - 4y + 2z}{\sqrt{9 - x^2 - y^2 - z^2}}$

b. $g(x, y, t) = \dfrac{\sqrt{2t - 4}}{x^2 - y^2}$

### Solution

a. For the function $f(x, y, z) = \dfrac{3x - 4y + 2z}{\sqrt{9 - x^2 - y^2 - z^2}}$ to be defined (and be a real value), two conditions must

hold:

    1.  The denominator cannot be zero.

    2.  The radicand cannot be negative.

Combining these conditions leads to the inequality

$$9 - x^2 - y^2 - z^2 > 0.$$

Moving the variables to the other side and reversing the inequality gives the domain as

$$\text{domain}(f) = \left\{(x, y, z) \in \mathbb{R}^3 \middle| x^2 + y^2 + z^2 < 9\right\},$$

which describes a ball of radius 3 centered at the origin. (*Note*: The surface of the ball is not included in this domain.)

b. For the function $g(x, y, t) = \dfrac{\sqrt{2t - 4}}{x^2 - y^2}$ to be defined (and be a real value), two conditions must hold:

    1.  The radicand cannot be negative.

    2.  The denominator cannot be zero.

Since the radicand cannot be negative, this implies $2t - 4 \geq 0$, and therefore that $t \geq 2$. Since the denominator cannot be zero, $x^2 - y^2 \neq 0$, or $x^2 \neq y^2$, Which can be rewritten as $y = \pm x$, which are the equations of two lines passing through the origin. Therefore, the domain of $g$ is

$$\text{domain}(g) = \{(x, y, t) | y \neq \pm x, t \geq 2\}.$$

**4.4** Find the domain of the function $h(x, y, t) = (3t - 6)\sqrt{y - 4x^2 + 4}$.

Functions of two variables have level curves, which are shown as curves in the $xy$-plane. However, when the function has three variables, the curves become surfaces, so we can define level surfaces for functions of three variables.

**Definition**

Given a function $f(x, y, z)$ and a number $c$ in the range of $f$, a **level surface of a function of three variables** is defined to be the set of points satisfying the equation $f(x, y, z) = c$.

## Example 4.7

### Finding a Level Surface

Find the level surface for the function $f(x, y, z) = 4x^2 + 9y^2 - z^2$ corresponding to $c = 1$.

### Solution

The level surface is defined by the equation $4x^2 + 9y^2 - z^2 = 1$. This equation describes a hyperboloid of one sheet as shown in the following figure.

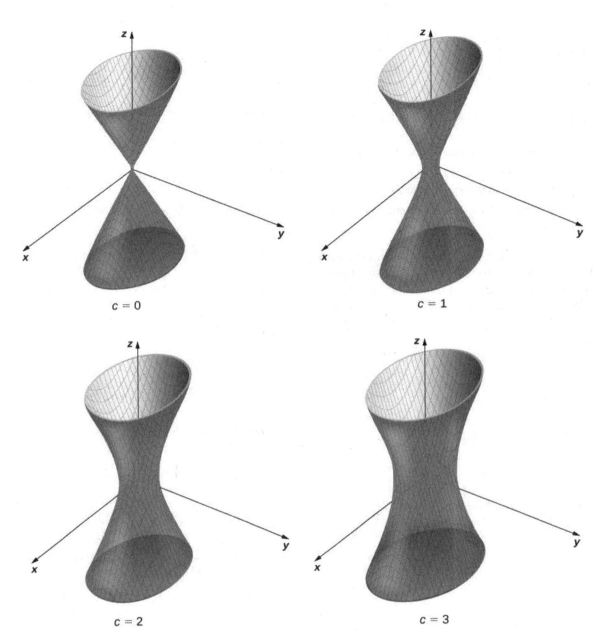

$c = 0$

$c = 1$

$c = 2$

$c = 3$

**Figure 4.13** A hyperboloid of one sheet with some of its level surfaces.

**4.5** Find the equation of the level surface of the function

$$g(x,\, y,\, z) = x^2 + y^2 + z^2 - 2x + 4y - 6z$$

corresponding to $c = 2$, and describe the surface, if possible.

# 4.1 EXERCISES

For the following exercises, evaluate each function at the indicated values.

1. $W(x, y) = 4x^2 + y^2$. Find $W(2, -1)$, $W(-3, 6)$.

2. $W(x, y) = 4x^2 + y^2$. Find $W(2 + h, 3 + h)$.

3. The volume of a right circular cylinder is calculated by a function of two variables, $V(x, y) = \pi x^2 y$, where $x$ is the radius of the right circular cylinder and $y$ represents the height of the cylinder. Evaluate $V(2, 5)$ and explain what this means.

4. An oxygen tank is constructed of a right cylinder of height $y$ and radius $x$ with two hemispheres of radius $x$ mounted on the top and bottom of the cylinder. Express the volume of the cylinder as a function of two variables, $x$ and $y$, find $V(10, 2)$, and explain what this means.

For the following exercises, find the domain of the function.

5. $V(x, y) = 4x^2 + y^2$

6. $f(x, y) = \sqrt{x^2 + y^2 - 4}$

7. $f(x, y) = 4\ln(y^2 - x)$

8. $g(x, y) = \sqrt{16 - 4x^2 - y^2}$

9. $z(x, y) = y^2 - x^2$

10. $f(x, y) = \dfrac{y + 2}{x^2}$

Find the range of the functions.

11. $g(x, y) = \sqrt{16 - 4x^2 - y^2}$

12. $V(x, y) = 4x^2 + y^2$

13. $z = y^2 - x^2$

For the following exercises, find the level curves of each function at the indicated value of $c$ to visualize the given function.

14. $z(x, y) = y^2 - x^2$, $c = 1$

15. $z(x, y) = y^2 - x^2$, $c = 4$

16. $g(x, y) = x^2 + y^2$; $c = 4, c = 9$

17. $g(x, y) = 4 - x - y$; $c = 0, 4$

18. $f(x, y) = xy$; $c = 1$; $c = -1$

19. $h(x, y) = 2x - y$; $c = 0, -2, 2$

20. $f(x, y) = x^2 - y$; $c = 1, 2$

21. $g(x, y) = \dfrac{x}{x + y}$; $c = -1, 0, 2$

22. $g(x, y) = x^3 - y$; $c = -1, 0, 2$

23. $g(x, y) = e^{xy}$; $c = \dfrac{1}{2}, 3$

24. $f(x, y) = x^2$; $c = 4, 9$

25. $f(x, y) = xy - x$; $c = -2, 0, 2$

26. $h(x, y) = \ln(x^2 + y^2)$; $c = -1, 0, 1$

27. $g(x, y) = \ln\left(\dfrac{y}{x^2}\right)$; $c = -2, 0, 2$

28. $z = f(x, y) = \sqrt{x^2 + y^2}$, $c = 3$

29. $f(x, y) = \dfrac{y + 2}{x^2}$, $c =$ any constant

For the following exercises, find the vertical traces of the functions at the indicated values of $x$ and $y$, and plot the traces.

30. $z = 4 - x - y$; $x = 2$

31. $f(x, y) = 3x + y^3$, $x = 1$

32. $z = \cos\sqrt{x^2 + y^2}$ $x = 1$

Find the domain of the following functions.

33. $z = \sqrt{100 - 4x^2 - 25y^2}$

34. $z = \ln(x - y^2)$

35. $f(x, y, z) = \dfrac{1}{\sqrt{36 - 4x^2 - 9y^2 - z^2}}$

36. $f(x, y, z) = \sqrt{49 - x^2 - y^2 - z^2}$

37. $f(x, y, z) = \sqrt[3]{16 - x^2 - y^2 - z^2}$

38. $f(x, y) = \cos\sqrt{x^2 + y^2}$

For the following exercises, plot a graph of the function.

39. $z = f(x, y) = \sqrt{x^2 + y^2}$

40. $z = x^2 + y^2$

41. Use technology to graph $z = x^2 y$.

Sketch the following by finding the level curves. Verify the graph using technology.

42. $f(x, y) = \sqrt{4 - x^2 - y^2}$

43. $f(x, y) = 2 - \sqrt{x^2 + y^2}$

44. $z = 1 + e^{-x^2 - y^2}$

45. $z = \cos\sqrt{x^2 + y^2}$

46. $z = y^2 - x^2$

47. Describe the contour lines for several values of $c$ for $z = x^2 + y^2 - 2x - 2y$.

Find the level surface for the functions of three variables and describe it.

48. $w(x, y, z) = x - 2y + z, \ c = 4$

49. $w(x, y, z) = x^2 + y^2 + z^2, \ c = 9$

50. $w(x, y, z) = x^2 + y^2 - z^2, \ c = -4$

51. $w(x, y, z) = x^2 + y^2 - z^2, \ c = 4$

52. $w(x, y, z) = 9x^2 - 4y^2 + 36z^2, \ c = 0$

For the following exercises, find an equation of the level curve of $f$ that contains the point $P$.

53. $f(x, y) = 1 - 4x^2 - y^2, \ P(0, 1)$

54. $g(x, y) = y^2 \arctan x, \ P(1, 2)$

55. $g(x, y) = e^{xy}(x^2 + y^2), \ P(1, 0)$

56. The strength $E$ of an electric field at point $(x, y, z)$ resulting from an infinitely long charged wire lying along the $y$-axis is given by $E(x, y, z) = k/\sqrt{x^2 + y^2}$, where $k$ is a positive constant. For simplicity, let $k = 1$ and find the equations of the level surfaces for $E = 10$ and $E = 100$.

57. A thin plate made of iron is located in the $xy$-plane. The temperature $T$ in degrees Celsius at a point $P(x, y)$ is inversely proportional to the square of its distance from the origin. Express $T$ as a function of $x$ and $y$.

58. Refer to the preceding problem. Using the temperature function found there, determine the proportionality constant if the temperature at point $P(1, 2)$ is $50°C$. Use this constant to determine the temperature at point $Q(3, 4)$.

59. Refer to the preceding problem. Find the level curves for $T = 40°C$ and $T = 100°C$, and describe what the level curves represent.

# 4.2 | Limits and Continuity

We have now examined functions of more than one variable and seen how to graph them. In this section, we see how to take the limit of a function of more than one variable, and what it means for a function of more than one variable to be continuous at a point in its domain. It turns out these concepts have aspects that just don't occur with functions of one variable.

## Limit of a Function of Two Variables

Recall from Section 2.2 the definition of a limit of a function of one variable:

Let $f(x)$ be defined for all $x \neq a$ in an open interval containing $a$. Let $L$ be a real number. Then

$$\lim_{x \to a} f(x) = L$$

if for every $\varepsilon > 0$, there exists a $\delta > 0$, such that if $0 < |x - a| < \delta$ for all $x$ in the domain of $f$, then

$$|f(x) - L| > \varepsilon.$$

Before we can adapt this definition to define a limit of a function of two variables, we first need to see how to extend the idea of an open interval in one variable to an open interval in two variables.

**Definition**

Consider a point $(a, b) \in \mathbb{R}^2$. A **$\delta$ disk** centered at point $(a, b)$ is defined to be an open disk of radius $\delta$ centered at point $(a, b)$—that is,

$$\left\{ (x, y) \in \mathbb{R}^2 \,\middle|\, (x - a)^2 + (y - b)^2 < \delta^2 \right\}$$

as shown in the following graph.

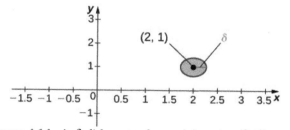

**Figure 4.14** A $\delta$ disk centered around the point $(2, 1)$.

The idea of a $\delta$ disk appears in the definition of the limit of a function of two variables. If $\delta$ is small, then all the points $(x, y)$ in the $\delta$ disk are close to $(a, b)$. This is completely analogous to $x$ being close to $a$ in the definition of a limit of a function of one variable. In one dimension, we express this restriction as

$$a - \delta < x < a + \delta.$$

In more than one dimension, we use a $\delta$ disk.

Let $f$ be a function of two variables, $x$ and $y$. The limit of $f(x, y)$ as $(x, y)$ approaches $(a, b)$ is $L$, written

$$\lim_{(x, y) \to (a, b)} f(x, y) = L$$

if for each $\varepsilon > 0$ there exists a small enough $\delta > 0$ such that for all points $(x, y)$ in a $\delta$ disk around $(a, b)$, except possibly for $(a, b)$ itself, the value of $f(x, y)$ is no more than $\varepsilon$ away from $L$ **(Figure 4.15)**. Using symbols, we write the following: For any $\varepsilon > 0$, there exists a number $\delta > 0$ such that

$$|f(x, y) - L| < \varepsilon \text{ whenever } 0 < \sqrt{(x-a)^2 + (y-b)^2} < \delta.$$

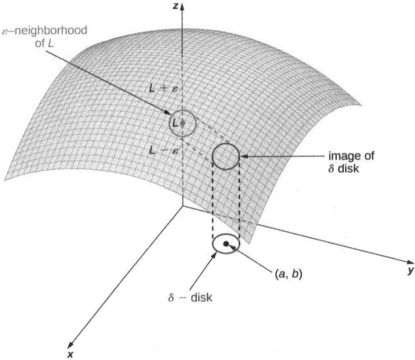

**Figure 4.15** The limit of a function involving two variables requires that $f(x, y)$ be within $\varepsilon$ of $L$ whenever $(x, y)$ is within $\delta$ of $(a, b)$. The smaller the value of $\varepsilon$, the smaller the value of $\delta$.

Proving that a limit exists using the definition of a limit of a function of two variables can be challenging. Instead, we use the following theorem, which gives us shortcuts to finding limits. The formulas in this theorem are an extension of the formulas in the limit laws theorem in **The Limit Laws (http://cnx.org/content/m53492/latest/)** .

Let $f(x, y)$ and $g(x, y)$ be defined for all $(x, y) \neq (a, b)$ in a neighborhood around $(a, b)$, and assume the neighborhood is contained completely inside the domain of $f$. Assume that $L$ and $M$ are real numbers such that $\lim_{(x, y) \to (a, b)} f(x, y) = L$ and $\lim_{(x, y) \to (a, b)} g(x, y) = M$, and let $c$ be a constant. Then each of the following statements holds:

**Constant Law:**

$$\lim_{(x, y) \to (a, b)} c = c \qquad (4.2)$$

**Identity Laws:**

$$\lim_{(x, y) \to (a, b)} x = a \qquad (4.3)$$

$$\lim_{(x, y) \to (a, b)} y = b \qquad (4.4)$$

**Sum Law:**

$$\lim_{(x, y) \to (a, b)} (f(x, y) + g(x, y)) = L + M \qquad (4.5)$$

**Difference Law:**

$$\lim_{(x, y) \to (a, b)} (f(x, y) - g(x, y)) = L - M \qquad (4.6)$$

**Constant Multiple Law:**

$$\lim_{(x, y) \to (a, b)} (cf(x, y)) = cL \qquad (4.7)$$

**Product Law:**

$$\lim_{(x, y) \to (a, b)} (f(x, y)g(x, y)) = LM \qquad (4.8)$$

**Quotient Law:**

$$\lim_{(x, y) \to (a, b)} \frac{f(x, y)}{g(x, y)} = \frac{L}{M} \text{ for } M \neq 0 \qquad (4.9)$$

**Power Law:**

$$\lim_{(x, y) \to (a, b)} (f(x, y))^n = L^n \qquad (4.10)$$

for any positive integer $n$.

**Root Law:**

$$\lim_{(x, y) \to (a, b)} \sqrt[n]{f(x, y)} = \sqrt[n]{L} \qquad (4.11)$$

for all $L$ if $n$ is odd and positive, and for $L \geq 0$ if $n$ is even and positive.

The proofs of these properties are similar to those for the limits of functions of one variable. We can apply these laws to finding limits of various functions.

## Example 4.8

### Finding the Limit of a Function of Two Variables

Find each of the following limits:

a. $\lim_{(x, y) \to (2, -1)} \left(x^2 - 2xy + 3y^2 - 4x + 3y - 6\right)$

b. $\lim_{(x, y) \to (2, -1)} \frac{2x + 3y}{4x - 3y}$

## Solution

a.  First use the sum and difference laws to separate the terms:

$$\lim_{(x, y) \to (2, -1)} \left(x^2 - 2xy + 3y^2 - 4x + 3y - 6\right)$$

$$= \left(\lim_{(x, y) \to (2, -1)} x^2\right) - \left(\lim_{(x, y) \to (2, -1)} 2xy\right) + \left(\lim_{(x, y) \to (2, -1)} 3y^2\right) - \left(\lim_{(x, y) \to (2, -1)} 4x\right)$$

$$+ \left(\lim_{(x, y) \to (2, -1)} 3y\right) - \left(\lim_{(x, y) \to (2, -1)} 6\right).$$

Next, use the constant multiple law on the second, third, fourth, and fifth limits:

$$= \left(\lim_{(x, y) \to (2, -1)} x^2\right) - 2\left(\lim_{(x, y) \to (2, -1)} xy\right) + 3\left(\lim_{(x, y) \to (2, -1)} y^2\right) - 4\left(\lim_{(x, y) \to (2, -1)} x\right)$$

$$+ 3\left(\lim_{(x, y) \to (2, -1)} y\right) - \lim_{(x, y) \to (2, -1)} 6.$$

Now, use the power law on the first and third limits, and the product law on the second limit:

$$= \left(\lim_{(x, y) \to (2, -1)} x\right)^2 - 2\left(\lim_{(x, y) \to (2, -1)} x\right)\left(\lim_{(x, y) \to (2, -1)} y\right) + 3\left(\lim_{(x, y) \to (2, -1)} y\right)^2$$

$$- 4\left(\lim_{(x, y) \to (2, -1)} x\right) + 3\left(\lim_{(x, y) \to (2, -1)} y\right) - \lim_{(x, y) \to (2, -1)} 6.$$

Last, use the identity laws on the first six limits and the constant law on the last limit:

$$\lim_{(x, y) \to (2, -1)} \left(x^2 - 2xy + 3y^2 - 4x + 3y - 6\right) = (2)^2 - 2(2)(-1) + 3(-1)^2 - 4(2) + 3(-1) - 6$$

$$= -6.$$

b.  Before applying the quotient law, we need to verify that the limit of the denominator is nonzero. Using the difference law, constant multiple law, and identity law,

$$\lim_{(x, y) \to (2, -1)} (4x - 3y) = \lim_{(x, y) \to (2, -1)} 4x - \lim_{(x, y) \to (2, -1)} 3y$$

$$= 4\left(\lim_{(x, y) \to (2, -1)} x\right) - 3\left(\lim_{(x, y) \to (2, -1)} y\right)$$

$$= 4(2) - 3(-1) = 11.$$

Since the limit of the denominator is nonzero, the quotient law applies. We now calculate the limit of the numerator using the difference law, constant multiple law, and identity law:

$$\lim_{(x, y) \to (2, -1)} (2x + 3y) = \lim_{(x, y) \to (2, -1)} 2x + \lim_{(x, y) \to (2, -1)} 3y$$

$$= 2\left(\lim_{(x, y) \to (2, -1)} x\right) + 3\left(\lim_{(x, y) \to (2, -1)} y\right)$$

$$= 2(2) + 3(-1)$$

$$= 1.$$

Therefore, according to the quotient law we have

$$\lim_{(x,\,y)\,\to\,(2,\,-1)}\frac{2x+3y}{4x-3y}=\frac{\displaystyle\lim_{(x,\,y)\,\to\,(2,\,-1)}(2x+3y)}{\displaystyle\lim_{(x,\,y)\,\to\,(2,\,-1)}(4x-3y)}=\frac{1}{11}.$$

 **4.6**   Evaluate the following limit:

$$\lim_{(x,\,y)\,\to\,(5,\,-2)}\sqrt[3]{\frac{x^2-y}{y^2+x-1}}.$$

Since we are taking the limit of a function of two variables, the point $(a,\,b)$ is in $\mathbb{R}^2,$ and it is possible to approach this point from an infinite number of directions. Sometimes when calculating a limit, the answer varies depending on the path taken toward $(a,\,b).$ If this is the case, then the limit fails to exist. In other words, the limit must be unique, regardless of path taken.

## Example 4.9

### Limits That Fail to Exist

Show that neither of the following limits exist:

a.   $\displaystyle\lim_{(x,\,y)\,\to\,(0,\,0)}\frac{2xy}{3x^2+y^2}$

b.   $\displaystyle\lim_{(x,\,y)\,\to\,(0,\,0)}\frac{4xy^2}{x^2+3y^4}$

### Solution

a.   The domain of the function $f(x,\,y)=\dfrac{2xy}{3x^2+y^2}$ consists of all points in the $xy$-plane except for the point $(0,\,0)$ (**Figure 4.16**). To show that the limit does not exist as $(x,\,y)$ approaches $(0,\,0),$ we note that it is impossible to satisfy the definition of a limit of a function of two variables because of the fact that the function takes different values along different lines passing through point $(0,\,0).$ First, consider the line $y=0$ in the $xy$-plane. Substituting $y=0$ into $f(x,\,y)$ gives

$$f(x,\,0)=\frac{2x(0)}{3x^2+0^2}=0$$

for any value of $x.$ Therefore the value of $f$ remains constant for any point on the $x$-axis, and as $y$ approaches zero, the function remains fixed at zero.
Next, consider the line $y=x.$ Substituting $y=x$ into $f(x,\,y)$ gives

$$f(x,\,x)=\frac{2x(x)}{3x^2+x^2}=\frac{2x^2}{4x^2}=\frac{1}{2}.$$

This is true for any point on the line $y=x.$ If we let $x$ approach zero while staying on this line, the value of the function remains fixed at $\frac{1}{2}$, regardless of how small $x$ is.

Choose a value for $\varepsilon$ that is less than $1/2$ —say, $1/4$. Then, no matter how small a $\delta$ disk we draw around $(0, 0)$, the values of $f(x, y)$ for points inside that $\delta$ disk will include both $0$ and $\frac{1}{2}$. Therefore, the definition of limit at a point is never satisfied and the limit fails to exist.

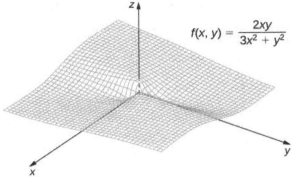

$$f(x, y) = \frac{2xy}{3x^2 + y^2}$$

**Figure 4.16** Graph of the function $f(x, y) = (2xy)/(3x^2 + y^2)$. Along the line $y = 0$, the function is equal to zero; along the line $y = x$, the function is equal to $\frac{1}{2}$.

In a similar fashion to a., we can approach the origin along any straight line passing through the origin. If we try the $x$-axis (i.e., $y = 0$), then the function remains fixed at zero. The same is true for the $y$-axis. Suppose we approach the origin along a straight line of slope $k$. The equation of this line is $y = kx$. Then the limit becomes

$$\lim_{(x, y) \to (0, 0)} \frac{4xy^2}{x^2 + 3y^4} = \lim_{(x, y) \to (0, 0)} \frac{4x(kx)^2}{x^2 + 3(kx)^4}$$

$$= \lim_{(x, y) \to (0, 0)} \frac{4k^2 x^3}{x^2 + 3k^4 x^4}$$

$$= \lim_{(x, y) \to (0, 0)} \frac{4k^2 x}{1 + 3k^4 x^2}$$

$$= \frac{\lim_{(x, y) \to (0, 0)} \left(4k^2 x\right)}{\lim_{(x, y) \to (0, 0)} \left(1 + 3k^4 x^2\right)}$$

$$= 0$$

regardless of the value of $k$. It would seem that the limit is equal to zero. What if we chose a curve passing through the origin instead? For example, we can consider the parabola given by the equation $x = y^2$. Substituting $y^2$ in place of $x$ in $f(x, y)$ gives

$$\lim_{(x,\,y) \to (0,\,0)} \frac{4xy^2}{x^2 + 3y^4} = \lim_{(x,\,y) \to (0,\,0)} \frac{4(y^2)y^2}{(y^2)^2 + 3y^4}$$

$$= \lim_{(x,\,y) \to (0,\,0)} \frac{4y^4}{y^4 + 3y^4}$$

$$= \lim_{(x,\,y) \to (0,\,0)} 1$$

$$= 1.$$

By the same logic in a., it is impossible to find a $\delta$ disk around the origin that satisfies the definition of the limit for any value of $\varepsilon < 1$. Therefore, $\displaystyle\lim_{(x,\,y) \to (0,\,0)} \frac{4xy^2}{x^2 + 3y^4}$ does not exist.

 **4.7**   Show that

$$\lim_{(x,\,y) \to (2,\,1)} \frac{(x - 2)(y - 1)}{(x - 2)^2 + (y - 1)^2}$$

does not exist.

## Interior Points and Boundary Points

To study continuity and differentiability of a function of two or more variables, we first need to learn some new terminology.

**Definition**

Let $S$ be a subset of $\mathbb{R}^2$ (Figure 4.17).

1.  A point $P_0$ is called an **interior point** of $S$ if there is a $\delta$ disk centered around $P_0$ contained completely in $S$.

2.  A point $P_0$ is called a **boundary point** of $S$ if every $\delta$ disk centered around $P_0$ contains points both inside and outside $S$.

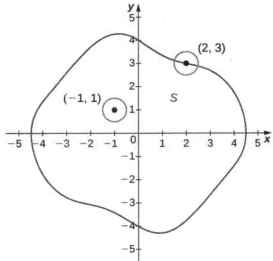

**Figure 4.17** In the set $S$ shown, $(-1, 1)$ is an interior point and $(2, 3)$ is a boundary point.

**Definition**

Let $S$ be a subset of $\mathbb{R}^2$ (**Figure 4.17**).

1. $S$ is called an **open set** if every point of $S$ is an interior point.

2. $S$ is called a **closed set** if it contains all its boundary points.

An example of an open set is a $\delta$ disk. If we include the boundary of the disk, then it becomes a closed set. A set that contains some, but not all, of its boundary points is neither open nor closed. For example if we include half the boundary of a $\delta$ disk but not the other half, then the set is neither open nor closed.

**Definition**

Let $S$ be a subset of $\mathbb{R}^2$ (**Figure 4.17**).

1. An open set $S$ is a **connected set** if it cannot be represented as the union of two or more disjoint, nonempty open subsets.

2. A set $S$ is a **region** if it is open, connected, and nonempty.

The definition of a limit of a function of two variables requires the $\delta$ disk to be contained inside the domain of the function. However, if we wish to find the limit of a function at a boundary point of the domain, the $\delta$ disk is not contained inside the domain. By definition, some of the points of the $\delta$ disk are inside the domain and some are outside. Therefore, we need only consider points that are inside both the $\delta$ disk and the domain of the function. This leads to the definition of the limit of a function at a boundary point.

**Definition**

Let $f$ be a function of two variables, $x$ and $y$, and suppose $(a, b)$ is on the boundary of the domain of $f$. Then, the limit of $f(x, y)$ as $(x, y)$ approaches $(a, b)$ is $L$, written

$$\lim_{(x, y) \to (a, b)} f(x, y) = L,$$

if for any $\varepsilon > 0$, there exists a number $\delta > 0$ such that for any point $(x, y)$ inside the domain of $f$ and within a suitably small distance positive $\delta$ of $(a, b)$, the value of $f(x, y)$ is no more than $\varepsilon$ away from $L$ (Figure 4.15). Using symbols, we can write: For any $\varepsilon > 0$, there exists a number $\delta > 0$ such that

$$|f(x, y) - L| < \varepsilon \text{ whenever } 0 < \sqrt{(x - a)^2 + (y - b)^2} < \delta.$$

## Example 4.10

### Limit of a Function at a Boundary Point

Prove $\displaystyle\lim_{(x, y) \to (4, 3)} \sqrt{25 - x^2 - y^2} = 0$.

### Solution

The domain of the function $f(x, y) = \sqrt{25 - x^2 - y^2}$ is $\{(x, y) \in \mathbb{R}^2 \,|\, x^2 + y^2 \leq 25\}$, which is a circle of radius $5$ centered at the origin, along with its interior as shown in the following graph.

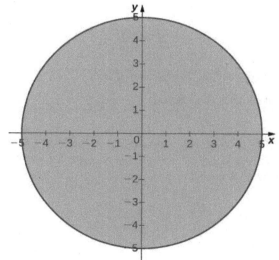

**Figure 4.18** Domain of the function
$f(x, y) = \sqrt{25 - x^2 - y^2}$.

We can use the limit laws, which apply to limits at the boundary of domains as well as interior points:

$$\lim_{(x, y) \to (4, 3)} \sqrt{25 - x^2 - y^2} = \sqrt{\lim_{(x, y) \to (4, 3)} (25 - x^2 - y^2)}$$

$$= \sqrt{\lim_{(x, y) \to (4, 3)} 25 - \lim_{(x, y) \to (4, 3)} x^2 - \lim_{(x, y) \to (4, 3)} y^2}$$

$$= \sqrt{25 - 4^2 - 3^2}$$

$$= 0.$$

See the following graph.

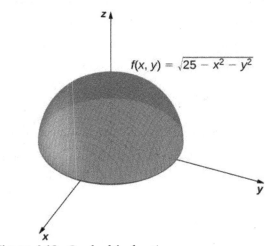

**Figure 4.19** Graph of the function $f(x, y) = \sqrt{25 - x^2 - y^2}$.

 **4.8** Evaluate the following limit:

$$\lim_{(x, y) \to (5, -2)} \sqrt{29 - x^2 - y^2}.$$

## Continuity of Functions of Two Variables

In **Continuity (http://cnx.org/content/m53489/latest/)** , we defined the continuity of a function of one variable and saw how it relied on the limit of a function of one variable. In particular, three conditions are necessary for $f(x)$ to be continuous at point $x = a$:

1.  $f(a)$ exists.

2.  $\lim\limits_{x \to a} f(x)$ exists.

3.  $\lim\limits_{x \to a} f(x) = f(a)$.

These three conditions are necessary for continuity of a function of two variables as well.

---

**Definition**

A function $f(x, y)$ is continuous at a point $(a, b)$ in its domain if the following conditions are satisfied:

1.  $f(a, b)$ exists.

2.  $\lim\limits_{(x, y) \to (a, b)} f(x, y)$ exists.

3.  $\lim\limits_{(x, y) \to (a, b)} f(x, y) = f(a, b)$.

## Example 4.11

### Demonstrating Continuity for a Function of Two Variables

Show that the function $f(x, y) = \dfrac{3x + 2y}{x + y + 1}$ is continuous at point $(5, -3)$.

### Solution

There are three conditions to be satisfied, per the definition of continuity. In this example, $a = 5$ and $b = -3$.

1. $f(a, b)$ exists. This is true because the domain of the function $f$ consists of those ordered pairs for which the denominator is nonzero (i.e., $x + y + 1 \neq 0$). Point $(5, -3)$ satisfies this condition. Furthermore,

$$f(a, b) = f(5, -3) = \frac{3(5) + 2(-3)}{5 + (-3) + 1} = \frac{15 - 6}{2 + 1} = 3.$$

2. $\displaystyle\lim_{(x, y) \to (a, b)} f(x, y)$ exists. This is also true:

$$
\begin{aligned}
\lim_{(x, y) \to (a, b)} f(x, y) &= \lim_{(x, y) \to (5, -3)} \frac{3x + 2y}{x + y + 1} \\
&= \frac{\displaystyle\lim_{(x, y) \to (5, -3)} (3x + 2y)}{\displaystyle\lim_{(x, y) \to (5, -3)} (x + y + 1)} \\
&= \frac{15 - 6}{5 - 3 + 1} \\
&= 3.
\end{aligned}
$$

3. $\displaystyle\lim_{(x, y) \to (a, b)} f(x, y) = f(a, b)$. This is true because we have just shown that both sides of this equation equal three.

 **4.9** Show that the function $f(x, y) = \sqrt{26 - 2x^2 - y^2}$ is continuous at point $(2, -3)$.

Continuity of a function of any number of variables can also be defined in terms of delta and epsilon. A function of two variables is continuous at a point $(x_0, y_0)$ in its domain if for every $\varepsilon > 0$ there exists a $\delta > 0$ such that, whenever $\sqrt{(x - x_0)^2 + (y - y_0)^2} < \delta$ it is true, $|f(x, y) - f(a, b)| < \varepsilon$. This definition can be combined with the formal definition (that is, the *epsilon–delta definition*) of continuity of a function of one variable to prove the following theorems:

### Theorem 4.2: The Sum of Continuous Functions Is Continuous

If $f(x, y)$ is continuous at $(x_0, y_0)$, and $g(x, y)$ is continuous at $(x_0, y_0)$, then $f(x, y) + g(x, y)$ is continuous at $(x_0, y_0)$.

### Theorem 4.3: The Product of Continuous Functions Is Continuous

If $g(x)$ is continuous at $x_0$ and $h(y)$ is continuous at $y_0$, then $f(x, y) = g(x)h(y)$ is continuous at $(x_0, y_0)$.

### Theorem 4.4: The Composition of Continuous Functions Is Continuous

Let $g$ be a function of two variables from a domain $D \subseteq \mathbb{R}^2$ to a range $R \subseteq \mathbb{R}$. Suppose $g$ is continuous at some point $(x_0, y_0) \in D$ and define $z_0 = g(x_0, y_0)$. Let $f$ be a function that maps $\mathbb{R}$ to $\mathbb{R}$ such that $z_0$ is in the domain of $f$. Last, assume $f$ is continuous at $z_0$. Then $f \circ g$ is continuous at $(x_0, y_0)$ as shown in the following figure.

**Figure 4.20**  The composition of two continuous functions is continuous.

Let's now use the previous theorems to show continuity of functions in the following examples.

### Example 4.12

**More Examples of Continuity of a Function of Two Variables**

Show that the functions $f(x, y) = 4x^3 y^2$ and $g(x, y) = \cos\left(4x^3 y^2\right)$ are continuous everywhere.

**Solution**

The polynomials $g(x) = 4x^3$ and $h(y) = y^2$ are continuous at every real number, and therefore by the product of continuous functions theorem, $f(x, y) = 4x^3 y^2$ is continuous at every point $(x, y)$ in the $xy$-plane. Since $f(x, y) = 4x^3 y^2$ is continuous at every point $(x, y)$ in the $xy$-plane and $g(x) = \cos x$ is continuous at every real number $x$, the continuity of the composition of functions tells us that $g(x, y) = \cos\left(4x^3 y^2\right)$ is continuous at every point $(x, y)$ in the $xy$-plane.

 **4.10**   Show that the functions $f(x, y) = 2x^2 y^3 + 3$ and $g(x, y) = \left(2x^2 y^3 + 3\right)^4$ are continuous everywhere.

## Functions of Three or More Variables

The limit of a function of three or more variables occurs readily in applications. For example, suppose we have a function $f(x, y, z)$ that gives the temperature at a physical location $(x, y, z)$ in three dimensions. Or perhaps a function $g(x, y, z, t)$ can indicate air pressure at a location $(x, y, z)$ at time $t$. How can we take a limit at a point in $\mathbb{R}^3$? What does it mean to be continuous at a point in four dimensions?

The answers to these questions rely on extending the concept of a $\delta$ disk into more than two dimensions. Then, the ideas of the limit of a function of three or more variables and the continuity of a function of three or more variables are very similar to the definitions given earlier for a function of two variables.

## Definition

Let $(x_0, y_0, z_0)$ be a point in $\mathbb{R}^3$. Then, a $\delta$ **ball** in three dimensions consists of all points in $\mathbb{R}^3$ lying at a distance of less than $\delta$ from $(x_0, y_0, z_0)$ —that is,

$$\left\{ (x, y, z) \in \mathbb{R}^3 \middle| \sqrt{(x - x_0)^2 + (y - y_0)^2 + (z - z_0)^2} < \delta \right\}.$$

To define a $\delta$ ball in higher dimensions, add additional terms under the radical to correspond to each additional dimension. For example, given a point $P = (w_0, x_0, y_0, z_0)$ in $\mathbb{R}^4$, a $\delta$ ball around $P$ can be described by

$$\left\{ (w, x, y, z) \in \mathbb{R}^4 \middle| \sqrt{(w - w_0)^2 + (x - x_0)^2 + (y - y_0)^2 + (z - z_0)^2} < \delta \right\}.$$

To show that a limit of a function of three variables exists at a point $(x_0, y_0, z_0)$, it suffices to show that for any point in a $\delta$ ball centered at $(x_0, y_0, z_0)$, the value of the function at that point is arbitrarily close to a fixed value (the limit value). All the limit laws for functions of two variables hold for functions of more than two variables as well.

## Example 4.13

### Finding the Limit of a Function of Three Variables

Find $\displaystyle\lim_{(x,\, y,\, z) \to (4,\, 1,\, -3)} \frac{x^2 y - 3z}{2x + 5y - z}$.

#### Solution

Before we can apply the quotient law, we need to verify that the limit of the denominator is nonzero. Using the difference law, the identity law, and the constant law,

$$\begin{aligned}
\lim_{(x,\, y,\, z) \to (4,\, 1,\, -3)} (2x + 5y - z) &= 2 \left( \lim_{(x,\, y,\, z) \to (4,\, 1,\, -3)} x \right) + 5 \left( \lim_{(x,\, y,\, z) \to (4,\, 1,\, -3)} y \right) - \left( \lim_{(x,\, y,\, z) \to (4,\, 1,\, -3)} z \right) \\
&= 2(4) + 5(1) - (-3) \\
&= 16.
\end{aligned}$$

Since this is nonzero, we next find the limit of the numerator. Using the product law, difference law, constant multiple law, and identity law,

$$\begin{aligned}
\lim_{(x,\, y,\, z) \to (4,\, 1,\, -3)} (x^2 y - 3z) &= \left( \lim_{(x,\, y,\, z) \to (4,\, 1,\, -3)} x \right)^2 \left( \lim_{(x,\, y,\, z) \to (4,\, 1,\, -3)} y \right) - 3 \lim_{(x,\, y,\, z) \to (4,\, 1,\, -3)} z \\
&= (4^2)(1) - 3(-3) \\
&= 16 + 9 \\
&= 25.
\end{aligned}$$

Last, applying the quotient law:

$$\lim_{(x,\, y,\, z) \to (4,\, 1,\, -3)} \frac{x^2 y - 3z}{2x + 5y - z} = \frac{\displaystyle\lim_{(x,\, y,\, z) \to (4,\, 1,\, -3)} (x^2 y - 3z)}{\displaystyle\lim_{(x,\, y,\, z) \to (4,\, 1,\, -3)} (2x + 5y - z)}$$

$$= \frac{25}{16}.$$

**4.11** Find $\displaystyle\lim_{(x,\,y,\,z)\,\to\,(4,\,-1,\,3)}\sqrt{13 - x^2 - 2y^2 + z^2}$.

## 4.2 EXERCISES

For the following exercises, find the limit of the function.

60. $\displaystyle\lim_{(x,\,y)\to(1,\,2)} x$

61. $\displaystyle\lim_{(x,\,y)\to(1,\,2)} \frac{5x^2 y}{x^2 + y^2}$

62. Show that the limit $\displaystyle\lim_{(x,\,y)\to(0,\,0)} \frac{5x^2 y}{x^2 + y^2}$ exists and is the same along the paths: $y$-axis and $x$-axis, and along $y = x$.

For the following exercises, evaluate the limits at the indicated values of $x$ and $y$. If the limit does not exist, state this and explain why the limit does not exist.

63. $\displaystyle\lim_{(x,\,y)\to(0,\,0)} \frac{4x^2 + 10y^2 + 4}{4x^2 - 10y^2 + 6}$

64. $\displaystyle\lim_{(x,\,y)\to(11,\,13)} \sqrt{\frac{1}{xy}}$

65. $\displaystyle\lim_{(x,\,y)\to(0,\,1)} \frac{y^2 \sin x}{x}$

66. $\displaystyle\lim_{(x,\,y)\to(0,\,0)} \sin\!\left(\frac{x^8 + y^7}{x - y + 10}\right)$

67. $\displaystyle\lim_{(x,\,y)\to(\pi/4,\,1)} \frac{y \tan x}{y + 1}$

68. $\displaystyle\lim_{(x,\,y)\to(0,\,\pi/4)} \frac{\sec x + 2}{3x - \tan y}$

69. $\displaystyle\lim_{(x,\,y)\to(2,\,5)} \left(\frac{1}{x} - \frac{5}{y}\right)$

70. $\displaystyle\lim_{(x,\,y)\to(4,\,4)} x \ln y$

71. $\displaystyle\lim_{(x,\,y)\to(4,\,4)} e^{-x^2 - y^2}$

72. $\displaystyle\lim_{(x,\,y)\to(0,\,0)} \sqrt{9 - x^2 - y^2}$

73. $\displaystyle\lim_{(x,\,y)\to(1,\,2)} \left(x^2 y^3 - x^3 y^2 + 3x + 2y\right)$

74. $\displaystyle\lim_{(x,\,y)\to(\pi,\,\pi)} x \sin\!\left(\frac{x + y}{4}\right)$

75. $\displaystyle\lim_{(x,\,y)\to(0,\,0)} \frac{xy + 1}{x^2 + y^2 + 1}$

76. $\displaystyle\lim_{(x,\,y)\to(0,\,0)} \frac{x^2 + y^2}{\sqrt{x^2 + y^2 + 1} - 1}$

77. $\displaystyle\lim_{(x,\,y)\to(0,\,0)} \ln\!\left(x^2 + y^2\right)$

For the following exercises, complete the statement.

78. A point $(x_0, y_0)$ in a plane region $R$ is an interior point of $R$ if _____.

79. A point $(x_0, y_0)$ in a plane region $R$ is called a boundary point of $R$ if _____.

For the following exercises, use algebraic techniques to evaluate the limit.

80. $\displaystyle\lim_{(x,\,y)\to(2,\,1)} \frac{x - y - 1}{\sqrt{x - y} - 1}$

81. $\displaystyle\lim_{(x,\,y)\to(0,\,0)} \frac{x^4 - 4y^4}{x^2 + 2y^2}$

82. $\displaystyle\lim_{(x,\,y)\to(0,\,0)} \frac{x^3 - y^3}{x - y}$

83. $\displaystyle\lim_{(x,\,y)\to(0,\,0)} \frac{x^2 - xy}{\sqrt{x} - \sqrt{y}}$

For the following exercises, evaluate the limits of the functions of three variables.

84. $\displaystyle\lim_{(x,\,y,\,z)\to(1,\,2,\,3)} \frac{xz^2 - y^2 z}{xyz - 1}$

85. $\displaystyle\lim_{(x,\,y,\,z)\to(0,\,0,\,0)} \frac{x^2 - y^2 - z^2}{x^2 + y^2 - z^2}$

For the following exercises, evaluate the limit of the function by determining the value the function approaches along the indicated paths. If the limit does not exist, explain why not.

86. $\lim\limits_{(x,\,y)\to(0,\,0)}\dfrac{xy+y^3}{x^2+y^2}$

  a. Along the $x$-axis $(y=0)$

  b. Along the $y$-axis $(x=0)$

  c. Along the path $y=2x$

87. Evaluate $\lim\limits_{(x,\,y)\to(0,\,0)}\dfrac{xy+y^3}{x^2+y^2}$ using the results of previous problem.

88. $\lim\limits_{(x,\,y)\to(0,\,0)}\dfrac{x^2y}{x^4+y^2}$

  a. Along the $x$-axis $(y=0)$

  b. Along the $y$-axis $(x=0)$

  c. Along the path $y=x^2$

89. Evaluate $\lim\limits_{(x,\,y)\to(0,\,0)}\dfrac{x^2y}{x^4+y^2}$ using the results of previous problem.

Discuss the continuity of the following functions. Find the largest region in the $xy$-plane in which the following functions are continuous.

90. $f(x,y)=\sin(xy)$

91. $f(x,y)=\ln(x+y)$

92. $f(x,y)=e^{3xy}$

93. $f(x,y)=\frac{1}{xy}$

For the following exercises, determine the region in which the function is continuous. Explain your answer.

94. $f(x,y)=\dfrac{x^2y}{x^2+y^2}$

95. $f(x,y)=\begin{cases}\dfrac{x^2y}{x^2+y^2} & \text{if }(x,y)\neq(0,0)\\ 0 & \text{if }(x,y)=(0,0)\end{cases}$  (*Hint*:

Show that the function approaches different values along two different paths.)

96. $f(x,y)=\dfrac{\sin(x^2+y^2)}{x^2+y^2}$

97. Determine whether $g(x,y)=\dfrac{x^2-y^2}{x^2+y^2}$ is continuous at $(0,0)$.

98. Create a plot using graphing software to determine where the limit does not exist. Determine the region of the coordinate plane in which $f(x,y)=\dfrac{1}{x^2-y}$ is continuous.

99. Determine the region of the $xy$-plane in which the composite function $g(x,y)=\arctan\left(\dfrac{xy^2}{x+y}\right)$ is continuous. Use technology to support your conclusion.

100. Determine the region of the $xy$-plane in which $f(x,y)=\ln(x^2+y^2-1)$ is continuous. Use technology to support your conclusion. (*Hint*: Choose the range of values for $x$ and $y$ carefully!)

101. At what points in space is $g(x,y,z)=x^2+y^2-2z^2$ continuous?

102. At what points in space is $g(x,y,z)=\dfrac{1}{x^2+z^2-1}$ continuous?

103. Show that $\lim\limits_{(x,\,y)\to(0,\,0)}\dfrac{1}{x^2+y^2}$ does not exist at $(0,0)$ by plotting the graph of the function.

104. **[T]** Evaluate $\lim\limits_{(x,\,y)\to(0,\,0)}\dfrac{-xy^2}{x^2+y^4}$ by plotting the function using a CAS. Determine analytically the limit along the path $x=y^2$.

105. **[T]**

  a. Use a CAS to draw a contour map of $z=\sqrt{9-x^2-y^2}$.

  b. What is the name of the geometric shape of the level curves?

  c. Give the general equation of the level curves.

  d. What is the maximum value of $z$?

  e. What is the domain of the function?

  f. What is the range of the function?

106. *True or False*: If we evaluate $\lim\limits_{(x,\,y)\to(0,\,0)}f(x)$ along several paths and each time the limit is $1$, we can conclude that $\lim\limits_{(x,\,y)\to(0,\,0)}f(x)=1$.

107. Use polar coordinates to find $\lim_{(x,\, y) \to (0,\, 0)} \dfrac{\sin\sqrt{x^2 + y^2}}{\sqrt{x^2 + y^2}}$. You can also find the limit using

L'Hôpital's rule.

108. Use polar coordinates to find $\lim_{(x,\, y) \to (0,\, 0)} \cos\left(x^2 + y^2\right)$.

109. Discuss the continuity of $f(g(x,\, y))$ where $f(t) = 1/t$ and $g(x,\, y) = 2x - 5y$.

110. Given $f(x,\, y) = x^2 - 4y$, find $\lim_{h \to 0} \dfrac{f(x + h,\, y) - f(x,\, y)}{h}$.

111. Given $f(x,\, y) = x^2 - 4y$, find $\lim_{h \to 0} \dfrac{f(1 + h,\, y) - f(1,\, y)}{h}$.

# 4.3 | Partial Derivatives

## Learning Objectives

**4.3.1** Calculate the partial derivatives of a function of two variables.
**4.3.2** Calculate the partial derivatives of a function of more than two variables.
**4.3.3** Determine the higher-order derivatives of a function of two variables.
**4.3.4** Explain the meaning of a partial differential equation and give an example.

Now that we have examined limits and continuity of functions of two variables, we can proceed to study derivatives. Finding derivatives of functions of two variables is the key concept in this chapter, with as many applications in mathematics, science, and engineering as differentiation of single-variable functions. However, we have already seen that limits and continuity of multivariable functions have new issues and require new terminology and ideas to deal with them. This carries over into differentiation as well.

## Derivatives of a Function of Two Variables

When studying derivatives of functions of one variable, we found that one interpretation of the derivative is an instantaneous rate of change of $y$ as a function of $x$. Leibniz notation for the derivative is $dy/dx$, which implies that $y$ is the dependent variable and $x$ is the independent variable. For a function $z = f(x, y)$ of two variables, $x$ and $y$ are the independent variables and $z$ is the dependent variable. This raises two questions right away: How do we adapt Leibniz notation for functions of two variables? Also, what is an interpretation of the derivative? The answer lies in partial derivatives.

### Definition

Let $f(x, y)$ be a function of two variables. Then the **partial derivative** of $f$ with respect to $x$, written as $\partial f/\partial x$, or $f_x$, is defined as

$$\frac{\partial f}{\partial x} = \lim_{h \to 0} \frac{f(x+h, y) - f(x, y)}{h}. \tag{4.12}$$

The partial derivative of $f$ with respect to $y$, written as $\partial f/\partial y$, or $f_y$, is defined as

$$\frac{\partial f}{\partial y} = \lim_{k \to 0} \frac{f(x, y+k) - f(x, y)}{k}. \tag{4.13}$$

This definition shows two differences already. First, the notation changes, in the sense that we still use a version of Leibniz notation, but the $d$ in the original notation is replaced with the symbol $\partial$. (This rounded "d" is usually called "partial," so $\partial f/\partial x$ is spoken as the "partial of $f$ with respect to $x$.") This is the first hint that we are dealing with partial derivatives.

Second, we now have two different derivatives we can take, since there are two different independent variables. Depending on which variable we choose, we can come up with different partial derivatives altogether, and often do.

## Example 4.14

### Calculating Partial Derivatives from the Definition

Use the definition of the partial derivative as a limit to calculate $\partial f/\partial x$ and $\partial f/\partial y$ for the function

$$f(x, y) = x^2 - 3xy + 2y^2 - 4x + 5y - 12.$$

### Solution

First, calculate $f(x + h, y)$.

$$f(x + h, y) = (x + h)^2 - 3(x + h)y + 2y^2 - 4(x + h) + 5y - 12$$
$$= x^2 + 2xh + h^2 - 3xy - 3hy + 2y^2 - 4x - 4h + 5y - 12.$$

Next, substitute this into **Equation 4.12** and simplify:

$$\frac{\partial f}{\partial x} = \lim_{h \to 0} \frac{f(x + h, y) - f(x, y)}{h}$$

$$= \lim_{h \to 0} \frac{\left(x^2 + 2xh + h^2 - 3xy - 3hy + 2y^2 - 4x - 4h + 5y - 12\right) - \left(x^2 - 3xy + 2y^2 - 4x + 5y - 12\right)}{h}$$

$$= \lim_{h \to 0} \frac{x^2 + 2xh + h^2 - 3xy - 3hy + 2y^2 - 4x - 4h + 5y - 12 - x^2 + 3xy - 2y^2 + 4x - 5y + 12}{h}$$

$$= \lim_{h \to 0} \frac{2xh + h^2 - 3hy - 4h}{h}$$

$$= \lim_{h \to 0} \frac{h(2x + h - 3y - 4)}{h}$$

$$= \lim_{h \to 0} (2x + h - 3y - 4)$$

$$= 2x - 3y - 4.$$

To calculate $\frac{\partial f}{\partial y}$, first calculate $f(x, y + h)$:

$$f(x + h, y) = x^2 - 3x(y + h) + 2(y + h)^2 - 4x + 5(y + h) - 12$$
$$= x^2 - 3xy - 3xh + 2y^2 + 4yh + 2h^2 - 4x + 5y + 5h - 12.$$

Next, substitute this into **Equation 4.13** and simplify:

$$\frac{\partial f}{\partial y} = \lim_{h \to 0} \frac{f(x, y + h) - f(x, y)}{h}$$

$$= \lim_{h \to 0} \frac{\left(x^2 - 3xy - 3xh + 2y^2 + 4yh + 2h^2 - 4x + 5y + 5h - 12\right) - \left(x^2 - 3xy + 2y^2 - 4x + 5y - 12\right)}{h}$$

$$= \lim_{h \to 0} \frac{x^2 - 3xy - 3xh + 2y^2 + 4yh + 2h^2 - 4x + 5y + 5h - 12 - x^2 + 3xy - 2y^2 + 4x - 5y + 12}{h}$$

$$= \lim_{h \to 0} \frac{-3xh + 4yh + 2h^2 + 5h}{h}$$

$$= \lim_{h \to 0} \frac{h(-3x + 4y + 2h + 5)}{h}$$

$$= \lim_{h \to 0} (-3x + 4y + 2h + 5)$$

$$= -3x + 4y + 5.$$

 **4.12**   Use the definition of the partial derivative as a limit to calculate $\partial f/\partial x$ and $\partial f/\partial y$ for the function

$$f(x, y) = 4x^2 + 2xy - y^2 + 3x - 2y + 5.$$

The idea to keep in mind when calculating partial derivatives is to treat all independent variables, other than the variable with respect to which we are differentiating, as constants. Then proceed to differentiate as with a function of a single variable. To see why this is true, first fix $y$ and define $g(x) = f(x, y)$ as a function of $x$. Then

$$g'(x) = \lim_{h \to 0} \frac{g(x+h) - g(x)}{h} = \lim_{h \to 0} \frac{f(x+h, \ y) - f(x, \ y)}{h} = \frac{\partial f}{\partial x}.$$

The same is true for calculating the partial derivative of $f$ with respect to $y$. This time, fix $x$ and define $h(y) = f(x, y)$ as a function of $y$. Then

$$h'(x) = \lim_{k \to 0} \frac{h(x+k) - h(x)}{k} = \lim_{k \to 0} \frac{f(x, \ y+k) - f(x, \ y)}{k} = \frac{\partial f}{\partial y}.$$

All differentiation rules from **Introduction to Derivatives (http://cnx.org/content/m53494/latest/)** apply.

## Example 4.15

### Calculating Partial Derivatives

Calculate $\partial f/\partial x$ and $\partial f/\partial y$ for the following functions by holding the opposite variable constant then differentiating:

a. $f(x, \ y) = x^2 - 3xy + 2y^2 - 4x + 5y - 12$

b. $g(x, \ y) = \sin\!\left(x^2 y - 2x + 4\right)$

### Solution

a. To calculate $\partial f/\partial x$, treat the variable $y$ as a constant. Then differentiate $f(x, y)$ with respect to $x$ using the sum, difference, and power rules:

$$\begin{aligned}
\frac{\partial f}{\partial x} &= \frac{\partial}{\partial x}\!\left[x^2 - 3xy + 2y^2 - 4x + 5y - 12\right] \\
&= \frac{\partial}{\partial x}\!\left[x^2\right] - \frac{\partial}{\partial x}[3xy] + \frac{\partial}{\partial x}\!\left[2y^2\right] - \frac{\partial}{\partial x}[4x] + \frac{\partial}{\partial x}[5y] - \frac{\partial}{\partial x}[12] \\
&= 2x - 3y + 0 - 4 + 0 - 0 \\
&= 2x - 3y - 4.
\end{aligned}$$

The derivatives of the third, fifth, and sixth terms are all zero because they do not contain the variable $x$, so they are treated as constant terms. The derivative of the second term is equal to the coefficient of $x$, which is $-3y$. Calculating $\partial f/\partial y$:

$$\begin{aligned}
\frac{\partial f}{\partial y} &= \frac{\partial}{\partial y}\!\left[x^2 - 3xy + 2y^2 - 4x + 5y - 12\right] \\
&= \frac{\partial}{\partial y}\!\left[x^2\right] - \frac{\partial}{\partial y}[3xy] + \frac{\partial}{\partial y}\!\left[2y^2\right] - \frac{\partial}{\partial y}[4x] + \frac{\partial}{\partial y}[5y] - \frac{\partial}{\partial y}[12] \\
&= -3x + 4y - 0 + 5 - 0 \\
&= -3x + 4y + 5.
\end{aligned}$$

These are the same answers obtained in **Example 4.14**.

b. To calculate $\partial g/\partial x$, treat the variable $y$ as a constant. Then differentiate $g(x, y)$ with respect to $x$ using the chain rule and power rule:

$$\begin{aligned}
\frac{\partial g}{\partial x} &= \frac{\partial}{\partial x}\!\left[\sin\!\left(x^2 y - 2x + 4\right)\right] \\
&= \cos\!\left(x^2 y - 2x + 4\right)\frac{\partial}{\partial x}\!\left[x^2 y - 2x + 4\right] \\
&= (2xy - 2)\cos\!\left(x^2 y - 2x + 4\right).
\end{aligned}$$

To calculate $\partial g/\partial y$, treat the variable $x$ as a constant. Then differentiate $g(x, y)$ with respect to $y$ using the chain rule and power rule:

$$\begin{aligned}
\frac{\partial g}{\partial y} &= \frac{\partial}{\partial y}\left[\sin\left(x^2 y - 2x + 4\right)\right] \\
&= \cos\left(x^2 y - 2x + 4\right)\frac{\partial}{\partial y}\left[x^2 y - 2x + 4\right] \\
&= x^2 \cos\left(x^2 y - 2x + 4\right).
\end{aligned}$$

**4.13**   Calculate $\partial f/\partial x$ and $\partial f/\partial y$ for the function $f(x, y) = \tan\left(x^3 - 3x^2 y^2 + 2y^4\right)$ by holding the opposite variable constant, then differentiating.

How can we interpret these partial derivatives? Recall that the graph of a function of two variables is a surface in $\mathbb{R}^3$. If we remove the limit from the definition of the partial derivative with respect to $x$, the difference quotient remains:

$$\frac{f(x + h, y) - f(x, y)}{h}.$$

This resembles the difference quotient for the derivative of a function of one variable, except for the presence of the $y$ variable. **Figure 4.21** illustrates a surface described by an arbitrary function $z = f(x, y)$.

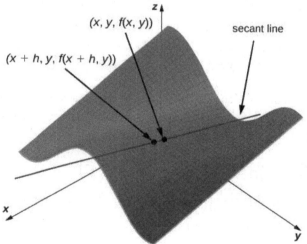

**Figure 4.21**   Secant line passing through the points $(x, y, f(x, y))$ and $(x + h, y, f(x + h, y))$.

In **Figure 4.21**, the value of $h$ is positive. If we graph $f(x, y)$ and $f(x + h, y)$ for an arbitrary point $(x, y)$, then the slope of the secant line passing through these two points is given by

$$\frac{f(x + h, y) - f(x, y)}{h}.$$

This line is parallel to the $x$-axis. Therefore, the slope of the secant line represents an average rate of change of the function $f$ as we travel parallel to the $x$-axis. As $h$ approaches zero, the slope of the secant line approaches the slope of the tangent line.

If we choose to change $y$ instead of $x$ by the same incremental value $h$, then the secant line is parallel to the $y$-axis and so is the tangent line. Therefore, $\partial f/\partial x$ represents the slope of the tangent line passing through the point $(x, y, f(x, y))$ parallel to the $x$-axis and $\partial f/\partial y$ represents the slope of the tangent line passing through the point $(x, y, f(x, y))$ parallel to the $y$-axis. If we wish to find the slope of a tangent line passing through the same point in any other direction, then we need what are called *directional derivatives*, which we discuss in Directional Derivatives and the Gradient.

We now return to the idea of contour maps, which we introduced in Functions of Several Variables. We can use a contour map to estimate partial derivatives of a function $g(x, y)$.

## Example 4.16

### Partial Derivatives from a Contour Map

Use a contour map to estimate $\partial g/\partial x$ at the point $(\sqrt{5}, 0)$ for the function $g(x, y) = \sqrt{9 - x^2 - y^2}$.

### Solution

The following graph represents a contour map for the function $g(x, y) = \sqrt{9 - x^2 - y^2}$.

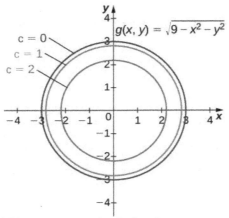

**Figure 4.22** Contour map for the function
$g(x, y) = \sqrt{9 - x^2 - y^2}$, using c $= 0, 1, 2$, and $3$
($c = 3$ corresponds to the origin).

The inner circle on the contour map corresponds to $c = 2$ and the next circle out corresponds to $c = 1$. The first circle is given by the equation $2 = \sqrt{9 - x^2 - y^2}$; the second circle is given by the equation $1 = \sqrt{9 - x^2 - y^2}$. The first equation simplifies to $x^2 + y^2 = 5$ and the second equation simplifies to $x^2 + y^2 = 8$. The $x$-intercept of the first circle is $(\sqrt{5}, 0)$ and the $x$-intercept of the second circle is $(2\sqrt{2}, 0)$. We can estimate the value of $\partial g/\partial x$ evaluated at the point $(\sqrt{5}, 0)$ using the slope formula:

$$\frac{\partial g}{\partial x}\Big|_{(x, y) = (\sqrt{5}, 0)} \approx \frac{g(\sqrt{5}, 0) - g(2\sqrt{2}, 0)}{\sqrt{5} - 2\sqrt{2}} = \frac{2 - 1}{\sqrt{5} - 2\sqrt{2}} = \frac{1}{\sqrt{5} - 2\sqrt{2}} \approx -1.688.$$

To calculate the exact value of $\partial g/\partial x$ evaluated at the point $(\sqrt{5}, 0)$, we start by finding $\partial g/\partial x$ using the chain rule. First, we rewrite the function as $g(x, y) = \sqrt{9 - x^2 - y^2} = \left(9 - x^2 - y^2\right)^{1/2}$ and then differentiate with respect to $x$ while holding $y$ constant:

$$\frac{\partial g}{\partial x} = \frac{1}{2}\left(9 - x^2 - y^2\right)^{-1/2}(-2x) = -\frac{x}{\sqrt{9 - x^2 - y^2}}.$$

Next, we evaluate this expression using $x = \sqrt{5}$ and $y = 0$:

$$\left.\frac{\partial g}{\partial x}\right|_{(x, y) = (\sqrt{5}, 0)} = -\frac{\sqrt{5}}{\sqrt{9 - \left(\sqrt{5}\right)^2 - (0)^2}} = -\frac{\sqrt{5}}{\sqrt{4}} = -\frac{\sqrt{5}}{2} \approx -1.118.$$

The estimate for the partial derivative corresponds to the slope of the secant line passing through the points $\left(\sqrt{5}, 0, g(\sqrt{5}, 0)\right)$ and $\left(2\sqrt{2}, 0, g(2\sqrt{2}, 0)\right)$. It represents an approximation to the slope of the tangent line to the surface through the point $\left(\sqrt{5}, 0, g(\sqrt{5}, 0)\right)$, which is parallel to the $x$-axis.

 **4.14** Use a contour map to estimate $\partial f/\partial y$ at point $\left(0, \sqrt{2}\right)$ for the function

$$f(x, y) = x^2 - y^2.$$

Compare this with the exact answer.

## Functions of More Than Two Variables

Suppose we have a function of three variables, such as $w = f(x, y, z)$. We can calculate partial derivatives of $w$ with respect to any of the independent variables, simply as extensions of the definitions for partial derivatives of functions of two variables.

---

**Definition**

Let $f(x, y, z)$ be a function of three variables. Then, the *partial derivative of $f$ with respect to x*, written as $\partial f/\partial x$, or $f_x$, is defined to be

$$\frac{\partial f}{\partial x} = \lim_{h \to 0} \frac{f(x + h, y, z) - f(x, y, z)}{h}. \tag{4.14}$$

The *partial derivative of $f$ with respect to $y$*, written as $\partial f/\partial y$, or $f_y$, is defined to be

$$\frac{\partial f}{\partial y} = \lim_{k \to 0} \frac{f(x, y + k, z) - f(x, y, z)}{k}. \tag{4.15}$$

The *partial derivative of $f$ with respect to $z$*, written as $\partial f/\partial z$, or $f_z$, is defined to be

$$\frac{\partial f}{\partial z} = \lim_{m \to 0} \frac{f(x, y, z + m) - f(x, y, z)}{m}. \tag{4.16}$$

---

We can calculate a partial derivative of a function of three variables using the same idea we used for a function of two variables. For example, if we have a function $f$ of $x$, $y$, and $z$, and we wish to calculate $\partial f/\partial x$, then we treat the other two independent variables as if they are constants, then differentiate with respect to $x$.

## Example 4.17

### Calculating Partial Derivatives for a Function of Three Variables

Use the limit definition of partial derivatives to calculate $\partial f/\partial x$ for the function

$$f(x, y, z) = x^2 - 3xy + 2y^2 - 4xz + 5yz^2 - 12x + 4y - 3z.$$

Then, find $\partial f/\partial y$ and $\partial f/\partial z$ by setting the other two variables constant and differentiating accordingly.

### Solution

We first calculate $\partial f/\partial x$ using **Equation 4.14**, then we calculate the other two partial derivatives by holding the remaining variables constant. To use the equation to find $\partial f/\partial x$, we first need to calculate $f(x + h, y, z)$:

$$
\begin{aligned}
f(x + h, y, z) &= (x + h)^2 - 3(x + h)y + 2y^2 - 4(x + h)z + 5yz^2 - 12(x + h) + 4y - 3z \\
&= x^2 + 2xh + h^2 - 3xy - 3xh + 2y^2 - 4xz - 4hz + 5yz^2 - 12x - 12h + 4y - 3z
\end{aligned}
$$

and recall that $f(x, y, z) = x^2 - 3xy + 2y^2 - 4zx + 5yz^2 - 12x + 4y - 3z$. Next, we substitute these two expressions into the equation:

$$
\begin{aligned}
\frac{\partial f}{\partial x} &= \lim_{h \to 0} \left[ \frac{x^2 + 2xh + h^2 - 3xy - 3hy + 2y^2 - 4xz - 4hz + 5yz^2 - 12x - 12h + 4y - 3z}{h} \right. \\
&\qquad \left. - \frac{x^2 - 3xy + 2y^2 - 4xz + 5yz^2 - 12x + 4y - 3z}{h} \right] \\
&= \lim_{h \to 0} \left[ \frac{2xh + h^2 - 3hy - 4hz - 12h}{h} \right] \\
&= \lim_{h \to 0} \left[ \frac{h(2x + h - 3y - 4z - 12)}{h} \right] \\
&= \lim_{h \to 0} (2x + h - 3y - 4z - 12) \\
&= 2x - 3y - 4z - 12.
\end{aligned}
$$

Then we find $\partial f/\partial y$ by holding $x$ and $z$ constant. Therefore, any term that does not include the variable $y$ is constant, and its derivative is zero. We can apply the sum, difference, and power rules for functions of one variable:

$$
\begin{aligned}
&\frac{\partial}{\partial y}\left[x^2 - 3xy + 2y^2 - 4xz + 5yz^2 - 12x + 4y - 3z\right] \\
&= \frac{\partial}{\partial y}\left[x^2\right] - \frac{\partial}{\partial y}[3xy] + \frac{\partial}{\partial y}\left[2y^2\right] - \frac{\partial}{\partial y}[4xz] + \frac{\partial}{\partial y}\left[5yz^2\right] - \frac{\partial}{\partial y}[12x] + \frac{\partial}{\partial y}[4y] - \frac{\partial}{\partial y}[3z] \\
&= 0 - 3x + 4y - 0 + 5z^2 - 0 + 4 - 0 \\
&= -3x + 4y + 5z^2 + 4.
\end{aligned}
$$

To calculate $\partial f/\partial z$, we hold $x$ and $y$ constant and apply the sum, difference, and power rules for functions of one variable:

$$
\begin{aligned}
&\frac{\partial}{\partial z}\left[x^2 - 3xy + 2y^2 - 4xz + 5yz^2 - 12x + 4y - 3z\right] \\
&= \frac{\partial}{\partial z}\left[x^2\right] - \frac{\partial}{\partial z}[3xy] + \frac{\partial}{\partial z}\left[2y^2\right] - \frac{\partial}{\partial z}[4xz] + \frac{\partial}{\partial z}\left[5yz^2\right] - \frac{\partial}{\partial z}[12x] + \frac{\partial}{\partial z}[4y] - \frac{\partial}{\partial z}[3z] \\
&= 0 - 0 + 0 - 4x + 10yz - 0 + 0 - 3 \\
&= -4x + 10yz - 3.
\end{aligned}
$$

**4.15** Use the limit definition of partial derivatives to calculate $\partial f/\partial x$ for the function

$$f(x,\ y,\ z) = 2x^2 - 4x^2 y + 2y^2 + 5xz^2 - 6x + 3z - 8.$$

Then find $\partial f/\partial y$ and $\partial f/\partial z$ by setting the other two variables constant and differentiating accordingly.

## Example 4.18

### Calculating Partial Derivatives for a Function of Three Variables

Calculate the three partial derivatives of the following functions.

a. $f(x,\ y,\ z) = \dfrac{x^2 y - 4xz + y^2}{x - 3yz}$

b. $g(x,\ y,\ z) = \sin\!\left(x^2 y - z\right) + \cos\!\left(x^2 - yz\right)$

### Solution

In each case, treat all variables as constants except the one whose partial derivative you are calculating.

a.
$$\frac{\partial f}{\partial x} = \frac{\partial}{\partial x}\!\left[\frac{x^2 y - 4xz + y^2}{x - 3yz}\right]$$

$$= \frac{\frac{\partial}{\partial x}\!\left(x^2 y - 4xz + y^2\right)\!\left(x - 3yz\right) - \left(x^2 y - 4xz + y^2\right)\frac{\partial}{\partial x}(x - 3yz)}{(x - 3yz)^2}$$

$$= \frac{(2xy - 4z)(x - 3yz) - \left(x^2 y - 4xz + y^2\right)(1)}{(x - 3yz)^2}$$

$$= \frac{2x^2 y - 6xy^2 z - 4xz + 12yz^2 - x^2 y + 4xz - y^2}{(x - 3yz)^2}$$

$$= \frac{x^2 y - 6xy^2 z - 4xz + 12yz^2 + 4xz - y^2}{(x - 3yz)^2}$$

$$\frac{\partial f}{\partial y} = \frac{\partial}{\partial y}\!\left[\frac{x^2 y - 4xz + y^2}{x - 3yz}\right]$$

$$= \frac{\frac{\partial}{\partial y}\!\left(x^2 y - 4xz + y^2\right)\!\left(x - 3yz\right) - \left(x^2 y - 4xz + y^2\right)\frac{\partial}{\partial y}(x - 3yz)}{(x - 3yz)^2}$$

$$= \frac{\left(x^2 + 2y\right)\!\left(x - 3yz\right) - \left(x^2 y - 4xz + y^2\right)(-3z)}{(x - 3yz)^2}$$

$$= \frac{x^3 - 3x^2 yz + 2xy - 6y^2 z + 3x^2 yz - 12xz^2 + 3y^2 z}{(x - 3yz)^2}$$

$$= \frac{x^3 + 2xy - 3y^2 z - 12xz^2}{(x - 3yz)^2}$$

$$\frac{\partial f}{\partial z} = \frac{\partial}{\partial z}\left[\frac{x^2 y - 4xz + y^2}{x - 3yz}\right]$$

$$= \frac{\frac{\partial}{\partial z}(x^2 y - 4xz + y^2)(x - 3yz) - (x^2 y - 4xz + y^2)\frac{\partial}{\partial z}(x - 3yz)}{(x - 3yz)^2}$$

$$= \frac{(-4x)(x - 3yz) - (x^2 y - 4xz + y^2)(-3y)}{(x - 3yz)^2}$$

$$= \frac{-4x^2 + 12xyz + 3x^2 y^2 - 12xyz + 3y^3}{(x - 3yz)^2}$$

$$= \frac{-4x^2 + 3x^2 y^2 + 3y^3}{(x - 3yz)^2}$$

$$\frac{\partial f}{\partial x} = \frac{\partial}{\partial x}\left[\sin(x^2 y - z) + \cos(x^2 - yz)\right]$$

$$= \left(\cos(x^2 y - z)\right)\frac{\partial}{\partial x}(x^2 y - z) - \left(\sin(x^2 - yz)\right)\frac{\partial}{\partial x}(x^2 - yz)$$

$$= 2xy\cos(x^2 y - z) - 2x\sin(x^2 - yz)$$

$$\frac{\partial f}{\partial y} = \frac{\partial}{\partial y}\left[\sin(x^2 y - z) + \cos(x^2 - yz)\right]$$

b.

$$= \left(\cos(x^2 y - z)\right)\frac{\partial}{\partial y}(x^2 y - z) - \left(\sin(x^2 - yz)\right)\frac{\partial}{\partial y}(x^2 - yz)$$

$$= x^2\cos(x^2 y - z) + z\sin(x^2 - yz)$$

$$\frac{\partial f}{\partial z} = \frac{\partial}{\partial z}\left[\sin(x^2 y - z) + \cos(x^2 - yz)\right]$$

$$= \left(\cos(x^2 y - z)\right)\frac{\partial}{\partial z}(x^2 y - z) - \left(\sin(x^2 - yz)\right)\frac{\partial}{\partial z}(x^2 - yz)$$

$$= -\cos(x^2 y - z) + y\sin(x^2 - yz)$$

**4.16** Calculate $\partial f/\partial x$, $\partial f/\partial y$, and $\partial f/\partial z$ for the function $f(x, y, z) = \sec(x^2 y) - \tan(x^3 yz^2)$.

## Higher-Order Partial Derivatives

Consider the function

$$f(x, y) = 2x^3 - 4xy^2 + 5y^3 - 6xy + 5x - 4y + 12.$$

Its partial derivatives are

$$\frac{\partial f}{\partial x} = 6x^2 - 4y^2 - 6y + 5 \text{ and } \frac{\partial f}{\partial y} = -8xy + 15y^2 - 6x - 4.$$

Each of these partial derivatives is a function of two variables, so we can calculate partial derivatives of these functions. Just as with derivatives of single-variable functions, we can call these *second-order derivatives, third-order derivatives*, and so on. In general, they are referred to as **higher-order partial derivatives**. There are four second-order partial derivatives for any function (provided they all exist):

$$\frac{\partial^2 f}{\partial x^2} = \frac{\partial}{\partial x}\left[\frac{\partial f}{\partial x}\right], \quad \frac{\partial^2 f}{\partial x \partial y} = \frac{\partial}{\partial x}\left[\frac{\partial f}{\partial y}\right], \quad \frac{\partial^2 f}{\partial y \partial x} = \frac{\partial}{\partial y}\left[\frac{\partial f}{\partial x}\right], \quad \frac{\partial^2 f}{\partial y^2} = \frac{\partial}{\partial y}\left[\frac{\partial f}{\partial y}\right].$$

An alternative notation for each is $f_{xx}$, $f_{yx}$, $f_{xy}$, and $f_{yy}$, respectively. Higher-order partial derivatives calculated with respect to different variables, such as $f_{xy}$ and $f_{yx}$, are commonly called **mixed partial derivatives**.

## Example 4.19

### Calculating Second Partial Derivatives

Calculate all four second partial derivatives for the function

$$f(x, y) = xe^{-3y} + \sin(2x - 5y).$$

### Solution

To calculate $\partial^2 f/\partial x^2$ and $\partial^2 f/\partial y \partial x$, we first calculate $\partial f/\partial x$:

$$\frac{\partial f}{\partial x} = e^{-3y} + 2\cos(2x - 5y).$$

To calculate $\partial^2 f/\partial x^2$, differentiate $\partial f/\partial x$ with respect to $x$:

$$\begin{aligned}
\frac{\partial^2 f}{\partial x^2} &= \frac{\partial}{\partial x}\left[\frac{\partial f}{\partial x}\right] \\
&= \frac{\partial}{\partial x}\left[e^{-3y} + 2\cos(2x - 5y)\right] \\
&= -4\sin(2x - 5y).
\end{aligned}$$

To calculate $\partial^2 f/\partial y \partial x$, differentiate $\partial f/\partial x$ with respect to $y$:

$$\begin{aligned}
\frac{\partial^2 f}{\partial y \partial x} &= \frac{\partial}{\partial y}\left[\frac{\partial f}{\partial x}\right] \\
&= \frac{\partial}{\partial y}\left[e^{-3y} + 2\cos(2x - 5y)\right] \\
&= -3e^{-3y} + 10\sin(2x - 5y).
\end{aligned}$$

To calculate $\partial^2 f/\partial x \partial y$ and $\partial^2 f/\partial y^2$, first calculate $\partial f/\partial y$:

$$\frac{\partial f}{\partial y} = -3xe^{-3y} - 5\cos(2x - 5y).$$

To calculate $\partial^2 f/\partial x \partial y$, differentiate $\partial f/\partial y$ with respect to $x$:

$$\begin{aligned}
\frac{\partial^2 f}{\partial x \partial y} &= \frac{\partial}{\partial x}\left[\frac{\partial f}{\partial y}\right] \\
&= \frac{\partial}{\partial x}\left[-3xe^{-3y} - 5\cos(2x - 5y)\right] \\
&= -3e^{-3y} + 10\sin(2x - 5y).
\end{aligned}$$

To calculate $\partial^2 f/\partial y^2$, differentiate $\partial f/\partial y$ with respect to $y$:

$$\frac{\partial^2 f}{\partial y^2} = \frac{\partial}{\partial y}\left[\frac{\partial f}{\partial y}\right]$$

$$= \frac{\partial}{\partial y}\left[-3xe^{-3y} - 5\cos(2x - 5y)\right]$$

$$= 9xe^{-3y} - 25\sin(2x - 5y).$$

 **4.17** Calculate all four second partial derivatives for the function

$$f(x, y) = \sin(3x - 2y) + \cos(x + 4y).$$

At this point we should notice that, in both **Example 4.19** and the checkpoint, it was true that $\partial^2 f/\partial x\partial y = \partial^2 f/\partial y\partial x$. Under certain conditions, this is always true. In fact, it is a direct consequence of the following theorem.

### Theorem 4.5: Equality of Mixed Partial Derivatives (Clairaut's Theorem)

Suppose that $f(x, y)$ is defined on an open disk $D$ that contains the point $(a, b)$. If the functions $f_{xy}$ and $f_{yx}$ are continuous on $D$, then $f_{xy} = f_{yx}$.

Clairaut's theorem guarantees that as long as mixed second-order derivatives are continuous, the order in which we choose to differentiate the functions (i.e., which variable goes first, then second, and so on) does not matter. It can be extended to higher-order derivatives as well. The proof of Clairaut's theorem can be found in most advanced calculus books.

Two other second-order partial derivatives can be calculated for any function $f(x, y)$. The partial derivative $f_{xx}$ is equal to the partial derivative of $f_x$ with respect to $x$, and $f_{yy}$ is equal to the partial derivative of $f_y$ with respect to $y$.

## Partial Differential Equations

In **Introduction to Differential Equations (http://cnx.org/content/m53696/latest/)** , we studied differential equations in which the unknown function had one independent variable. A **partial differential equation** is an equation that involves an unknown function of more than one independent variable and one or more of its partial derivatives. Examples of partial differential equations are

$$u_t = c^2\left(u_{xx} + u_{yy}\right) \tag{4.17}$$

( heat equation in two dimensions)

$$u_{tt} = c^2\left(u_{xx} + u_{yy}\right) \tag{4.18}$$

( wave equation in two dimensions)

$$u_{xx} + u_{yy} = 0 \tag{4.19}$$

( Laplace's equation in two dimensions)

In the first two equations, the unknown function $u$ has three independent variables—$t$, $x$, and $y$—and $c$ is an arbitrary constant. The independent variables $x$ and $y$ are considered to be spatial variables, and the variable $t$ represents time. In Laplace's equation, the unknown function $u$ has two independent variables $x$ and $y$.

## Example 4.20

### A Solution to the Wave Equation

Verify that

$$u(x, y, t) = 5 \sin(3\pi x)\sin(4\pi y)\cos(10\pi t)$$

is a solution to the wave equation

$$u_{tt} = 4(u_{xx} + u_{yy}). \tag{4.20}$$

### Solution

First, we calculate $u_{tt}$, $u_{xx}$, and $u_{yy}$:

$$
\begin{aligned}
u_{tt} &= \frac{\partial}{\partial t}\left[\frac{\partial u}{\partial t}\right] \\
&= \frac{\partial}{\partial t}[5 \sin(3\pi x)\sin(4\pi y)(-10\pi \sin(10\pi t))] \\
&= \frac{\partial}{\partial t}[-50\pi \sin(3\pi x)\sin(4\pi y)\sin(10\pi t)] \\
&= -500\pi^2 \sin(3\pi x)\sin(4\pi y)\cos(10\pi t) \\
u_{xx} &= \frac{\partial}{\partial x}\left[\frac{\partial u}{\partial x}\right] \\
&= \frac{\partial}{\partial x}[15\pi \cos(3\pi x)\sin(4\pi y)\cos(10\pi t)] \\
&= -45\pi^2 \sin(3\pi x)\sin(4\pi y)\cos(10\pi t) \\
u_{yy} &= \frac{\partial}{\partial y}\left[\frac{\partial u}{\partial y}\right] \\
&= \frac{\partial}{\partial y}[5 \sin(3\pi x)(4\pi \cos(4\pi y))\cos(10\pi t)] \\
&= \frac{\partial}{\partial y}[20\pi \sin(3\pi x)\cos(4\pi y)\cos(10\pi t)] \\
&= -80\pi^2 \sin(3\pi x)\sin(4\pi y)\cos(10\pi t).
\end{aligned}
$$

Next, we substitute each of these into the right-hand side of **Equation 4.20** and simplify:

$$
\begin{aligned}
4(u_{xx} + u_{yy}) &= 4\left(-45\pi^2 \sin(3\pi x)\sin(4\pi y)\cos(10\pi t) + -80\pi^2 \sin(3\pi x)\sin(4\pi y)\cos(10\pi t)\right) \\
&= 4\left(-125\pi^2 \sin(3\pi x)\sin(4\pi y)\cos(10\pi t)\right) \\
&= -500\pi^2 \sin(3\pi x)\sin(4\pi y)\cos(10\pi t) \\
&= u_{tt}.
\end{aligned}
$$

This verifies the solution.

 **4.18**   Verify that $u(x, y, t) = 2 \sin\left(\frac{x}{3}\right)\sin\left(\frac{y}{4}\right)e^{-25t/16}$ is a solution to the heat equation

$$u_t = 9(u_{xx} + u_{yy}). \tag{4.21}$$

Since the solution to the two-dimensional heat equation is a function of three variables, it is not easy to create a visual representation of the solution. We can graph the solution for fixed values of $t$, which amounts to snapshots of the heat distributions at fixed times. These snapshots show how the heat is distributed over a two-dimensional surface as time progresses. The graph of the preceding solution at time $t = 0$ appears in the following figure. As time progresses, the extremes level out, approaching zero as $t$ approaches infinity.

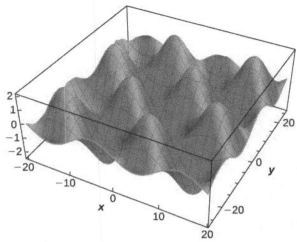

Figure 4.23

If we consider the heat equation in one dimension, then it is possible to graph the solution over time. The heat equation in one dimension becomes

$$u_t = c^2 u_{xx},$$

where $c^2$ represents the thermal diffusivity of the material in question. A solution of this differential equation can be written in the form

$$u_m(x, t) = e^{-\pi^2 m^2 c^2 t} \sin(m\pi x) \tag{4.22}$$

where $m$ is any positive integer. A graph of this solution using $m = 1$ appears in Figure 4.24, where the initial temperature distribution over a wire of length 1 is given by $u(x, 0) = \sin \pi x$. Notice that as time progresses, the wire cools off. This is seen because, from left to right, the highest temperature (which occurs in the middle of the wire) decreases and changes color from red to blue.

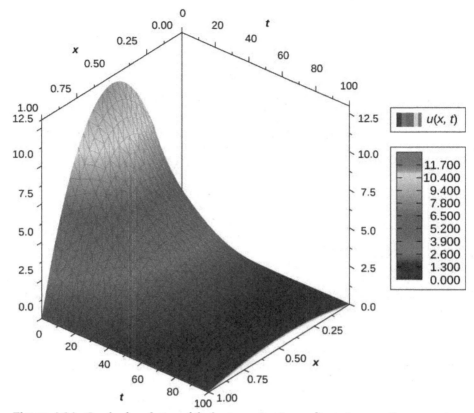

**Figure 4.24** Graph of a solution of the heat equation in one dimension over time.

# Student PROJECT

## Lord Kelvin and the Age of Earth

| (a) | (b) |

**Figure 4.25** (a) William Thomson (Lord Kelvin), 1824-1907, was a British physicist and electrical engineer; (b) Kelvin used the heat diffusion equation to estimate the age of Earth (credit: modification of work by NASA).

During the late 1800s, the scientists of the new field of geology were coming to the conclusion that Earth must be "millions and millions" of years old. At about the same time, Charles Darwin had published his treatise on evolution. Darwin's view was that evolution needed many millions of years to take place, and he made a bold claim that the Weald chalk fields, where important fossils were found, were the result of $300$ million years of erosion.

At that time, eminent physicist William Thomson (Lord Kelvin) used an important partial differential equation, known as the *heat diffusion equation*, to estimate the age of Earth by determining how long it would take Earth to cool from molten rock to what we had at that time. His conclusion was a range of $20$ to $400$ million years, but most likely about $50$ million years. For many decades, the proclamations of this irrefutable icon of science did not sit well with geologists or with Darwin.

▶ Read Kelvin's paper (http://www.openstaxcollege.org/l/20_KelEarthAge) on estimating the age of the Earth.

Kelvin made reasonable assumptions based on what was known in his time, but he also made several assumptions that turned out to be wrong. One incorrect assumption was that Earth is solid and that the cooling was therefore via conduction only, hence justifying the use of the diffusion equation. But the most serious error was a forgivable one—omission of the fact that Earth contains radioactive elements that continually supply heat beneath Earth's mantle. The discovery of radioactivity came near the end of Kelvin's life and he acknowledged that his calculation would have to be modified.

Kelvin used the simple one-dimensional model applied only to Earth's outer shell, and derived the age from graphs and the roughly known temperature gradient near Earth's surface. Let's take a look at a more appropriate version of the diffusion equation in radial coordinates, which has the form

$$\frac{\partial T}{\partial t} = K\left[\frac{\partial^2 T}{\partial^2 r} + \frac{2}{r}\frac{\partial T}{\partial r}\right].$$

(4.23)

Here, $T(r, t)$ is temperature as a function of $r$ (measured from the center of Earth) and time $t$. $K$ is the heat conductivity—for molten rock, in this case. The standard method of solving such a partial differential equation is by separation of variables, where we express the solution as the product of functions containing each variable separately. In this case, we would write the temperature as

$$T(r, t) = R(r)f(t).$$

1. Substitute this form into Equation 4.13 and, noting that $f(t)$ is constant with respect to distance $(r)$ and $R(r)$ is constant with respect to time $(t)$, show that

$$\frac{1}{f}\frac{\partial f}{\partial t} = \frac{K}{R}\left[\frac{\partial^2 R}{\partial r^2} + \frac{2}{r}\frac{\partial R}{\partial r}\right].$$

2. This equation represents the separation of variables we want. The left-hand side is only a function of $t$ and the right-hand side is only a function of $r$, and they must be equal for all values of $r$ and $t$. Therefore, they both must be equal to a constant. Let's call that constant $-\lambda^2$. (The convenience of this choice is seen on substitution.) So, we have

$$\frac{1}{f}\frac{\partial f}{\partial t} = -\lambda^2 \quad \text{and} \quad \frac{K}{R}\left[\frac{\partial^2 R}{\partial r^2} + \frac{2}{r}\frac{\partial R}{\partial r}\right] = -\lambda^2.$$

Now, we can verify through direct substitution for each equation that the solutions are $f(t) = Ae^{-\lambda^2 t}$ and $R(r) = B\left(\frac{\sin \alpha r}{r}\right) + C\left(\frac{\cos \alpha r}{r}\right)$, where $\alpha = \lambda/\sqrt{K}$. Note that $f(t) = Ae^{+\lambda n^2 t}$ is also a valid solution, so we could have chosen $+\lambda^2$ for our constant. Can you see why it would not be valid for this case as time increases?

3. Let's now apply boundary conditions.

    a. The temperature must be finite at the center of Earth, $r = 0$. Which of the two constants, $B$ or $C$, must therefore be zero to keep $R$ finite at $r = 0$? (Recall that $\sin(\alpha r)/r \to \alpha =$ as $r \to 0$, but $\cos(\alpha r)/r$ behaves very differently.)

    b. Kelvin argued that when magma reaches Earth's surface, it cools very rapidly. A person can often touch the surface within weeks of the flow. Therefore, the surface reached a moderate temperature very early and remained nearly constant at a surface temperature $T_s$. For simplicity, let's set $T = 0$ at $r = R_E$ and find $\alpha$ such that this is the temperature there for all time $t$. (Kelvin took the value to be $300 \text{ K} \approx 80°\text{F}$. We can add this $300 \text{ K}$ constant to our solution later.) For this to be true, the sine argument must be zero at $r = R_E$. Note that $\alpha$ has an infinite series of values that satisfies this condition. Each value of $\alpha$ represents a valid solution (each with its own value for $A$). The total or general solution is the sum of all these solutions.

    c. At $t = 0$, we assume that all of Earth was at an initial hot temperature $T_0$ (Kelvin took this to be about $7000 \text{ K}$.) The application of this boundary condition involves the more advanced application of Fourier coefficients. As noted in part b. each value of $\alpha_n$ represents a valid solution, and the general solution is a sum of all these solutions. This results in a series solution:

$$T(r, t) = \left(\frac{T_0 R_E}{\pi}\right)\sum_n \frac{(-1)^{n-1}}{n}e^{-\lambda n^2 t}\frac{\sin(\alpha_n r)}{r}, \quad \text{where } \alpha_n = n\pi/R_E.$$

Note how the values of $\alpha_n$ come from the boundary condition applied in part b. The term $\frac{-1^{n-1}}{n}$ is the constant $A_n$ for each term in the series, determined from applying the Fourier method. Letting $\beta = \frac{\pi}{R_E}$, examine the first few terms of this solution shown here and note how $\lambda^2$ in the exponential causes the higher terms to decrease quickly as time progresses:

$$T(r,\ t) = \frac{T_0 R_E}{\pi r}\left(\begin{array}{l} e^{-K\beta^2 t}(\sin \beta r) - \frac{1}{2}e^{-4K\beta^2 t}(\sin 2\beta r) + \frac{1}{3}e^{-9K\beta^2 t}(\sin 3\beta r) \\ -\frac{1}{4}e^{-16K\beta^2 t}(\sin 4\beta r) + \frac{1}{5}e^{-25K\beta^2 t}(\sin 5\beta r)\ldots \end{array}\right).$$

Near time $t = 0$, many terms of the solution are needed for accuracy. Inserting values for the conductivity $K$ and $\beta = \pi/R_E$ for time approaching merely thousands of years, only the first few terms make a significant contribution. Kelvin only needed to look at the solution near Earth's surface (Figure 4.26) and, after a long time, determine what time best yielded the estimated temperature gradient known during his era ($1°F$ increase per $50$ ft). He simply chose a range of times with a gradient close to this value. In Figure 4.26, the solutions are plotted and scaled, with the $300 - K$ surface temperature added. Note that the center of Earth would be relatively cool. At the time, it was thought Earth must be solid.

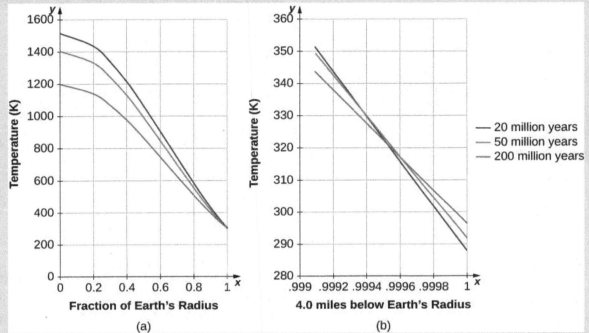

Figure 4.26 Temperature versus radial distance from the center of Earth. (a) Kelvin's results, plotted to scale. (b) A close-up of the results at a depth of $4.0$ mi below Earth's surface.

**Epilog**

On May 20, 1904, physicist Ernest Rutherford spoke at the Royal Institution to announce a revised calculation that included the contribution of radioactivity as a source of Earth's heat. In Rutherford's own words:

"I came into the room, which was half-dark, and presently spotted Lord Kelvin in the audience, and realised that I was in for trouble at the last part of my speech dealing with the age of the Earth, where my views conflicted with his. To my relief, Kelvin fell fast asleep, but as I came to the important point, I saw the old bird sit up, open an eye and cock a baleful glance at me.

Then a sudden inspiration came, and I said Lord Kelvin had limited the age of the Earth, *provided no new source* [*of heat*] *was discovered*. That prophetic utterance referred to what we are now considering tonight, radium! Behold! The old boy beamed upon me."

Rutherford calculated an age for Earth of about $500$ million years. Today's accepted value of Earth's age is about $4.6$ billion years.

# 4.3 EXERCISES

For the following exercises, calculate the partial derivative using the limit definitions only.

112. $\frac{\partial z}{\partial x}$ for $z = x^2 - 3xy + y^2$

113. $\frac{\partial z}{\partial y}$ for $z = x^2 - 3xy + y^2$

For the following exercises, calculate the sign of the partial derivative using the graph of the surface.

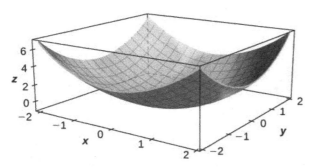

114. $f_x(1, 1)$

115. $f_x(-1, 1)$

116. $f_y(1, 1)$

117. $f_x(0, 0)$

For the following exercises, calculate the partial derivatives.

118. $\frac{\partial z}{\partial x}$ for $z = \sin(3x)\cos(3y)$

119. $\frac{\partial z}{\partial y}$ for $z = \sin(3x)\cos(3y)$

120. $\frac{\partial z}{\partial x}$ and $\frac{\partial z}{\partial y}$ for $z = x^8 e^{3y}$

121. $\frac{\partial z}{\partial x}$ and $\frac{\partial z}{\partial y}$ for $z = \ln(x^6 + y^4)$

122. Find $f_y(x, y)$ for $f(x, y) = e^{xy}\cos(x)\sin(y)$.

123. Let $z = e^{xy}$. Find $\frac{\partial z}{\partial x}$ and $\frac{\partial z}{\partial y}$.

124. Let $z = \ln\left(\frac{x}{y}\right)$. Find $\frac{\partial z}{\partial x}$ and $\frac{\partial z}{\partial y}$.

125. Let $z = \tan(2x - y)$. Find $\frac{\partial z}{\partial x}$ and $\frac{\partial z}{\partial y}$.

126. Let $z = \sinh(2x + 3y)$. Find $\frac{\partial z}{\partial x}$ and $\frac{\partial z}{\partial y}$.

127. Let $f(x, y) = \arctan\left(\frac{y}{x}\right)$. Evaluate $f_x(2, -2)$ and $f_y(2, -2)$.

128. Let $f(x, y) = \frac{xy}{x - y}$. Find $f_x(2, -2)$ and $f_y(2, -2)$.

Evaluate the partial derivatives at point $P(0, 1)$.

129. Find $\frac{\partial z}{\partial x}$ at $(0, 1)$ for $z = e^{-x}\cos(y)$.

130. Given $f(x, y, z) = x^3 yz^2$, find $\frac{\partial^2 f}{\partial x \partial y}$ and $f_z(1, 1, 1)$.

131. Given $f(x, y, z) = 2\sin(x + y)$, find $f_x\left(0, \frac{\pi}{2}, -4\right)$, $f_y\left(0, \frac{\pi}{2}, -4\right)$, and $f_z\left(0, \frac{\pi}{2}, -4\right)$.

132. The area of a parallelogram with adjacent side lengths that are $a$ and $b$, and in which the angle between these two sides is $\theta$, is given by the function $A(a, b, \theta) = ba\sin(\theta)$. Find the rate of change of the area of the parallelogram with respect to the following:
    a.  Side $a$
    b.  Side $b$
    c.  Angle $\theta$

133. Express the volume of a right circular cylinder as a function of two variables:
    a.  its radius $r$ and its height $h$.
    b.  Show that the rate of change of the volume of the cylinder with respect to its radius is the product of its circumference multiplied by its height.
    c.  Show that the rate of change of the volume of the cylinder with respect to its height is equal to the area of the circular base.

134. Calculate $\frac{\partial w}{\partial z}$ for $w = z\sin(xy^2 + 2z)$.

Find the indicated higher-order partial derivatives.

135. $f_{xy}$ for $z = \ln(x - y)$

136. $f_{yx}$ for $z = \ln(x - y)$

137. Let $z = x^2 + 3xy + 2y^2$. Find $\dfrac{\partial^2 z}{\partial x^2}$ and $\dfrac{\partial^2 z}{\partial y^2}$.

138. Given $z = e^x \tan y$, find $\dfrac{\partial^2 z}{\partial x \partial y}$ and $\dfrac{\partial^2 z}{\partial y \partial x}$.

139. Given $f(x, y, z) = xyz$, find $f_{xyy}$, $f_{yxy}$, and $f_{yyx}$.

140. Given $f(x, y, z) = e^{-2x} \sin(z^2 y)$, show that $f_{xyy} = f_{yxy}$.

141. Show that $z = \frac{1}{2}(e^y - e^{-y})\sin x$ is a solution of the differential equation $\dfrac{\partial^2 z}{\partial x^2} + \dfrac{\partial^2 z}{\partial y^2} = 0$.

142. Find $f_{xx}(x, y)$ for $f(x, y) = \dfrac{4x^2}{y} + \dfrac{y^2}{2x}$.

143. Let $f(x, y, z) = x^2 y^3 z - 3xy^2 z^3 + 5x^2 z - y^3 z$. Find $f_{xyz}$.

144. Let $F(x, y, z) = x^3 yz^2 - 2x^2 yz + 3xz - 2y^3 z$. Find $F_{xyz}$.

145. Given $f(x, y) = x^2 + x - 3xy + y^3 - 5$, find all points at which $f_x = f_y = 0$ simultaneously.

146. Given $f(x, y) = 2x^2 + 2xy + y^2 + 2x - 3$, find all points at which $\dfrac{\partial f}{\partial x} = 0$ and $\dfrac{\partial f}{\partial y} = 0$ simultaneously.

147. Given $f(x, y) = y^3 - 3yx^2 - 3y^2 - 3x^2 + 1$, find all points on $f$ at which $f_x = f_y = 0$ simultaneously.

148. Given $f(x, y) = 15x^3 - 3xy + 15y^3$, find all points at which $f_x(x, y) = f_y(x, y) = 0$ simultaneously.

149. Show that $z = e^x \sin y$ satisfies the equation $\dfrac{\partial^2 z}{\partial x^2} + \dfrac{\partial^2 z}{\partial y^2} = 0$.

150. Show that $f(x, y) = \ln(x^2 + y^2)$ solves Laplace's equation $\dfrac{\partial^2 z}{\partial x^2} + \dfrac{\partial^2 z}{\partial y^2} = 0$.

151. Show that $z = e^{-t} \cos(\frac{x}{c})$ satisfies the heat equation $\dfrac{\partial z}{\partial t} = -e^{-t} \cos(\frac{x}{c})$.

152. Find $\displaystyle\lim_{\Delta x \to 0} \dfrac{f(x + \Delta x) - f(x, y)}{\Delta x}$ for $f(x, y) = -7x - 2xy + 7y$.

153. Find $\displaystyle\lim_{\Delta y \to 0} \dfrac{f(x, y + \Delta y) - f(x, y)}{\Delta y}$ for $f(x, y) = -7x - 2xy + 7y$.

154. Find $\displaystyle\lim_{\Delta x \to 0} \dfrac{\Delta f}{\Delta x} = \lim_{\Delta x \to 0} \dfrac{f(x + \Delta x, y) - f(x, y)}{\Delta x}$ for $f(x, y) = x^2 y^2 + xy + y$.

155. Find $\displaystyle\lim_{\Delta x \to 0} \dfrac{\Delta f}{\Delta x} = \lim_{\Delta x \to 0} \dfrac{f(x + \Delta x, y) - f(x, y)}{\Delta x}$ for $f(x, y) = \sin(xy)$.

156. The function $P(T, V) = \dfrac{nRT}{V}$ gives the pressure at a point in a gas as a function of temperature $T$ and volume $V$. The letters $n$ and $R$ are constants. Find $\dfrac{\partial P}{\partial V}$ and $\dfrac{\partial P}{\partial T}$, and explain what these quantities represent.

157. The equation for heat flow in the $xy$-plane is $\dfrac{\partial f}{\partial t} = \dfrac{\partial^2 f}{\partial x^2} + \dfrac{\partial^2 f}{\partial y^2}$. Show that $f(x, y, t) = e^{-2t} \sin x \sin y$ is a solution.

158. The basic wave equation is $f_{tt} = f_{xx}$. Verify that $f(x, t) = \sin(x + t)$ and $f(x, t) = \sin(x - t)$ are solutions.

159. The law of cosines can be thought of as a function of three variables. Let $x$, $y$, and $\theta$ be two sides of any triangle where the angle $\theta$ is the included angle between the two sides. Then, $F(x, y, \theta) = x^2 + y^2 - 2xy \cos \theta$ gives the square of the third side of the triangle. Find $\dfrac{\partial F}{\partial \theta}$ and $\dfrac{\partial F}{\partial x}$ when $x = 2$, $y = 3$, and $\theta = \frac{\pi}{6}$.

160. Suppose the sides of a rectangle are changing with respect to time. The first side is changing at a rate of 2 in./sec whereas the second side is changing at the rate of 4 in/sec. How fast is the diagonal of the rectangle changing when the first side measures 16 in. and the second side measures 20 in.? (Round answer to three decimal places.)

161. A Cobb-Douglas production function is $f(x, y) = 200x^{0.7}y^{0.3}$, where $x$ and $y$ represent the amount of labor and capital available. Let $x = 500$ and $y = 1000$. Find $\frac{\delta f}{\delta x}$ and $\frac{\delta f}{\delta y}$ at these values, which represent the marginal productivity of labor and capital, respectively.

162. The apparent temperature index is a measure of how the temperature feels, and it is based on two variables: $h$, which is relative humidity, and $t$, which is the air temperature. $A = 0.885t - 22.4h + 1.20th - 0.544$. Find $\frac{\partial A}{\partial t}$ and $\frac{\partial A}{\partial h}$ when $t = 20°F$ and $h = 0.90$.

# 4.4 | Tangent Planes and Linear Approximations

## Learning Objectives

4.4.1  Determine the equation of a plane tangent to a given surface at a point.

4.4.2  Use the tangent plane to approximate a function of two variables at a point.

4.4.3  Explain when a function of two variables is differentiable.

4.4.4  Use the total differential to approximate the change in a function of two variables.

In this section, we consider the problem of finding the tangent plane to a surface, which is analogous to finding the equation of a tangent line to a curve when the curve is defined by the graph of a function of one variable, $y = f(x)$. The slope of the tangent line at the point $x = a$ is given by $m = f'(a)$; what is the slope of a tangent plane? We learned about the equation of a plane in Equations of Lines and Planes in Space; in this section, we see how it can be applied to the problem at hand.

## Tangent Planes

Intuitively, it seems clear that, in a plane, only one line can be tangent to a curve at a point. However, in three-dimensional space, many lines can be tangent to a given point. If these lines lie in the same plane, they determine the tangent plane at that point. A tangent plane at a regular point contains all of the lines tangent to that point. A more intuitive way to think of a tangent plane is to assume the surface is smooth at that point (no corners). Then, a tangent line to the surface at that point in any direction does not have any abrupt changes in slope because the direction changes smoothly.

### Definition

Let $P_0 = (x_0, y_0, z_0)$ be a point on a surface $S$, and let $C$ be any curve passing through $P_0$ and lying entirely in $S$. If the tangent lines to all such curves $C$ at $P_0$ lie in the same plane, then this plane is called the **tangent plane** to $S$ at $P_0$ (Figure 4.27).

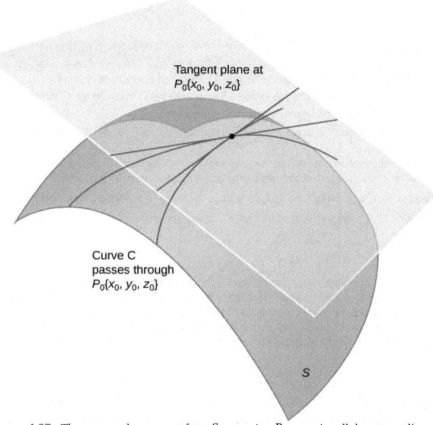

**Figure 4.27** The tangent plane to a surface $S$ at a point $P_0$ contains all the tangent lines to curves in $S$ that pass through $P_0$.

For a tangent plane to a surface to exist at a point on that surface, it is sufficient for the function that defines the surface to be differentiable at that point. We define the term tangent plane here and then explore the idea intuitively.

**Definition**

Let $S$ be a surface defined by a differentiable function $z = f(x, y)$, and let $P_0 = (x_0, y_0)$ be a point in the domain of $f$. Then, the equation of the tangent plane to $S$ at $P_0$ is given by

$$z = f(x_0, y_0) + f_x(x_0, y_0)(x - x_0) + f_y(x_0, y_0)(y - y_0). \tag{4.24}$$

To see why this formula is correct, let's first find two tangent lines to the surface $S$. The equation of the tangent line to the curve that is represented by the intersection of $S$ with the vertical trace given by $x = x_0$ is $z = f(x_0, y_0) + f_y(x_0, y_0)(y - y_0)$. Similarly, the equation of the tangent line to the curve that is represented by the intersection of $S$ with the vertical trace given by $y = y_0$ is $z = f(x_0, y_0) + f_x(x_0, y_0)(x - x_0)$. A parallel vector to the first tangent line is $\mathbf{a} = \mathbf{j} + f_y(x_0, y_0)\mathbf{k}$; a parallel vector to the second tangent line is $\mathbf{b} = \mathbf{i} + f_x(x_0, y_0)\mathbf{k}$. We can take the cross product of these two vectors:

$$\mathbf{a} \times \mathbf{b} = \left(\mathbf{j} + f_y(x_0, y_0)\mathbf{k}\right) \times \left(\mathbf{i} + f_x(x_0, y_0)\mathbf{k}\right)$$

$$= \begin{vmatrix} \mathbf{i} & \mathbf{j} & \mathbf{k} \\ 0 & 1 & f_y(x_0, y_0) \\ 1 & 0 & f_x(x_0, y_0) \end{vmatrix}$$

$$= f_x(x_0, y_0)\mathbf{i} + f_y(x_0, y_0)\mathbf{j} - \mathbf{k}.$$

This vector is perpendicular to both lines and is therefore perpendicular to the tangent plane. We can use this vector as a normal vector to the tangent plane, along with the point $P_0 = (x_0, y_0, f(x_0, y_0))$ in the equation for a plane:

$$\mathbf{n} \cdot \left((x - x_0)\mathbf{i} + (y - y_0)\mathbf{j} + (z - f(x_0, y_0))\mathbf{k}\right) = 0$$

$$\left(f_x(x_0, y_0)\mathbf{i} + f_y(x_0, y_0)\mathbf{j} - \mathbf{k}\right) \cdot \left((x - x_0)\mathbf{i} + (y - y_0)\mathbf{j} + (z - f(x_0, y_0))\mathbf{k}\right) = 0$$

$$f_x(x_0, y_0)(x - x_0) + f_y(x_0, y_0)(y - y_0) - (z - f(x_0, y_0)) = 0.$$

Solving this equation for $z$ gives Equation 4.24.

## Example 4.21

### Finding a Tangent Plane

Find the equation of the tangent plane to the surface defined by the function $f(x, y) = 2x^2 - 3xy + 8y^2 + 2x - 4y + 4$ at point $(2, -1)$.

### Solution

First, we must calculate $f_x(x, y)$ and $f_y(x, y)$, then use Equation 4.24 with $x_0 = 2$ and $y_0 = -1$:

$$\begin{aligned} f_x(x, y) &= 4x - 3y + 2 \\ f_y(x, y) &= -3x + 16y - 4 \\ f(2, -1) &= 2(2)^2 - 3(2)(-1) + 8(-1)^2 + 2(2) - 4(-1) + 4 = 34. \\ f_x(2, -1) &= 4(2) - 3(-1) + 2 = 13 \\ f_y(2, -1) &= -3(2) + 16(-1) - 4 = -26. \end{aligned}$$

Then Equation 4.24 becomes

$$\begin{aligned} z &= f(x_0, y_0) + f_x(x_0, y_0)(x - x_0) + f_y(x_0, y_0)(y - y_0) \\ z &= 34 + 13(x - 2) - 26(y - (-1)) \\ z &= 34 + 13x - 26 - 26y - 26 \\ z &= 13x - 26y - 18. \end{aligned}$$

(See the following figure).

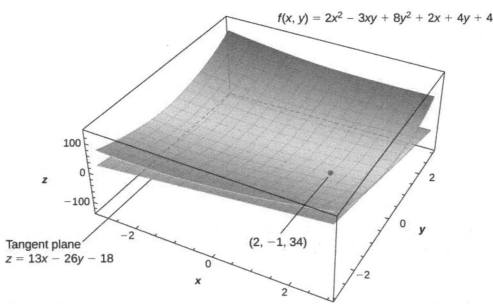

$f(x, y) = 2x^2 - 3xy + 8y^2 + 2x + 4y + 4$

Tangent plane
$z = 13x - 26y - 18$

$(2, -1, 34)$

**Figure 4.28** Calculating the equation of a tangent plane to a given surface at a given point.

 **4.19** Find the equation of the tangent plane to the surface defined by the function $f(x, y) = x^3 - x^2 y + y^2 - 2x + 3y - 2$ at point $(-1, 3)$.

## Example 4.22

### Finding Another Tangent Plane

Find the equation of the tangent plane to the surface defined by the function $f(x, y) = \sin(2x)\cos(3y)$ at the point $(\pi/3, \pi/4)$.

### Solution

First, calculate $f_x(x, y)$ and $f_y(x, y)$, then use **Equation 4.24** with $x_0 = \pi/3$ and $y_0 = \pi/4$:

$$f_x(x, y) = 2\cos(2x)\cos(3y)$$
$$f_y(x, y) = -3\sin(2x)\sin(3y)$$
$$f\left(\frac{\pi}{3}, \frac{\pi}{4}\right) = \sin\left(2\left(\frac{\pi}{3}\right)\right)\cos\left(3\left(\frac{\pi}{4}\right)\right) = \left(\frac{\sqrt{3}}{2}\right)\left(-\frac{\sqrt{2}}{2}\right) = -\frac{\sqrt{6}}{4}$$
$$f_x\left(\frac{\pi}{3}, \frac{\pi}{4}\right) = 2\cos\left(2\left(\frac{\pi}{3}\right)\right)\cos\left(3\left(\frac{\pi}{4}\right)\right) = 2\left(-\frac{1}{2}\right)\left(-\frac{\sqrt{2}}{2}\right) = \frac{\sqrt{2}}{2}$$
$$f_y\left(\frac{\pi}{3}, \frac{\pi}{4}\right) = -3\sin\left(2\left(\frac{\pi}{3}\right)\right)\sin\left(3\left(\frac{\pi}{4}\right)\right) = -3\left(\frac{\sqrt{3}}{2}\right)\left(\frac{\sqrt{2}}{2}\right) = -\frac{3\sqrt{6}}{4}.$$

Then **Equation 4.24** becomes

$$z = f(x_0, y_0) + f_x(x_0, y_0)(x - x_0) + f_y(x_0, y_0)(y - y_0)$$
$$z = -\frac{\sqrt{6}}{4} + \frac{\sqrt{2}}{2}\left(x - \frac{\pi}{3}\right) - \frac{3\sqrt{6}}{4}\left(y - \frac{\pi}{4}\right)$$
$$z = \frac{\sqrt{2}}{2}x - \frac{3\sqrt{6}}{4}y - \frac{\sqrt{6}}{4} - \frac{\pi\sqrt{2}}{6} + \frac{3\pi\sqrt{6}}{16}.$$

A tangent plane to a surface does not always exist at every point on the surface. Consider the function

$$f(x, y) = \begin{cases} \dfrac{xy}{\sqrt{x^2 + y^2}} & (x, y) \neq (0, 0) \\ 0 & (x, y) = (0, 0). \end{cases}$$

The graph of this function follows.

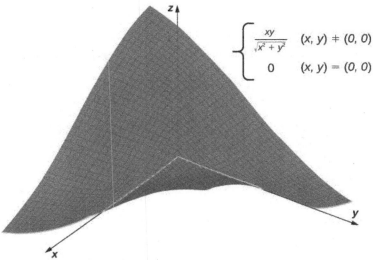

**Figure 4.29** Graph of a function that does not have a tangent plane at the origin.

If either $x = 0$ or $y = 0$, then $f(x, y) = 0$, so the value of the function does not change on either the $x$- or $y$-axis. Therefore, $f_x(x, 0) = f_y(0, y) = 0$, so as either $x$ or $y$ approach zero, these partial derivatives stay equal to zero. Substituting them into **Equation 4.24** gives $z = 0$ as the equation of the tangent line. However, if we approach the origin from a different direction, we get a different story. For example, suppose we approach the origin along the line $y = x$. If we put $y = x$ into the original function, it becomes

$$f(x, x) = \frac{x(x)}{\sqrt{x^2 + (x)^2}} = \frac{x^2}{\sqrt{2x^2}} = \frac{|x|}{\sqrt{2}}.$$

When $x > 0$, the slope of this curve is equal to $\sqrt{2}/2$; when $x < 0$, the slope of this curve is equal to $-(\sqrt{2}/2)$. This presents a problem. In the definition of *tangent plane*, we presumed that all tangent lines through point $P$ (in this case, the origin) lay in the same plane. This is clearly not the case here. When we study differentiable functions, we will see that this function is not differentiable at the origin.

## Linear Approximations

Recall from **Linear Approximations and Differentials** (http://cnx.org/content/m53605/latest/) that the formula for the linear approximation of a function $f(x)$ at the point $x = a$ is given by

$$y \approx f(a) + f'(a)(x - a).$$

The diagram for the linear approximation of a function of one variable appears in the following graph.

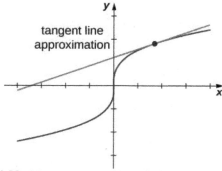

**Figure 4.30** Linear approximation of a function in one variable.

The tangent line can be used as an approximation to the function $f(x)$ for values of $x$ reasonably close to $x = a$. When working with a function of two variables, the tangent line is replaced by a tangent plane, but the approximation idea is much the same.

**Definition**

Given a function $z = f(x, y)$ with continuous partial derivatives that exist at the point $(x_0, y_0)$, the **linear approximation** of $f$ at the point $(x_0, y_0)$ is given by the equation

$$L(x, y) = f(x_0, y_0) + f_x(x_0, y_0)(x - x_0) + f_y(x_0, y_0)(y - y_0). \tag{4.25}$$

Notice that this equation also represents the tangent plane to the surface defined by $z = f(x, y)$ at the point $(x_0, y_0)$. The idea behind using a linear approximation is that, if there is a point $(x_0, y_0)$ at which the precise value of $f(x, y)$ is known, then for values of $(x, y)$ reasonably close to $(x_0, y_0)$, the linear approximation (i.e., tangent plane) yields a value that is also reasonably close to the exact value of $f(x, y)$ (**Figure 4.31**). Furthermore the plane that is used to find the linear approximation is also the tangent plane to the surface at the point $(x_0, y_0)$.

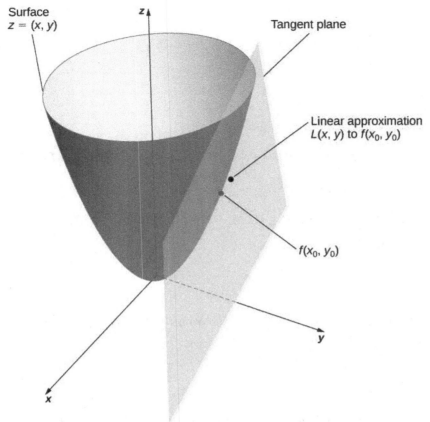

**Figure 4.31** Using a tangent plane for linear approximation at a point.

## Example 4.23

### Using a Tangent Plane Approximation

Given the function $f(x, y) = \sqrt{41 - 4x^2 - y^2}$, approximate $f(2.1, 2.9)$ using point $(2, 3)$ for $(x_0, y_0)$. What is the approximate value of $f(2.1, 2.9)$ to four decimal places?

### Solution

To apply **Equation 4.25**, we first must calculate $f(x_0, y_0)$, $f_x(x_0, y_0)$, and $f_y(x_0, y_0)$ using $x_0 = 2$ and $y_0 = 3$:

$$
\begin{aligned}
f(x_0, y_0) &= f(2, 3) = \sqrt{41 - 4(2)^2 - (3)^2} = \sqrt{41 - 16 - 9} = \sqrt{16} = 4 \\
f_x(x, y) &= -\frac{4x}{\sqrt{41 - 4x^2 - y^2}} \text{ so } f_x(x_0, y_0) = -\frac{4(2)}{\sqrt{41 - 4(2)^2 - (3)^2}} = -2 \\
f_y(x, y) &= -\frac{y}{\sqrt{41 - 4x^2 - y^2}} \text{ so } f_y(x_0, y_0) = -\frac{3}{\sqrt{41 - 4(2)^2 - (3)^2}} = -\frac{3}{4}.
\end{aligned}
$$

Now we substitute these values into **Equation 4.25**:

$$L(x, y) = f(x_0, y_0) + f_x(x_0, y_0)(x - x_0) + f_y(x_0, y_0)(y - y_0)$$
$$= 4 - 2(x - 2) - \frac{3}{4}(y - 3)$$
$$= \frac{41}{4} - 2x - \frac{3}{4}y.$$

Last, we substitute $x = 2.1$ and $y = 2.9$ into $L(x, y)$:

$$L(2.1, 2.9) = \frac{41}{4} - 2(2.1) - \frac{3}{4}(2.9) = 10.25 - 4.2 - 2.175 = 3.875.$$

The approximate value of $f(2.1, 2.9)$ to four decimal places is

$$f(2.1, 2.9) = \sqrt{41 - 4(2.1)^2 - (2.9)^2} = \sqrt{14.95} \approx 3.8665,$$

which corresponds to a $0.2\%$ error in approximation.

 **4.20** Given the function $f(x, y) = e^{5 - 2x + 3y}$, approximate $f(4.1, 0.9)$ using point $(4, 1)$ for $(x_0, y_0)$. What is the approximate value of $f(4.1, 0.9)$ to four decimal places?

## Differentiability

When working with a function $y = f(x)$ of one variable, the function is said to be differentiable at a point $x = a$ if $f'(a)$ exists. Furthermore, if a function of one variable is differentiable at a point, the graph is "smooth" at that point (i.e., no corners exist) and a tangent line is well-defined at that point.

The idea behind differentiability of a function of two variables is connected to the idea of smoothness at that point. In this case, a surface is considered to be smooth at point $P$ if a tangent plane to the surface exists at that point. If a function is differentiable at a point, then a tangent plane to the surface exists at that point. Recall the formula for a tangent plane at a point $(x_0, y_0)$ is given by

$$z = f(x_0, y_0) + f_x(x_0, y_0)(x - x_0) + f_y(x_0, y_0)(y - y_0),$$

For a tangent plane to exist at the point $(x_0, y_0)$, the partial derivatives must therefore exist at that point. However, this is not a sufficient condition for smoothness, as was illustrated in Figure 4.29. In that case, the partial derivatives existed at the origin, but the function also had a corner on the graph at the origin.

### Definition

A function $f(x, y)$ is **differentiable** at a point $P(x_0, y_0)$ if, for all points $(x, y)$ in a $\delta$ disk around $P$, we can write

$$f(x, y) = f(x_0, y_0) + f_x(x_0, y_0)(x - x_0) + f_y(x_0, y_0)(y - y_0) + E(x, y), \tag{4.26}$$

where the error term $E$ satisfies

$$\lim_{(x, y) \to (x_0, y_0)} \frac{E(x, y)}{\sqrt{(x - x_0)^2 + (y - y_0)^2}} = 0.$$

The last term in Equation 4.26 is referred to as the *error term* and it represents how closely the tangent plane comes to the surface in a small neighborhood ($\delta$ disk) of point $P$. For the function $f$ to be differentiable at $P$, the function must be smooth—that is, the graph of $f$ must be close to the tangent plane for points near $P$.

## Example 4.24

### Demonstrating Differentiability

Show that the function $f(x, y) = 2x^2 - 4y$ is differentiable at point $(2, -3)$.

### Solution

First, we calculate $f(x_0, y_0)$, $f_x(x_0, y_0)$, and $f_y(x_0, y_0)$ using $x_0 = 2$ and $y_0 = -3$, then we use **Equation 4.26**:

$$f(2, -3) = 2(2)^2 - 4(-3) = 8 + 12 = 20$$
$$f_x(2, -3) = 4(2) = 8$$
$$f_y(2, -3) = -4.$$

Therefore $m_1 = 8$ and $m_2 = -4$, and **Equation 4.26** becomes

$$f(x, y) = f(2, -3) + f_x(2, -3)(x - 2) + f_y(2, -3)(y + 3) + E(x, y)$$
$$2x^2 - 4y = 20 + 8(x - 2) - 4(y + 3) + E(x, y)$$
$$2x^2 - 4y = 20 + 8x - 16 - 4y - 12 + E(x, y)$$
$$2x^2 - 4y = 8x - 4y - 8 + E(x, y)$$
$$E(x, y) = 2x^2 - 8x + 8.$$

Next, we calculate $\lim\limits_{(x, y) \to (x_0, y_0)} \dfrac{E(x, y)}{\sqrt{(x - x_0)^2 + (y - y_0)^2}}$:

$$\lim_{(x, y) \to (x_0, y_0)} \frac{E(x, y)}{\sqrt{(x - x_0)^2 + (y - y_0)^2}} = \lim_{(x, y) \to (2, -3)} \frac{2x^2 - 8x + 8}{\sqrt{(x - 2)^2 + (y + 3)^2}}$$

$$= \lim_{(x, y) \to (2, -3)} \frac{2(x^2 - 4x + 4)}{\sqrt{(x - 2)^2 + (y + 3)^2}}$$

$$= \lim_{(x, y) \to (2, -3)} \frac{2(x - 2)^2}{\sqrt{(x - 2)^2 + (y + 3)^2}}$$

$$\leq \lim_{(x, y) \to (2, -3)} \frac{2\left((x - 2)^2 + (y + 3)^2\right)}{\sqrt{(x - 2)^2 + (y + 3)^2}}$$

$$= \lim_{(x, y) \to (2, -3)} 2\sqrt{(x - 2)^2 + (y + 3)^2}$$

$$= 0.$$

Since $E(x, y) \geq 0$ for any value of $x$ or $y$, the original limit must be equal to zero. Therefore, $f(x, y) = 2x^2 - 4y$ is differentiable at point $(2, -3)$.

 **4.21** Show that the function $f(x, y) = 3x - 4y^2$ is differentiable at point $(-1, 2)$.

The function $f(x, y) = \begin{cases} \dfrac{xy}{\sqrt{x^2 + y^2}} & (x, y) \neq (0, 0) \\ 0 & (x, y) = (0, 0) \end{cases}$ is not differentiable at the origin. We can see this by calculating the partial derivatives. This function appeared earlier in the section, where we showed that $f_x(0, 0) = f_y(0, 0) = 0$.

Substituting this information into **Equation 4.26** using $x_0 = 0$ and $y_0 = 0$, we get

$$\begin{aligned} f(x, y) &= f(0, 0) + f_x(0, 0)(x - 0) + f_y(0, 0)(y - 0) + E(x, y) \\ E(x, y) &= \frac{xy}{\sqrt{x^2 + y^2}}. \end{aligned}$$

Calculating $\displaystyle\lim_{(x, y) \to (x_0, y_0)} \frac{E(x, y)}{\sqrt{(x - x_0)^2 + (y - y_0)^2}}$ gives

$$\lim_{(x, y) \to (x_0, y_0)} \frac{E(x, y)}{\sqrt{(x - x_0)^2 + (y - y_0)^2}} = \lim_{(x, y) \to (0, 0)} \frac{\frac{xy}{\sqrt{x^2 + y^2}}}{\sqrt{x^2 + y^2}}$$

$$= \lim_{(x, y) \to (0, 0)} \frac{xy}{x^2 + y^2}.$$

Depending on the path taken toward the origin, this limit takes different values. Therefore, the limit does not exist and the function $f$ is not differentiable at the origin as shown in the following figure.

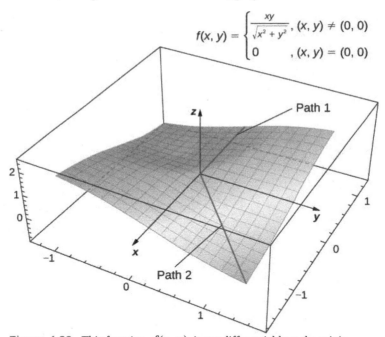

**Figure 4.32** This function $f(x, y)$ is not differentiable at the origin.

Differentiability and continuity for functions of two or more variables are connected, the same as for functions of one variable. In fact, with some adjustments of notation, the basic theorem is the same.

### Theorem 4.6: Differentiability Implies Continuity

Let $z = f(x, y)$ be a function of two variables with $(x_0, y_0)$ in the domain of $f$. If $f(x, y)$ is differentiable at $(x_0, y_0)$, then $f(x, y)$ is continuous at $(x_0, y_0)$.

**Differentiability Implies Continuity** shows that if a function is differentiable at a point, then it is continuous there. However, if a function is continuous at a point, then it is not necessarily differentiable at that point. For example,

$$f(x, y) = \begin{cases} \dfrac{xy}{\sqrt{x^2 + y^2}} & (x, y) \neq (0, 0) \\ 0 & (x, y) = (0, 0) \end{cases}$$

is continuous at the origin, but it is not differentiable at the origin. This observation is also similar to the situation in single-variable calculus.

**Continuity of First Partials Implies Differentiability** further explores the connection between continuity and differentiability at a point. This theorem says that if the function and its partial derivatives are continuous at a point, the function is differentiable.

---

**Theorem 4.7: Continuity of First Partials Implies Differentiability**

Let $z = f(x, y)$ be a function of two variables with $(x_0, y_0)$ in the domain of $f$. If $f(x, y)$, $f_x(x, y)$, and $f_y(x, y)$ all exist in a neighborhood of $(x_0, y_0)$ and are continuous at $(x_0, y_0)$, then $f(x, y)$ is differentiable there.

---

Recall that earlier we showed that the function

$$f(x, y) = \begin{cases} \dfrac{xy}{\sqrt{x^2 + y^2}} & (x, y) \neq (0, 0) \\ 0 & (x, y) = (0, 0) \end{cases}$$

was not differentiable at the origin. Let's calculate the partial derivatives $f_x$ and $f_y$:

$$\frac{\partial f}{\partial x} = \frac{y^3}{\left(x^2 + y^2\right)^{3/2}} \quad \text{and} \quad \frac{\partial f}{\partial y} = \frac{x^3}{\left(x^2 + y^2\right)^{3/2}}.$$

The contrapositive of the preceding theorem states that if a function is not differentiable, then at least one of the hypotheses must be false. Let's explore the condition that $f_x(0, 0)$ must be continuous. For this to be true, it must be true that $\lim\limits_{(x, y) \to (0, 0)} f_x(0, 0) = f_x(0, 0)$:

$$\lim_{(x, y) \to (0, 0)} f_x(x, y) = \lim_{(x, y) \to (0, 0)} \frac{y^3}{\left(x^2 + y^2\right)^{3/2}}.$$

Let $x = ky$. Then

$$\lim_{(x, y) \to (0, 0)} \frac{y^3}{\left(x^2 + y^2\right)^{3/2}} = \lim_{y \to 0} \frac{y^3}{\left((ky)^2 + y^2\right)^{3/2}}$$

$$= \lim_{y \to 0} \frac{y^3}{\left(k^2 y^2 + y^2\right)^{3/2}}$$

$$= \lim_{y \to 0} \frac{y^3}{|y|^3 \left(k^2 + 1\right)^{3/2}}$$

$$= \frac{1}{\left(k^2 + 1\right)^{3/2}} \lim_{y \to 0} \frac{|y|}{y}.$$

If $y > 0$, then this expression equals $1/\left(k^2 + 1\right)^{3/2}$; if $y < 0$, then it equals $-\left(1/\left(k^2 + 1\right)^{3/2}\right)$. In either case, the value depends on $k$, so the limit fails to exist.

## Differentials

In **Linear Approximations and Differentials (http://cnx.org/content/m53605/latest/)** we first studied the concept of differentials. The differential of $y$, written $dy$, is defined as $f'(x)dx$. The differential is used to approximate $\Delta y = f(x + \Delta x) - f(x)$, where $\Delta x = dx$. Extending this idea to the linear approximation of a function of two variables at the point $(x_0, y_0)$ yields the formula for the total differential for a function of two variables.

---

**Definition**

Let $z = f(x, y)$ be a function of two variables with $(x_0, y_0)$ in the domain of $f$, and let $\Delta x$ and $\Delta y$ be chosen so that $(x_0 + \Delta x, y_0 + \Delta y)$ is also in the domain of $f$. If $f$ is differentiable at the point $(x_0, y_0)$, then the differentials $dx$ and $dy$ are defined as

$$dx = \Delta x \text{ and } dy = \Delta y.$$

The differential $dz$, also called the **total differential** of $z = f(x, y)$ at $(x_0, y_0)$, is defined as

$$dz = f_x(x_0, y_0)dx + f_y(x_0, y_0)dy. \tag{4.27}$$

---

Notice that the symbol $\partial$ is not used to denote the total differential; rather, $d$ appears in front of $z$. Now, let's define $\Delta z = f(x + \Delta x, y + \Delta y) - f(x, y)$. We use $dz$ to approximate $\Delta z$, so

$$\Delta z \approx dz = f_x(x_0, y_0)dx + f_y(x_0, y_0)dy.$$

Therefore, the differential is used to approximate the change in the function $z = f(x_0, y_0)$ at the point $(x_0, y_0)$ for given values of $\Delta x$ and $\Delta y$. Since $\Delta z = f(x + \Delta x, y + \Delta y) - f(x, y)$, this can be used further to approximate $f(x + \Delta x, y + \Delta y)$:

$$
\begin{aligned}
f(x + \Delta x, y + \Delta y) &= f(x, y) + \Delta z \\
&\approx f(x, y) + f_x(x_0, y_0)\Delta x + f_y(x_0, y_0)\Delta y.
\end{aligned}
$$

See the following figure.

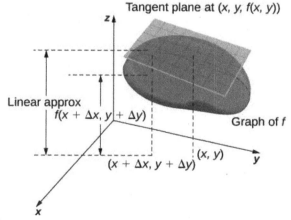

**Figure 4.33** The linear approximation is calculated via the formula
$$f(x + \Delta x, y + \Delta y) \approx f(x, y) + f_x(x_0, y_0)\Delta x + f_y(x_0, y_0)\Delta y.$$

One such application of this idea is to determine error propagation. For example, if we are manufacturing a gadget and are off by a certain amount in measuring a given quantity, the differential can be used to estimate the error in the total volume of the gadget.

## Example 4.25

### Approximation by Differentials

Find the differential $dz$ of the function $f(x, y) = 3x^2 - 2xy + y^2$ and use it to approximate $\Delta z$ at point $(2, -3)$. Use $\Delta x = 0.1$ and $\Delta y = -0.05$. What is the exact value of $\Delta z$?

### Solution

First, we must calculate $f(x_0, y_0)$, $f_x(x_0, y_0)$, and $f_y(x_0, y_0)$ using $x_0 = 2$ and $y_0 = -3$:

$$
\begin{aligned}
f(x_0, y_0) &= f(2, -3) = 3(2)^2 - 2(2)(-3) + (-3)^2 = 12 + 12 + 9 = 33 \\
f_x(x, y) &= 6x - 2y \\
f_y(x, y) &= -2x + 2y \\
f_x(x_0, y_0) &= f_x(2, -3) = 6(2) - 2(-3) = 12 + 6 = 18 \\
f_y(x_0, y_0) &= f_y(2, -3) = -2(2) + 2(-3) = -4 - 6 = -10.
\end{aligned}
$$

Then, we substitute these quantities into Equation 4.27:

$$
\begin{aligned}
dz &= f_x(x_0, y_0)dx + f_y(x_0, y_0)dy \\
dz &= 18(0.1) - 10(-0.05) = 1.8 + 0.5 = 2.3.
\end{aligned}
$$

This is the approximation to $\Delta z = f(x_0 + \Delta x, y_0 + \Delta y) - f(x_0, y_0)$. The exact value of $\Delta z$ is given by

$$
\begin{aligned}
\Delta z &= f(x_0 + \Delta x, y_0 + \Delta y) - f(x_0, y_0) \\
&= f(2 + 0.1, -3 - 0.05) - f(2, -3) \\
&= f(2.1, -3.05) - f(2, -3) \\
&= 2.3425.
\end{aligned}
$$

 **4.22** Find the differential $dz$ of the function $f(x, y) = 4y^2 + x^2 y - 2xy$ and use it to approximate $\Delta z$ at point $(1, -1)$. Use $\Delta x = 0.03$ and $\Delta y = -0.02$. What is the exact value of $\Delta z$?

## Differentiability of a Function of Three Variables

All of the preceding results for differentiability of functions of two variables can be generalized to functions of three variables. First, the definition:

### Definition

A function $f(x, y, z)$ is differentiable at a point $P(x_0, y_0, z_0)$ if for all points $(x, y, z)$ in a $\delta$ disk around $P$ we can write

$$
\begin{aligned}
f(x, y) &= f(x_0, y_0, z_0) + f_x(x_0, y_0, z_0)(x - x_0) + f_y(x_0, y_0, z_0)(y - y_0) \\
&\quad + f_z(x_0, y_0, z_0)(z - z_0) + E(x, y, z),
\end{aligned}
\tag{4.28}
$$

where the error term $E$ satisfies

$$\lim_{(x,\, y,\, z) \to (x_0,\, y_0,\, z_0)} \frac{E(x,\, y,\, z)}{\sqrt{(x - x_0)^2 + (y - y_0)^2 + (z - z_0)^2}} = 0.$$

If a function of three variables is differentiable at a point $(x_0,\, y_0,\, z_0),$ then it is continuous there. Furthermore, continuity of first partial derivatives at that point guarantees differentiability.

# 4.4 EXERCISES

For the following exercises, find a unit normal vector to the surface at the indicated point.

163. $f(x, y) = x^3$, $(2, -1, 8)$

164. $\ln\left(\frac{x}{y-z}\right) = 0$ when $x = y = 1$

For the following exercises, as a useful review for techniques used in this section, find a normal vector and a tangent vector at point $P$.

165. $x^2 + xy + y^2 = 3$, $P(-1, -1)$

166. $\left(x^2 + y^2\right)^2 = 9\left(x^2 - y^2\right)$, $P(\sqrt{2}, 1)$

167. $xy^2 - 2x^2 + y + 5x = 6$, $P(4, 2)$

168. $2x^3 - x^2 y^2 = 3x - y - 7$, $P(1, -2)$

169. $ze^{x^2 - y^2} - 3 = 0$, $P(2, 2, 3)$

For the following exercises, find the equation for the tangent plane to the surface at the indicated point. (*Hint:* Solve for $z$ in terms of $x$ and $y$.)

170. $-8x - 3y - 7z = -19$, $P(1, -1, 2)$

171. $z = -9x^2 - 3y^2$, $P(2, 1, -39)$

172. $x^2 + 10xyz + y^2 + 8z^2 = 0$, $P(-1, -1, -1)$

173. $z = \ln(10x^2 + 2y^2 + 1)$, $P(0, 0, 0)$

174. $z = e^{7x^2 + 4y^2}$, $P(0, 0, 1)$

175. $xy + yz + zx = 11$, $P(1, 2, 3)$

176. $x^2 + 4y^2 = z^2$, $P(3, 2, 5)$

177. $x^3 + y^3 = 3xyz$, $P\left(1, 2, \frac{3}{2}\right)$

178. $z = axy$, $P\left(1, \frac{1}{a}, 1\right)$

179. $z = \sin x + \sin y + \sin(x + y)$, $P(0, 0, 0)$

180. $h(x, y) = \ln\sqrt{x^2 + y^2}$, $P(3, 4)$

181. $z = x^2 - 2xy + y^2$, $P(1, 2, 1)$

For the following exercises, find parametric equations for the normal line to the surface at the indicated point. (Recall that to find the equation of a line in space, you need a point on the line, $P_0(x_0, y_0, z_0)$, and a vector $\mathbf{n} = \langle a, b, c \rangle$ that is parallel to the line. Then the equation of the line is $x - x_0 = at$, $y - y_0 = bt$, $z - z_0 = ct$.)

182. $-3x + 9y + 4z = -4$, $P(1, -1, 2)$

183. $z = 5x^2 - 2y^2$, $P(2, 1, 18)$

184. $x^2 - 8xyz + y^2 + 6z^2 = 0$, $P(1, 1, 1)$

185. $z = \ln\left(3x^2 + 7y^2 + 1\right)$, $P(0, 0, 0)$

186. $z = e^{4x^2 + 6y^2}$, $P(0, 0, 1)$

187. $z = x^2 - 2xy + y^2$ at point $P(1, 2, 1)$

For the following exercises, use the figure shown here.

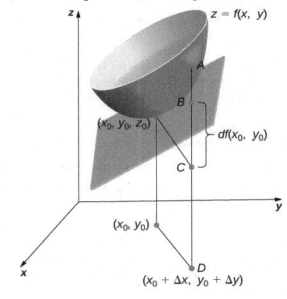

188. The length of line segment $AC$ is equal to what mathematical expression?

189. The length of line segment $BC$ is equal to what mathematical expression?

190. Using the figure, explain what the length of line segment $AB$ represents.

For the following exercises, complete each task.

**191.** Show that $f(x, y) = e^{xy}x$ is differentiable at point $(1, 0)$.

**192.** Find the total differential of the function $w = e^y \cos(x) + z^2$.

**193.** Show that $f(x, y) = x^2 + 3y$ is differentiable at every point. In other words, show that $\Delta z = f(x + \Delta x, y + \Delta y) - f(x, y) = f_x \Delta x + f_y \Delta y + \varepsilon_1 \Delta x + \varepsilon_2 \Delta y$, where both $\varepsilon_1$ and $\varepsilon_2$ approach zero as $(\Delta x, \Delta y)$ approaches $(0, 0)$.

**194.** Find the total differential of the function $z = \dfrac{xy}{y + x}$ where $x$ changes from $10$ to $10.5$ and $y$ changes from $15$ to $13$.

**195.** Let $z = f(x, y) = xe^y$. Compute $\Delta z$ from $P(1, 2)$ to $Q(1.05, 2.1)$ and then find the approximate change in $z$ from point $P$ to point $Q$. Recall $\Delta z = f(x + \Delta x, y + \Delta y) - f(x, y)$, and $dz$ and $\Delta z$ are approximately equal.

**196.** The volume of a right circular cylinder is given by $V(r, h) = \pi r^2 h$. Find the differential $dV$. Interpret the formula geometrically.

**197.** See the preceding problem. Use differentials to estimate the amount of aluminum in an enclosed aluminum can with diameter $8.0\,\text{cm}$ and height $12\,\text{cm}$ if the aluminum is $0.04$ cm thick.

**198.** Use the differential $dz$ to approximate the change in $z = \sqrt{4 - x^2 - y^2}$ as $(x, y)$ moves from point $(1, 1)$ to point $(1.01, 0.97)$. Compare this approximation with the actual change in the function.

**199.** Let $z = f(x, y) = x^2 + 3xy - y^2$. Find the exact change in the function and the approximate change in the function as $x$ changes from $2.00$ to $2.05$ and $y$ changes from $3.00$ to $2.96$.

**200.** The centripetal acceleration of a particle moving in a circle is given by $a(r, v) = \dfrac{v^2}{r}$, where $v$ is the velocity and $r$ is the radius of the circle. Approximate the maximum percent error in measuring the acceleration resulting from errors of $3\%$ in $v$ and $2\%$ in $r$. (Recall that the percentage error is the ratio of the amount of error over the original amount. So, in this case, the percentage error in $a$ is given by $\dfrac{da}{a}$.)

**201.** The radius $r$ and height $h$ of a right circular cylinder are measured with possible errors of $4\%$ and $5\%$, respectively. Approximate the maximum possible percentage error in measuring the volume (Recall that the percentage error is the ratio of the amount of error over the original amount. So, in this case, the percentage error in $V$ is given by $\dfrac{dV}{V}$.)

**202.** The base radius and height of a right circular cone are measured as $10$ in. and $25$ in., respectively, with a possible error in measurement of as much as $0.1$ in. each. Use differentials to estimate the maximum error in the calculated volume of the cone.

**203.** The electrical resistance $R$ produced by wiring resistors $R_1$ and $R_2$ in parallel can be calculated from the formula $\dfrac{1}{R} = \dfrac{1}{R_1} + \dfrac{1}{R_2}$. If $R_1$ and $R_2$ are measured to be $7\Omega$ and $6\Omega$, respectively, and if these measurements are accurate to within $0.05\Omega$, estimate the maximum possible error in computing $R$. (The symbol $\Omega$ represents an ohm, the unit of electrical resistance.)

**204.** The area of an ellipse with axes of length $2a$ and $2b$ is given by the formula $A = \pi ab$. Approximate the percent change in the area when $a$ increases by $2\%$ and $b$ increases by $1.5\%$.

**205.** The period $T$ of a simple pendulum with small oscillations is calculated from the formula $T = 2\pi\sqrt{\dfrac{L}{g}}$, where $L$ is the length of the pendulum and $g$ is the acceleration resulting from gravity. Suppose that $L$ and $g$ have errors of, at most, $0.5\%$ and $0.1\%$, respectively. Use differentials to approximate the maximum percentage error in the calculated value of $T$.

206. Electrical power $P$ is given by $P = \dfrac{V^2}{R}$, where $V$ is the voltage and $R$ is the resistance. Approximate the maximum percentage error in calculating power if $120$ $V$ is applied to a $2000 - \Omega$ resistor and the possible percent errors in measuring $V$ and $R$ are $3\%$ and $4\%$, respectively.

For the following exercises, find the linear approximation of each function at the indicated point.

207. $f(x, y) = x\sqrt{y}, \quad P(1, 4)$

208. $f(x, y) = e^x \cos y; \, P(0, 0)$

209. $f(x, y) = \arctan(x + 2y), \, P(1, 0)$

210. $f(x, y) = \sqrt{20 - x^2 - 7y^2}, \quad P(2, 1)$

211. $f(x, y, z) = \sqrt{x^2 + y^2 + z^2}, \quad P(3, 2, 6)$

212. **[T]** Find the equation of the tangent plane to the surface $f(x, y) = x^2 + y^2$ at point $(1, 2, 5),$ and graph the surface and the tangent plane at the point.

213. **[T]** Find the equation for the tangent plane to the surface at the indicated point, and graph the surface and the tangent plane: $z = \ln(10x^2 + 2y^2 + 1), \, P(0, 0, 0).$

214. **[T]** Find the equation of the tangent plane to the surface $z = f(x, y) = \sin(x + y^2)$ at point $\left(\dfrac{\pi}{4}, 0, \dfrac{\sqrt{2}}{2}\right),$ and graph the surface and the tangent plane.

# 4.5 | The Chain Rule

| Learning Objectives |
|---|
| **4.5.1** State the chain rules for one or two independent variables. |
| **4.5.2** Use tree diagrams as an aid to understanding the chain rule for several independent and intermediate variables. |
| **4.5.3** Perform implicit differentiation of a function of two or more variables. |

In single-variable calculus, we found that one of the most useful differentiation rules is the chain rule, which allows us to find the derivative of the composition of two functions. The same thing is true for multivariable calculus, but this time we have to deal with more than one form of the chain rule. In this section, we study extensions of the chain rule and learn how to take derivatives of compositions of functions of more than one variable.

## Chain Rules for One or Two Independent Variables

Recall that the chain rule for the derivative of a composite of two functions can be written in the form

$$\frac{d}{dx}(f(g(x))) = f'(g(x))g'(x).$$

In this equation, both $f(x)$ and $g(x)$ are functions of one variable. Now suppose that $f$ is a function of two variables and $g$ is a function of one variable. Or perhaps they are both functions of two variables, or even more. How would we calculate the derivative in these cases? The following theorem gives us the answer for the case of one independent variable.

---

**Theorem 4.8: Chain Rule for One Independent Variable**

Suppose that $x = g(t)$ and $y = h(t)$ are differentiable functions of $t$ and $z = f(x, y)$ is a differentiable function of $x$ and $y$. Then $z = f(x(t), y(t))$ is a differentiable function of $t$ and

$$\frac{dz}{dt} = \frac{\partial z}{\partial x} \cdot \frac{dx}{dt} + \frac{\partial z}{\partial y} \cdot \frac{dy}{dt}, \tag{4.29}$$

where the ordinary derivatives are evaluated at $t$ and the partial derivatives are evaluated at $(x, y)$.

---

### Proof

The proof of this theorem uses the definition of differentiability of a function of two variables. Suppose that $f$ is differentiable at the point $P(x_0, y_0)$, where $x_0 = g(t_0)$ and $y_0 = h(t_0)$ for a fixed value of $t_0$. We wish to prove that $z = f(x(t), y(t))$ is differentiable at $t = t_0$ and that Equation 4.29 holds at that point as well.

Since $f$ is differentiable at $P$, we know that

$$z(t) = f(x, y) = f(x_0, y_0) + f_x(x_0, y_0)(x - x_0) + f_y(x_0, y_0)(y - y_0) + E(x, y), \tag{4.30}$$

where $\displaystyle \lim_{(x, y) \to (x_0, y_0)} \frac{E(x, y)}{\sqrt{(x - x_0)^2 + (y - y_0)^2}} = 0$. We then subtract $z_0 = f(x_0, y_0)$ from both sides of this equation:

$$
\begin{aligned}
z(t) - z(t_0) &= f(x(t), y(t)) - f(x(t_0), y(t_0)) \\
&= f_x(x_0, y_0)(x(t) - x(t_0)) + f_y(x_0, y_0)(y(t) - y(t_0)) + E(x(t), y(t)).
\end{aligned}
$$

Next, we divide both sides by $t - t_0$:

$$\frac{z(t) - z(t_0)}{t - t_0} = f_x(x_0, y_0)\left(\frac{x(t) - x(t_0)}{t - t_0}\right) + f_y(x_0, y_0)\left(\frac{y(t) - y(t_0)}{t - t_0}\right) + \frac{E(x(t), y(t))}{t - t_0}.$$

Then we take the limit as $t$ approaches $t_0$:

$$\lim_{t \to t_0} \frac{z(t) - z(t_0)}{t - t_0} = f_x(x_0, y_0) \lim_{t \to t_0} \left( \frac{x(t) - x(t_0)}{t - t_0} \right) + f_y(x_0, y_0) \lim_{t \to t_0} \left( \frac{y(t) - y(t_0)}{t - t_0} \right)$$

$$+ \lim_{t \to t_0} \frac{E(x(t), y(t))}{t - t_0}.$$

The left-hand side of this equation is equal to $dz/dt$, which leads to

$$\frac{dz}{dt} = f_x(x_0, y_0)\frac{dx}{dt} + f_y(x_0, y_0)\frac{dy}{dt} + \lim_{t \to t_0} \frac{E(x(t), y(t))}{t - t_0}.$$

The last term can be rewritten as

$$\lim_{t \to t_0} \frac{E(x(t), y(t))}{t - t_0} = \lim_{t \to t_0} \left( \frac{E(x, y)}{\sqrt{(x - x_0)^2 + (y - y_0)^2}} \frac{\sqrt{(x - x_0)^2 + (y - y_0)^2}}{t - t_0} \right)$$

$$= \lim_{t \to t_0} \left( \frac{E(x, y)}{\sqrt{(x - x_0)^2 + (y - y_0)^2}} \right) \lim_{t \to t_0} \left( \frac{\sqrt{(x - x_0)^2 + (y - y_0)^2}}{t - t_0} \right).$$

As $t$ approaches $t_0$, $(x(t), y(t))$ approaches $(x(t_0), y(t_0))$, so we can rewrite the last product as

$$\lim_{(x, y) \to (x_0, y_0)} \left( \frac{E(x, y)}{\sqrt{(x - x_0)^2 + (y - y_0)^2}} \right) \lim_{(x, y) \to (x_0, y_0)} \left( \frac{\sqrt{(x - x_0)^2 + (y - y_0)^2}}{t - t_0} \right).$$

Since the first limit is equal to zero, we need only show that the second limit is finite:

$$\lim_{(x, y) \to (x_0, y_0)} \left( \frac{\sqrt{(x - x_0)^2 + (y - y_0)^2}}{t - t_0} \right) = \lim_{(x, y) \to (x_0, y_0)} \left( \sqrt{\frac{(x - x_0)^2 + (y - y_0)^2}{(t - t_0)^2}} \right)$$

$$= \lim_{(x, y) \to (x_0, y_0)} \left( \sqrt{\left( \frac{x - x_0}{t - t_0} \right)^2 + \left( \frac{y - y_0}{t - t_0} \right)^2} \right)$$

$$= \sqrt{\left( \lim_{(x, y) \to (x_0, y_0)} \left( \frac{x - x_0}{t - t_0} \right) \right)^2 + \left( \lim_{(x, y) \to (x_0, y_0)} \left( \frac{y - y_0}{t - t_0} \right) \right)^2}.$$

Since $x(t)$ and $y(t)$ are both differentiable functions of $t$, both limits inside the last radical exist. Therefore, this value is finite. This proves the chain rule at $t = t_0$; the rest of the theorem follows from the assumption that all functions are differentiable over their entire domains.

□

Closer examination of **Equation 4.29** reveals an interesting pattern. The first term in the equation is $\frac{\partial f}{\partial x} \cdot \frac{dx}{dt}$ and the second term is $\frac{\partial f}{\partial y} \cdot \frac{dy}{dt}$. Recall that when multiplying fractions, cancelation can be used. If we treat these derivatives as fractions, then each product "simplifies" to something resembling $\partial f/dt$. The variables $x$ and $y$ that disappear in this simplification are often called **intermediate variables**: they are independent variables for the function $f$, but are dependent variables for the variable $t$. Two terms appear on the right-hand side of the formula, and $f$ is a function of two variables. This pattern works with functions of more than two variables as well, as we see later in this section.

## Example 4.26

## Using the Chain Rule

Calculate $dz/dt$ for each of the following functions:

a.   $z = f(x, y) = 4x^2 + 3y^2$, $x = x(t) = \sin t$, $y = y(t) = \cos t$

b.   $z = f(x, y) = \sqrt{x^2 - y^2}$, $x = x(t) = e^{2t}$, $y = y(t) = e^{-t}$

### Solution

a.   To use the chain rule, we need four quantities— $\partial z/\partial x$, $\partial z/\partial y$, $dx/dt$,   and  $dy/dt$:

$$\frac{\partial z}{\partial x} = 8x \qquad \frac{\partial z}{\partial y} = 6y$$

$$\frac{dx}{dt} = \cos t \qquad \frac{dy}{dt} = -\sin t$$

Now, we substitute each of these into **Equation 4.29**:

$$\frac{dz}{dt} = \frac{\partial z}{\partial x} \cdot \frac{dx}{dt} + \frac{\partial z}{\partial y} \cdot \frac{dy}{dt}$$
$$= (8x)(\cos t) + (6y)(-\sin t)$$
$$= 8x \cos t - 6y \sin t.$$

This answer has three variables in it. To reduce it to one variable, use the fact that $x(t) = \sin t$ and $y(t) = \cos t$. We obtain

$$\frac{dz}{dt} = 8x \cos t - 6y \sin t$$
$$= 8(\sin t)\cos t - 6(\cos t)\sin t$$
$$= 2 \sin t \cos t.$$

This derivative can also be calculated by first substituting $x(t)$ and $y(t)$ into $f(x, y)$,   then differentiating with respect to $t$:

$$z = f(x, y)$$
$$= f(x(t), y(t))$$
$$= 4(x(t))^2 + 3(y(t))^2$$
$$= 4\sin^2 t + 3\cos^2 t.$$

Then

$$\frac{dz}{dt} = 2(4 \sin t)(\cos t) + 2(3 \cos t)(-\sin t)$$
$$= 8 \sin t \cos t - 6 \sin t \cos t$$
$$= 2 \sin t \cos t,$$

which is the same solution. However, it may not always be this easy to differentiate in this form.

b.   To use the chain rule, we again need four quantities— $\partial z/\partial x$, $\partial z/\partial y$, $dx/dt$,   and  $dy/dt$:

$$\frac{\partial z}{\partial x} = \frac{x}{\sqrt{x^2 - y^2}} \qquad \frac{\partial z}{\partial y} = \frac{-y}{\sqrt{x^2 - y^2}}$$

$$\frac{dx}{dt} = 2e^{2t} \qquad \frac{dx}{dt} = -e^{-t}.$$

We substitute each of these into **Equation 4.29**:

$$\frac{dz}{dt} = \frac{\partial z}{\partial x} \cdot \frac{dx}{dt} + \frac{\partial z}{\partial y} \cdot \frac{dy}{dt}$$

$$= \left(\frac{x}{\sqrt{x^2 - y^2}}\right)(2e^{2t}) + \left(\frac{-y}{\sqrt{x^2 - y^2}}\right)(-e^{-t})$$

$$= \frac{2xe^{2t} - ye^{-t}}{\sqrt{x^2 - y^2}}.$$

To reduce this to one variable, we use the fact that $x(t) = e^{2t}$ and $y(t) = e^{-t}$. Therefore,

$$\frac{dz}{dt} = \frac{2xe^{2t} + ye^{-t}}{\sqrt{x^2 - y^2}}$$

$$= \frac{2(e^{2t})e^{2t} + (e^{-t})e^{-t}}{\sqrt{e^{4t} - e^{-2t}}}$$

$$= \frac{2e^{4t} + e^{-2t}}{\sqrt{e^{4t} - e^{-2t}}}.$$

To eliminate negative exponents, we multiply the top by $e^{2t}$ and the bottom by $\sqrt{e^{4t}}$:

$$\frac{dz}{dt} = \frac{2e^{4t} + e^{-2t}}{\sqrt{e^{4t} - e^{-2t}}} \cdot \frac{e^{2t}}{\sqrt{e^{4t}}}$$

$$= \frac{2e^{6t} + 1}{\sqrt{e^{8t} - e^{2t}}}$$

$$= \frac{2e^{6t} + 1}{\sqrt{e^{2t}(e^{6t} - 1)}}$$

$$= \frac{2e^{6t} + 1}{e^t \sqrt{e^{6t} - 1}}.$$

Again, this derivative can also be calculated by first substituting $x(t)$ and $y(t)$ into $f(x, y)$, then differentiating with respect to $t$:

$$z = f(x, y)$$

$$= f(x(t), y(t))$$

$$= \sqrt{(x(t))^2 - (y(t))^2}$$

$$= \sqrt{e^{4t} - e^{-2t}}$$

$$= \left(e^{4t} - e^{-2t}\right)^{1/2}.$$

Then

$$\frac{dz}{dt} = \frac{1}{2}\left(e^{4t} - e^{-2t}\right)^{-1/2}\left(4e^{4t} + 2e^{-2t}\right)$$

$$= \frac{2e^{4t} + e^{-2t}}{\sqrt{e^{4t} - e^{-2t}}}.$$

This is the same solution.

 **4.23** Calculate $dz/dt$ given the following functions. Express the final answer in terms of $t$.

$$z = f(x, y) = x^2 - 3xy + 2y^2, \; x = x(t) = 3\sin 2t, \; y = y(t) = 4\cos 2t$$

It is often useful to create a visual representation of **Equation 4.29** for the chain rule. This is called a **tree diagram** for the chain rule for functions of one variable and it provides a way to remember the formula (**Figure 4.34**). This diagram can be expanded for functions of more than one variable, as we shall see very shortly.

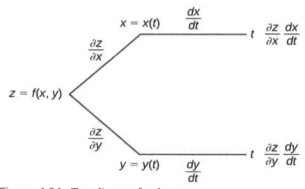

**Figure 4.34** Tree diagram for the case
$$\frac{dz}{dt} = \frac{\partial z}{\partial x} \cdot \frac{dx}{dt} + \frac{\partial z}{\partial y} \cdot \frac{dy}{dt}.$$

In this diagram, the leftmost corner corresponds to $z = f(x, y)$. Since $f$ has two independent variables, there are two lines coming from this corner. The upper branch corresponds to the variable $x$ and the lower branch corresponds to the variable $y$. Since each of these variables is then dependent on one variable $t$, one branch then comes from $x$ and one branch comes from $y$. Last, each of the branches on the far right has a label that represents the path traveled to reach that branch. The top branch is reached by following the $x$ branch, then the $t$ branch; therefore, it is labeled $(\partial z/\partial x) \times (dx/dt)$. The bottom branch is similar: first the $y$ branch, then the $t$ branch. This branch is labeled $(\partial z/\partial y) \times (dy/dt)$. To get the formula for $dz/dt$, add all the terms that appear on the rightmost side of the diagram. This gives us **Equation 4.29**.

In **Chain Rule for Two Independent Variables**, $z = f(x, y)$ is a function of $x$ and $y$, and both $x = g(u, v)$ and $y = h(u, v)$ are functions of the independent variables $u$ and $v$.

**Theorem 4.9: Chain Rule for Two Independent Variables**

Suppose $x = g(u, v)$ and $y = h(u, v)$ are differentiable functions of $u$ and $v$, and $z = f(x, y)$ is a differentiable function of $x$ and $y$. Then, $z = f(g(u, v), h(u, v))$ is a differentiable function of $u$ and $v$, and

$$\frac{\partial z}{\partial u} = \frac{\partial z}{\partial x}\frac{\partial x}{\partial u} + \frac{\partial z}{\partial y}\frac{\partial x}{\partial u} \tag{4.31}$$

and

$$\frac{\partial z}{\partial v} = \frac{\partial z}{\partial x}\frac{\partial x}{\partial v} + \frac{\partial z}{\partial y}\frac{\partial y}{\partial v}. \tag{4.32}$$

We can draw a tree diagram for each of these formulas as well as follows.

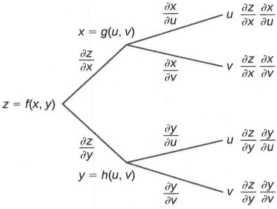

**Figure 4.35** Tree diagram for $\frac{\partial z}{\partial u} = \frac{\partial z}{\partial x} \cdot \frac{\partial x}{\partial u} + \frac{\partial z}{\partial y} \cdot \frac{\partial y}{\partial u}$ and

$$\frac{\partial z}{\partial v} = \frac{\partial z}{\partial x} \cdot \frac{\partial x}{\partial v} + \frac{\partial z}{\partial y} \cdot \frac{\partial y}{\partial v}.$$

To derive the formula for $\partial z/\partial u$, start from the left side of the diagram, then follow only the branches that end with $u$ and add the terms that appear at the end of those branches. For the formula for $\partial z/\partial v$, follow only the branches that end with $v$ and add the terms that appear at the end of those branches.

There is an important difference between these two chain rule theorems. In **Chain Rule for One Independent Variable**, the left-hand side of the formula for the derivative is not a partial derivative, but in **Chain Rule for Two Independent Variables** it is. The reason is that, in **Chain Rule for One Independent Variable**, $z$ is ultimately a function of $t$ alone, whereas in **Chain Rule for Two Independent Variables**, $z$ is a function of both $u$ and $v$.

## Example 4.27

### Using the Chain Rule for Two Variables

Calculate $\partial z/\partial u$ and $\partial z/\partial v$ using the following functions:

$$z = f(x, y) = 3x^2 - 2xy + y^2,\ x = x(u, v) = 3u + 2v,\ y = y(u, v) = 4u - v.$$

### Solution

To implement the chain rule for two variables, we need six partial derivatives—$\partial z/\partial x,\ \partial z/\partial y,\ \partial x/\partial u,\ \partial x/\partial v,\ \partial y/\partial u,$ and $\partial y/\partial v$:

$$\frac{\partial z}{\partial x} = 6x - 2y \qquad \frac{\partial z}{\partial y} = -2x + 2y$$

$$\frac{\partial x}{\partial u} = 3 \qquad\qquad \frac{\partial x}{\partial v} = 2$$

$$\frac{\partial y}{\partial u} = 4 \qquad\qquad \frac{\partial y}{\partial v} = -1.$$

To find $\partial z/\partial u$, we use **Equation 4.31**:

$$\begin{aligned}
\frac{\partial z}{\partial u} &= \frac{\partial z}{\partial x} \cdot \frac{\partial x}{\partial u} + \frac{\partial z}{\partial y} \cdot \frac{\partial y}{\partial u} \\
&= 3(6x - 2y) + 4(-2x + 2y) \\
&= 10x + 2y.
\end{aligned}$$

Next, we substitute $x(u, v) = 3u + 2v$ and $y(u, v) = 4u - v$:

$$\begin{aligned}
\frac{\partial z}{\partial u} &= 10x + 2y \\
&= 10(3u + 2v) + 2(4u - v) \\
&= 38u + 18v.
\end{aligned}$$

To find $\partial z/\partial v$, we use **Equation 4.32**:

$$\begin{aligned}
\frac{\partial z}{\partial v} &= \frac{\partial z}{\partial x} \frac{\partial x}{\partial v} + \frac{\partial z}{\partial y} \frac{\partial y}{\partial v} \\
&= 2(6x - 2y) + (-1)(-2x + 2y) \\
&= 14x - 6y.
\end{aligned}$$

Then we substitute $x(u, v) = 3u + 2v$ and $y(u, v) = 4u - v$:

$$\begin{aligned}
\frac{\partial z}{\partial v} &= 14x - 6y \\
&= 14(3u + 2v) - 6(4u - v) \\
&= 18u + 34v.
\end{aligned}$$

 **4.24** Calculate $\partial z/\partial u$ and $\partial z/\partial v$ given the following functions:

$$z = f(x, y) = \frac{2x - y}{x + 3y}, \; x(u, v) = e^{2u} \cos 3v, \; y(u, v) = e^{2u} \sin 3v.$$

## The Generalized Chain Rule

Now that we've see how to extend the original chain rule to functions of two variables, it is natural to ask: Can we extend the rule to more than two variables? The answer is yes, as the **generalized chain rule** states.

---

### Theorem 4.10: Generalized Chain Rule

Let $w = f(x_1, x_2, ..., x_m)$ be a differentiable function of $m$ independent variables, and for each $i \in \{1, ..., m\}$, let $x_i = x_i(t_1, t_2, ..., t_n)$ be a differentiable function of $n$ independent variables. Then

$$\frac{\partial w}{\partial t_j} = \frac{\partial w}{\partial x_1} \frac{\partial x_1}{\partial t_j} + \frac{\partial w}{\partial x_2} \frac{\partial x_2}{\partial t_j} + \cdots + \frac{\partial w}{\partial x_m} \frac{\partial x_m}{\partial t_j} \qquad (4.33)$$

for any $j \in \{1, 2,\ldots, n\}$.

In the next example we calculate the derivative of a function of three independent variables in which each of the three variables is dependent on two other variables.

## Example 4.28

### Using the Generalized Chain Rule

Calculate $\partial w/\partial u$ and $\partial w/\partial v$ using the following functions:

$$
\begin{aligned}
w &= f(x, y, z) = 3x^2 - 2xy + 4z^2 \\
x &= x(u, v) = e^u \sin v \\
y &= y(u, v) = e^u \cos v \\
z &= z(u, v) = e^u.
\end{aligned}
$$

### Solution

The formulas for $\partial w/\partial u$ and $\partial w/\partial v$ are

$$
\frac{\partial w}{\partial u} = \frac{\partial w}{\partial x} \cdot \frac{\partial x}{\partial u} + \frac{\partial w}{\partial y} \cdot \frac{\partial y}{\partial u} + \frac{\partial w}{\partial z} \cdot \frac{\partial z}{\partial u}
$$

$$
\frac{\partial w}{\partial v} = \frac{\partial w}{\partial x} \cdot \frac{\partial x}{\partial v} + \frac{\partial w}{\partial y} \cdot \frac{\partial y}{\partial v} + \frac{\partial w}{\partial z} \cdot \frac{\partial z}{\partial v}.
$$

Therefore, there are nine different partial derivatives that need to be calculated and substituted. We need to calculate each of them:

$$
\begin{array}{lll}
\dfrac{\partial w}{\partial x} = 6x - 2y & \dfrac{\partial w}{\partial y} = -2x & \dfrac{\partial w}{\partial z} = 8z \\[2ex]
\dfrac{\partial x}{\partial u} = e^u \sin v & \dfrac{\partial y}{\partial u} = e^u \cos v & \dfrac{\partial z}{\partial u} = e^u \\[2ex]
\dfrac{\partial x}{\partial v} = e^u \cos v & \dfrac{\partial y}{\partial v} = -e^u \sin v & \dfrac{\partial z}{\partial v} = 0.
\end{array}
$$

Now, we substitute each of them into the first formula to calculate $\partial w/\partial u$:

$$
\begin{aligned}
\frac{\partial w}{\partial u} &= \frac{\partial w}{\partial x} \cdot \frac{\partial x}{\partial u} + \frac{\partial w}{\partial y} \cdot \frac{\partial y}{\partial u} + \frac{\partial w}{\partial z} \cdot \frac{\partial z}{\partial u} \\
&= (6x - 2y)e^u \sin v - 2xe^u \cos v + 8ze^u,
\end{aligned}
$$

then substitute $x(u, v) = e^u \sin v$, $y(u, v) = e^u \cos v$, and $z(u, v) = e^u$ into this equation:

$$
\begin{aligned}
\frac{\partial w}{\partial u} &= (6x - 2y)e^u \sin v - 2xe^u \cos v + 8ze^u \\
&= (6e^u \sin v - 2e^u \cos v)e^u \sin v - 2(e^u \sin v)e^u \cos v + 8e^{2u} \\
&= 6e^{2u} \sin^2 v - 4e^{2u} \sin v \cos v + 8e^{2u} \\
&= 2e^{2u}\left(3 \sin^2 v - 2 \sin v \cos v + 4\right).
\end{aligned}
$$

Next, we calculate $\partial w/\partial v$:

$$\frac{\partial w}{\partial v} = \frac{\partial w}{\partial x} \cdot \frac{\partial x}{\partial v} + \frac{\partial w}{\partial y} \cdot \frac{\partial y}{\partial v} + \frac{\partial w}{\partial z} \cdot \frac{\partial z}{\partial v}$$

$$= (6x - 2y)e^u \cos v - 2x(-e^u \sin v) + 8z(0),$$

then we substitute $x(u, v) = e^u \sin v,\ y(u, v) = e^u \cos v,$ and $z(u, v) = e^u$ into this equation:

$$\frac{\partial w}{\partial v} = (6x - 2y)e^u \cos v - 2x(-e^u \sin v)$$

$$= (6e^u \sin v - 2e^u \cos v)e^u \cos v + 2(e^u \sin v)(e^u \sin v)$$

$$= 2e^{2u} \sin^2 v + 6e^{2u} \sin v \cos v - 2e^{2u} \cos^2 v$$

$$= 2e^{2u}\left(\sin^2 v + \sin v \cos v - \cos^2 v\right).$$

 **4.25**   Calculate $\partial w/\partial u$ and $\partial w/\partial v$ given the following functions:

$$w = f(x, y, z) = \frac{x + 2y - 4z}{2x - y + 3z}$$

$$x = x(u, v) = e^{2u} \cos 3v$$

$$y = y(u, v) = e^{2u} \sin 3v$$

$$z = z(u, v) = e^{2u}.$$

## Example 4.29

### Drawing a Tree Diagram

Create a tree diagram for the case when

$$w = f(x, y, z),\ x = x(t, u, v),\ y = y(t, u, v),\ z = z(t, u, v)$$

and write out the formulas for the three partial derivatives of $w$.

### Solution

Starting from the left, the function $f$ has three independent variables: $x,\ y,$ and $z$. Therefore, three branches must be emanating from the first node. Each of these three branches also has three branches, for each of the variables $t,\ u,$ and $v$.

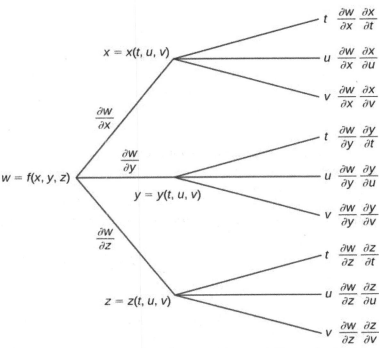

**Figure 4.36** Tree diagram for a function of three variables, each of which is a function of three independent variables.

The three formulas are

$$\frac{\partial w}{\partial t} = \frac{\partial w}{\partial x}\frac{\partial x}{\partial t} + \frac{\partial w}{\partial y}\frac{\partial y}{\partial t} + \frac{\partial w}{\partial z}\frac{\partial z}{\partial t}$$

$$\frac{\partial w}{\partial u} = \frac{\partial w}{\partial x}\frac{\partial x}{\partial u} + \frac{\partial w}{\partial y}\frac{\partial y}{\partial u} + \frac{\partial w}{\partial z}\frac{\partial z}{\partial u}$$

$$\frac{\partial w}{\partial v} = \frac{\partial w}{\partial x}\frac{\partial x}{\partial v} + \frac{\partial w}{\partial y}\frac{\partial y}{\partial v} + \frac{\partial w}{\partial z}\frac{\partial z}{\partial v}.$$

 **4.26** Create a tree diagram for the case when

$$w = f(x, y), \ x = x(t, u, v), \ y = y(t, u, v)$$

and write out the formulas for the three partial derivatives of $w$.

# Implicit Differentiation

Recall from **Implicit Differentiation** (http://cnx.org/content/m53585/latest/) that implicit differentiation provides a method for finding $dy/dx$ when $y$ is defined implicitly as a function of $x$. The method involves differentiating both sides of the equation defining the function with respect to $x$, then solving for $dy/dx$. Partial derivatives provide an alternative to this method.

Consider the ellipse defined by the equation $x^2 + 3y^2 + 4y - 4 = 0$ as follows.

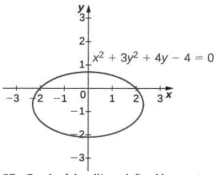

**Figure 4.37** Graph of the ellipse defined by
$x^2 + 3y^2 + 4y - 4 = 0$.

This equation implicitly defines $y$ as a function of $x$. As such, we can find the derivative $dy/dx$ using the method of implicit differentiation:

$$\frac{d}{dx}\left(x^2 + 3y^2 + 4y - 4\right) = \frac{d}{dx}(0)$$
$$2x + 6y\frac{dy}{dx} + 4\frac{dy}{dx} = 0$$
$$(6y + 4)\frac{dy}{dx} = -2x$$
$$\frac{dy}{dx} = -\frac{x}{3y + 2}.$$

We can also define a function $z = f(x, y)$ by using the left-hand side of the equation defining the ellipse. Then $f(x, y) = x^2 + 3y^2 + 4y - 4$. The ellipse $x^2 + 3y^2 + 4y - 4 = 0$ can then be described by the equation $f(x, y) = 0$. Using this function and the following theorem gives us an alternative approach to calculating $dy/dx$.

---

**Theorem 4.11: Implicit Differentiation of a Function of Two or More Variables**

Suppose the function $z = f(x, y)$ defines $y$ implicitly as a function $y = g(x)$ of $x$ via the equation $f(x, y) = 0$. Then

$$\frac{dy}{dx} = -\frac{\partial f/\partial x}{\partial f/\partial y} \qquad (4.34)$$

provided $f_y(x, y) \neq 0$.

If the equation $f(x, y, z) = 0$ defines $z$ implicitly as a differentiable function of $x$ and $y$, then

$$\frac{\partial z}{\partial x} = -\frac{\partial f/\partial x}{\partial f/\partial z} \quad \text{and} \quad \frac{\partial z}{\partial y} = -\frac{\partial f/\partial y}{\partial f/\partial z} \qquad (4.35)$$

as long as $f_z(x, y, z) \neq 0$.

---

**Equation 4.34** is a direct consequence of **Equation 4.31**. In particular, if we assume that $y$ is defined implicitly as a function of $x$ via the equation $f(x, y) = 0$, we can apply the chain rule to find $dy/dx$:

$$\frac{d}{dx}f(x, y) = \frac{d}{dx}(0)$$

$$\frac{\partial f}{\partial x} \cdot \frac{dx}{dx} + \frac{\partial f}{\partial y} \cdot \frac{dy}{dx} = 0$$

$$\frac{\partial f}{\partial x} + \frac{\partial f}{\partial y} \cdot \frac{dy}{dx} = 0.$$

Solving this equation for $dy/dx$ gives Equation 4.34. Equation 4.35 can be derived in a similar fashion.

Let's now return to the problem that we started before the previous theorem. Using Implicit Differentiation of a Function of Two or More Variables and the function $f(x, y) = x^2 + 3y^2 + 4y - 4$, we obtain

$$\frac{\partial f}{\partial x} = 2x$$

$$\frac{\partial f}{\partial y} = 6y + 4.$$

Then Equation 4.34 gives

$$\frac{dy}{dx} = -\frac{\partial f/\partial x}{\partial f/\partial y} = -\frac{2x}{6y + 4} = -\frac{x}{3y + 2},$$

which is the same result obtained by the earlier use of implicit differentiation.

## Example 4.30

### Implicit Differentiation by Partial Derivatives

a. Calculate $dy/dx$ if $y$ is defined implicitly as a function of $x$ via the equation $3x^2 - 2xy + y^2 + 4x - 6y - 11 = 0$. What is the equation of the tangent line to the graph of this curve at point $(2, 1)$?

b. Calculate $\partial z/\partial x$ and $\partial z/\partial y$, given $x^2 e^y - yze^x = 0$.

### Solution

a. Set $f(x, y) = 3x^2 - 2xy + y^2 + 4x - 6y - 11 = 0$, then calculate $f_x$ and $f_y$: $\begin{aligned} f_x &= 6x - 2y + 4 \\ f_y &= -2x + 2y - 6. \end{aligned}$

The derivative is given by

$$\frac{dy}{dx} = -\frac{\partial f/\partial x}{\partial f/\partial y} = -\frac{6x - 2y + 4}{-2x + 2y - 6} = \frac{3x - y + 2}{x - y + 3}.$$

The slope of the tangent line at point $(2, 1)$ is given by

$$\left.\frac{dy}{dx}\right|_{(x, y) = (2, 1)} = \frac{3(2) - 1 + 2}{2 - 1 + 3} = \frac{7}{4}.$$

To find the equation of the tangent line, we use the point-slope form (Figure 4.38):

$$\begin{aligned} y - y_0 &= m(x - x_0) \\ y - 1 &= \frac{7}{4}(x - 2) \\ y &= \frac{7}{4}x - \frac{7}{2} + 1 \\ y &= \frac{7}{4}x - \frac{5}{2}. \end{aligned}$$

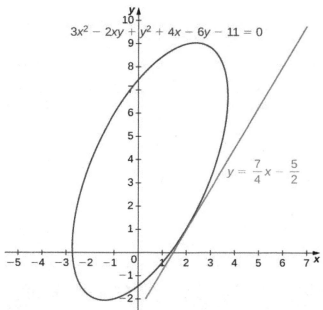

**Figure 4.38** Graph of the rotated ellipse defined by
$3x^2 - 2xy + y^2 + 4x - 6y - 11 = 0$.

b.  We have $f(x, y, z) = x^2 e^y - yze^x$. Therefore,

$$\frac{\partial f}{\partial x} = 2xe^y - yze^x$$

$$\frac{\partial f}{\partial y} = x^2 e^y - ze^x$$

$$\frac{\partial f}{\partial z} = -ye^x.$$

Using **Equation 4.35**,

$$\frac{\partial z}{\partial x} = -\frac{\partial f/\partial x}{\partial f/\partial y} \qquad\qquad \frac{\partial z}{\partial y} = -\frac{\partial f/\partial y}{\partial f/\partial z}$$

$$= -\frac{2xe^y - yze^x}{-ye^x} \quad \text{and} \quad = -\frac{x^2 e^y - ze^x}{-ye^x}$$

$$= \frac{2xe^y - yze^x}{ye^x} \qquad\qquad = \frac{x^2 e^y - ze^x}{ye^x}.$$

 **4.27** Find $dy/dx$ if $y$ is defined implicitly as a function of $x$ by the equation $x^2 + xy - y^2 + 7x - 3y - 26 = 0$. What is the equation of the tangent line to the graph of this curve at point $(3, -2)$?

# 4.5 EXERCISES

For the following exercises, use the information provided to solve the problem.

215. Let $w(x, y, z) = xy \cos z$, where $x = t$, $y = t^2$, and $z = \arcsin t$. Find $\frac{dw}{dt}$.

216. Let $w(t, v) = e^{tv}$ where $t = r + s$ and $v = rs$. Find $\frac{\partial w}{\partial r}$ and $\frac{\partial w}{\partial s}$.

217. If $w = 5x^2 + 2y^2$, $x = -3s + t$, and $y = s - 4t$, find $\frac{\partial w}{\partial s}$ and $\frac{\partial w}{\partial t}$.

218. If $w = xy^2$, $x = 5 \cos(2t)$, and $y = 5 \sin(2t)$, find $\frac{\partial w}{\partial t}$.

219. If $f(x, y) = xy$, $x = r \cos \theta$, and $y = r \sin \theta$, find $\frac{\partial f}{\partial r}$ and express the answer in terms of $r$ and $\theta$.

220. Suppose $f(x, y) = x + y$, $u = e^x \sin y$, $x = t^2$, and $y = \pi t$, where $x = r \cos \theta$ and $y = r \sin \theta$. Find $\frac{\partial f}{\partial \theta}$.

For the following exercises, find $\frac{df}{dt}$ using the chain rule and direct substitution.

221. $f(x, y) = x^2 + y^2$, $x = t$, $y = t^2$

222. $f(x, y) = \sqrt{x^2 + y^2}$, $y = t^2$, $x = t$

223. $f(x, y) = xy$, $x = 1 - \sqrt{t}$, $y = 1 + \sqrt{t}$

224. $f(x, y) = \frac{x}{y}$, $x = e^t$, $y = 2e^t$

225. $f(x, y) = \ln(x + y)$, $x = e^t$, $y = e^t$

226. $f(x, y) = x^4$, $x = t$, $y = t$

227. Let $w(x, y, z) = x^2 + y^2 + z^2$, $x = \cos t$, $y = \sin t$, and $z = e^t$. Express $w$ as a function of $t$ and find $\frac{dw}{dt}$ directly. Then, find $\frac{dw}{dt}$ using the chain rule.

228. Let $z = x^2 y$, where $x = t^2$ and $y = t^3$. Find $\frac{dz}{dt}$.

229. Let $u = e^x \sin y$, where $x = t^2$ and $y = \pi t$. Find $\frac{du}{dt}$ when $x = \ln 2$ and $y = \frac{\pi}{4}$.

For the following exercises, find $\frac{dy}{dx}$ using partial derivatives.

230. $\sin(6x) + \tan(8y) + 5 = 0$

231. $x^3 + y^2 x - 3 = 0$

232. $\sin(x + y) + \cos(x - y) = 4$

233. $x^2 - 2xy + y^4 = 4$

234. $xe^y + ye^x - 2x^2 y = 0$

235. $x^{2/3} + y^{2/3} = a^{2/3}$

236. $x \cos(xy) + y \cos x = 2$

237. $e^{xy} + ye^y = 1$

238. $x^2 y^3 + \cos y = 0$

239. Find $\frac{dz}{dt}$ using the chain rule where $z = 3x^2 y^3$, $x = t^4$, and $y = t^2$.

240. Let $z = 3 \cos x - \sin(xy)$, $x = \frac{1}{t}$, and $y = 3t$. Find $\frac{dz}{dt}$.

241. Let $z = e^{1-xy}$, $x = t^{1/3}$, and $y = t^3$. Find $\frac{dz}{dt}$.

242. Find $\frac{dz}{dt}$ by the chain rule where $z = \cosh^2(xy)$, $x = \frac{1}{2}t$, and $y = e^t$.

243. Let $z = \frac{x}{y}$, $x = 2 \cos u$, and $y = 3 \sin v$. Find $\frac{\partial z}{\partial u}$ and $\frac{\partial z}{\partial v}$.

244. Let $z = e^{x^2 y}$, where $x = \sqrt{uv}$ and $y = \frac{1}{v}$. Find $\frac{\partial z}{\partial u}$ and $\frac{\partial z}{\partial v}$.

245. If $z = xye^{x/y}$, $x = r\cos\theta$, and $y = r\sin\theta$, find $\frac{\partial z}{\partial r}$ and $\frac{\partial z}{\partial \theta}$ when $r = 2$ and $\theta = \frac{\pi}{6}$.

246. Find $\frac{\partial w}{\partial s}$ if $w = 4x + y^2 + z^3$, $x = e^{rs^2}$, $y = \ln\left(\frac{r+s}{t}\right)$, and $z = rst^2$.

247. If $w = \sin(xyz)$, $x = 1 - 3t$, $y = e^{1-t}$, and $z = 4t$, find $\frac{\partial w}{\partial t}$.

For the following exercises, use this information: A function $f(x, y)$ is said to be homogeneous of degree $n$ if $f(tx, ty) = t^n f(x, y)$. For all homogeneous functions of degree $n$, the following equation is true: $x\frac{\partial f}{\partial x} + y\frac{\partial f}{\partial y} = nf(x, y)$. Show that the given function is homogeneous and verify that $x\frac{\partial f}{\partial x} + y\frac{\partial f}{\partial y} = nf(x, y)$.

248. $f(x, y) = 3x^2 + y^2$

249. $f(x, y) = \sqrt{x^2 + y^2}$

250. $f(x, y) = x^2 y - 2y^3$

251. The volume of a right circular cylinder is given by $V(x, y) = \pi x^2 y$, where $x$ is the radius of the cylinder and $y$ is the cylinder height. Suppose $x$ and $y$ are functions of $t$ given by $x = \frac{1}{2}t$ and $y = \frac{1}{3}t$ so that $x$ and $y$ are both increasing with time. How fast is the volume increasing when $x = 2$ and $y = 5$?

252. The pressure $P$ of a gas is related to the volume and temperature by the formula $PV = kT$, where temperature is expressed in kelvins. Express the pressure of the gas as a function of both $V$ and $T$. Find $\frac{dP}{dt}$ when $k = 1$, $\frac{dV}{dt} = 2$ cm$^3$/min, $\frac{dT}{dt} = \frac{1}{2}$ K/min, $V = 20$ cm$^3$, and $T = 20°$F.

253. The radius of a right circular cone is increasing at 3 cm/min whereas the height of the cone is decreasing at 2 cm/min. Find the rate of change of the volume of the cone when the radius is 13 cm and the height is 18 cm.

254. The volume of a frustum of a cone is given by the formula $V = \frac{1}{3}\pi z(x^2 + y^2 + xy)$, where $x$ is the radius of the smaller circle, $y$ is the radius of the larger circle, and $z$ is the height of the frustum (see figure). Find the rate of change of the volume of this frustum when $x = 10$ in., $y = 12$ in., and $z = 18$ in.

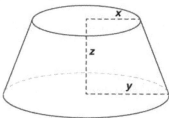

255. A closed box is in the shape of a rectangular solid with dimensions $x$, $y$, and $z$. (Dimensions are in inches.) Suppose each dimension is changing at the rate of 0.5 in./min. Find the rate of change of the total surface area of the box when $x = 2$ in., $y = 3$ in., and $z = 1$ in.

256. The total resistance in a circuit that has three individual resistances represented by $x$, $y$, and $z$ is given by the formula $R(x, y, z) = \frac{xyz}{yz + xz + xy}$. Suppose at a given time the $x$ resistance is $100\Omega$, the $y$ resistance is $200\Omega$, and the $z$ resistance is $300\Omega$. Also, suppose the $x$ resistance is changing at a rate of $2\Omega$/min, the $y$ resistance is changing at the rate of $1\Omega$/min, and the $z$ resistance has no change. Find the rate of change of the total resistance in this circuit at this time.

257. The temperature $T$ at a point $(x, y)$ is $T(x, y)$ and is measured using the Celsius scale. A fly crawls so that its position after $t$ seconds is given by $x = \sqrt{1 + t}$ and $y = 2 + \frac{1}{3}t$, where $x$ and $y$ are measured in centimeters. The temperature function satisfies $T_x(2, 3) = 4$ and $T_y(2, 3) = 3$. How fast is the temperature increasing on the fly's path after 3 sec?

258. The $x$ and $y$ components of a fluid moving in two dimensions are given by the following functions: $u(x, y) = 2y$ and $v(x, y) = -2x$; $x \geq 0; y \geq 0$. The speed of the fluid at the point $(x, y)$ is $s(x, y) = \sqrt{u(x, y)^2 + v(x, y)^2}$. Find $\frac{\partial s}{\partial x}$ and $\frac{\partial s}{\partial y}$ using the chain rule.

259. Let $u = u(x, y, z)$, where $x = x(w, t), y = y(w, t), z = z(w, t), w = w(r, s), \text{ and } t = t(r, s)$. Use a tree diagram and the chain rule to find an expression for $\frac{\partial u}{\partial r}$.

# 4.6 | Directional Derivatives and the Gradient

## Learning Objectives

**4.6.1** Determine the directional derivative in a given direction for a function of two variables.

**4.6.2** Determine the gradient vector of a given real-valued function.

**4.6.3** Explain the significance of the gradient vector with regard to direction of change along a surface.

**4.6.4** Use the gradient to find the tangent to a level curve of a given function.

**4.6.5** Calculate directional derivatives and gradients in three dimensions.

In **Partial Derivatives** we introduced the partial derivative. A function $z = f(x, y)$ has two partial derivatives: $\partial z/\partial x$ and $\partial z/\partial y$. These derivatives correspond to each of the independent variables and can be interpreted as instantaneous rates of change (that is, as slopes of a tangent line). For example, $\partial z/\partial x$ represents the slope of a tangent line passing through a given point on the surface defined by $z = f(x, y)$, assuming the tangent line is parallel to the $x$-axis. Similarly, $\partial z/\partial y$ represents the slope of the tangent line parallel to the $y$-axis. Now we consider the possibility of a tangent line parallel to neither axis.

## Directional Derivatives

We start with the graph of a surface defined by the equation $z = f(x, y)$. Given a point $(a, b)$ in the domain of $f$, we choose a direction to travel from that point. We measure the direction using an angle $\theta$, which is measured counterclockwise in the $x, y$-plane, starting at zero from the positive $x$-axis (**Figure 4.39**). The distance we travel is $h$ and the direction we travel is given by the unit vector $\mathbf{u} = (\cos \theta)\mathbf{i} + (\sin \theta)\mathbf{j}$. Therefore, the $z$-coordinate of the second point on the graph is given by $z = f(a + h \cos \theta, b + h \sin \theta)$.

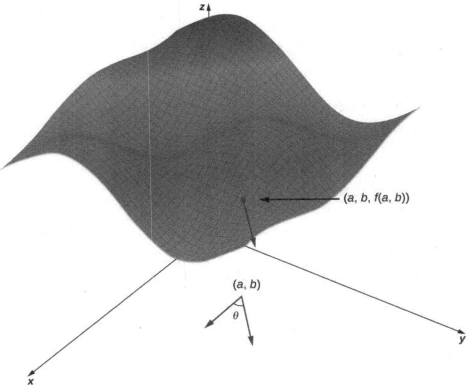

**Figure 4.39** Finding the directional derivative at a point on the graph of $z = f(x, y)$. The slope of the black arrow on the graph indicates the value of the directional derivative at that point.

We can calculate the slope of the secant line by dividing the difference in $z$-values by the length of the line segment connecting the two points in the domain. The length of the line segment is $h$. Therefore, the slope of the secant line is

$$m_{\text{sec}} = \frac{f(a + h \cos \theta, \, b + h \sin \theta) - f(a, \, b)}{h}.$$

To find the slope of the tangent line in the same direction, we take the limit as $h$ approaches zero.

### Definition

Suppose $z = f(x, y)$ is a function of two variables with a domain of $D$. Let $(a, b) \in D$ and define $\mathbf{u} = \cos \theta \mathbf{i} + \sin \theta \mathbf{j}$. Then the **directional derivative** of $f$ in the direction of $u$ is given by

$$D_{\mathbf{u}} f(a, b) = \lim_{h \to 0} \frac{f(a + h \cos \theta, \, b + h \sin \theta) - f(a, \, b)}{h}, \tag{4.36}$$

provided the limit exists.

Equation 4.36 provides a formal definition of the directional derivative that can be used in many cases to calculate a directional derivative.

### Example 4.31

#### Finding a Directional Derivative from the Definition

Let $\theta = \arccos(3/5)$. Find the directional derivative $D_{\mathbf{u}} f(x, y)$ of $f(x, y) = x^2 - xy + 3y^2$ in the direction of $\mathbf{u} = (\cos \theta)\mathbf{i} + (\sin \theta)\mathbf{j}$. What is $D_{\mathbf{u}} f(-1, 2)$?

## Solution

First of all, since $\cos \theta = 3/5$ and $\theta$ is acute, this implies

$$\sin \theta = \sqrt{1 - \left(\frac{3}{5}\right)^2} = \sqrt{\frac{16}{25}} = \frac{4}{5}.$$

Using $f(x, y) = x^2 - xy + 3y^2$, we first calculate $f(x + h \cos \theta, y + h \sin \theta)$:

$$
\begin{aligned}
f(x + h \cos \theta, y + h \sin \theta) &= (x + h \cos \theta)^2 - (x + h \cos \theta)(y + h \sin \theta) + 3(y + h \sin \theta)^2 \\
&= x^2 + 2xh \cos \theta + h^2 \cos^2 \theta - xy - xh \sin \theta - yh \cos \theta \\
&\quad - h^2 \sin \theta \cos \theta + 3y^2 + 6yh \sin \theta + 3h^2 \sin^2 \theta \\
&= x^2 + 2xh\left(\frac{3}{5}\right) + \frac{9h^2}{25} - xy - \frac{4xh}{5} - \frac{3yh}{5} - \frac{12h^2}{25} + 3y^2 \\
&\quad + 6yh\left(\frac{4}{5}\right) + 3h^2\left(\frac{16}{25}\right) \\
&= x^2 - xy + 3y^2 + \frac{2xh}{5} + \frac{9h^2}{5} + \frac{21yh}{5}.
\end{aligned}
$$

We substitute this expression into **Equation 4.36**:

$$
\begin{aligned}
D_{\mathbf{u}} f(a, b) &= \lim_{h \to 0} \frac{f(a + h \cos \theta, b + h \sin \theta) - f(a, b)}{h} \\
&= \lim_{h \to 0} \frac{\left(x^2 - xy + 3y^2 + \frac{2xh}{5} + \frac{9h^2}{5} + \frac{21yh}{5}\right) - \left(x^2 - xy + 3y^2\right)}{h} \\
&= \lim_{h \to 0} \frac{\frac{2xh}{5} + \frac{9h^2}{5} + \frac{21yh}{5}}{h} \\
&= \lim_{h \to 0} \frac{2x}{5} + \frac{9h}{5} + \frac{21y}{5} \\
&= \frac{2x + 21y}{5}.
\end{aligned}
$$

To calculate $D_{\mathbf{u}} f(-1, 2)$, we substitute $x = -1$ and $y = 2$ into this answer:

$$
\begin{aligned}
D_{\mathbf{u}} f(-1, 2) &= \frac{2(-1) + 21(2)}{5} \\
&= \frac{-2 + 42}{5} \\
&= 8.
\end{aligned}
$$

(See the following figure.)

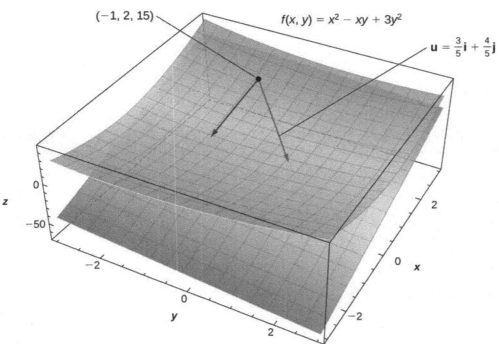

**Figure 4.40** Finding the directional derivative in a given direction **u** at a given point on a surface. The plane is tangent to the surface at the given point $(-1, 2, 15)$.

Another approach to calculating a directional derivative involves partial derivatives, as outlined in the following theorem.

---

### Theorem 4.12: Directional Derivative of a Function of Two Variables

Let $z = f(x, y)$ be a function of two variables $x$ and $y$, and assume that $f_x$ and $f_y$ exist. Then the directional derivative of $f$ in the direction of $u = \cos\theta i + \sin\theta j$ is given by

$$D_{\mathbf{u}} f(x, y) = f_x(x, y)\cos\theta + f_y(x, y)\sin\theta. \tag{4.37}$$

---

**Proof**

Equation 4.36 states that the directional derivative of $f$ in the direction of $u = \cos\theta i + \sin\theta j$ is given by

$$D_{\mathbf{u}} f(a, b) = \lim_{t \to 0} \frac{f(a + t\cos\theta,\ b + t\sin\theta) - f(a, b)}{t}.$$

Let $x = a + t\cos\theta$ and $y = b + t\sin\theta$, and define $g(t) = f(x, y)$. Since $f_x$ and $f_y$ both exist, we can use the chain rule for functions of two variables to calculate $g'(t)$:

$$\begin{aligned} g'(t) &= \frac{\partial f}{\partial x}\frac{dx}{dt} + \frac{\partial f}{\partial y}\frac{dy}{dt} \\ &= f_x(x, y)\cos\theta + f_y(x, y)\sin\theta. \end{aligned}$$

If $t = 0$, then $x = x_0$ and $y = y_0$, so

$$g'(0) = f_x(x_0, y_0)\cos\theta + f_y(x_0, y_0)\sin\theta.$$

By the definition of $g'(t)$, it is also true that

$$
\begin{aligned}
g'(0) &= \lim_{t \to 0} \frac{g(t) - g(0)}{t} \\
&= \lim_{t \to 0} \frac{f(x_0 + t\cos\theta, \, y_0 + t\sin\theta) - f(x_0, \, y_0)}{t}.
\end{aligned}
$$

Therefore, $D_{\mathbf{u}} f(x_0, \, y_0) = f_x(x, \, y)\cos\theta + f_y(x, \, y)\sin\theta$.

□

### Example 4.32

#### Finding a Directional Derivative: Alternative Method

Let $\theta = \arccos(3/5)$. Find the directional derivative $D_{\mathbf{u}} f(x, \, y)$ of $f(x, \, y) = x^2 - xy + 3y^2$ in the direction of $\mathbf{u} = (\cos\theta)\mathbf{i} + (\sin\theta)\mathbf{j}$. What is $D_{\mathbf{u}} f(-1, \, 2)$?

#### Solution
First, we must calculate the partial derivatives of $f$:

$$
\begin{aligned}
f_x &= 2x - y \\
f_y &= -x + 6y,
\end{aligned}
$$

Then we use **Equation 4.37** with $\theta = \arccos(3/5)$:

$$
\begin{aligned}
D_{\mathbf{u}} f(x, \, y) &= f_x(x, \, y)\cos\theta + f_y(x, \, y)\sin\theta \\
&= (2x - y)\tfrac{3}{5} + (-x + 6y)\tfrac{4}{5} \\
&= \frac{6x}{5} - \frac{3y}{5} - \frac{4x}{5} + \frac{24y}{5} \\
&= \frac{2x + 21y}{5}.
\end{aligned}
$$

To calculate $D_{\mathbf{u}} f(-1, \, 2)$, let $x = -1$ and $y = 2$:

$$
D_{\mathbf{u}} f(-1, \, 2) = \frac{2(-1) + 21(2)}{5} = \frac{-2 + 42}{5} = 8.
$$

This is the same answer obtained in **Example 4.31**.

 **4.28** Find the directional derivative $D_{\mathbf{u}} f(x, \, y)$ of $f(x, \, y) = 3x^2 y - 4xy^3 + 3y^2 - 4x$ in the direction of $\mathbf{u} = \left(\cos\frac{\pi}{3}\right)\mathbf{i} + \left(\sin\frac{\pi}{3}\right)\mathbf{j}$ using **Equation 4.37**. What is $D_{\mathbf{u}} f(3, \, 4)$?

If the vector that is given for the direction of the derivative is not a unit vector, then it is only necessary to divide by the norm of the vector. For example, if we wished to find the directional derivative of the function in **Example 4.32** in the direction of the vector $\langle -5, \, 12 \rangle$, we would first divide by its magnitude to get $\mathbf{u}$. This gives us $\mathbf{u} = \langle -(5/13), \, 12/13 \rangle$. Then

$$\begin{aligned}
D_{\mathbf{u}} f(x,\ y) &= \nabla f(x,\ y) \cdot \mathbf{u} \\
&= -\frac{5}{13}(2x - y) + \frac{12}{13}(-x + 6y) \\
&= -\frac{22}{13}x + \frac{17}{13}y.
\end{aligned}$$

## Gradient

The right-hand side of Equation 4.37 is equal to $f_x(x,\ y)\cos\theta + f_y(x,\ y)\sin\theta$, which can be written as the dot product of two vectors. Define the first vector as $\nabla f(x,\ y) = f_x(x,\ y)\mathbf{i} + f_y(x,\ y)\mathbf{j}$ and the second vector as $\mathbf{u} = (\cos\theta)\mathbf{i} + (\sin\theta)\mathbf{j}$. Then the right-hand side of the equation can be written as the dot product of these two vectors:

$$D_{\mathbf{u}} f(x,\ y) = \nabla f(x,\ y) \cdot \mathbf{u}. \tag{4.38}$$

The first vector in Equation 4.38 has a special name: the gradient of the function $f$. The symbol $\nabla$ is called *nabla* and the vector $\nabla f$ is read "del $f$."

---

**Definition**

Let $z = f(x,\ y)$ be a function of $x$ and $y$ such that $f_x$ and $f_y$ exist. The vector $\nabla f(x,\ y)$ is called the **gradient** of $f$ and is defined as

$$\nabla f(x,\ y) = f_x(x,\ y)\mathbf{i} + f_y(x,\ y)\mathbf{j}. \tag{4.39}$$

The vector $\nabla f(x,\ y)$ is also written as "grad $f$."

---

## Example 4.33

### Finding Gradients

Find the gradient $\nabla f(x,\ y)$ of each of the following functions:

a.  $f(x,\ y) = x^2 - xy + 3y^2$

b.  $f(x,\ y) = \sin 3x \cos 3y$

### Solution

For both parts a. and b., we first calculate the partial derivatives $f_x$ and $f_y$, then use Equation 4.39.

a.
$$\begin{aligned}
f_x(x,\ y) &= 2x - y \text{ and } f_y(x,\ y) = -x + 6y, \text{ so} \\
\nabla f(x,\ y) &= f_x(x,\ y)\mathbf{i} + f_y(x,\ y)\mathbf{j} \\
&= (2x - y)\mathbf{i} + (-x + 6y)\mathbf{j}.
\end{aligned}$$

b.
$$\begin{aligned}
f_x(x,\ y) &= 3\cos 3x \cos 3y \text{ and } f_y(x,\ y) = -3\sin 3x \sin 3y, \text{ so} \\
\nabla f(x,\ y) &= f_x(x,\ y)\mathbf{i} + f_y(x,\ y)\mathbf{j} \\
&= (3\cos 3x \cos 3y)\mathbf{i} - (3\sin 3x \sin 3y)\mathbf{j}.
\end{aligned}$$

**4.29** Find the gradient $\nabla f(x, y)$ of $f(x, y) = \left(x^2 - 3y^2\right)/(2x + y)$.

The gradient has some important properties. We have already seen one formula that uses the gradient: the formula for the directional derivative. Recall from **The Dot Product** that if the angle between two vectors $\mathbf{a}$ and $\mathbf{b}$ is $\varphi$, then $\mathbf{a} \cdot \mathbf{b} = \| \mathbf{a} \| \ \| \mathbf{b} \| \cos \varphi$. Therefore, if the angle between $\nabla f(x_0, y_0)$ and $\mathbf{u} = (\cos \theta)\mathbf{i} + (\sin \theta)\mathbf{j}$ is $\varphi$, we have

$$D_{\mathbf{u}} f(x_0, y_0) = \nabla f(x_0, y_0) \cdot \mathbf{u} = \| \nabla f(x_0, y_0) \| \ \| \mathbf{u} \| \cos \varphi = \| \nabla f(x_0, y_0) \| \cos \varphi.$$

The $\| \mathbf{u} \|$ disappears because $\mathbf{u}$ is a unit vector. Therefore, the directional derivative is equal to the magnitude of the gradient evaluated at $(x_0, y_0)$ multiplied by $\cos \varphi$. Recall that $\cos \varphi$ ranges from $-1$ to $1$. If $\varphi = 0$, then $\cos \varphi = 1$ and $\nabla f(x_0, y_0)$ and $\mathbf{u}$ both point in the same direction. If $\varphi = \pi$, then $\cos \varphi = -1$ and $\nabla f(x_0, y_0)$ and $\mathbf{u}$ point in opposite directions. In the first case, the value of $D_{\mathbf{u}} f(x_0, y_0)$ is maximized; in the second case, the value of $D_{\mathbf{u}} f(x_0, y_0)$ is minimized. If $\nabla f(x_0, y_0) = 0$, then $D_{\mathbf{u}} f(x_0, y_0) = \nabla f(x_0, y_0) \cdot \mathbf{u} = 0$ for any vector $\mathbf{u}$. These three cases are outlined in the following theorem.

---

**Theorem 4.13: Properties of the Gradient**

Suppose the function $z = f(x, y)$ is differentiable at $(x_0, y_0)$ (**Figure 4.41**).

   i.   If $\nabla f(x_0, y_0) = \mathbf{0}$, then $D_{\mathbf{u}} f(x_0, y_0) = 0$ for any unit vector $\mathbf{u}$.

  ii.   If $\nabla f(x_0, y_0) \neq \mathbf{0}$, then $D_{\mathbf{u}} f(x_0, y_0)$ is maximized when $\mathbf{u}$ points in the same direction as $\nabla f(x_0, y_0)$. The maximum value of $D_{\mathbf{u}} f(x_0, y_0)$ is $\| \nabla f(x_0, y_0) \|$.

 iii.   If $\nabla f(x_0, y_0) \neq \mathbf{0}$, then $D_{\mathbf{u}} f(x_0, y_0)$ is minimized when $\mathbf{u}$ points in the opposite direction from $\nabla f(x_0, y_0)$. The minimum value of $D_{\mathbf{u}} f(x_0, y_0)$ is $- \| \nabla f(x_0, y_0) \|$.

---

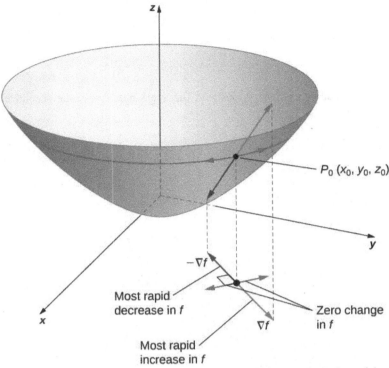

**Figure 4.41** The gradient indicates the maximum and minimum values of the directional derivative at a point.

## Example 4.34

### Finding a Maximum Directional Derivative

Find the direction for which the directional derivative of $f(x, y) = 3x^2 - 4xy + 2y^2$ at $(-2, 3)$ is a maximum. What is the maximum value?

### Solution

The maximum value of the directional derivative occurs when $\nabla f$ and the unit vector point in the same direction. Therefore, we start by calculating $\nabla f(x, y)$:

$$f_x(x, y) = 6x - 4y \text{ and } f_y(x, y) = -4x + 4y, \text{ so}$$
$$\nabla f(x, y) = f_x(x, y)\mathbf{i} + f_y(x, y)\mathbf{j} = (6x - 4y)\mathbf{i} + (-4x + 4y)\mathbf{j}.$$

Next, we evaluate the gradient at $(-2, 3)$:

$$\nabla f(-2, 3) = (6(-2) - 4(3))\mathbf{i} + (-4(-2) + 4(3))\mathbf{j} = -24\mathbf{i} + 20\mathbf{j}.$$

We need to find a unit vector that points in the same direction as $\nabla f(-2, 3)$, so the next step is to divide $\nabla f(-2, 3)$ by its magnitude, which is $\sqrt{(-24)^2 + (20)^2} = \sqrt{976} = 4\sqrt{61}$. Therefore,

$$\frac{\nabla f(-2, 3)}{\| \nabla f(-2, 3) \|} = \frac{-24}{4\sqrt{61}}\mathbf{i} + \frac{20}{4\sqrt{61}}\mathbf{j} = \frac{-6\sqrt{61}}{61}\mathbf{i} + \frac{5\sqrt{61}}{61}\mathbf{j}.$$

This is the unit vector that points in the same direction as $\nabla f(-2, 3)$. To find the angle corresponding to this

unit vector, we solve the equations

$$\cos\theta = \frac{-6\sqrt{61}}{61} \text{ and } \sin\theta = \frac{5\sqrt{61}}{61}$$

for $\theta$. Since cosine is negative and sine is positive, the angle must be in the second quadrant. Therefore, $\theta = \pi - \arcsin\left((5\sqrt{61})/61\right) \approx 2.45 \text{ rad}$.

The maximum value of the directional derivative at $(-2, 3)$ is $\|\nabla f(-2, 3)\| = 4\sqrt{61}$ (see the following figure).

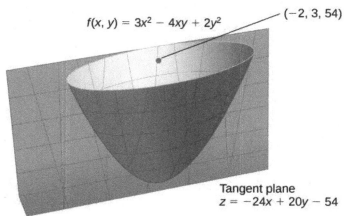

**Figure 4.42** The maximum value of the directional derivative at $(-2, 3)$ is in the direction of the gradient.

 **4.30** Find the direction for which the directional derivative of $g(x, y) = 4x - xy + 2y^2$ at $(-2, 3)$ is a maximum. What is the maximum value?

Figure 4.43 shows a portion of the graph of the function $f(x, y) = 3 + \sin x \sin y$. Given a point $(a, b)$ in the domain of $f$, the maximum value of the gradient at that point is given by $\|\nabla f(a, b)\|$. This would equal the rate of greatest ascent if the surface represented a topographical map. If we went in the opposite direction, it would be the rate of greatest descent.

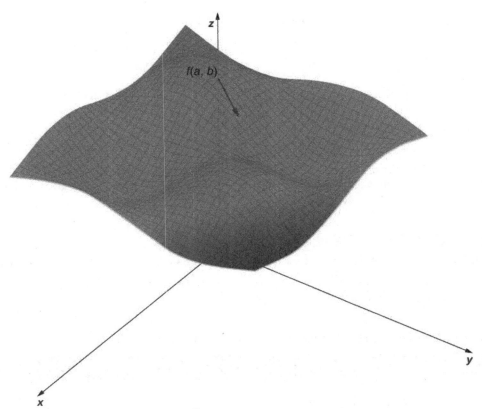

**Figure 4.43** A typical surface in $\mathbb{R}^3$. Given a point on the surface, the directional derivative can be calculated using the gradient.

When using a topographical map, the steepest slope is always in the direction where the contour lines are closest together (see **Figure 4.44**). This is analogous to the contour map of a function, assuming the level curves are obtained for equally spaced values throughout the range of that function.

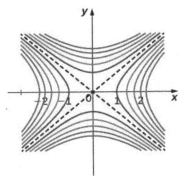

**Figure 4.44** Contour map for the function $f(x, y) = x^2 - y^2$ using level values between $-5$ and $5$.

## Gradients and Level Curves

Recall that if a curve is defined parametrically by the function pair $(x(t), y(t))$, then the vector $x'(t)\mathbf{i} + y'(t)\mathbf{j}$ is tangent to the curve for every value of $t$ in the domain. Now let's assume $z = f(x, y)$ is a differentiable function of $x$ and $y$, and $(x_0, y_0)$ is in its domain. Let's suppose further that $x_0 = x(t_0)$ and $y_0 = y(t_0)$ for some value of $t$, and consider the level curve $f(x, y) = k$. Define $g(t) = f(x(t), y(t))$ and calculate $g'(t)$ on the level curve. By the chain Rule,

$$g'(t) = f_x(x(t), y(t))x'(t) + f_y(x(t), y(t))y'(t).$$

But $g'(t) = 0$ because $g(t) = k$ for all $t$. Therefore, on the one hand,

$$f_x(x(t), y(t))x'(t) + f_y(x(t), y(t))y'(t) = 0;$$

on the other hand,

$$f_x(x(t), y(t))x'(t) + f_y(x(t), y(t))y'(t) = \nabla f(x, y) \cdot \langle x'(t), y'(t) \rangle.$$

Therefore,

$$\nabla f(x, y) \cdot \langle x'(t), y'(t) \rangle = 0.$$

Thus, the dot product of these vectors is equal to zero, which implies they are orthogonal. However, the second vector is tangent to the level curve, which implies the gradient must be normal to the level curve, which gives rise to the following theorem.

### Theorem 4.14: Gradient Is Normal to the Level Curve

Suppose the function $z = f(x, y)$ has continuous first-order partial derivatives in an open disk centered at a point $(x_0, y_0)$. If $\nabla f(x_0, y_0) \neq \mathbf{0}$, then $\nabla f(x_0, y_0)$ is normal to the level curve of $f$ at $(x_0, y_0)$.

We can use this theorem to find tangent and normal vectors to level curves of a function.

### Example 4.35

#### Finding Tangents to Level Curves

For the function $f(x, y) = 2x^2 - 3xy + 8y^2 + 2x - 4y + 4$, find a tangent vector to the level curve at point $(-2, 1)$. Graph the level curve corresponding to $f(x, y) = 18$ and draw in $\nabla f(-2, 1)$ and a tangent vector.

#### Solution
First, we must calculate $\nabla f(x, y)$:

$$f_x(x, y) = 4x - 3y + 2 \text{ and } f_y = -3x + 16y - 4 \text{ so } \nabla f(x, y) = (4x - 3y + 2)\mathbf{i} + (-3x + 16y - 4)\mathbf{j}.$$

Next, we evaluate $\nabla f(x, y)$ at $(-2, 1)$:

$$\nabla f(-2, 1) = (4(-2) - 3(1) + 2)\mathbf{i} + (-3(-2) + 16(1) - 4)\mathbf{j} = -9\mathbf{i} + 18\mathbf{j}.$$

This vector is orthogonal to the curve at point $(-2, 1)$. We can obtain a tangent vector by reversing the components and multiplying either one by $-1$. Thus, for example, $-18\mathbf{i} - 9\mathbf{j}$ is a tangent vector (see the following graph).

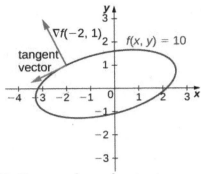

Figure 4.45  Tangent and normal vectors to
$2x^2 - 3xy + 8y^2 + 2x - 4y + 4 = 18$ at point $(-2, 1)$.

 **4.31**  For the function $f(x, y) = x^2 - 2xy + 5y^2 + 3x - 2y + 4$, find the tangent to the level curve at point $(1, 1)$. Draw the graph of the level curve corresponding to $f(x, y) = 8$ and draw $\nabla f(1, 1)$ and a tangent vector.

## Three-Dimensional Gradients and Directional Derivatives

The definition of a gradient can be extended to functions of more than two variables.

---

**Definition**

Let $w = f(x, y, z)$ be a function of three variables such that $f_x$, $f_y$, and $f_z$ exist. The vector $\nabla f(x, y, z)$ is called the gradient of $f$ and is defined as

$$\nabla f(x, y, z) = f_x(x, y, z)\mathbf{i} + f_y(x, y, z)\mathbf{j} + f_z(x, y, z)\mathbf{k}. \tag{4.40}$$

$\nabla f(x, y, z)$ can also be written as grad $f(x, y, z)$.

---

Calculating the gradient of a function in three variables is very similar to calculating the gradient of a function in two variables. First, we calculate the partial derivatives $f_x$, $f_y$, and $f_z$, and then we use Equation 4.40.

### Example 4.36

#### Finding Gradients in Three Dimensions

Find the gradient $\nabla f(x, y, z)$ of each of the following functions:

a.  $f(x, y) = 5x^2 - 2xy + y^2 - 4yz + z^2 + 3xz$

b.  $f(x, y, z) = e^{-2z} \sin 2x \cos 2y$

**Solution**

For both parts a. and b., we first calculate the partial derivatives $f_x$, $f_y$, and $f_z$, then use **Equation 4.40**.

a.

$$f_z(x, y, z) = 10x - 2y + 3z, \ f_y(x, y, z) = -2x + 2y - 4z \text{ and } f_z(x, y, z) = 3x - 4y + 2z, \text{ so}$$

$$\nabla f(x, y, z) = f_x(x, y, z)\mathbf{i} + f_y(x, y, z)\mathbf{j} + f_z(x, y, z)\mathbf{k}$$

$$= (10x - 2y + 3z)\mathbf{i} + (-2x + 2y - 4z)\mathbf{j} + (-4x + 3y + 2z)\mathbf{k}.$$

b.

$$f_x(x, y, z) = -2e^{-2z}\cos 2x \cos 2y, \ f_y(x, y, z) = -2e^{-2z}\sin 2x \sin 2y \text{ and}$$

$$f_z(x, y, z) = -2e^{-2z}\sin 2x \cos 2y, \text{ so}$$

$$\nabla f(x, y, z) = f_x(x, y, z)\mathbf{i} + f_y(x, y, z)\mathbf{j} + f_z(x, y, z)\mathbf{k}$$

$$= \left(2e^{-2z}\cos 2x \cos 2y\right)\mathbf{i} + \left(-2e^{-2z}\right)\mathbf{j} + \left(-2e^{-2z}\right)$$

$$= 2e^{-2z}(\cos 2x \cos 2y \, \mathbf{i} - \sin 2x \sin 2y \, \mathbf{j} - \sin 2x \cos 2y \, \mathbf{k}).$$

 **4.32**  Find the gradient $\nabla f(x, y, z)$ of $f(x, y, z) = \dfrac{x^2 - 3y^2 + z^2}{2x + y - 4z}$.

The directional derivative can also be generalized to functions of three variables. To determine a direction in three dimensions, a vector with three components is needed. This vector is a unit vector, and the components of the unit vector are called *directional cosines*. Given a three-dimensional unit vector $\mathbf{u}$ in standard form (i.e., the initial point is at the origin), this vector forms three different angles with the positive $x-$, $y-$, and z-axes. Let's call these angles $\alpha$, $\beta$, and $\gamma$. Then the directional cosines are given by $\cos\alpha$, $\cos\beta$, and $\cos\gamma$. These are the components of the unit vector $\mathbf{u}$; since $\mathbf{u}$ is a unit vector, it is true that $\cos^2\alpha + \cos^2\beta + \cos^2\gamma = 1$.

---

**Definition**

Suppose $w = f(x, y, z)$ is a function of three variables with a domain of $D$. Let $(x_0, y_0, z_0) \in D$ and let $\mathbf{u} = \cos\alpha\mathbf{i} + \cos\beta\mathbf{j} + \cos\gamma\mathbf{k}$ be a unit vector. Then, the directional derivative of $f$ in the direction of $u$ is given by

$$D_{\mathbf{u}} f(x_0, y_0, z_0) = \lim_{t \to 0} \frac{f(x_0 + t\cos\alpha, \ y_0 + t\cos\beta, \ z_0 + t\cos\gamma) - f(x_0, y_0, z_0)}{t}, \tag{4.41}$$

provided the limit exists.

---

We can calculate the directional derivative of a function of three variables by using the gradient, leading to a formula that is analogous to **Equation 4.38**.

---

**Theorem 4.15: Directional Derivative of a Function of Three Variables**

Let $f(x, y, z)$ be a differentiable function of three variables and let $\mathbf{u} = \cos\alpha\mathbf{i} + \cos\beta\mathbf{j} + \cos\gamma\mathbf{k}$ be a unit vector. Then, the directional derivative of $f$ in the direction of $\mathbf{u}$ is given by

$$D_{\mathbf{u}} f(x, y, z) = \nabla f(x, y, z) \cdot \mathbf{u} \tag{4.42}$$

$$= f_x(x, y, z)\cos\alpha + f_y(x, y, z)\cos\beta + f_z(x, y, z)\cos\gamma.$$

The three angles $\alpha$, $\beta$, and $\gamma$ determine the unit vector **u**. In practice, we can use an arbitrary (nonunit) vector, then divide by its magnitude to obtain a unit vector in the desired direction.

## Example 4.37

### Finding a Directional Derivative in Three Dimensions

Calculate $D_{\mathbf{u}} f(1, -2, 3)$ in the direction of $\mathbf{v} = -\mathbf{i} + 2\mathbf{j} + 2\mathbf{k}$ for the function

$$f(x, y, z) = 5x^2 - 2xy + y^2 - 4yz + z^2 + 3xz.$$

**Solution**

First, we find the magnitude of **v**:

$$\| \mathbf{v} \| = \sqrt{(-1)^2 + (2)^2} = 3.$$

Therefore, $\dfrac{\mathbf{v}}{\| \mathbf{v} \|} = \dfrac{-\mathbf{i} + 2\mathbf{j} + 2\mathbf{k}}{3} = -\dfrac{1}{3}\mathbf{i} + \dfrac{2}{3}\mathbf{j} + \dfrac{2}{3}\mathbf{k}$ is a unit vector in the direction of **v**, so $\cos \alpha = -\dfrac{1}{3}$, $\cos \beta = \dfrac{2}{3}$, and $\cos \gamma = \dfrac{2}{3}$. Next, we calculate the partial derivatives of $f$:

$$\begin{aligned}
f_x(x, y, z) &= 10x - 2y + 3z \\
f_y(x, y, z) &= -2x + 2y - 4z \\
f_z(x, y, z) &= -4y + 2z + 3x,
\end{aligned}$$

then substitute them into **Equation 4.42**:

$$\begin{aligned}
D_{\mathbf{u}} f(x, y, z) &= f_x(x, y, z)\cos \alpha + f_y(x, y, z)\cos \beta + f_z(x, y, z)\cos \gamma \\
&= (10x - 2y + 3z)\left(-\frac{1}{3}\right) + (-2x + 2y - 4z)\left(\frac{2}{3}\right) + (-4y + 2z + 3x)\left(\frac{2}{3}\right) \\
&= -\frac{10x}{3} + \frac{2y}{3} - \frac{3z}{3} - \frac{4x}{3} + \frac{4y}{3} - \frac{8z}{3} - \frac{8y}{3} + \frac{4z}{3} + \frac{6x}{3} \\
&= -\frac{8x}{3} - \frac{2y}{3} - \frac{7z}{3}.
\end{aligned}$$

Last, to find $D_{\mathbf{u}} f(1, -2, 3)$, we substitute $x = 1$, $y = -2$, and $z = 3$:

$$\begin{aligned}
D_{\mathbf{u}} f(1, -2, 3) &= -\frac{8(1)}{3} - \frac{2(-2)}{3} - \frac{7(3)}{3} \\
&= -\frac{8}{3} + \frac{4}{3} - \frac{21}{3} \\
&= -\frac{25}{3}.
\end{aligned}$$

 **4.33** Calculate $D_{\mathbf{u}} f(x, y, z)$ and $D_{\mathbf{u}} f(0, -2, 5)$ in the direction of $\mathbf{v} = -3\mathbf{i} + 12\mathbf{j} - 4\mathbf{k}$ for the function $f(x, y, z) = 3x^2 + xy - 2y^2 + 4yz - z^2 + 2xz.$

# 4.6 EXERCISES

For the following exercises, find the directional derivative using the limit definition only.

260. $f(x, y) = 5 - 2x^2 - \frac{1}{2}y^2$ at point $P(3, 4)$ in the direction of $u = \left(\cos\frac{\pi}{4}\right)i + \left(\sin\frac{\pi}{4}\right)j$

261. $f(x, y) = y^2 \cos(2x)$ at point $P\left(\frac{\pi}{3}, 2\right)$ in the direction of $u = \left(\cos\frac{\pi}{4}\right)i + \left(\sin\frac{\pi}{4}\right)j$

262. Find the directional derivative of $f(x, y) = y^2 \sin(2x)$ at point $P\left(\frac{\pi}{4}, 2\right)$ in the direction of $u = 5i + 12j$.

For the following exercises, find the directional derivative of the function at point $P$ in the direction of $v$.

263. $f(x, y) = xy$, $P(0, -2)$, $v = \frac{1}{2}i + \frac{\sqrt{3}}{2}j$

264. $h(x, y) = e^x \sin y$, $P\left(1, \frac{\pi}{2}\right)$, $v = -i$

265. $h(x, y, z) = xyz$, $P(2, 1, 1)$, $v = 2i + j - k$

266. $f(x, y) = xy$, $P(1, 1)$, $u = \langle \frac{\sqrt{2}}{2}, \frac{\sqrt{2}}{2} \rangle$

267. $f(x, y) = x^2 - y^2$, $u = \langle \frac{\sqrt{3}}{2}, \frac{1}{2} \rangle$, $P(1, 0)$

268. $f(x, y) = 3x + 4y + 7$, $u = \langle \frac{3}{5}, \frac{4}{5} \rangle$, $P\left(0, \frac{\pi}{2}\right)$

269. $f(x, y) = e^x \cos y$, $u = \langle 0, 1 \rangle$, $P = \left(0, \frac{\pi}{2}\right)$

270. $f(x, y) = y^{10}$, $u = \langle 0, -1 \rangle$, $P = (1, -1)$

271. $f(x, y) = \ln(x^2 + y^2)$, $u = \langle \frac{3}{5}, \frac{4}{5} \rangle$, $P(1, 2)$

272. $f(x, y) = x^2 y$, $P(-5, 5)$, $v = 3i - 4j$

273. $f(x, y) = y^2 + xz$, $P(1, 2, 2)$, $v = \langle 2, -1, 2 \rangle$

For the following exercises, find the directional derivative of the function in the direction of the unit vector $u = \cos\theta i + \sin\theta j$.

274. $f(x, y) = x^2 + 2y^2$, $\theta = \frac{\pi}{6}$

275. $f(x, y) = \frac{y}{x + 2y}$, $\theta = -\frac{\pi}{4}$

276. $f(x, y) = \cos(3x + y)$, $\theta = \frac{\pi}{4}$

277. $w(x, y) = ye^x$, $\theta = \frac{\pi}{3}$

278. $f(x, y) = x \arctan(y)$, $\theta = \frac{\pi}{2}$

279. $f(x, y) = \ln(x + 2y)$, $\theta = \frac{\pi}{3}$

For the following exercises, find the gradient.

280. Find the gradient of $f(x, y) = \frac{14 - x^2 - y^2}{3}$. Then, find the gradient at point $P(1, 2)$.

281. Find the gradient of $f(x, y, z) = xy + yz + xz$ at point $P(1, 2, 3)$.

282. Find the gradient of $f(x, y, z)$ at $P$ and in the direction of $u$: $f(x, y, z) = \ln(x^2 + 2y^2 + 3z^2)$, $P(2, 1, 4)$, $u = \frac{-3}{13}i - \frac{4}{13}j - \frac{12}{13}k$.

283. $f(x, y, z) = 4x^5 y^2 z^3$, $P(2, -1, 1)$, $u = \frac{1}{3}i + \frac{2}{3}j - \frac{2}{3}k$

For the following exercises, find the directional derivative of the function at point $P$ in the direction of $Q$.

284. $f(x, y) = x^2 + 3y^2$, $P(1, 1)$, $Q(4, 5)$

285. $f(x, y, z) = \frac{y}{x + z}$, $P(2, 1, -1)$, $Q(-1, 2, 0)$

For the following exercises, find the derivative of the function at $P$ in the direction of $u$.

286. $f(x, y) = -7x + 2y$, $P(2, -4)$, $u = 4i - 3j$

287. $f(x, y) = \ln(5x + 4y)$, $P(3, 9)$, $u = 6i + 8j$

288. [T] Use technology to sketch the level curve of $f(x, y) = 4x - 2y + 3$ that passes through $P(1, 2)$ and draw the gradient vector at $P$.

**289.** **[T]** Use technology to sketch the level curve of $f(x, y) = x^2 + 4y^2$ that passes through $P(-2, 0)$ and draw the gradient vector at $P$.

For the following exercises, find the gradient vector at the indicated point.

**290.** $f(x, y) = xy^2 - yx^2,\ P(-1, 1)$

**291.** $f(x, y) = xe^y - \ln(x),\ P(-3, 0)$

**292.** $f(x, y, z) = xy - \ln(z),\ P(2, -2, 2)$

**293.** $f(x, y, z) = x\sqrt{y^2 + z^2},\ P(-2, -1, -1)$

For the following exercises, find the derivative of the function.

**294.** $f(x, y) = x^2 + xy + y^2$ at point $(-5, -4)$ in the direction the function increases most rapidly

**295.** $f(x, y) = e^{xy}$ at point $(6, 7)$ in the direction the function increases most rapidly

**296.** $f(x, y) = \arctan\left(\frac{y}{x}\right)$ at point $(-9, 9)$ in the direction the function increases most rapidly

**297.** $f(x, y, z) = \ln(xy + yz + zx)$ at point $(-9, -18, -27)$ in the direction the function increases most rapidly

**298.** $f(x, y, z) = \frac{x}{y} + \frac{y}{z} + \frac{z}{x}$ at point $(5, -5, 5)$ in the direction the function increases most rapidly

For the following exercises, find the maximum rate of change of $f$ at the given point and the direction in which it occurs.

**299.** $f(x, y) = xe^{-y},\quad (1, 0)$

**300.** $f(x, y) = \sqrt{x^2 + 2y},\quad (4, 10)$

**301.** $f(x, y) = \cos(3x + 2y),\ \left(\frac{\pi}{6}, -\frac{\pi}{8}\right)$

For the following exercises, find equations of

a. the tangent plane and

b. the normal line to the given surface at the given point.

**302.** The level curve $f(x, y, z) = 12$ for $f(x, y, z) = 4x^2 - 2y^2 + z^2$ at point $(2, 2, 2)$.

**303.** $f(x, y, z) = xy + yz + xz = 3$ at point $(1, 1, 1)$

**304.** $f(x, y, z) = xyz = 6$ at point $(1, 2, 3)$

**305.** $f(x, y, z) = xe^y \cos z - z = 1$ at point $(1, 0, 0)$

For the following exercises, solve the problem.

**306.** The temperature $T$ in a metal sphere is inversely proportional to the distance from the center of the sphere (the origin: $(0, 0, 0)$). The temperature at point $(1, 2, 2)$ is $120°C$.

    a. Find the rate of change of the temperature at point $(1, 2, 2)$ in the direction toward point $(2, 1, 3)$.

    b. Show that, at any point in the sphere, the direction of greatest increase in temperature is given by a vector that points toward the origin.

**307.** The electrical potential (voltage) in a certain region of space is given by the function $V(x, y, z) = 5x^2 - 3xy + xyz$.

    a. Find the rate of change of the voltage at point $(3, 4, 5)$ in the direction of the vector $\langle 1, 1, -1 \rangle$.

    b. In which direction does the voltage change most rapidly at point $(3, 4, 5)$?

    c. What is the maximum rate of change of the voltage at point $(3, 4, 5)$?

**308.** If the electric potential at a point $(x, y)$ in the $xy$-plane is $V(x, y) = e^{-2x} \cos(2y)$, then the electric intensity vector at $(x, y)$ is $\mathbf{E} = -\nabla V(x, y)$.

    a. Find the electric intensity vector at $\left(\frac{\pi}{4}, 0\right)$.

    b. Show that, at each point in the plane, the electric potential decreases most rapidly in the direction of the vector $\mathbf{E}$.

**309.** In two dimensions, the motion of an ideal fluid is governed by a velocity potential $\varphi$. The velocity components of the fluid $u$ in the $x$-direction and $v$ in the $y$-direction, are given by $\langle u, v \rangle = \nabla \varphi$. Find the velocity components associated with the velocity potential $\varphi(x, y) = \sin \pi x \sin 2\pi y$.

# 4.7 | Maxima/Minima Problems

## Learning Objectives

**4.7.1** Use partial derivatives to locate critical points for a function of two variables.

**4.7.2** Apply a second derivative test to identify a critical point as a local maximum, local minimum, or saddle point for a function of two variables.

**4.7.3** Examine critical points and boundary points to find absolute maximum and minimum values for a function of two variables.

One of the most useful applications for derivatives of a function of one variable is the determination of maximum and/or minimum values. This application is also important for functions of two or more variables, but as we have seen in earlier sections of this chapter, the introduction of more independent variables leads to more possible outcomes for the calculations. The main ideas of finding critical points and using derivative tests are still valid, but new wrinkles appear when assessing the results.

## Critical Points

For functions of a single variable, we defined critical points as the values of the function when the derivative equals zero or does not exist. For functions of two or more variables, the concept is essentially the same, except for the fact that we are now working with partial derivatives.

### Definition

Let $z = f(x, y)$ be a function of two variables that is defined on an open set containing the point $(x_0, y_0)$. The point $(x_0, y_0)$ is called a **critical point of a function of two variables** $f$ if one of the two following conditions holds:

1. $f_x(x_0, y_0) = f_y(x_0, y_0) = 0$

2. Either $f_x(x_0, y_0)$ or $f_y(x_0, y_0)$ does not exist.

### Example 4.38

#### Finding Critical Points

Find the critical points of each of the following functions:

a. $f(x, y) = \sqrt{4y^2 - 9x^2 + 24y + 36x + 36}$

b. $g(x, y) = x^2 + 2xy - 4y^2 + 4x - 6y + 4$

#### Solution

a. First, we calculate $f_x(x, y)$ and $f_y(x, y)$:

$$f_x(x, y) = \tfrac{1}{2}(-18x + 36)\left(4y^2 - 9x^2 + 24y + 36x + 36\right)^{-1/2}$$

$$= \frac{-9x + 18}{\sqrt{4y^2 - 9x^2 + 24y + 36x + 36}}$$

$$f_y(x, y) = \tfrac{1}{2}(8y + 24)\left(4y^2 - 9x^2 + 24y + 36x + 36\right)^{-1/2}$$

$$= \frac{4y + 12}{\sqrt{4y^2 - 9x^2 + 24y + 36x + 36}}.$$

Next, we set each of these expressions equal to zero:

$$\frac{-9x + 18}{\sqrt{4y^2 - 9x^2 + 24y + 36x + 36}} = 0$$

$$\frac{4y + 12}{\sqrt{4y^2 - 9x^2 + 24y + 36x + 36}} = 0.$$

Then, multiply each equation by its common denominator:

$$-9x + 18 = 0$$

$$4y + 12 = 0.$$

Therefore, $x = 2$ and $y = -3$, so $(2, -3)$ is a critical point of $f$.

We must also check for the possibility that the denominator of each partial derivative can equal zero, thus causing the partial derivative not to exist. Since the denominator is the same in each partial derivative, we need only do this once:

$$4y^2 - 9x^2 + 24y + 36x + 36 = 0.$$

This equation represents a hyperbola. We should also note that the domain of $f$ consists of points satisfying the inequality

$$4y^2 - 9x^2 + 24y + 36x + 36 \geq 0.$$

Therefore, any points on the hyperbola are not only critical points, they are also on the boundary of the domain. To put the hyperbola in standard form, we use the method of completing the square:

$$4y^2 - 9x^2 + 24y + 36x + 36 = 0$$
$$4y^2 - 9x^2 + 24y + 36x = -36$$
$$4y^2 + 24y - 9x^2 + 36x = -36$$
$$4(y^2 + 6y) - 9(x^2 - 4x) = -36$$
$$4(y^2 + 6y + 9) - 9(x^2 - 4x + 4) = -36 + 36 - 36$$
$$4(y + 3)^2 - 9(x - 2)^2 = -36.$$

Dividing both sides by $-36$ puts the equation in standard form:

$$\frac{4(y+3)^2}{-36} - \frac{9(x-2)^2}{-36} = 1$$

$$\frac{(x-2)^2}{4} - \frac{(y+3)^2}{9} = 1.$$

Notice that point $(2, -3)$ is the center of the hyperbola.

b.  First, we calculate $g_x(x, y)$ and $g_y(x, y)$:

$$g_x(x, y) = 2x + 2y + 4$$
$$g_y(x, y) = 2x - 8y - 6.$$

Next, we set each of these expressions equal to zero, which gives a system of equations in $x$ and $y$:

$$2x + 2y + 4 = 0$$
$$2x - 8y - 6 = 0.$$

Subtracting the second equation from the first gives $10y + 10 = 0$, so $y = -1$. Substituting this into the first equation gives $2x + 2(-1) + 4 = 0$, so $x = -1$. Therefore $(-1, -1)$ is a critical point of $g$ (Figure 4.46). There are no points in $\mathbb{R}^2$ that make either partial derivative not exist.

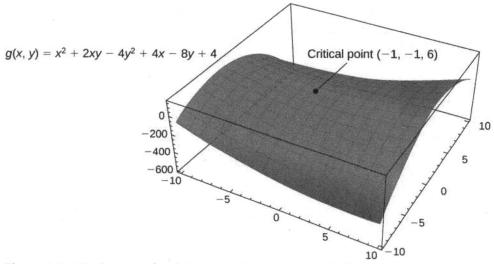

**Figure 4.46** The function $g(x, y)$ has a critical point at $(-1, -1, 6)$.

 **4.34** Find the critical point of the function $f(x, y) = x^3 + 2xy - 2x - 4y$.

The main purpose for determining critical points is to locate relative maxima and minima, as in single-variable calculus. When working with a function of one variable, the definition of a local extremum involves finding an interval around the critical point such that the function value is either greater than or less than all the other function values in that interval. When working with a function of two or more variables, we work with an open disk around the point.

## Definition

Let $z = f(x, y)$ be a function of two variables that is defined and continuous on an open set containing the point $(x_0, y_0)$. Then $f$ has a *local maximum* at $(x_0, y_0)$ if

$$f(x_0, y_0) \geq f(x, y)$$

for all points $(x, y)$ within some disk centered at $(x_0, y_0)$. The number $f(x_0, y_0)$ is called a *local maximum value*. If the preceding inequality holds for every point $(x, y)$ in the domain of $f$, then $f$ has a *global maximum* (also called an *absolute maximum*) at $(x_0, y_0)$.

The function $f$ has a *local minimum* at $(x_0, y_0)$ if

$$f(x_0, y_0) \leq f(x, y)$$

for all points $(x, y)$ within some disk centered at $(x_0, y_0)$. The number $f(x_0, y_0)$ is called a *local minimum value*. If the preceding inequality holds for every point $(x, y)$ in the domain of $f$, then $f$ has a *global minimum* (also called an *absolute minimum*) at $(x_0, y_0)$.

If $f(x_0, y_0)$ is either a local maximum or local minimum value, then it is called a *local extremum* (see the following figure).

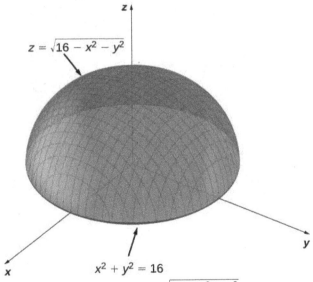

**Figure 4.47** The graph of $z = \sqrt{16 - x^2 - y^2}$ has a maximum value when $(x, y) = (0, 0)$. It attains its minimum value at the boundary of its domain, which is the circle $x^2 + y^2 = 16$.

In **Maxima and Minima (http://cnx.org/content/m53611/latest/)** , we showed that extrema of functions of one variable occur at critical points. The same is true for functions of more than one variable, as stated in the following theorem.

## Theorem 4.16: Fermat's Theorem for Functions of Two Variables

Let $z = f(x, y)$ be a function of two variables that is defined and continuous on an open set containing the point

$(x_0, y_0)$. Suppose $f_x$ and $f_y$ each exists at $(x_0, y_0)$. If $f$ has a local extremum at $(x_0, y_0)$, then $(x_0, y_0)$ is a critical point of $f$.

## Second Derivative Test

Consider the function $f(x) = x^3$. This function has a critical point at $x = 0$, since $f'(0) = 3(0)^2 = 0$. However, $f$ does not have an extreme value at $x = 0$. Therefore, the existence of a critical value at $x = x_0$ does not guarantee a local extremum at $x = x_0$. The same is true for a function of two or more variables. One way this can happen is at a **saddle point**. An example of a saddle point appears in the following figure.

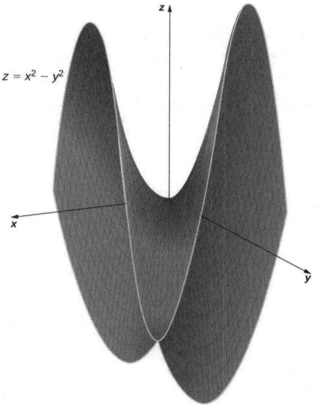

**Figure 4.48** Graph of the function $z = x^2 - y^2$. This graph has a saddle point at the origin.

In this graph, the origin is a saddle point. This is because the first partial derivatives of $f(x, y) = x^2 - y^2$ are both equal to zero at this point, but it is neither a maximum nor a minimum for the function. Furthermore the vertical trace corresponding to $y = 0$ is $z = x^2$ (a parabola opening upward), but the vertical trace corresponding to $x = 0$ is $z = -y^2$ (a parabola opening downward). Therefore, it is both a global maximum for one trace and a global minimum for another.

### Definition

Given the function $z = f(x, y)$, the point $\left(x_0, y_0, f(x_0, y_0)\right)$ is a saddle point if both $f_0(x_0, y_0) = 0$ and $f_y(x_0, y_0) = 0$, but $f$ does not have a local extremum at $(x_0, y_0)$.

The second derivative test for a function of one variable provides a method for determining whether an extremum occurs at a critical point of a function. When extending this result to a function of two variables, an issue arises related to the fact that there are, in fact, four different second-order partial derivatives, although equality of mixed partials reduces this to three. The second derivative test for a function of two variables, stated in the following theorem, uses a **discriminant** $D$ that replaces $f''(x_0)$ in the second derivative test for a function of one variable.

---

### Theorem 4.17: Second Derivative Test

Let $z = f(x, y)$ be a function of two variables for which the first- and second-order partial derivatives are continuous on some disk containing the point $(x_0, y_0)$. Suppose $f_x(x_0, y_0) = 0$ and $f_y(x_0, y_0) = 0$. Define the quantity

$$D = f_{xx}(x_0, y_0)f_{yy}(x_0, y_0) - \left(f_{xy}(x_0, y_0)\right)^2. \tag{4.43}$$

i.   If $D > 0$ and $f_{xx}(x_0, y_0) > 0$, then $f$ has a local minimum at $(x_0, y_0)$.

ii.  If $D > 0$ and $f_{xx}(x_0, y_0) < 0$, then $f$ has a local maximum at $(x_0, y_0)$.

iii. If $D < 0$, , then $f$ has a saddle point at $(x_0, y_0)$.

iv.  If $D = 0$, then the test is inconclusive.

See Figure 4.49.

---

(a)                              (b)                              (c)

**Figure 4.49** The second derivative test can often determine whether a function of two variables has a local minima (a), a local maxima (b), or a saddle point (c).

To apply the second derivative test, it is necessary that we first find the critical points of the function. There are several steps involved in the entire procedure, which are outlined in a problem-solving strategy.

---

### Problem-Solving Strategy: Using the Second Derivative Test for Functions of Two Variables

Let $z = f(x, y)$ be a function of two variables for which the first- and second-order partial derivatives are continuous on some disk containing the point $(x_0, y_0)$. To apply the second derivative test to find local extrema, use the following steps:

1. Determine the critical points $(x_0, y_0)$ of the function $f$ where $f_x(x_0, y_0) = f_y(x_0, y_0) = 0$. Discard any points where at least one of the partial derivatives does not exist.

2. Calculate the discriminant $D = f_{xx}(x_0, y_0)f_{yy}(x_0, y_0) - \left(f_{xy}(x_0, y_0)\right)^2$ for each critical point of $f$.

3. Apply **Second Derivative Test** to determine whether each critical point is a local maximum, local minimum, or saddle point, or whether the theorem is inconclusive.

## Example 4.39

### Using the Second Derivative Test

Find the critical points for each of the following functions, and use the second derivative test to find the local extrema:

a. $f(x, y) = 4x^2 + 9y^2 + 8x - 36y + 24$

b. $g(x, y) = \frac{1}{3}x^3 + y^2 + 2xy - 6x - 3y + 4$

### Solution

a. Step 1 of the problem-solving strategy involves finding the critical points of $f$. To do this, we first calculate $f_x(x, y)$ and $f_y(x, y)$, then set each of them equal to zero:

$$\begin{aligned} f_x(x, y) &= 8x + 8 \\ f_y(x, y) &= 18y - 36. \end{aligned}$$

Setting them equal to zero yields the system of equations

$$\begin{aligned} 8x + 8 &= 0 \\ 18y - 36 &= 0. \end{aligned}$$

The solution to this system is $x = -1$ and $y = 2$. Therefore $(-1, 2)$ is a critical point of $f$.

Step 2 of the problem-solving strategy involves calculating $D$. To do this, we first calculate the second partial derivatives of $f$:

$$\begin{aligned} f_{xx}(x, y) &= 8 \\ f_{xy}(x, y) &= 0 \\ f_{yy}(x, y) &= 18. \end{aligned}$$

Therefore, $D = f_{xx}(-1, 2)f_{yy}(-1, 2) - \left(f_{xy}(-1, 2)\right)^2 = (8)(18) - (0)^2 = 144.$

Step 3 states to check **Fermat's Theorem for Functions of Two Variables**. Since $D > 0$ and $f_{xx}(-1, 2) > 0$, this corresponds to case 1. Therefore, $f$ has a local minimum at $(-1, 2)$ as shown in the following figure.

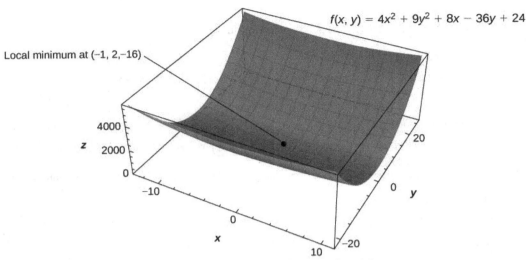

**Figure 4.50** The function $f(x, y)$ has a local minimum at $(-1, 2, -16)$.

b. For step 1, we first calculate $g_x(x, y)$ and $g_y(x, y)$, then set each of them equal to zero:

$$g_x(x, y) = x^2 + 2y - 6$$
$$g_y(x, y) = 2y + 2x - 3.$$

Setting them equal to zero yields the system of equations

$$x^2 + 2y - 6 = 0$$
$$2y + 2x - 3 = 0.$$

To solve this system, first solve the second equation for $y$. This gives $y = \dfrac{3 - 2x}{2}$. Substituting this into the first equation gives

$$x^2 + 3 - 2x - 6 = 0$$
$$x^2 - 2x - 3 = 0$$
$$(x - 3)(x + 1) = 0.$$

Therefore, $x = -1$ or $x = 3$. Substituting these values into the equation $y = \dfrac{3 - 2x}{2}$ yields the critical points $\left(-1, \frac{5}{2}\right)$ and $\left(3, -\frac{3}{2}\right)$.

Step 2 involves calculating the second partial derivatives of $g$:

$$g_{xx}(x, y) = 2x$$
$$g_{xy}(x, y) = 2$$
$$g_{yy}(x, y) = 2.$$

Then, we find a general formula for $D$:

$$D = g_{xx}(x_0, y_0)g_{yy}(x_0, y_0) - \left(g_{xy}(x_0, y_0)\right)^2$$
$$= (2x_0)(2) - 2^2$$
$$= 4x_0 - 4.$$

Next, we substitute each critical point into this formula:

$$D\left(-1, \frac{5}{2}\right) = (2(-1))(2) - (2)^2 = -4 - 4 = -8$$

$$D\left(3, -\frac{3}{2}\right) = (2(3))(2) - (2)^2 = 12 - 4 = 8.$$

In step 3, we note that, applying **Fermat's Theorem for Functions of Two Variables** to point $\left(-1, \frac{5}{2}\right)$ leads to case 3, which means that $\left(-1, \frac{5}{2}\right)$ is a saddle point. Applying the theorem to point $\left(3, -\frac{3}{2}\right)$ leads to case 1, which means that $\left(3, -\frac{3}{2}\right)$ corresponds to a local minimum as shown in the following figure.

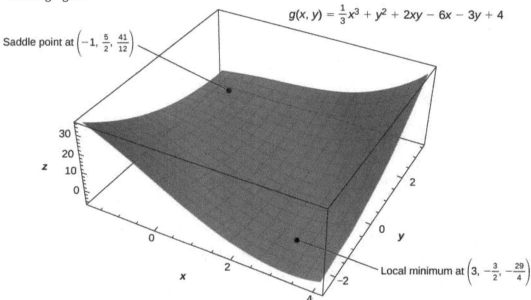

**Figure 4.51** The function $g(x, y)$ has a local minimum and a saddle point.

 **4.35** Use the second derivative to find the local extrema of the function

$$f(x, y) = x^3 + 2xy - 6x - 4y^2.$$

## Absolute Maxima and Minima

When finding global extrema of functions of one variable on a closed interval, we start by checking the critical values over that interval and then evaluate the function at the endpoints of the interval. When working with a function of two variables, the closed interval is replaced by a closed, bounded set. A set is *bounded* if all the points in that set can be contained within a ball (or disk) of finite radius. First, we need to find the critical points inside the set and calculate the corresponding critical values. Then, it is necessary to find the maximum and minimum value of the function on the boundary of the set. When we have all these values, the largest function value corresponds to the global maximum and the smallest function value corresponds to the absolute minimum. First, however, we need to be assured that such values exist. The following theorem does this.

## Theorem 4.18: Extreme Value Theorem

A continuous function $f(x, y)$ on a closed and bounded set $D$ in the plane attains an absolute maximum value at some point of $D$ and an absolute minimum value at some point of $D$.

Now that we know any continuous function $f$ defined on a closed, bounded set attains its extreme values, we need to know how to find them.

## Theorem 4.19: Finding Extreme Values of a Function of Two Variables

Assume $z = f(x, y)$ is a differentiable function of two variables defined on a closed, bounded set $D$. Then $f$ will attain the absolute maximum value and the absolute minimum value, which are, respectively, the largest and smallest values found among the following:

   i.   The values of $f$ at the critical points of $f$ in $D$.

   ii.  The values of $f$ on the boundary of $D$.

The proof of this theorem is a direct consequence of the extreme value theorem and Fermat's theorem. In particular, if either extremum is not located on the boundary of $D$, then it is located at an interior point of $D$. But an interior point $(x_0, y_0)$ of $D$ that's an absolute extremum is also a local extremum; hence, $(x_0, y_0)$ is a critical point of $f$ by Fermat's theorem. Therefore the only possible values for the global extrema of $f$ on $D$ are the extreme values of $f$ on the interior or boundary of $D$.

## Problem-Solving Strategy: Finding Absolute Maximum and Minimum Values

Let $z = f(x, y)$ be a continuous function of two variables defined on a closed, bounded set $D$, and assume $f$ is differentiable on $D$. To find the absolute maximum and minimum values of $f$ on $D$, do the following:

   1.  Determine the critical points of $f$ in $D$.

   2.  Calculate $f$ at each of these critical points.

   3.  Determine the maximum and minimum values of $f$ on the boundary of its domain.

   4.  The maximum and minimum values of $f$ will occur at one of the values obtained in steps 2 and 3.

Finding the maximum and minimum values of $f$ on the boundary of $D$ can be challenging. If the boundary is a rectangle or set of straight lines, then it is possible to parameterize the line segments and determine the maxima on each of these segments, as seen in **Example 4.40**. The same approach can be used for other shapes such as circles and ellipses.

If the boundary of the set $D$ is a more complicated curve defined by a function $g(x, y) = c$ for some constant $c$, and the first-order partial derivatives of $g$ exist, then the method of Lagrange multipliers can prove useful for determining the extrema of $f$ on the boundary. The method of Lagrange multipliers is introduced in **Lagrange Multipliers**.

## Example 4.40

### Finding Absolute Extrema

Use the problem-solving strategy for finding absolute extrema of a function to determine the absolute extrema of each of the following functions:

a.  $f(x, y) = x^2 - 2xy + 4y^2 - 4x - 2y + 24$  on the domain defined by  $0 \leq x \leq 4$  and  $0 \leq y \leq 2$

b.  $g(x, y) = x^2 + y^2 + 4x - 6y$  on the domain defined by  $x^2 + y^2 \leq 16$

### Solution

a.  Using the problem-solving strategy, step 1 involves finding the critical points of  $f$  on its domain. Therefore, we first calculate  $f_x(x, y)$  and  $f_y(x, y)$,  then set them each equal to zero:

$$\begin{aligned} f_x(x, y) &= 2x - 2y - 4 \\ f_y(x, y) &= -2x + 8y - 2. \end{aligned}$$

Setting them equal to zero yields the system of equations

$$\begin{aligned} 2x - 2y - 4 &= 0 \\ -2x + 8y - 2 &= 0. \end{aligned}$$

The solution to this system is  $x = 3$  and  $y = 1$.  Therefore  $(3, 1)$  is a critical point of  $f$.  Calculating  $f(3, 1)$  gives  $f(3, 1) = 17$.

The next step involves finding the extrema of  $f$  on the boundary of its domain. The boundary of its domain consists of four line segments as shown in the following graph:

**Figure 4.52**  Graph of the domain of the function
$f(x, y) = x^2 - 2xy + 4y^2 - 4x - 2y + 24.$

$L_1$  is the line segment connecting  $(0, 0)$  and  $(4, 0)$,  and it can be parameterized by the equations  $x(t) = t, y(t) = 0$  for  $0 \leq t \leq 4$.  Define  $g(t) = f(x(t), y(t))$.  This gives  $g(t) = t^2 - 4t + 24$.  Differentiating  $g$  leads to  $g'(t) = 2t - 4$.  Therefore,  $g$  has a critical value at  $t = 2$,  which corresponds to the point  $(2, 0)$.  Calculating  $f(2, 0)$  gives the z-value 20.

$L_2$  is the line segment connecting  $(4, 0)$  and  $(4, 2)$,  and it can be parameterized by the equations  $x(t) = 4, y(t) = t$  for  $0 \leq t \leq 2$.  Again, define  $g(t) = f(x(t), y(t))$.  This gives  $g(t) = 4t^2 - 10t + 24$.  Then,  $g'(t) = 8t - 10$.  $g$  has a critical value at  $t = \frac{5}{4}$,  which corresponds to the point  $\left(0, \frac{5}{4}\right)$.

Calculating $f\left(0, \frac{5}{4}\right)$ gives the z-value 27.75.

$L_3$ is the line segment connecting $(0, 2)$ and $(4, 2)$, and it can be parameterized by the equations $x(t) = t$, $y(t) = 2$ for $0 \le t \le 4$. Again, define $g(t) = f(x(t), y(t))$. This gives $g(t) = t^2 - 8t + 36$. The critical value corresponds to the point $(4, 2)$. So, calculating $f(4, 2)$ gives the z-value 20.

$L_4$ is the line segment connecting $(0, 0)$ and $(0, 2)$, and it can be parameterized by the equations $x(t) = 0$, $y(t) = t$ for $0 \le t \le 2$. This time, $g(t) = 4t^2 - 2t + 24$ and the critical value $t = \frac{1}{4}$ correspond to the point $\left(0, \frac{1}{4}\right)$. Calculating $f\left(0, \frac{1}{4}\right)$ gives the z-value 23.75.

We also need to find the values of $f(x, y)$ at the corners of its domain. These corners are located at $(0, 0)$, $(4, 0)$, $(4, 2)$ and $(0, 2)$:

$$\begin{aligned}
f(0, 0) &= (0)^2 - 2(0)(0) + 4(0)^2 - 4(0) - 2(0) + 24 = 24 \\
f(4, 0) &= (4)^2 - 2(4)(0) + 4(0)^2 - 4(4) - 2(0) + 24 = 24 \\
f(4, 2) &= (4)^2 - 2(4)(2) + 4(2)^2 - 4(4) - 2(2) + 24 = 20 \\
f(0, 2) &= (0)^2 - 2(0)(2) + 4(2)^2 - 4(0) - 2(2) + 24 = 36.
\end{aligned}$$

The absolute maximum value is 36, which occurs at $(0, 2)$, and the global minimum value is 20, which occurs at both $(4, 2)$ and $(2, 0)$ as shown in the following figure.

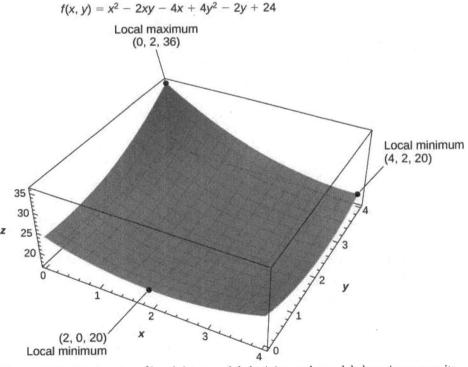

Figure 4.53 The function $f(x, y)$ has two global minima and one global maximum over its domain.

b.  Using the problem-solving strategy, step 1 involves finding the critical points of $g$ on its domain. Therefore, we first calculate $g_x(x, y)$ and $g_y(x, y)$, then set them each equal to zero:

$$g_x(x, y) = 2x + 4$$
$$g_y(x, y) = 2y - 6.$$

Setting them equal to zero yields the system of equations

$$2x + 4 = 0$$
$$2y - 6 = 0.$$

The solution to this system is $x = -2$ and $y = 3$. Therefore, $(-2, 3)$ is a critical point of $g$. Calculating $g(-2, 3)$, we get

$$g(-2, 3) = (-2)^2 + 3^2 + 4(-2) - 6(3) = 4 + 9 - 8 - 18 = -13.$$

The next step involves finding the extrema of $g$ on the boundary of its domain. The boundary of its domain consists of a circle of radius 4 centered at the origin as shown in the following graph.

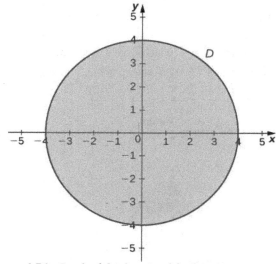

**Figure 4.54** Graph of the domain of the function $g(x, y) = x^2 + y^2 + 4x - 6y$.

The boundary of the domain of $g$ can be parameterized using the functions $x(t) = 4 \cos t$, $y(t) = 4 \sin t$ for $0 \le t \le 2\pi$. Define $h(t) = g(x(t), y(t))$:

$$
\begin{aligned}
h(t) &= g(x(t), y(t)) \\
&= (4 \cos t)^2 + (4 \sin t)^2 + 4(4 \cos t) - 6(4 \sin t) \\
&= 16\cos^2 t + 16\sin^2 t + 16 \cos t - 24 \sin t \\
&= 16 + 16 \cos t - 24 \sin t.
\end{aligned}
$$

Setting $h'(t) = 0$ leads to

$$
\begin{aligned}
-16 \sin t - 24 \cos t &= 0 \\
-16 \sin t &= 24 \cos t \\
\frac{-16 \sin t}{-16 \cos t} &= \frac{24 \cos t}{-16 \cos t} \\
\tan t &= -\frac{3}{2}.
\end{aligned}
$$

This equation has two solutions over the interval $0 \le t \le 2\pi$. One is $t = \pi - \arctan\left(\frac{3}{2}\right)$ and the other is $t = 2\pi - \arctan\left(\frac{3}{2}\right)$. For the first angle,

$$
\begin{aligned}
\sin t &= \sin\left(\pi - \arctan\left(\frac{3}{2}\right)\right) = \sin\left(\arctan\left(\frac{3}{2}\right)\right) = \frac{3\sqrt{13}}{13} \\
\cos t &= \cos\left(\pi - \arctan\left(\frac{3}{2}\right)\right) = -\cos\left(\arctan\left(\frac{3}{2}\right)\right) = -\frac{2\sqrt{13}}{13}.
\end{aligned}
$$

Therefore, $x(t) = 4 \cos t = -\frac{8\sqrt{13}}{13}$ and $y(t) = 4 \sin t = \frac{12\sqrt{13}}{13}$, so $\left(-\frac{8\sqrt{13}}{13}, \frac{12\sqrt{13}}{13}\right)$ is a critical point on the boundary and

$$
\begin{aligned}
g\left(-\frac{8\sqrt{13}}{13}, \frac{12\sqrt{13}}{13}\right) &= \left(-\frac{8\sqrt{13}}{13}\right)^2 + \left(\frac{12\sqrt{13}}{13}\right)^2 + 4\left(-\frac{8\sqrt{13}}{13}\right) - 6\left(\frac{12\sqrt{13}}{13}\right) \\
&= \frac{144}{13} + \frac{64}{13} - \frac{32\sqrt{13}}{13} - \frac{72\sqrt{13}}{13} \\
&= \frac{208 - 104\sqrt{13}}{13} \approx -12.844.
\end{aligned}
$$

For the second angle,

$$
\begin{aligned}
\sin t &= \sin\left(2\pi - \arctan\left(\frac{3}{2}\right)\right) = -\sin\left(\arctan\left(\frac{3}{2}\right)\right) = -\frac{3\sqrt{13}}{13} \\
\cos t &= \cos\left(2\pi - \arctan\left(\frac{3}{2}\right)\right) = \cos\left(\arctan\left(\frac{3}{2}\right)\right) = \frac{2\sqrt{13}}{13}.
\end{aligned}
$$

Therefore, $x(t) = 4 \cos t = \frac{8\sqrt{13}}{13}$ and $y(t) = 4 \sin t = -\frac{12\sqrt{13}}{13}$, so $\left(\frac{8\sqrt{13}}{13}, -\frac{12\sqrt{13}}{13}\right)$ is a critical point on the boundary and

$$
\begin{aligned}
g\left(\frac{8\sqrt{13}}{13}, -\frac{12\sqrt{13}}{13}\right) &= \left(\frac{8\sqrt{13}}{13}\right)^2 + \left(-\frac{12\sqrt{13}}{13}\right)^2 + 4\left(\frac{8\sqrt{13}}{13}\right) - 6\left(-\frac{12\sqrt{13}}{13}\right) \\
&= \frac{144}{13} + \frac{64}{13} + \frac{32\sqrt{13}}{13} + \frac{72\sqrt{13}}{13} \\
&= \frac{208 + 104\sqrt{13}}{13} \approx 44.844.
\end{aligned}
$$

The absolute minimum of $g$ is $-13$, which is attained at the point $(-2, 3)$, which is an interior point of $D$. The absolute maximum of $g$ is approximately equal to 44.844, which is attained at the boundary point $\left(\frac{8\sqrt{13}}{13}, -\frac{12\sqrt{13}}{13}\right)$. These are the absolute extrema of $g$ on $D$ as shown in the following figure.

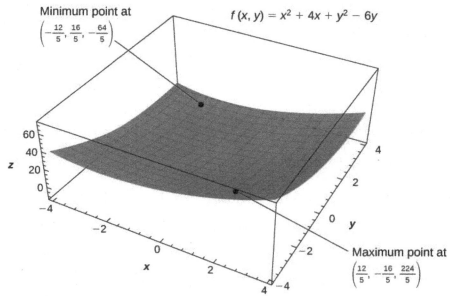

**Figure 4.55** The function $f(x, y)$ has a local minimum and a local maximum.

 **4.36** Use the problem-solving strategy for finding absolute extrema of a function to find the absolute extrema of the function

$$f(x, y) = 4x^2 - 2xy + 6y^2 - 8x + 2y + 3$$

on the domain defined by $0 \le x \le 2$ and $-1 \le y \le 3$.

## Example 4.41

### Chapter Opener: Profitable Golf Balls

**Figure 4.56** (credit: modification of work by oatsy40, Flickr)

Pro-T company has developed a profit model that depends on the number $x$ of golf balls sold per month (measured in thousands), and the number of hours per month of advertising $y$, according to the function

$$z = f(x, y) = 48x + 96y - x^2 - 2xy - 9y^2,$$

where $z$ is measured in thousands of dollars. The maximum number of golf balls that can be produced and sold is $50,000$, and the maximum number of hours of advertising that can be purchased is $25$. Find the values of $x$ and $y$ that maximize profit, and find the maximum profit.

### Solution

Using the problem-solving strategy, step $1$ involves finding the critical points of $f$ on its domain. Therefore, we first calculate $f_x(x, y)$ and $f_y(x, y)$, then set them each equal to zero:

$$\begin{aligned} f_x(x, y) &= 48 - 2x - 2y \\ f_y(x, y) &= 96 - 2x - 18y. \end{aligned}$$

Setting them equal to zero yields the system of equations

$$\begin{aligned} 48 - 2x - 2y &= 0 \\ 96 - 2x - 18y &= 0. \end{aligned}$$

The solution to this system is $x = 21$ and $y = 3$. Therefore $(21, 3)$ is a critical point of $f$. Calculating $f(21, 3)$ gives $f(21, 3) = 48(21) + 96(3) - 21^2 - 2(21)(3) - 9(3)^2 = 648$.

The domain of this function is $0 \le x \le 50$ and $0 \le y \le 25$ as shown in the following graph.

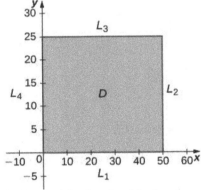

**Figure 4.57** Graph of the domain of the function $f(x, y) = 48x + 96y - x^2 - 2xy - 9y^2$.

$L_1$ is the line segment connecting $(0, 0)$ and $(50, 0)$, and it can be parameterized by the equations $x(t) = t$, $y(t) = 0$ for $0 \le t \le 50$. We then define $g(t) = f(x(t), y(t))$:

$$\begin{aligned} g(t) &= f(x(t), y(t)) \\ &= f(t, 0) \\ &= 48t + 96(0) - y^2 - 2(t)(0) - 9(0)^2 \\ &= 48t - t^2. \end{aligned}$$

Setting $g'(t) = 0$ yields the critical point $t = 24$, which corresponds to the point $(24, 0)$ in the domain of $f$.

Calculating $f(24, 0)$ gives $576$.

$L_2$ is the line segment connecting    and $(50, 25)$,  and it can be parameterized by the equations $x(t) = 50$, $y(t) = t$ for $0 \leq t \leq 25$. Once again, we define $g(t) = f(x(t), y(t))$:

$$\begin{aligned} g(t) &= f(x(t), y(t)) \\ &= f(50, t) \\ &= 48(50) + 96t - 50^2 - 2(50)t - 9t^2 \\ &= -9t^2 - 4t - 100. \end{aligned}$$

This function has a critical point at $t = -\frac{2}{9}$,  which corresponds to the point $\left(50, -\frac{2}{9}\right)$. This point is not in the domain of $f$.

$L_3$ is the line segment connecting $(0, 25)$ and $(50, 25)$,  and it can be parameterized by the equations $x(t) = t$, $y(t) = 25$ for $0 \leq t \leq 50$. We define $g(t) = f(x(t), y(t))$:

$$\begin{aligned} g(t) &= f(x(t), y(t)) \\ &= f(t, 25) \\ &= 48t + 96(25) - t^2 - 2t(25) - 9\left(25^2\right) \\ &= -t^2 - 2t - 3225. \end{aligned}$$

This function has a critical point at $t = -1$,  which corresponds to the point $(-1, 25)$,  which is not in the domain.

$L_4$ is the line segment connecting $(0, 0)$ to $(0, 25)$,  and it can be parameterized by the equations $x(t) = 0$, $y(t) = t$ for $0 \leq t \leq 25$. We define $g(t) = f(x(t), y(t))$:

$$\begin{aligned} g(t) &= f(x(t), y(t)) \\ &= f(0, t) \\ &= 48(0) + 96t - (0)^2 - 2(0)t - 9t^2 \\ &= 96t - t^2. \end{aligned}$$

This function has a critical point at $t = \frac{16}{3}$,  which corresponds to the point $\left(0, \frac{16}{3}\right)$,  which is on the boundary of the domain. Calculating $f\left(0, \frac{16}{3}\right)$ gives $256$.

We also need to find the values of $f(x, y)$ at the corners of its domain. These corners are located at $(0, 0)$, $(50, 0)$, $(50, 25)$ and $(0, 25)$:

$$\begin{aligned} f(0, 0) &= 48(0) + 96(0) - (0)^2 - 2(0)(0) - 9(0)^2 = 0 \\ f(50, 0) &= 48(50) + 96(0) - (50)^2 - 2(50)(0) - 9(0)^2 = -100 \\ f(50, 25) &= 48(50) + 96(25) - (50)^2 - 2(50)(25) - 9(25)^2 = -5825 \\ f(0, 25) &= 48(0) + 96(25) - (0)^2 - 2(0)(25) - 9(25)^2 = -3225. \end{aligned}$$

The maximum critical value is $648$,  which occurs at $(21, 3)$. Therefore, a maximum profit of $\$648,000$ is realized when $21,000$ golf balls are sold and $3$ hours of advertising are purchased per month as shown in the following figure.

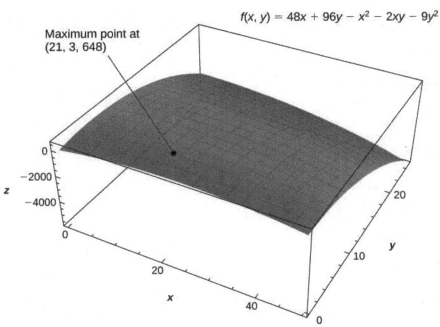

**Figure 4.58** The profit function $f(x, y)$ has a maximum at $(21, 3, 648)$.

# 4.7 EXERCISES

For the following exercises, find all critical points.

310. $f(x, y) = 1 + x^2 + y^2$

311. $f(x, y) = (3x - 2)^2 + (y - 4)^2$

312. $f(x, y) = x^4 + y^4 - 16xy$

313. $f(x, y) = 15x^3 - 3xy + 15y^3$

For the following exercises, find the critical points of the function by using algebraic techniques (completing the square) or by examining the form of the equation. Verify your results using the partial derivatives test.

314. $f(x, y) = \sqrt{x^2 + y^2 + 1}$

315. $f(x, y) = -x^2 - 5y^2 + 8x - 10y - 13$

316. $f(x, y) = x^2 + y^2 + 2x - 6y + 6$

317. $f(x, y) = \sqrt{x^2 + y^2} + 1$

For the following exercises, use the second derivative test to identify any critical points and determine whether each critical point is a maximum, minimum, saddle point, or none of these.

318. $f(x, y) = -x^3 + 4xy - 2y^2 + 1$

319. $f(x, y) = x^2 y^2$

320. $f(x, y) = x^2 - 6x + y^2 + 4y - 8$

321. $f(x, y) = 2xy + 3x + 4y$

322. $f(x, y) = 8xy(x + y) + 7$

323. $f(x, y) = x^2 + 4xy + y^2$

324. $f(x, y) = x^3 + y^3 - 300x - 75y - 3$

325. $f(x, y) = 9 - x^4 y^4$

326. $f(x, y) = 7x^2 y + 9xy^2$

327. $f(x, y) = 3x^2 - 2xy + y^2 - 8y$

328. $f(x, y) = 3x^2 + 2xy + y^2$

329. $f(x, y) = y^2 + xy + 3y + 2x + 3$

330. $f(x, y) = x^2 + xy + y^2 - 3x$

331. $f(x, y) = x^2 + 2y^2 - x^2 y$

332. $f(x, y) = x^2 + y - e^y$

333. $f(x, y) = e^{-(x^2 + y^2 + 2x)}$

334. $f(x, y) = x^2 + xy + y^2 - x - y + 1$

335. $f(x, y) = x^2 + 10xy + y^2$

336. $f(x, y) = -x^2 - 5y^2 + 10x - 30y - 62$

337. $f(x, y) = 120x + 120y - xy - x^2 - y^2$

338. $f(x, y) = 2x^2 + 2xy + y^2 + 2x - 3$

339. $f(x, y) = x^2 + x - 3xy + y^3 - 5$

340. $f(x, y) = 2xye^{-x^2 - y^2}$

For the following exercises, determine the extreme values and the saddle points. Use a CAS to graph the function.

341. **[T]** $f(x, y) = ye^x - e^y$

342. **[T]** $f(x, y) = x \sin(y)$

343.                                                    **[T]**
$f(x, y) = \sin(x)\sin(y), \ x \in (0, 2\pi), \ y \in (0, 2\pi)$

Find the absolute extrema of the given function on the indicated closed and bounded set $R$.

344. $f(x, y) = xy - x - 3y$; $R$ is the triangular region with vertices $(0, 0), \ (0, 4), \ $ and $(5, 0)$.

345. Find the absolute maximum and minimum values of $f(x, y) = x^2 + y^2 - 2y + 1$ on the region $R = \{(x, y)|x^2 + y^2 \le 4\}$.

346.                    $f(x, y) = x^3 - 3xy - y^3$                    on
$R = \{(x, y): -2 \le x \le 2, -2 \le y \le 2\}$

347. $$f(x, y) = \frac{-2y}{x^2 + y^2 + 1} \qquad \text{on}$$

$R = \left\{(x, y): x^2 + y^2 \leq 4\right\}$

348. Find three positive numbers the sum of which is 27, such that the sum of their squares is as small as possible.

349. Find the points on the surface $x^2 - yz = 5$ that are closest to the origin.

350. Find the maximum volume of a rectangular box with three faces in the coordinate planes and a vertex in the first octant on the plane $x + y + z = 1$.

351. The sum of the length and the girth (perimeter of a cross-section) of a package carried by a delivery service cannot exceed 108 in. Find the dimensions of the rectangular package of largest volume that can be sent.

352. A cardboard box without a lid is to be made with a volume of 4 ft$^3$. Find the dimensions of the box that requires the least amount of cardboard.

353. Find the point on the surface $f(x, y) = x^2 + y^2 + 10$ nearest the plane $x + 2y - z = 0$. Identify the point on the plane.

354. Find the point in the plane $2x - y + 2z = 16$ that is closest to the origin.

355. A company manufactures two types of athletic shoes: jogging shoes and cross-trainers. The total revenue from $x$ units of jogging shoes and $y$ units of cross-trainers is given by $R(x, y) = -5x^2 - 8y^2 - 2xy + 42x + 102y$, where $x$ and $y$ are in thousands of units. Find the values of $x$ and $y$ to maximize the total revenue.

356. A shipping company handles rectangular boxes provided the sum of the length, width, and height of the box does not exceed 96 in. Find the dimensions of the box that meets this condition and has the largest volume.

357. Find the maximum volume of a cylindrical soda can such that the sum of its height and circumference is 120 cm.

# 4.8 | Lagrange Multipliers

| Learning Objectives |
| --- |
| **4.8.1** Use the method of Lagrange multipliers to solve optimization problems with one constraint. |
| **4.8.2** Use the method of Lagrange multipliers to solve optimization problems with two constraints. |

Solving optimization problems for functions of two or more variables can be similar to solving such problems in single-variable calculus. However, techniques for dealing with multiple variables allow us to solve more varied optimization problems for which we need to deal with additional conditions or constraints. In this section, we examine one of the more common and useful methods for solving optimization problems with constraints.

## Lagrange Multipliers

Example 4.41 was an applied situation involving maximizing a profit function, subject to certain **constraints**. In that example, the constraints involved a maximum number of golf balls that could be produced and sold in 1 month $(x)$, and a maximum number of advertising hours that could be purchased per month $(y)$. Suppose these were combined into a budgetary constraint, such as $20x + 4y \le 216$, that took into account the cost of producing the golf balls and the number of advertising hours purchased per month. The goal is, still, be to maximize profit, but now there is a different type of constraint on the values of $x$ and $y$. This constraint, when combined with the profit function $f(x, y) = 48x + 96y - x^2 - 2xy - 9y^2$, is an example of an **optimization problem**, and the function $f(x, y)$ is called the **objective function**. A graph of various level curves of the function $f(x, y)$ follows.

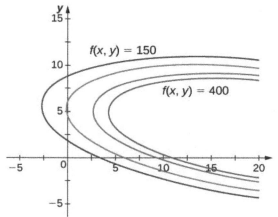

**Figure 4.59** Graph of level curves of the function $f(x, y) = 48x + 96y - x^2 - 2xy - 9y^2$ corresponding to $c = 150, 250, 350,$ and $400.$

In Figure 4.59, the value $c$ represents different profit levels (i.e., values of the function $f$). As the value of $c$ increases, the curve shifts to the right. Since our goal is to maximize profit, we want to choose a curve as far to the right as possible. If there was no restriction on the number of golf balls the company could produce, or the number of units of advertising available, then we could produce as many golf balls as we want, and advertise as much as we want, and there would be not be a maximum profit for the company. Unfortunately, we have a budgetary constraint that is modeled by the inequality $20x + 4y \le 216$. To see how this constraint interacts with the profit function, Figure 4.60 shows the graph of the line $20x + 4y = 216$ superimposed on the previous graph.

**Figure 4.60**  Graph of level curves of the function
$f(x, y) = 48x + 96y - x^2 - 2xy - 9y^2$ corresponding to
$c = 150, 250, 350,$ and $395.$ The red graph is the constraint
function.

As mentioned previously, the maximum profit occurs when the level curve is as far to the right as possible. However, the level of production corresponding to this maximum profit must also satisfy the budgetary constraint, so the point at which this profit occurs must also lie on (or to the left of) the red line in **Figure 4.60**. Inspection of this graph reveals that this point exists where the line is tangent to the level curve of $f$. Trial and error reveals that this profit level seems to be around $395,$ when $x$ and $y$ are both just less than $5.$ We return to the solution of this problem later in this section.

From a theoretical standpoint, at the point where the profit curve is tangent to the constraint line, the gradient of both of the functions evaluated at that point must point in the same (or opposite) direction. Recall that the gradient of a function of more than one variable is a vector. If two vectors point in the same (or opposite) directions, then one must be a constant multiple of the other. This idea is the basis of the **method of Lagrange multipliers**.

---

**Theorem 4.20: Method of Lagrange Multipliers: One Constraint**

Let $f$ and $g$ be functions of two variables with continuous partial derivatives at every point of some open set containing the smooth curve $g(x, y) = 0.$ Suppose that $f,$ when restricted to points on the curve $g(x, y) = 0,$ has a local extremum at the point $(x_0, y_0)$ and that $\nabla g(x_0, y_0) \neq 0.$ Then there is a number $\lambda$ called a **Lagrange multiplier**, for which

$$\nabla f(x_0, y_0) = \lambda \nabla g(x_0, y_0).$$

---

**Proof**

Assume that a constrained extremum occurs at the point $(x_0, y_0).$ Furthermore, we assume that the equation $g(x, y) = 0$ can be smoothly parameterized as

$$x = x(s) \text{ and } y = y(s)$$

where $s$ is an arc length parameter with reference point $(x_0, y_0)$ at $s = 0.$ Therefore, the quantity $z = f(x(s), y(s))$ has a relative maximum or relative minimum at $s = 0,$ and this implies that $\frac{dz}{ds} = 0$ at that point. From the chain rule,

$$\frac{dz}{ds} = \frac{\partial f}{\partial x} \cdot \frac{\partial x}{\partial s} + \frac{\partial f}{\partial y} \cdot \frac{\partial y}{\partial s} = \left(\frac{\partial f}{\partial x}\mathbf{i} + \mathbf{j}\frac{\partial x}{\partial s}\right) + \left(\frac{\partial f}{\partial y} \cdot \frac{\partial y}{\partial s}\right) = 0,$$

where the derivatives are all evaluated at $s = 0.$ However, the first factor in the dot product is the gradient of $f,$ and the second factor is the unit tangent vector $\mathbf{T}(0)$ to the constraint curve. Since the point $(x_0, y_0)$ corresponds to $s = 0,$ it follows from this equation that

$$\nabla f(x_0, y_0) \cdot \mathbf{T}(0) = 0,$$

which implies that the gradient is either $\mathbf{0}$ or is normal to the constraint curve at a constrained relative extremum. However, the constraint curve $g(x, y) = 0$ is a level curve for the function $g(x, y)$ so that if $\nabla g(x_0, y_0) \neq 0$ then $\nabla g(x_0, y_0)$ is normal to this curve at $(x_0, y_0)$ It follows, then, that there is some scalar $\lambda$ such that

$$\nabla f(x_0, y_0) = \lambda \nabla g(x_0, y_0)$$

□

To apply **Method of Lagrange Multipliers: One Constraint** to an optimization problem similar to that for the golf ball manufacturer, we need a problem-solving strategy.

---

### Problem-Solving Strategy: Steps for Using Lagrange Multipliers

1. Determine the objective function $f(x, y)$ and the constraint function $g(x, y)$. Does the optimization problem involve maximizing or minimizing the objective function?

2. Set up a system of equations using the following template:
$$\nabla f(x_0, y_0) = \lambda \nabla g(x_0, y_0)$$
$$g(x_0, y_0) = 0.$$

3. Solve for $x_0$ and $y_0$.

4. The largest of the values of $f$ at the solutions found in step 3 maximizes $f$; the smallest of those values minimizes $f$.

---

### Example 4.42

#### Using Lagrange Multipliers

Use the method of Lagrange multipliers to find the minimum value of $f(x, y) = x^2 + 4y^2 - 2x + 8y$ subject to the constraint $x + 2y = 7$.

#### Solution

Let's follow the problem-solving strategy:

1. The optimization function is $f(x, y) = x^2 + 4y^2 - 2x + 8y$. To determine the constraint function, we must first subtract 7 from both sides of the constraint. This gives $x + 2y - 7 = 0$. The constraint function is equal to the left-hand side, so $g(x, y) = x + 2y - 7$. The problem asks us to solve for the minimum value of $f$, subject to the constraint (see the following graph).

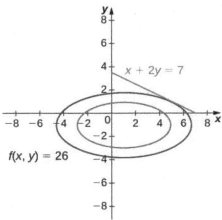

**Figure 4.61** Graph of level curves of the function
$f(x, y) = x^2 + 4y^2 - 2x + 8y$ corresponding to $c = 10$ and
26. The red graph is the constraint function.

2.  We then must calculate the gradients of both $f$ and $g$:

$$\nabla f(x, y) = (2x - 2)\mathbf{i} + (8y + 8)\mathbf{j}$$
$$\nabla g(x, y) = \mathbf{i} + 2\mathbf{j}.$$

The equation $\nabla f(x_0, y_0) = \lambda \nabla g(x_0, y_0)$ becomes

$$(2x_0 - 2)\mathbf{i} + (8y_0 + 8)\mathbf{j} = \lambda(\mathbf{i} + 2\mathbf{j}),$$

which can be rewritten as

$$(2x_0 - 2)\mathbf{i} + (8y_0 + 8)\mathbf{j} = \lambda\mathbf{i} + 2\lambda\mathbf{j}.$$

Next, we set the coefficients of $\mathbf{i}$ and $\mathbf{j}$ equal to each other:

$$2x_0 - 2 = \lambda$$
$$8y_0 + 8 = 2\lambda.$$

The equation $g(x_0, y_0) = 0$ becomes $x_0 + 2y_0 - 7 = 0$. Therefore, the system of equations that needs to be solved is

$$
\begin{aligned}
2x_0 - 2 &= \lambda \\
8y_0 + 8 &= 2\lambda \\
x_0 + 2y_0 - 7 &= 0.
\end{aligned}
$$

3.  This is a linear system of three equations in three variables. We start by solving the second equation for $\lambda$ and substituting it into the first equation. This gives $\lambda = 4y_0 + 4$, so substituting this into the first equation gives

$$2x_0 - 2 = 4y_0 + 4.$$

Solving this equation for $x_0$ gives $x_0 = 2y_0 + 3$. We then substitute this into the third equation:

$$\begin{aligned}(2y_0 + 3) + 2y_0 - 7 &= 0 \\ 4y_0 - 4 &= 0 \\ y_0 &= 1.\end{aligned}$$

Since $x_0 = 2y_0 + 3$, this gives $x_0 = 5$.

4.  Next, we substitute $(5, 1)$ into $f(x, y) = x^2 + 4y^2 - 2x + 8y$, gives $f(5, 1) = 5^2 + 4(1)^2 - 2(5) + 8(1) = 27$. To ensure this corresponds to a minimum value on the constraint function, let's try some other values, such as the intercepts of $g(x, y) = 0$, Which are $(7, 0)$ and $(0, 3.5)$. We get $f(7, 0) = 35$ and $f(0, 3.5) = 77$, so it appears $f$ has a minimum at $(5, 1)$.

 **4.37** Use the method of Lagrange multipliers to find the maximum value of $f(x, y) = 9x^2 + 36xy - 4y^2 - 18x - 8y$ subject to the constraint $3x + 4y = 32$.

Let's now return to the problem posed at the beginning of the section.

## Example 4.43

### Golf Balls and Lagrange Multipliers

The golf ball manufacturer, Pro-T, has developed a profit model that depends on the number $x$ of golf balls sold per month (measured in thousands), and the number of hours per month of advertising $y$, according to the function

$$z = f(x, y) = 48x + 96y - x^2 - 2xy - 9y^2,$$

where $z$ is measured in thousands of dollars. The budgetary constraint function relating the cost of the production of thousands golf balls and advertising units is given by $20x + 4y = 216$. Find the values of $x$ and $y$ that maximize profit, and find the maximum profit.

### Solution

Again, we follow the problem-solving strategy:

1.  The optimization function is $f(x, y) = 48x + 96y - x^2 - 2xy - 9y^2$. To determine the constraint function, we first subtract 216 from both sides of the constraint, then divide both sides by 4, which gives $5x + y - 54 = 0$. The constraint function is equal to the left-hand side, so $g(x, y) = 5x + y - 54$. The problem asks us to solve for the maximum value of $f$, subject to this constraint.

2.  So, we calculate the gradients of both $f$ and $g$:

$$\nabla f(x, y) = (48 - 2x - 2y)\mathbf{i} + (96 - 2x - 18y)\mathbf{j}$$
$$\nabla g(x, y) = 5\mathbf{i} + \mathbf{j}.$$

The equation $\nabla f(x_0, y_0) = \lambda \nabla g(x_0, y_0)$ becomes

$$(48 - 2x_0 - 2y_0)\mathbf{i} + (96 - 2x_0 - 18y_0)\mathbf{j} = \lambda(5\mathbf{i} + \mathbf{j}),$$

which can be rewritten as

$$(48 - 2x_0 - 2y_0)\mathbf{i} + (96 - 2x_0 - 18y_0)\mathbf{j} = \lambda 5\mathbf{i} + \lambda\mathbf{j}.$$

We then set the coefficients of $\mathbf{i}$ and $\mathbf{j}$ equal to each other:

$$48 - 2x_0 - 2y_0 = 5\lambda$$
$$96 - 2x_0 - 18y_0 = \lambda.$$

The equation $g(x_0, y_0) = 0$ becomes $5x_0 + y_0 - 54 = 0$. Therefore, the system of equations that needs to be solved is

$$48 - 2x_0 - 2y_0 = 5\lambda$$
$$96 - 2x_0 - 18y_0 = \lambda$$
$$5x_0 + y_0 - 54 = 0.$$

3. We use the left-hand side of the second equation to replace $\lambda$ in the first equation:

$$48 - 2x_0 - 2y_0 = 5(96 - 2x_0 - 18y_0)$$
$$48 - 2x_0 - 2y_0 = 480 - 10x_0 - 90y_0$$
$$8x_0 = 432 - 88y_0$$
$$x_0 = 54 - 11y_0.$$

Then we substitute this into the third equation:

$$5(54 - 11y_0) + y_0 - 54 = 0$$
$$270 - 55y_0 + y_0 = 0$$
$$216 - 54y_0 = 0$$
$$y_0 = 4.$$

Since $x_0 = 54 - 11y_0$, this gives $x_0 = 10$.

4. We then substitute $(10, 4)$ into $f(x, y) = 48x + 96y - x^2 - 2xy - 9y^2$, which gives

$$f(10, 4) = 48(10) + 96(4) - (10)^2 - 2(10)(4) - 9(4)^2$$
$$= 480 + 384 - 100 - 80 - 144 = 540.$$

Therefore the maximum profit that can be attained, subject to budgetary constraints, is $\$540,000$ with a production level of $10,000$ golf balls and $4$ hours of advertising bought per month. Let's check to make sure this truly is a maximum. The endpoints of the line that defines the constraint are $(10.8, 0)$ and $(0, 54)$ Let's evaluate $f$ at both of these points:

$$f(10.8, 0) = 48(10.8) + 96(0) - 10.8^2 - 2(10.8)(0) - 9(0^2) = 401.76$$
$$f(0, 54) = 48(0) + 96(54) - 0^2 - 2(0)(54) - 9(54^2) = -21,060.$$

The second value represents a loss, since no golf balls are produced. Neither of these values exceed $540$, so it seems that our extremum is a maximum value of $f$.

**4.38** A company has determined that its production level is given by the Cobb-Douglas function $f(x, y) = 2.5x^{0.45} y^{0.55}$ where $x$ represents the total number of labor hours in 1 year and $y$ represents the total capital input for the company. Suppose 1 unit of labor costs \$40 and 1 unit of capital costs \$50. Use the method of Lagrange multipliers to find the maximum value of $f(x, y) = 2.5x^{0.45} y^{0.55}$ subject to a budgetary constraint of \$500,000 per year.

In the case of an optimization function with three variables and a single constraint function, it is possible to use the method of Lagrange multipliers to solve an optimization problem as well. An example of an optimization function with three variables could be the Cobb-Douglas function in the previous example: $f(x, y, z) = x^{0.2} y^{0.4} z^{0.4}$, where $x$ represents the cost of labor, $y$ represents capital input, and $z$ represents the cost of advertising. The method is the same as for the method with a function of two variables; the equations to be solved are

$$\nabla f(x, y, z) = \lambda \nabla g(x, y, z)$$
$$g(x, y, z) = 0.$$

## Example 4.44

### Lagrange Multipliers with a Three-Variable Optimization Function

Maximize the function $f(x, y, z) = x^2 + y^2 + z^2$ subject to the constraint $x + y + z = 1$.

### Solution

1. The optimization function is $f(x, y, z) = x^2 + y^2 + z^2$. To determine the constraint function, we subtract 1 from each side of the constraint: $x + y + z - 1 = 0$ which gives the constraint function as $g(x, y, z) = x + y + z - 1$.

2. Next, we calculate $\nabla f(x, y, z)$ and $\nabla g(x, y, z)$:

$$\nabla f(x, y, z) = \langle 2x, 2y, 2z \rangle$$
$$\nabla g(x, y, z) = \langle 1, 1, 1 \rangle.$$

This leads to the equations

$$\langle 2x_0, 2y_0, 2z_0 \rangle = \lambda \langle 1, 1, 1 \rangle$$
$$x_0 + y_0 + z_0 - 1 = 0$$

which can be rewritten in the following form:

$$2x_0 = \lambda$$
$$2y_0 = \lambda$$
$$2z_0 = \lambda$$
$$x_0 + y_0 + z_0 - 1 = 0.$$

3. Since each of the first three equations has $\lambda$ on the right-hand side, we know that $2x_0 = 2y_0 = 2z_0$ and all three variables are equal to each other. Substituting $y_0 = x_0$ and $z_0 = x_0$ into the last equation yields $3x_0 - 1 = 0$, so $x_0 = \frac{1}{3}$ and $y_0 = \frac{1}{3}$ and $z_0 = \frac{1}{3}$ which corresponds to a critical point on the constraint curve.

4. Then, we evaluate $f$ at the point $\left(\frac{1}{3}, \frac{1}{3}, \frac{1}{3}\right)$:

$$f\left(\frac{1}{3}, \frac{1}{3}, \frac{1}{3}\right) = \left(\frac{1}{3}\right)^2 + \left(\frac{1}{3}\right)^2 + \left(\frac{1}{3}\right)^2 = \frac{3}{9} = \frac{1}{3}.$$

Therefore, an extremum of the function is $\frac{1}{3}$. To verify it is a minimum, choose other points that satisfy the constraint and calculate $f$ at that point. For example,

$$\begin{aligned} f(1, 0, 0) &= 1^2 + 0^2 + 0^2 = 1 \\ f(0, -2, 3) &= 0^2 + + (-2)^2 + 3^2 = 13. \end{aligned}$$

Both of these values are greater than $\frac{1}{3}$, leading us to believe the extremum is a minimum.

 **4.39** Use the method of Lagrange multipliers to find the minimum value of the function

$$f(x, y, z) = x + y + z$$

subject to the constraint $x^2 + y^2 + z^2 = 1$.

## Problems with Two Constraints

The method of Lagrange multipliers can be applied to problems with more than one constraint. In this case the optimization function, $w$ is a function of three variables:

$$w = f(x, y, z)$$

and it is subject to two constraints:

$$g(x, y, z) = 0 \text{ and } h(x, y, z) = 0.$$

There are two Lagrange multipliers, $\lambda_1$ and $\lambda_2$, and the system of equations becomes

$$\begin{aligned} \nabla f(x_0, y_0, z_0) &= \lambda_1 \nabla g(x_0, y_0, z_0) + \lambda_2 \nabla h(x_0, y_0, z_0) \\ g(x_0, y_0, z_0) &= 0 \\ h(x_0, y_0, z_0) &= 0. \end{aligned}$$

### Example 4.45

### Lagrange Multipliers with Two Constraints

Find the maximum and minimum values of the function

$$f(x, y, z) = x^2 + y^2 + z^2$$

subject to the constraints $z^2 = x^2 + y^2$ and $x + y - z + 1 = 0$.

### Solution

Let's follow the problem-solving strategy:

1. The optimization function is $f(x, y, z) = x^2 + y^2 + z^2$. To determine the constraint functions, we first subtract $z^2$ from both sides of the first constraint, which gives $x^2 + y^2 - z^2 = 0$, so $g(x, y, z) = x^2 + y^2 - z^2$. The second constraint function is $h(x, y, z) = x + y - z + 1$.

2. We then calculate the gradients of $f$, $g$, and $h$:

$$\nabla f(x, y, z) = 2x\mathbf{i} + 2y\mathbf{j} + 2z\mathbf{k}$$
$$\nabla g(x, y, z) = 2x\mathbf{i} + 2y\mathbf{j} - 2z\mathbf{k}$$
$$\nabla h(x, y, z) = \mathbf{i} + \mathbf{j} - \mathbf{k}.$$

The equation $\nabla f(x_0, y_0, z_0) = \lambda_1 \nabla g(x_0, y_0, z_0) + \lambda_2 \nabla h(x_0, y_0, z_0)$ becomes

$$2x_0\mathbf{i} + 2y_0\mathbf{j} + 2z_0\mathbf{k} = \lambda_1(2x_0\mathbf{i} + 2y_0\mathbf{j} - 2z_0\mathbf{k}) + \lambda_2(\mathbf{i} + \mathbf{j} - \mathbf{k}),$$

which can be rewritten as

$$2x_0\mathbf{i} + 2y_0\mathbf{j} + 2z_0\mathbf{k} = (2\lambda_1 x_0 + \lambda_2)\mathbf{i} + (2\lambda_1 y_0 + \lambda_2)\mathbf{j} - (2\lambda_1 z_0 + \lambda_2)\mathbf{k}.$$

Next, we set the coefficients of $\mathbf{i}$ and $\mathbf{j}$ equal to each other:

$$2x_0 = 2\lambda_1 x_0 + \lambda_2$$
$$2y_0 = 2\lambda_1 y_0 + \lambda_2$$
$$2z_0 = -2\lambda_1 z_0 - \lambda_2.$$

The two equations that arise from the constraints are $z_0{}^2 = x_0{}^2 + y_0{}^2$ and $x_0 + y_0 - z_0 + 1 = 0$. Combining these equations with the previous three equations gives

$$
\begin{aligned}
2x_0 &= 2\lambda_1 x_0 + \lambda_2 \\
2y_0 &= 2\lambda_1 y_0 + \lambda_2 \\
2z_0 &= -2\lambda_1 z_0 - \lambda_2 \\
z_0{}^2 &= x_0{}^2 + y_0{}^2 \\
x_0 + y_0 - z_0 + 1 &= 0.
\end{aligned}
$$

3. The first three equations contain the variable $\lambda_2$. Solving the third equation for $\lambda_2$ and replacing into the first and second equations reduces the number of equations to four:

$$
\begin{aligned}
2x_0 &= 2\lambda_1 x_0 - 2\lambda_1 z_0 - 2z_0 \\
2y_0 &= 2\lambda_1 y_0 - 2\lambda_1 z_0 - 2z_0 \\
z_0{}^2 &= x_0{}^2 + y_0{}^2 \\
x_0 + y_0 - z_0 + 1 &= 0.
\end{aligned}
$$

Next, we solve the first and second equation for $\lambda_1$. The first equation gives $\lambda_1 = \frac{x_0 + z_0}{x_0 - z_0}$, the second equation gives $\lambda_1 = \frac{y_0 + z_0}{y_0 - z_0}$. We set the right-hand side of each equation equal to each other and cross-multiply:

$$\frac{x_0 + z_0}{x_0 - z_0} = \frac{y_0 + z_0}{y_0 - z_0}$$

$$(x_0 + z_0)(y_0 - z_0) = (x_0 - z_0)(y_0 + z_0)$$

$$x_0 y_0 - x_0 z_0 + y_0 z_0 - z_0^2 = x_0 y_0 + x_0 z_0 - y_0 z_0 - z_0 2.$$

$$2y_0 z_0 - 2x_0 z_0 = 0$$

$$2z_0(y_0 - x_0) = 0.$$

Therefore, either $z_0 = 0$ or $y_0 = x_0$. If $z_0 = 0$, then the first constraint becomes $0 = x_0^2 + y_0^2$. The only real solution to this equation is $x_0 = 0$ and $y_0 = 0$, which gives the ordered triple $(0, 0, 0)$. This point does not satisfy the second constraint, so it is not a solution.

Next, we consider $y_0 = x_0$, which reduces the number of equations to three:

$$y_0 = x_0$$

$$z_0^2 = x_0^2 + y_0^2$$

$$x_0 + y_0 - z_0 + 1 = 0.$$

We substitute the first equation into the second and third equations:

$$z_0^2 = x_0^2 + x_0^2$$

$$x_0 + x_0 - z_0 + 1 = 0.$$

Then, we solve the second equation for $z_0$, which gives $z_0 = 2x_0 + 1$. We then substitute this into the first equation,

$$z_0^2 = 2x_0^2$$

$$(2x_0 + 1)^2 = 2x_0^2$$

$$4x_0^2 + 4x_0 + 1 = 2x_0^2$$

$$2x_0^2 + 4x_0 + 1 = 0,$$

and use the quadratic formula to solve for $x_0$:

$$x_0 = \frac{-4 \pm \sqrt{4^2 - 4(2)(1)}}{2(2)} = \frac{-4 \pm \sqrt{8}}{4} = \frac{-4 \pm 2\sqrt{2}}{4} = -1 \pm \frac{\sqrt{2}}{2}.$$

Recall $y_0 = x_0$, so this solves for $y_0$ as well. Then, $z_0 = 2x_0 + 1$, so

$$z_0 = 2x_0 + 1 = 2\left(-1 \pm \frac{\sqrt{2}}{2}\right) + 1 = -2 + 1 \pm \sqrt{2} = -1 \pm \sqrt{2}.$$

Therefore, there are two ordered triplet solutions:

$$\left(-1 + \frac{\sqrt{2}}{2}, -1 + \frac{\sqrt{2}}{2}, -1 + \sqrt{2}\right) \text{ and } \left(-1 - \frac{\sqrt{2}}{2}, -1 - \frac{\sqrt{2}}{2}, -1 - \sqrt{2}\right).$$

4.  We substitute $\left(-1 + \frac{\sqrt{2}}{2}, -1 + \frac{\sqrt{2}}{2}, -1 + \sqrt{2}\right)$ into $f(x, y, z) = x^2 + y^2 + z^2$, which gives

$$f\left(-1 + \frac{\sqrt{2}}{2}, -1 + \frac{\sqrt{2}}{2}, -1 + \sqrt{2}\right) = \left(-1 + \frac{\sqrt{2}}{2}\right)^2 + \left(-1 + \frac{\sqrt{2}}{2}\right)^2 + (-1 + \sqrt{2})^2$$

$$= \left(1 - \sqrt{2} + \frac{1}{2}\right) + \left(1 - \sqrt{2} + \frac{1}{2}\right) + (1 - 2\sqrt{2} + 2)$$

$$= 6 - 4\sqrt{2}.$$

Then, we substitute $\left(-1 - \frac{\sqrt{2}}{2}, -1 - \frac{\sqrt{2}}{2}, -1 - \sqrt{2}\right)$ into $f(x, y, z) = x^2 + y^2 + z^2$, which gives

$$f\left(-1 - \frac{\sqrt{2}}{2}, -1 - \frac{\sqrt{2}}{2}, -1 - \sqrt{2}\right) = \left(-1 - \frac{\sqrt{2}}{2}\right)^2 + \left(-1 - \frac{\sqrt{2}}{2}\right)^2 + (-1 - \sqrt{2})^2$$

$$= \left(1 + \sqrt{2} + \frac{1}{2}\right) + \left(1 + \sqrt{2} + \frac{1}{2}\right) + (1 + 2\sqrt{2} + 2)$$

$$= 6 + 4\sqrt{2}.$$

$6 + 4\sqrt{2}$ is the maximum value and $6 - 4\sqrt{2}$ is the minimum value of $f(x, y, z)$, subject to the given constraints.

 **4.40** Use the method of Lagrange multipliers to find the minimum value of the function

$$f(x, y, z) = x^2 + y^2 + z^2$$

subject to the constraints $2x + y + 2z = 9$ and $5x + 5y + 7z = 29$.

# 4.8 EXERCISES

For the following exercises, use the method of Lagrange multipliers to find the maximum and minimum values of the function subject to the given constraints.

358. $f(x, y) = x^2 y; \ x^2 + 2y^2 = 6$

359. $f(x, y, z) = xyz, \ x^2 + 2y^2 + 3z^2 = 6$

360. $f(x, y) = xy; \ 4x^2 + 8y^2 = 16$

361. $f(x, y) = 4x^3 + y^2; \ 2x^2 + y^2 = 1$

362. $f(x, y, z) = x^2 + y^2 + z^2, \ x^4 + y^4 + z^4 = 1$

363. $f(x, y, z) = yz + xy, \ xy = 1, \ y^2 + z^2 = 1$

364. $f(x, y) = x^2 + y^2, \ (x - 1)^2 + 4y^2 = 4$

365. $f(x, y) = 4xy, \ \dfrac{x^2}{9} + \dfrac{y^2}{16} = 1$

366. $f(x, y, z) = x + y + z, \ \dfrac{1}{x} + \dfrac{1}{y} + \dfrac{1}{z} = 1$

367. $f(x, y, z) = x + 3y - z, \ x^2 + y^2 + z^2 = 4$

368. $f(x, y, z) = x^2 + y^2 + z^2, \ xyz = 4$

369. Minimize $f(x, y) = x^2 + y^2$ on the hyperbola $xy = 1$.

370. Minimize $f(x, y) = xy$ on the ellipse $b^2 x^2 + a^2 y^2 = a^2 b^2$.

371. Maximize $f(x, y, z) = 2x + 3y + 5z$ on the sphere $x^2 + y^2 + z^2 = 19$.

372. Maximize $\begin{aligned} &f(x, y) = x^2 - y^2; \ x > 0, \ y > 0; \\ &g(x, y) = y - x^2 = 0 \end{aligned}$

373. The curve $x^3 - y^3 = 1$ is asymptotic to the line $y = x$. Find the point(s) on the curve $x^3 - y^3 = 1$ farthest from the line $y = x$.

374. Maximize $U(x, y) = 8x^{4/5} y^{1/5}; \ 4x + 2y = 12$

375. Minimize $f(x, y) = x^2 + y^2, \ x + 2y - 5 = 0.$

376. Maximize $f(x, y) = \sqrt{6 - x^2 - y^2}, \ x + y - 2 = 0.$

377. Minimize $f(x, y, z) = x^2 + y^2 + z^2, \ x + y + z = 1.$

378. Minimize $f(x, y) = x^2 - y^2$ subject to the constraint $x - 2y + 6 = 0.$

379. Minimize $f(x, y, z) = x^2 + y^2 + z^2$ when $x + y + z = 9$ and $x + 2y + 3z = 20.$

For the next group of exercises, use the method of Lagrange multipliers to solve the following applied problems.

380. A pentagon is formed by placing an isosceles triangle on a rectangle, as shown in the diagram. If the perimeter of the pentagon is 10 in., find the lengths of the sides of the pentagon that will maximize the area of the pentagon.

381. A rectangular box without a top (a topless box) is to be made from 12 ft$^2$ of cardboard. Find the maximum volume of such a box.

382. Find the minimum and maximum distances between the ellipse $x^2 + xy + 2y^2 = 1$ and the origin.

383. Find the point on the surface $x^2 - 2xy + y^2 - x + y = 0$ closest to the point $(1, 2, -3).$

384. Show that, of all the triangles inscribed in a circle of radius $R$ (see diagram), the equilateral triangle has the largest perimeter.

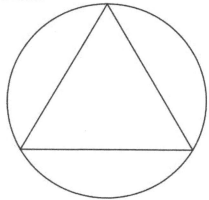

385. Find the minimum distance from point $(0, 1)$ to the parabola $x^2 = 4y$.

386. Find the minimum distance from the parabola $y = x^2$ to point $(0, 3)$.

387. Find the minimum distance from the plane $x + y + z = 1$ to point $(2, 1, 1)$.

388. A large container in the shape of a rectangular solid must have a volume of $480$ m³. The bottom of the container costs \$5/m² to construct whereas the top and sides cost \$3/m² to construct. Use Lagrange multipliers to find the dimensions of the container of this size that has the minimum cost.

389. Find the point on the line $y = 2x + 3$ that is closest to point $(4, 2)$.

390. Find the point on the plane $4x + 3y + z = 2$ that is closest to the point $(1, -1, 1)$.

391. Find the maximum value of $f(x, y) = \sin x \sin y$, where $x$ and $y$ denote the acute angles of a right triangle. Draw the contours of the function using a CAS.

392. A rectangular solid is contained within a tetrahedron with vertices at $(1, 0, 0), (0, 1, 0), (0, 0, 1),$ and the origin. The base of the box has dimensions $x, y,$ and the height of the box is $z$. If the sum of $x, y,$ and $z$ is 1.0, find the dimensions that maximizes the volume of the rectangular solid.

393. **[T]** By investing $x$ units of labor and $y$ units of capital, a watch manufacturer can produce $P(x, y) = 50x^{0.4}y^{0.6}$ watches. Find the maximum number of watches that can be produced on a budget of \$20,000 if labor costs \$100/unit and capital costs \$200/unit. Use a CAS to sketch a contour plot of the function.

# CHAPTER 4 REVIEW

## KEY TERMS

**boundary point** a point $P_0$ of $R$ is a boundary point if every $\delta$ disk centered around $P_0$ contains points both inside and outside $R$

**closed set** a set $S$ that contains all its boundary points

**connected set** an open set $S$ that cannot be represented as the union of two or more disjoint, nonempty open subsets

**constraint** an inequality or equation involving one or more variables that is used in an optimization problem; the constraint enforces a limit on the possible solutions for the problem

**contour map** a plot of the various level curves of a given function $f(x, y)$

**critical point of a function of two variables** the point $(x_0, y_0)$ is called a critical point of $f(x, y)$ if one of the two following conditions holds:

    1.   $f_x(x_0, y_0) = f_y(x_0, y_0) = 0$

    2.   At least one of $f_x(x_0, y_0)$ and $f_y(x_0, y_0)$ do not exist

**differentiable** a function $f(x, y)$ is differentiable at $(x_0, y_0)$ if $f(x, y)$ can be expressed in the form
$$f(x, y) = f(x_0, y_0) + f_x(x_0, y_0)(x - x_0) + f_y(x_0, y_0)(y - y_0) + E(x, y),$$
where the error term $E(x, y)$ satisfies $\lim\limits_{(x, y) \to (x_0, y_0)} \dfrac{E(x, y)}{\sqrt{(x - x_0)^2 + (y - y_0)^2}} = 0$

**directional derivative** the derivative of a function in the direction of a given unit vector

**discriminant** the discriminant of the function $f(x, y)$ is given by the formula
$$D = f_{xx}(x_0, y_0)f_{yy}(x_0, y_0) - \left(f_{xy}(x_0, y_0)\right)^2$$

**function of two variables** a function $z = f(x, y)$ that maps each ordered pair $(x, y)$ in a subset $D$ of $\mathbb{R}^2$ to a unique real number $z$

**generalized chain rule** the chain rule extended to functions of more than one independent variable, in which each independent variable may depend on one or more other variables

**gradient** the gradient of the function $f(x, y)$ is defined to be $\nabla f(x, y) = (\partial f/\partial x)\mathbf{i} + (\partial f/\partial y)\mathbf{j}$, which can be generalized to a function of any number of independent variables

**graph of a function of two variables** a set of ordered triples $(x, y, z)$ that satisfies the equation $z = f(x, y)$ plotted in three-dimensional Cartesian space

**higher-order partial derivatives** second-order or higher partial derivatives, regardless of whether they are mixed partial derivatives

**interior point** a point $P_0$ of $R$ is a boundary point if there is a $\delta$ disk centered around $P_0$ contained completely in $R$

**intermediate variable** given a composition of functions (e.g., $f(x(t), y(t))$), the intermediate variables are the variables that are independent in the outer function but dependent on other variables as well; in the function $f(x(t), y(t))$, the variables $x$ and $y$ are examples of intermediate variables

**Lagrange multiplier** the constant (or constants) used in the method of Lagrange multipliers; in the case of one constant, it is represented by the variable $\lambda$

**level curve of a function of two variables** the set of points satisfying the equation $f(x, y) = c$ for some real number $c$ in the range of $f$

**level surface of a function of three variables** the set of points satisfying the equation $f(x, y, z) = c$ for some real number $c$ in the range of $f$

**linear approximation** given a function $f(x, y)$ and a tangent plane to the function at a point $(x_0, y_0)$, we can approximate $f(x, y)$ for points near $(x_0, y_0)$ using the tangent plane formula

**method of Lagrange multipliers** a method of solving an optimization problem subject to one or more constraints

**mixed partial derivatives** second-order or higher partial derivatives, in which at least two of the differentiations are with respect to different variables

**objective function** the function that is to be maximized or minimized in an optimization problem

**open set** a set $S$ that contains none of its boundary points

**optimization problem** calculation of a maximum or minimum value of a function of several variables, often using Lagrange multipliers

**partial derivative** a derivative of a function of more than one independent variable in which all the variables but one are held constant

**partial differential equation** an equation that involves an unknown function of more than one independent variable and one or more of its partial derivatives

**region** an open, connected, nonempty subset of $\mathbb{R}^2$

**saddle point** given the function $z = f(x, y)$, the point $(x_0, y_0, f(x_0, y_0))$ is a saddle point if both $f_x(x_0, y_0) = 0$ and $f_y(x_0, y_0) = 0$, but $f$ does not have a local extremum at $(x_0, y_0)$

**surface** the graph of a function of two variables, $z = f(x, y)$

**tangent plane** given a function $f(x, y)$ that is differentiable at a point $(x_0, y_0)$, the equation of the tangent plane to the surface $z = f(x, y)$ is given by $z = f(x_0, y_0) + f_x(x_0, y_0)(x - x_0) + f_y(x_0, y_0)(y - y_0)$

**total differential** the total differential of the function $f(x, y)$ at $(x_0, y_0)$ is given by the formula $dz = f_x(x_0, y_0)dx + f_y(x_0, y_0)dy$

**tree diagram** illustrates and derives formulas for the generalized chain rule, in which each independent variable is accounted for

**vertical trace** the set of ordered triples $(c, y, z)$ that solves the equation $f(c, y) = z$ for a given constant $x = c$ or the set of ordered triples $(x, d, z)$ that solves the equation $f(x, d) = z$ for a given constant $y = d$

**$\delta$ ball** all points in $\mathbb{R}^3$ lying at a distance of less than $\delta$ from $(x_0, y_0, z_0)$

**$\delta$ disk** an open disk of radius $\delta$ centered at point $(a, b)$

## KEY EQUATIONS

- **Vertical trace**
  $f(a, y) = z$ for $x = a$ or $f(x, b) = z$ for $y = b$

- **Level surface of a function of three variables**
  $f(x, y, z) = c$

- **Partial derivative of $f$ with respect to $x$**
  $$\frac{\partial f}{\partial x} = \lim_{h \to 0} \frac{f(x + h, y) - f(x, y)}{h}$$

- **Partial derivative of $f$ with respect to $y$**

$$\frac{\partial f}{\partial y} = \lim_{k \to 0} \frac{f(x, y + k) - f(x, y)}{k}$$

- **Tangent plane**

$$z = f(x_0, y_0) + f_x(x_0, y_0)(x - x_0) + f_y(x_0, y_0)(y - y_0)$$

- **Linear approximation**

$$L(x, y) = f(x_0, y_0) + f_x(x_0, y_0)(x - x_0) + f_y(x_0, y_0)(y - y_0)$$

- **Total differential**

$$dz = f_x(x_0, y_0)dx + f_y(x_0, y_0)dy.$$

- **Differentiability (two variables)**

$$f(x, y) = f(x_0, y_0) + f_x(x_0, y_0)(x - x_0) + f_y(x_0, y_0)(y - y_0) + E(x, y),$$

where the error term $E$ satisfies

$$\lim_{(x, y) \to (x_0, y_0)} \frac{E(x, y)}{\sqrt{(x - x_0)^2 + (y - y_0)^2}} = 0.$$

- **Differentiability (three variables)**

$$f(x, y) = f(x_0, y_0, z_0) + f_x(x_0, y_0, z_0)(x - x_0) + f_y(x_0, y_0, z_0)(y - y_0)$$
$$+ f_z(x_0, y_0, z_0)(z - z_0) + E(x, y, z),$$

where the error term $E$ satisfies

$$\lim_{(x, y, z) \to (x_0, y_0, z_0)} \frac{E(x, y, z)}{\sqrt{(x - x_0)^2 + (y - y_0)^2 + (z - z_0)^2}} = 0.$$

- **Chain rule, one independent variable**

$$\frac{dz}{dt} = \frac{\partial z}{\partial x} \cdot \frac{dx}{dt} + \frac{\partial z}{\partial y} \cdot \frac{dy}{dt}$$

- **Chain rule, two independent variables**

$$\frac{dz}{du} = \frac{\partial z}{\partial x} \cdot \frac{\partial x}{\partial u} + \frac{\partial z}{\partial y} \cdot \frac{\partial y}{\partial u}$$

$$\frac{dz}{dv} = \frac{\partial z}{\partial x} \cdot \frac{\partial x}{\partial v} + \frac{\partial z}{\partial y} \cdot \frac{\partial y}{\partial v}$$

- **Generalized chain rule**

$$\frac{\partial w}{\partial t_j} = \frac{\partial w}{\partial x_1} \frac{\partial x_1}{\partial t_j} + \frac{\partial w}{\partial x_2} \frac{\partial x_1}{\partial t_j} + \cdots + \frac{\partial w}{\partial x_m} \frac{\partial x_m}{\partial t_j}$$

- **directional derivative (two dimensions)**

$$D_{\mathbf{u}} f(a, b) = \lim_{h \to 0} \frac{f(a + h\cos\theta, b + h\sin\theta) - f(a, b)}{h}$$

or

$$D_{\mathbf{u}} f(x, y) = f_x(x, y)\cos\theta + f_y(x, y)\sin\theta$$

- **gradient (two dimensions)**

$$\nabla f(x, y) = f_x(x, y)\mathbf{i} + f_y(x, y)\mathbf{j}$$

- **gradient (three dimensions)**

$$\nabla f(x, y, z) = f_x(x, y, z)\mathbf{i} + f_y(x, y, z)\mathbf{j} + f_z(x, y, z)\mathbf{k}$$

- **directional derivative (three dimensions)**

$$D_{\mathbf{u}} f(x, y, z) = \nabla f(x, y, z) \cdot \mathbf{u}$$
$$= f_x(x, y, z)\cos\alpha + f_y(x, y, z)\cos\beta + f_x(x, y, z)\cos\gamma$$

- **Discriminant**

$$D = f_{xx}(x_0, y_0) f_{yy}(x_0, y_0) - \left(f_{xy}(x_0, y_0)\right)^2$$

- **Method of Lagrange multipliers, one constraint**

$$\nabla f(x_0, y_0) = \lambda \nabla g(x_0, y_0)$$
$$g(x_0, y_0) = 0$$

- **Method of Lagrange multipliers, two constraints**

$$\nabla f(x_0, y_0, z_0) = \lambda_1 \nabla g(x_0, y_0, z_0) + \lambda_2 \nabla h(x_0, y_0, z_0)$$
$$g(x_0, y_0, z_0) = 0$$
$$h(x_0, y_0, z_0) = 0$$

# KEY CONCEPTS

## 4.1 Functions of Several Variables

- The graph of a function of two variables is a surface in $\mathbb{R}^3$ and can be studied using level curves and vertical traces.
- A set of level curves is called a contour map.

## 4.2 Limits and Continuity

- To study limits and continuity for functions of two variables, we use a $\delta$ disk centered around a given point.
- A function of several variables has a limit if for any point in a $\delta$ ball centered at a point $P$, the value of the function at that point is arbitrarily close to a fixed value (the limit value).
- The limit laws established for a function of one variable have natural extensions to functions of more than one variable.
- A function of two variables is continuous at a point if the limit exists at that point, the function exists at that point, and the limit and function are equal at that point.

## 4.3 Partial Derivatives

- A partial derivative is a derivative involving a function of more than one independent variable.
- To calculate a partial derivative with respect to a given variable, treat all the other variables as constants and use the usual differentiation rules.
- Higher-order partial derivatives can be calculated in the same way as higher-order derivatives.

## 4.4 Tangent Planes and Linear Approximations

- The analog of a tangent line to a curve is a tangent plane to a surface for functions of two variables.
- Tangent planes can be used to approximate values of functions near known values.
- A function is differentiable at a point if it is "smooth" at that point (i.e., no corners or discontinuities exist at that point).
- The total differential can be used to approximate the change in a function $z = f(x_0, y_0)$ at the point $(x_0, y_0)$ for given values of $\Delta x$ and $\Delta y$.

## 4.5 The Chain Rule

- The chain rule for functions of more than one variable involves the partial derivatives with respect to all the independent variables.
- Tree diagrams are useful for deriving formulas for the chain rule for functions of more than one variable, where each independent variable also depends on other variables.

## 4.6 Directional Derivatives and the Gradient

- A directional derivative represents a rate of change of a function in any given direction.
- The gradient can be used in a formula to calculate the directional derivative.
- The gradient indicates the direction of greatest change of a function of more than one variable.

## 4.7 Maxima/Minima Problems

- A critical point of the function $f(x, y)$ is any point $(x_0, y_0)$ where either $f_x(x_0, y_0) = f_y(x_0, y_0) = 0$, or at least one of $f_x(x_0, y_0)$ and $f_y(x_0, y_0)$ do not exist.
- A saddle point is a point $(x_0, y_0)$ where $f_x(x_0, y_0) = f_y(x_0, y_0) = 0$, but $(x_0, y_0)$ is neither a maximum nor a minimum at that point.
- To find extrema of functions of two variables, first find the critical points, then calculate the discriminant and apply the second derivative test.

## 4.8 Lagrange Multipliers

- An objective function combined with one or more constraints is an example of an optimization problem.
- To solve optimization problems, we apply the method of Lagrange multipliers using a four-step problem-solving strategy.

# CHAPTER 4 REVIEW EXERCISES

For the following exercises, determine whether the statement is *true or false*. Justify your answer with a proof or a counterexample.

**394.** The domain of $f(x, y) = x^3 \sin^{-1}(y)$ is $x = $ all real numbers, and $-\pi \le y \le \pi$.

**395.** If the function $f(x, y)$ is continuous everywhere, then $f_{xy} = f_{yx}$.

**396.** The linear approximation to the function of $f(x, y) = 5x^2 + x\tan(y)$ at $(2, \pi)$ is given by $L(x, y) = 22 + 21(x - 2) + (y - \pi)$.

**397.** $\left(\frac{3}{4}, \frac{9}{16}\right)$ is a critical point of $g(x, y) = 4x^3 - 2x^2 y + y^2 - 2$.

For the following exercises, sketch the function in one graph and, in a second, sketch several level curves.

**398.** $f(x, y) = e^{-\left(x^2 + 2y^2\right)}$.

**399.** $f(x, y) = x + 4y^2$.

For the following exercises, evaluate the following limits, if they exist. If they do not exist, prove it.

**400.** $\displaystyle \lim_{(x, y) \to (1, 1)} \frac{4xy}{x - 2y^2}$

**401.** $\displaystyle \lim_{(x, y) \to (0, 0)} \frac{4xy}{x - 2y^2}$

For the following exercises, find the largest interval of continuity for the function.

**402.** $f(x, y) = x^3 \sin^{-1}(y)$

**403.** $g(x, y) = \ln\left(4 - x^2 - y^2\right)$

For the following exercises, find all first partial derivatives.

**404.** $f(x, y) = \sqrt{x^2 - y^2}$

**405.** $u(x, y) = x^4 - 3xy + 1, \ x = 2t, \ y = t^3$

For the following exercises, find all second partial derivatives.

**406.** $g(t, x) = 3t^2 - \sin(x + t)$

**407.** $h(x, y, z) = \frac{x^3 e^{2y}}{z}$

For the following exercises, find the equation of the tangent plane to the specified surface at the given point.

**408.** $z = x^3 - 2y^2 + y - 1$ at point $(1, 1, -1)$

**409.** $3z^3 = e^x + \frac{2}{y}$ at point $(0, 1, 3)$

**410.** Approximate $f(x, y) = e^{x^2} + \sqrt{y}$ at $(0.1, 9.1)$. Write down your linear approximation function $L(x, y)$. How accurate is the approximation to the exact answer, rounded to four digits?

**411.** Find the differential $dz$ of $h(x, y) = 4x^2 + 2xy - 3y$ and approximate $\Delta z$ at the point $(1, -2)$. Let $\Delta x = 0.1$ and $\Delta y = 0.01$.

**412.** Find the directional derivative of $f(x, y) = x^2 + 6xy - y^2$ in the direction $\mathbf{v} = \mathbf{i} + 4\mathbf{j}$.

**413.** Find the maximal directional derivative magnitude and direction for the function $f(x, y) = x^3 + 2xy - \cos(\pi y)$ at point $(3, 0)$.

For the following exercises, find the gradient.

**414.** $c(x, t) = e(t - x)^2 + 3\cos(t)$

**415.** $f(x, y) = \frac{\sqrt{x} + y^2}{xy}$

For the following exercises, find and classify the critical points.

**416.** $z = x^3 - xy + y^2 - 1$

For the following exercises, use Lagrange multipliers to find the maximum and minimum values for the functions with the given constraints.

**417.** $f(x, y) = x^2 y, \; x^2 + y^2 = 4$

**418.** $f(x, y) = x^2 - y^2, \; x + 6y = 4$

**419.** A machinist is constructing a right circular cone out of a block of aluminum. The machine gives an error of $5\%$ in height and $2\%$ in radius. Find the maximum error in the volume of the cone if the machinist creates a cone of height $6$ cm and radius $2$ cm.

**420.** A trash compactor is in the shape of a cuboid. Assume the trash compactor is filled with incompressible liquid. The length and width are decreasing at rates of $2$ ft/sec and $3$ ft/sec, respectively. Find the rate at which the liquid level is rising when the length is $14$ ft, the width is $10$ ft, and the height is $4$ ft.

# ANSWER KEY for Chapters 1–4
## Chapter 1
## Checkpoint

**1.1.**

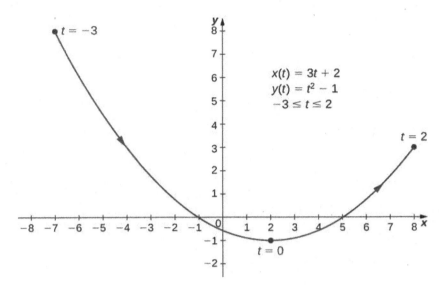

**1.2.** $x = 2 + \dfrac{3}{y+1}$, or $y = -1 + \dfrac{3}{x-2}$. This equation describes a portion of a rectangular hyperbola centered at $(2, -1)$.

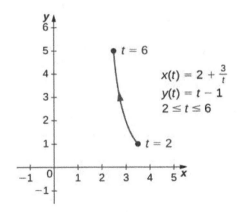

**1.3.** One possibility is $x(t) = t$, $y(t) = t^2 + 2t$. Another possibility is $x(t) = 2t - 3$, $y(t) = (2t - 3)^2 + 2(2t - 3) = 4t^2 - 8t + 3$. There are, in fact, an infinite number of possibilities.

**1.4.** $x'(t) = 2t - 4$ and $y'(t) = 6t^2 - 6$, so $\dfrac{dy}{dx} = \dfrac{6t^2 - 6}{2t - 4} = \dfrac{3t^2 - 3}{t - 2}$.

This expression is undefined when $t = 2$ and equal to zero when $t = \pm 1$.

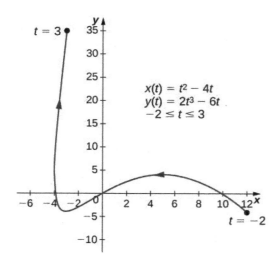

**1.5.** The equation of the tangent line is $y = 24x + 100$.

**1.6.** $\dfrac{d^2 y}{dx^2} = \dfrac{3t^2 - 12t + 3}{2(t-2)^3}$. Critical points $(5, 4)$, $(-3, -4)$, and $(-4, 6)$.

**1.7.** $A = 3\pi$ (Note that the integral formula actually yields a negative answer. This is due to the fact that $x(t)$ is a decreasing function over the interval $[0, 2\pi]$; that is, the curve is traced from right to left.)

**1.8.** $s = 2\left(10^{3/2} - 2^{3/2}\right) \approx 57.589$

**1.9.** $A = \dfrac{\pi\left(494\sqrt{13} + 128\right)}{1215}$

**1.10.** $\left(8\sqrt{2}, \dfrac{5\pi}{4}\right)$ and $\left(-2, 2\sqrt{3}\right)$

**1.11.**

**1.12.**

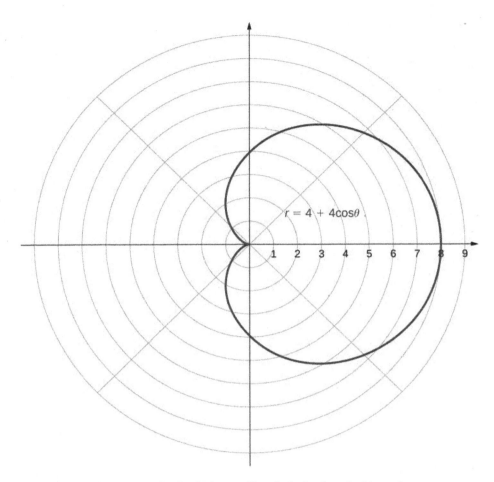

The name of this shape is a cardioid, which we will study further later in this section.

**1.13**. $y = x^2$, which is the equation of a parabola opening upward.

**1.14**. Symmetric with respect to the polar axis.

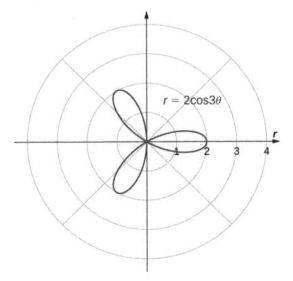

**1.15**. $A = 3\pi/2$

**1.16**. $A = \frac{4\pi}{3} + 4\sqrt{3}$

**1.17**. $s = 3\pi$

**1.18.** $x = 2(y + 3)^2 - 2$

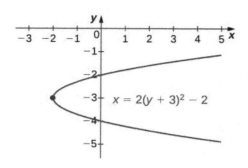

**1.19.** $\dfrac{(x + 1)^2}{16} + \dfrac{(y - 2)^2}{9} = 1$

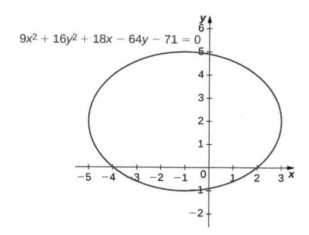

**1.20.** $\dfrac{(y + 2)^2}{9} - \dfrac{(x - 1)^2}{4} = 1$. This is a vertical hyperbola. Asymptotes $y = -2 \pm \dfrac{3}{2}(x - 1)$.

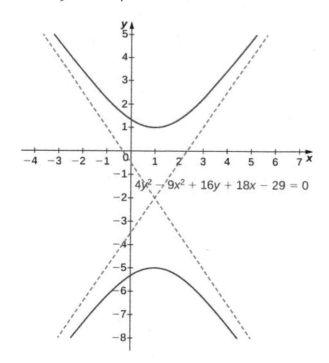

**1.21.** $e = \frac{c}{a} = \frac{\sqrt{74}}{7} \approx 1.229$

**1.22.** Here $e = 0.8$ and $p = 5$. This conic section is an ellipse.

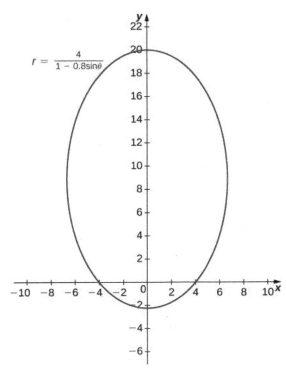

**1.23.** The conic is a hyperbola and the angle of rotation of the axes is $\theta = 22.5°$.

## Section Exercises

**1**.

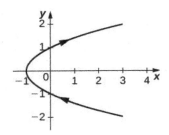

orientation: bottom to top

**3**.

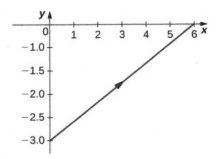

orientation: left to right

**5.** $y = \dfrac{x^2}{4} + 1$

**7.**

**9.**

**11.**

**13.**

**15.**

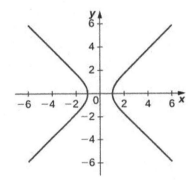

Asymptotes are $y = x$ and $y = -x$

**17.**

**19.**

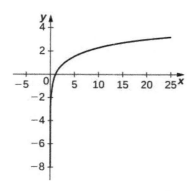

**21**. $x = 4y^2 - 1$; domain: $x \in [1, \infty)$.

**23**. $\dfrac{x^2}{16} + \dfrac{y^2}{9} = 1$; domain $x \in [-4, 4]$.

**25**. $y = 3x + 2$; domain: all real numbers.

**27**. $(x - 1)^2 + (y - 3)^2 = 1$; domain: $x \in [0, 2]$.

**29**. $y = \sqrt{x^2 - 1}$; domain: $x \in [-1, 1]$.

**31**. $y^2 = \dfrac{1 - x}{2}$; domain: $x \in [2, \infty) \cup (-\infty, -2]$.

**33**. $y = \ln x$; domain: $x \in (0, \infty)$.

**35**. $y = \ln x$; domain: $x \in (0, \infty)$.

**37**. $x^2 + y^2 = 4$; domain: $x \in [-2, 2]$.

**39**. line

**41**. parabola

**43**. circle

**45**. ellipse

**47**. hyperbola

**51**. The equations represent a cycloid.

**53**.

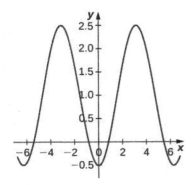

**55**. 22,092 meters at approximately 51 seconds.

**57**.

$x = 2\tan(t), y = 3\sec(t)$

**59**.

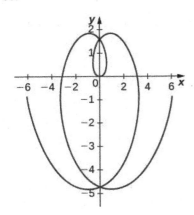

**61**.

$x = \cosh t, y = \sinh t$

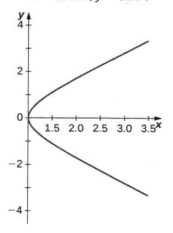

**63.** 0

**65.** $\dfrac{-3}{5}$

**67.** Slope $= 0$; $y = 8$.

**69.** Slope is undefined; $x = 2$.

**71.** $t = \arctan(-2)$; $\left(\dfrac{4}{\sqrt{5}}, \dfrac{-8}{\sqrt{5}}\right)$.

**73.** No points possible; undefined expression.

**75.** $y = -\left(\dfrac{2}{e}\right)x + 3$

**77.** $y = 2x - 7$

**79.** $\dfrac{\pi}{4}, \dfrac{5\pi}{4}, \dfrac{3\pi}{4}, \dfrac{7\pi}{4}$

**81.** $\dfrac{dy}{dx} = -\tan(t)$

**83.** $\dfrac{dy}{dx} = \dfrac{3}{4}$ and $\dfrac{d^2 y}{dx^2} = 0$, so the curve is neither concave up nor concave down at $t = 3$. Therefore the graph is linear and has a constant slope but no concavity.

**85.** $\dfrac{dy}{dx} = 4, \dfrac{d^2 y}{dx^2} = -6\sqrt{3}$; the curve is concave down at $\theta = \dfrac{\pi}{6}$.

**87.** No horizontal tangents. Vertical tangents at $(1, 0), (-1, 0)$.

**89.** $-\sec^3(\pi t)$

**91.** Horizontal $(0, -9)$; vertical $(\pm 2, -6)$.

**93.** 1

**95.** 0

**97.** 4

**99.** Concave up on $t > 0$.

**101.** 1

**103.** $\dfrac{3\pi}{2}$

**105.** $6\pi a^2$

**107.** $2\pi ab$

**109.** $\dfrac{1}{3}(2\sqrt{2} - 1)$

**111.** 7.075

**113.** $6a$

**115.** $6\sqrt{2}$

**119.** $\dfrac{2\pi(247\sqrt{13} + 64)}{1215}$

**121.** 59.101

**123.** $\dfrac{8\pi}{3}(17\sqrt{17} - 1)$

**125.**

**127.**

**129.**

**131.**

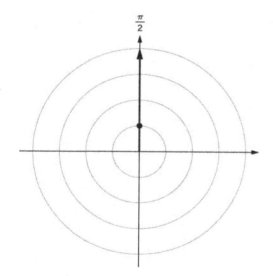

**133.** $B\left(3, \frac{-\pi}{3}\right)$ $B\left(-3, \frac{2\pi}{3}\right)$

**135.** $D\left(5, \frac{7\pi}{6}\right)D\left(-5, \frac{\pi}{6}\right)$

**137.** $(5, -0.927)$ $(-5, -0.927 + \pi)$

**139.** $(10, -0.927)(-10, -0.927 + \pi)$

**141.** $\left(2\sqrt{3}, -0.524\right)\left(-2\sqrt{3}, -0.524 + \pi\right)$

**143.** $(-\sqrt{3}, -1)$

**145.** $\left(-\frac{\sqrt{3}}{2}, \frac{-1}{2}\right)$

**147.** $(0, 0)$

**149.** Symmetry with respect to the $x$-axis, $y$-axis, and origin.

**151.** Symmetric with respect to $x$-axis only.

**153.** Symmetry with respect to $x$-axis only.

**155.** Line $y = x$

**157.** $y = 1$

**159.** Hyperbola; polar form $r^2 \cos(2\theta) = 16$ or $r^2 = 16 \sec \theta$.

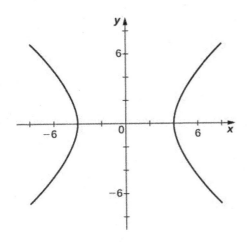

**161.** $r = \dfrac{2}{3\cos\theta - \sin\theta}$

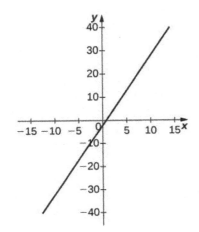

**163.** $x^2 + y^2 = 4y$

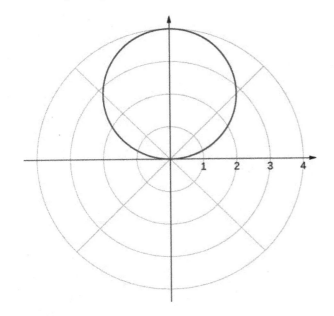

**165.** $x\tan\sqrt{x^2 + y^2} = y$

**167**.

*y*-axis symmetry
**169**.

*y*-axis symmetry

**171**.

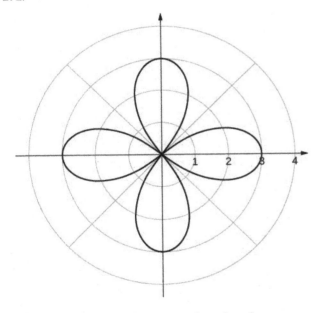

*x*- and *y*-axis symmetry and symmetry about the pole

**173**.

*x*-axis symmetry
**175**.

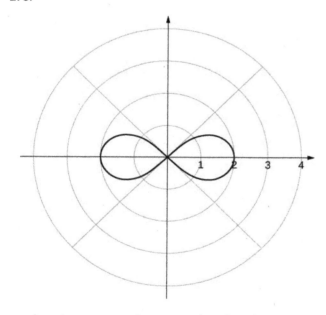

*x*- and *y*-axis symmetry and symmetry about the pole
**177**.

no symmetry
**179**.

a line
**181**.

**183**.

**185**.

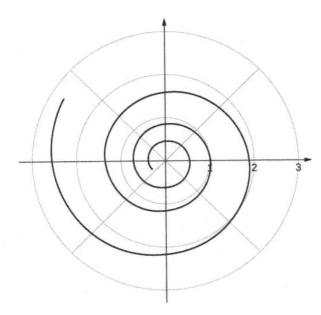

**187.** Answers vary. One possibility is the spiral lines become closer together and the total number of spirals increases.

**189.** $\frac{9}{2}\int_0^\pi \sin^2\theta\, d\theta$

**191.** $32\int_0^{\pi/2} \sin^2(2\theta)d\theta$

**193.** $\frac{1}{2}\int_\pi^{2\pi} (1-\sin\theta)^2\, d\theta$

**195.** $\int_{\sin^{-1}(2/3)}^{\pi/2} (2-3\sin\theta)^2 d\theta$

**197.** $\int_0^\pi (1-2\cos\theta)^2\, d\theta - \int_0^{\pi/3} (1-2\cos\theta)^2 d\theta$

**199.** $4\int_0^{\pi/3} d\theta + 16\int_{\pi/3}^{\pi/2} \left(\cos^2\theta\right)d\theta$

**201.** $9\pi$

**203.** $\frac{9\pi}{4}$

**205.** $\frac{9\pi}{8}$

**207.** $\frac{18\pi - 27\sqrt{3}}{2}$

**209.** $\frac{4}{3}\left(4\pi - 3\sqrt{3}\right)$

**211.** $\frac{3}{2}\left(4\pi - 3\sqrt{3}\right)$

**213.** $2\pi - 4$

**215.** $\int_0^{2\pi} \sqrt{(1+\sin\theta)^2 + \cos^2\theta}\, d\theta$

**217.** $\sqrt{2}\int_0^1 e^\theta\, d\theta$

**219.** $\frac{\sqrt{10}}{3}\left(e^6 - 1\right)$

**221.** 32

**223.** 6.238

**225.** 2

**227.** 4.39

**229.** $A = \pi\left(\frac{\sqrt{2}}{2}\right)^2 = \frac{\pi}{2}$ and $\frac{1}{2}\int_0^\pi (1 + 2\sin\theta\cos\theta)d\theta = \frac{\pi}{2}$

**231.** $C = 2\pi\left(\frac{3}{2}\right) = 3\pi$ and $\int_0^\pi 3d\theta = 3\pi$

**233.** $C = 2\pi(5) = 10\pi$ and $\int_0^\pi 10\,d\theta = 10\pi$

**235.** $\frac{dy}{dx} = \frac{f'(\theta)\sin\theta + f(\theta)\cos\theta}{f'(\theta)\cos\theta - f(\theta)\sin\theta}$

**237.** The slope is $\frac{1}{\sqrt{3}}$.

**239.** The slope is 0.

**241.** At $(4, 0)$, the slope is undefined. At $\left(-4, \frac{\pi}{2}\right)$, the slope is 0.

**243.** The slope is undefined at $\theta = \frac{\pi}{4}$.

**245.** Slope $= -1$.

**247.** Slope is $\frac{-2}{\pi}$.

**249.** Calculator answer: $-0.836$.

**251.** Horizontal tangent at $\left(\pm\sqrt{2}, \frac{\pi}{6}\right)$, $\left(\pm\sqrt{2}, -\frac{\pi}{6}\right)$.

**253.** Horizontal tangents at $\frac{\pi}{2}, \frac{7\pi}{6}, \frac{11\pi}{6}$. Vertical tangents at $\frac{\pi}{6}, \frac{5\pi}{6}$ and also at the pole $(0, 0)$.

**255.** $y^2 = 16x$

**257.** $x^2 = 2y$

**259.** $x^2 = -4(y - 3)$

**261.** $(x + 3)^2 = 8(y - 3)$

**263.** $\frac{x^2}{16} + \frac{y^2}{12} = 1$

**265.** $\frac{x^2}{13} + \frac{y^2}{4} = 1$

**267.** $\frac{(y - 1)^2}{16} + \frac{(x + 3)^2}{12} = 1$

**269.** $\frac{x^2}{16} + \frac{y^2}{12} = 1$

**271.** $\frac{x^2}{25} - \frac{y^2}{11} = 1$

**273.** $\frac{x^2}{7} - \frac{y^2}{9} = 1$

**275.** $\frac{(y + 2)^2}{4} - \frac{(x + 2)^2}{32} = 1$

**277.** $\frac{x^2}{4} - \frac{y^2}{32} = 1$

**279.** $e = 1$, parabola

**281.** $e = \frac{1}{2}$, ellipse

**283.** $e = 3$, hyperbola

**285.** $r = \dfrac{4}{5 + \cos\theta}$

**287.** $r = \dfrac{4}{1 + 2\sin\theta}$

**289.**

**291.**

**293.**

**295.**

**297**.

**299**.

**301**.

**303**.

**305**.

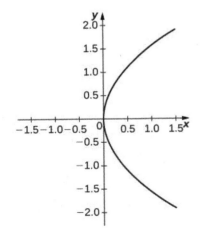

**307**. Hyperbola
**309**. Ellipse

**311**. Ellipse

**313**. At the point 2.25 feet above the vertex.

**315**. 0.5625 feet

**317**. Length is 96 feet and height is approximately 26.53 feet.

**319**. $r = \dfrac{2.616}{1 + 0.995 \cos \theta}$

**321**. $r = \dfrac{5.192}{1 + 0.0484 \cos \theta}$

## Review Exercises

**323**. True.

**325**. False. Imagine $y = t + 1, \quad x = -t + 1$.

**327**.

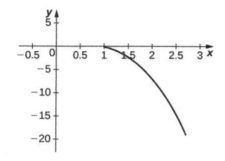

$y = 1 - x^3$

**329**.

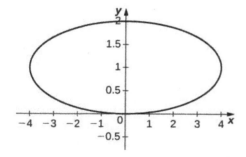

$\dfrac{x^2}{16} + (y - 1)^2 = 1$

**331**.

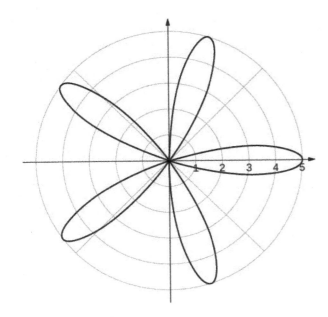

Symmetric about polar axis

**333**. $r^2 = \dfrac{4}{\sin^2\theta - \cos^2\theta}$

**335**.

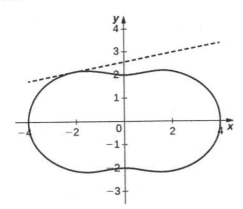

$y = \dfrac{3\sqrt{2}}{2} + \dfrac{1}{5}\left(x + \dfrac{3\sqrt{2}}{2}\right)$

**337**. $\dfrac{e^2}{2}$

**339**. $9\sqrt{10}$

**341**. $(y+5)^2 = -8x + 32$

**343**. $\dfrac{(y+1)^2}{16} - \dfrac{(x+2)^2}{9} = 1$

**345**. $e = \dfrac{2}{3}$, ellipse

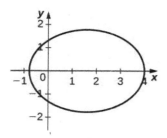

**347.** $\dfrac{y^2}{19.03^2} + \dfrac{x^2}{19.63^2} = 1, \quad e = 0.2447$

# Chapter 2

## Checkpoint

**2.1**.

**2.2**.

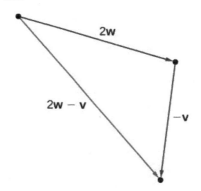

**2.3**. Vectors **a**, **b**, and **e** are equivalent.

**2.4**. $\langle 3, 7 \rangle$

**2.5**. a. $\| \mathbf{a} \| = 5\sqrt{2}$, b. $\mathbf{b} = \langle -4, -3 \rangle$, c. $3\mathbf{a} - 4\mathbf{b} = \langle 37, 15 \rangle$

**2.7**. $\mathbf{v} = \langle -5, 5\sqrt{3} \rangle$

**2.8**. $\langle -\dfrac{45}{\sqrt{85}}, -\dfrac{10}{\sqrt{85}} \rangle$

**2.9**. $\mathbf{a} = 16\mathbf{i} - 11\mathbf{j}, \quad \mathbf{b} = -\dfrac{\sqrt{2}}{2}\mathbf{i} - \dfrac{\sqrt{2}}{2}\mathbf{j}$

**2.10**. Approximately 516 mph

**2.11**.

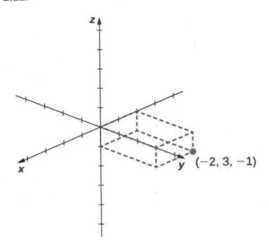

**2.12**. $5\sqrt{2}$

**2.13**. $z = -4$

**2.14**. $(x + 2)^2 + (y - 4)^2 + (z + 5)^2 = 52$

**2.15**. $x^2 + (y - 2)^2 + (z + 2)^2 = 14$

**2.16**. The set of points forms the two planes $y = -2$ and $z = 3$.

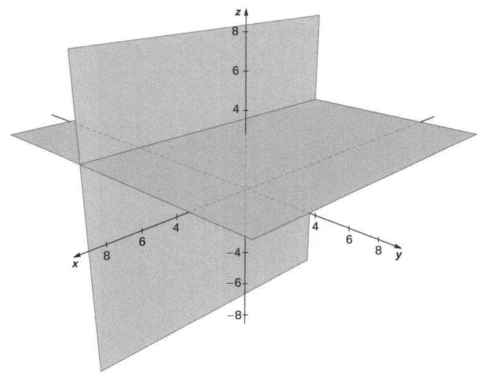

**2.17**. A cylinder of radius 4 centered on the line with $x = 0$ and $z = 2$.

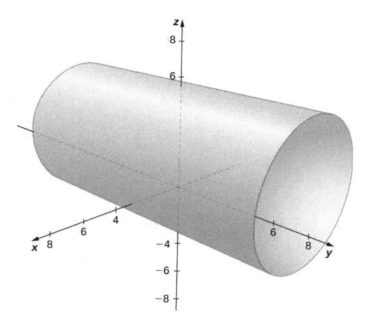

**2.18.** $\overrightarrow{ST} = \langle -1, -9, 1 \rangle = -\mathbf{i} - 9\mathbf{j} + \mathbf{k}$

**2.19.** $\langle \dfrac{1}{3\sqrt{10}}, -\dfrac{5}{3\sqrt{10}}, \dfrac{8}{3\sqrt{10}} \rangle$

**2.20.** $\mathbf{v} = \langle 16\sqrt{2}, 12\sqrt{2}, 20\sqrt{2} \rangle$

**2.21.** 7

**2.22.** a. $(\mathbf{r} \cdot \mathbf{p})\mathbf{q} = \langle 12, -12, 12 \rangle$; b. $\| \mathbf{p} \|^2 = 53$

**2.23.** $\theta \approx 0.22$ rad

**2.24.** $x = 5$

**2.25.** a. $\alpha \approx 1.04$ rad; b. $\beta \approx 2.58$ rad; c. $\gamma \approx 1.40$ rad

**2.26.** Sales = \$15,685.50; profit = \$14,073.15

**2.27.** $\mathbf{v} = \mathbf{p} + \mathbf{q}$, where $\mathbf{p} = \dfrac{18}{5}\mathbf{i} + \dfrac{9}{5}\mathbf{j}$ and $\mathbf{q} = \dfrac{7}{5}\mathbf{i} - \dfrac{14}{5}\mathbf{j}$

**2.28.** 21 knots

**2.29.** 150 ft-lb

**2.30.** $\mathbf{i} - 9\mathbf{j} + 2\mathbf{k}$

**2.31.** Up (the positive $z$-direction)

**2.32.** $-\mathbf{i}$

**2.33.** $-\mathbf{k}$

**2.34.** 16

**2.35.** 40

**2.36.** $8\mathbf{i} - 35\mathbf{j} + 2\mathbf{k}$

**2.37.** $\langle \dfrac{-3}{\sqrt{194}}, \dfrac{-13}{\sqrt{194}}, \dfrac{4}{\sqrt{194}} \rangle$

**2.38.** $6\sqrt{13}$

**2.39.** 17

**2.40.** 8 units$^3$

**2.41.** No, the triple scalar product is $-4 \neq 0$, so the three vectors form the adjacent edges of a parallelepiped. They are not coplanar.

**2.42.** 20 N

**2.43.** Possible set of parametric equations: $x = 1 + 4t$, $y = -3 + t$, $z = 2 + 6t$; related set of symmetric equations: $\dfrac{x-1}{4} = y + 3 = \dfrac{z-2}{6}$

**2.44**. $x = -1 - 7t,\ y = 3 - t,\ z = 6 - 2t,\ 0 \leq t \leq 1$

**2.45**. $\sqrt{\dfrac{10}{7}}$

**2.46**. These lines are skew because their direction vectors are not parallel and there is no point $(x,\ y,\ z)$ that lies on both lines.

**2.47**. $-2(x - 1) + (y + 1) + 3(z - 1) = 0$ or $-2x + y + 3z = 0$

**2.48**. $\dfrac{15}{\sqrt{21}}$

**2.49**. $x = t,\ y = 7 - 3t,\ z = 4 - 2t$

**2.50**. 1.44 rad

**2.51**. $\dfrac{9}{\sqrt{30}}$

**2.52**.

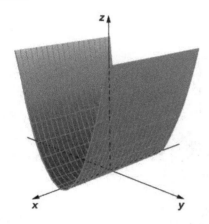

**2.53**. The traces parallel to the $xy$-plane are ellipses and the traces parallel to the $xz$- and $yz$-planes are hyperbolas. Specifically, the trace in the $xy$-plane is ellipse $\dfrac{x^2}{3^2} + \dfrac{y^2}{2^2} = 1$, the trace in the $xz$-plane is hyperbola $\dfrac{x^2}{3^2} - \dfrac{z^2}{5^2} = 1$, and the trace in the $yz$-plane is hyperbola $\dfrac{y^2}{2^2} - \dfrac{z^2}{5^2} = 1$ (see the following figure).

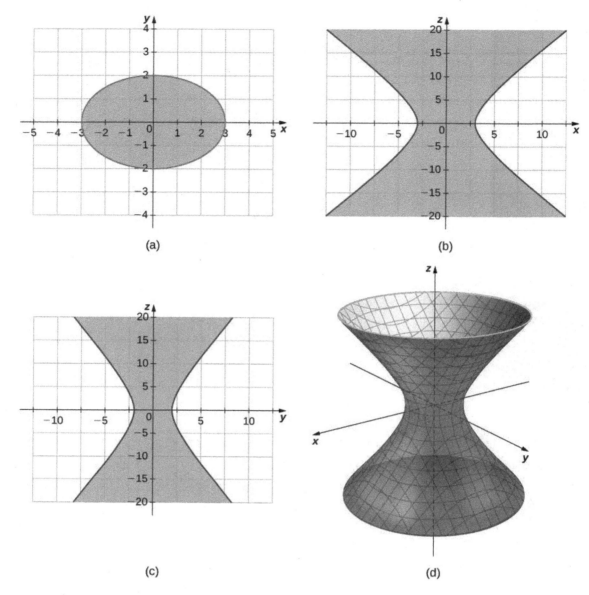

(a)

(b)

(c)

(d)

**2.54**. Hyperboloid of one sheet, centered at $(0, 0, 1)$

**2.55**. The rectangular coordinates of the point are $\left(\frac{5\sqrt{3}}{2}, \frac{5}{2}, 4\right)$.

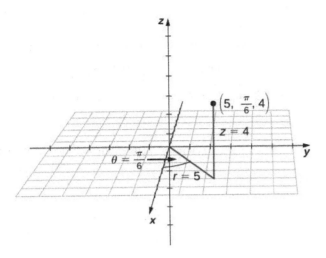

**2.56.** $\left(8\sqrt{2}, \frac{3\pi}{4}, -7\right)$

**2.57.** This surface is a cylinder with radius 6.

**2.58.**

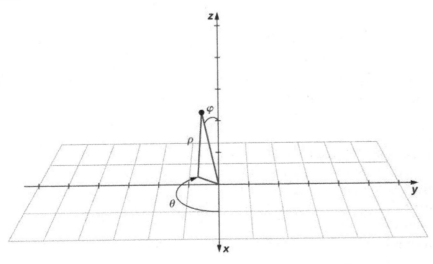

Cartesian: $\left(-\frac{\sqrt{3}}{2},\ -\frac{1}{2},\ \sqrt{3}\right)$, cylindrical: $\left(1,\ -\frac{5\pi}{6},\ \sqrt{3}\right)$

**2.59**. a. This is the set of all points $13$ units from the origin. This set forms a sphere with radius $13$. b. This set of points forms a half plane. The angle between the half plane and the positive $x$-axis is $\theta = \frac{2\pi}{3}$. c. Let $P$ be a point on this surface. The position vector of this point forms an angle of $\varphi = \frac{\pi}{4}$ with the positive $z$-axis, which means that points closer to the origin are closer to the axis. These points form a half-cone.

**2.60**. $(4000,\ 151°,\ 124°)$

**2.61**. Spherical coordinates with the origin located at the center of the earth, the $z$-axis aligned with the North Pole, and the $x$-axis aligned with the prime meridian

## Section Exercises

**1**. a. $\vec{PQ} = \langle 2, 2 \rangle$ ; b. $\vec{PQ} = 2\mathbf{i} + 2\mathbf{j}$

**3**. a. $\vec{QP} = \langle -2, -2 \rangle$ ; b. $\vec{QP} = -2\mathbf{i} - 2\mathbf{j}$

**5**. a. $\vec{PQ} + \vec{PR} = \langle 0, 6 \rangle$ ; b. $\vec{PQ} + \vec{PR} = 6\mathbf{j}$

**7**. a. $2\vec{PQ} - 2\vec{PR} = \langle 8, -4 \rangle$ ; b. $2\vec{PQ} - 2\vec{PR} = 8\mathbf{i} - 4\mathbf{j}$

**9**. a. $\langle \frac{1}{\sqrt{2}}, \frac{1}{\sqrt{2}} \rangle$ ; b. $\frac{1}{\sqrt{2}}\mathbf{i} + \frac{1}{\sqrt{2}}\mathbf{j}$

**11**. $\langle \frac{3}{5}, \frac{4}{5} \rangle$

**13**. $Q(0, 2)$

**15**. a. $\mathbf{a} + \mathbf{b} = 3\mathbf{i} + 4\mathbf{j}$, $\mathbf{a} + \mathbf{b} = \langle 3, 4 \rangle$ ; b. $\mathbf{a} - \mathbf{b} = \mathbf{i} - 2\mathbf{j}$, $\mathbf{a} - \mathbf{b} = \langle 1, -2 \rangle$ ; c. Answers will vary; d. $2\mathbf{a} = 4\mathbf{i} + 2\mathbf{j}$, $2\mathbf{a} = \langle 4, 2 \rangle$, $-\mathbf{b} = -\mathbf{i} - 3\mathbf{j}$, $-\mathbf{b} = \langle -1, -3 \rangle$, $2\mathbf{a} - \mathbf{b} = 3\mathbf{i} - \mathbf{j}$, $2\mathbf{a} - \mathbf{b} = \langle 3, -1 \rangle$

**17**. $15$

**19**. $\lambda = -3$

**21**. a. $\mathbf{a}(0) = \langle 1, 0 \rangle$, $\mathbf{a}(\pi) = \langle -1, 0 \rangle$ ; b. Answers may vary; c. Answers may vary

**23**. Answers may vary

**25**. $\mathbf{v} = \langle \frac{21}{5}, \frac{28}{5} \rangle$

**27**. $\mathbf{v} = \langle \frac{21\sqrt{34}}{34}, -\frac{35\sqrt{34}}{34} \rangle$

**29**. $\mathbf{u} = \langle \sqrt{3}, 1 \rangle$

**31**. $\mathbf{u} = \langle 0, 5 \rangle$

**33**. $\mathbf{u} = \langle -5\sqrt{3}, 5 \rangle$

**35**. $\theta = \frac{7\pi}{4}$

**37**. Answers may vary

**39**. a. $z_0 = f(x_0) + f'(x_0)$; b. $\mathbf{u} = \frac{1}{\sqrt{1 + [f'(x_0)]^2}} \langle 1, f'(x_0) \rangle$

**43**. $D(6, 1)$

**45**. $\langle 60.62, 35 \rangle$

**47**. The horizontal and vertical components are $750$ ft/sec and $1299.04$ ft/sec, respectively.

**49**. The magnitude of resultant force is $94.71$ lb; the direction angle is $13.42°$.

**51**. The magnitude of the third vector is $60.03$ N; the direction angle is $259.38°$.

**53**. The new ground speed of the airplane is $572.19$ mph; the new direction is N41.82E.

**55**. $\| \mathbf{T}_1 \| = 30.13$ lb, $\| \mathbf{T}_2 \| = 38.35$ lb

**57**. $\| \mathbf{v}_1 \| = 750$ lb, $\| \mathbf{v}_2 \| = 1299$ lb

**59**. The two horizontal and vertical components of the force of tension are $28$ lb and $42$ lb, respectively.

**61.** a. $(2, 0, 5), (2, 0, 0), (2, 3, 0), (0, 3, 0), (0, 3, 5), (0, 0, 5)$; b. $\sqrt{38}$

**63.** A union of two planes: $y = 5$ (a plane parallel to the $xz$-plane) and $z = 6$ (a plane parallel to the $xy$-plane)

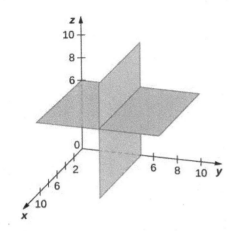

**65.** A cylinder of radius $1$ centered on the line $y = 1, z = 1$

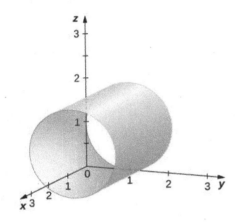

**67.** $z = 1$

**69.** $z = -2$

**71.** $(x + 1)^2 + (y - 7)^2 + (z - 4)^2 = 16$

**73.** $(x + 3)^2 + (y - 3.5)^2 + (z - 8)^2 = \frac{29}{4}$

**75.** Center $C(0, 0, 2)$ and radius $1$

**77.** a. $\overrightarrow{PQ} = \langle -4, -1, 2 \rangle$; b. $\overrightarrow{PQ} = -4\mathbf{i} - \mathbf{j} + 2\mathbf{k}$

**79.** a. $\overrightarrow{PQ} = \langle 6, -24, 24 \rangle$; b. $\overrightarrow{PQ} = 6\mathbf{i} - 24\mathbf{j} + 24\mathbf{k}$

**81.** $Q(5, 2, 8)$

**83.** $\mathbf{a} + \mathbf{b} = \langle -6, 4, -3 \rangle$, $4\mathbf{a} = \langle -4, -8, 16 \rangle$, $-5\mathbf{a} + 3\mathbf{b} = \langle -10, 28, -41 \rangle$

**85.** $\mathbf{a} + \mathbf{b} = \langle -1, 0, -1 \rangle$, $4\mathbf{a} = \langle 0, 0, -4 \rangle$, $-5\mathbf{a} + 3\mathbf{b} = \langle -3, 0, 5 \rangle$

**87.** $\| \mathbf{u} - \mathbf{v} \| = \sqrt{38}$, $\| -2\mathbf{u} \| = 2\sqrt{29}$

**89.** $\| \mathbf{u} - \mathbf{v} \| = 2$, $\| -2\mathbf{u} \| = 2\sqrt{13}$

**91.** $\mathbf{a} = \frac{3}{5}\mathbf{i} - \frac{4}{5}\mathbf{j}$

**93.** $\langle \frac{2}{\sqrt{62}}, -\frac{7}{\sqrt{62}}, \frac{3}{\sqrt{62}} \rangle$

**95.** $\langle -\frac{2}{\sqrt{6}}, \frac{1}{\sqrt{6}}, \frac{1}{\sqrt{6}} \rangle$

**97**. Equivalent vectors

**99**. $\mathbf{u} = \left\langle \dfrac{70}{\sqrt{59}}, \ -\dfrac{10}{\sqrt{59}}, \ \dfrac{30}{\sqrt{59}} \right\rangle$

**101**. $\mathbf{u} = \left\langle -\dfrac{4}{\sqrt{5}}\sin t, \ -\dfrac{4}{\sqrt{5}}\cos t, \ -\dfrac{2}{\sqrt{5}} \right\rangle$

**103**. $\left\langle \dfrac{5}{\sqrt{154}}, \dfrac{15}{\sqrt{154}}, \ -\dfrac{60}{\sqrt{154}} \right\rangle$

**105**. $\alpha = -\sqrt{7}, \quad \beta = -\sqrt{15}$

**111**. a. $\mathbf{F} = \left\langle 30, 40, 0 \right\rangle$ ; b. $53°$

**113**. $\mathbf{D} = 10\mathbf{k}$

**115**. $\mathbf{F}_4 = \left\langle -20, -7, -3 \right\rangle$

**117**. a. $\mathbf{F} = -19.6\mathbf{k}, \quad \|\mathbf{F}\| = 19.6$ N; b. $\mathbf{T} = 19.6\mathbf{k}, \quad \|\mathbf{T}\| = 19.6$ N

**119**. a. $\mathbf{F} = -294\mathbf{k}$ N; b. $\mathbf{F}_1 = \left\langle -\dfrac{49\sqrt{3}}{3}, 49, -98 \right\rangle$, $\mathbf{F}_2 = \left\langle -\dfrac{49\sqrt{3}}{3}, -49, -98 \right\rangle$, and $\mathbf{F}_3 = \left\langle \dfrac{98\sqrt{3}}{3}, 0, -98 \right\rangle$

(each component is expressed in newtons)

**121**. a. $\mathbf{v}(1) = \left\langle -0.84, 0.54, 2 \right\rangle$ (each component is expressed in centimeters per second); $\|\mathbf{v}(1)\| = 2.24$ (expressed in centimeters per second); $\mathbf{a}(1) = \left\langle -0.54, -0.84, 0 \right\rangle$ (each component expressed in centimeters per second squared); b.

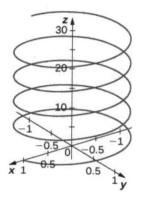

**123**. 6

**125**. 0

**127**. $(\mathbf{a} \cdot \mathbf{b})\mathbf{c} = \left\langle -11, -11, 11 \right\rangle$ ; $(\mathbf{a} \cdot \mathbf{c})\mathbf{b} = \left\langle -20, -35, 5 \right\rangle$

**129**. $(\mathbf{a} \cdot \mathbf{b})\mathbf{c} = \left\langle 1, 0, -2 \right\rangle$ ; $(\mathbf{a} \cdot \mathbf{c})\mathbf{b} = \left\langle 1, 0, -1 \right\rangle$

**131**. a. $\theta = 2.82$ rad; b. $\theta$ is not acute.

**133**. a. $\theta = \dfrac{\pi}{4}$ rad; b. $\theta$ is acute.

**135**. $\theta = \dfrac{\pi}{2}$

**137**. $\theta = \dfrac{\pi}{3}$

**139**. $\theta = 2$ rad

**141**. Orthogonal

**143**. Not orthogonal

**145**. $\mathbf{a} = \left\langle -\dfrac{4\alpha}{3}, \alpha \right\rangle$, where $\alpha \neq 0$ is a real number

**147**. $\mathbf{u} = -\alpha\mathbf{i} + \alpha\mathbf{j} + \beta\mathbf{k}$, where $\alpha$ and $\beta$ are real numbers such that $\alpha^2 + \beta^2 \neq 0$

**149**. $\alpha = -6$

**151**. a. $\overrightarrow{OP} = 4\mathbf{i} + 5\mathbf{j}, \quad \overrightarrow{OQ} = 5\mathbf{i} - 7\mathbf{j}$; b. $105.8°$

**153**. $68.33°$

**155**. $\mathbf{u}$ and $\mathbf{v}$ are orthogonal; $\mathbf{v}$ and $\mathbf{w}$ are orthogonal.

**161**. a. $\cos\alpha = \dfrac{2}{3}, \cos\beta = \dfrac{2}{3},$ and $\cos\gamma = \dfrac{1}{3}$; b. $\alpha = 48°, \quad \beta = 48°,$ and $\gamma = 71°$

**163.** a. $\cos\alpha = -\dfrac{1}{\sqrt{30}}$, $\cos\beta = \dfrac{5}{\sqrt{30}}$, and $\cos\gamma = \dfrac{2}{\sqrt{30}}$; b. $\alpha = 101°$, $\beta = 24°$, and $\gamma = 69°$

**167.** a. $\mathbf{w} = \left\langle \dfrac{80}{29}, \dfrac{32}{29} \right\rangle$; b. $\text{comp}_u\,\mathbf{v} = \dfrac{16}{\sqrt{29}}$

**169.** a. $\mathbf{w} = \left\langle \dfrac{24}{13}, 0, \dfrac{16}{13} \right\rangle$; b. $\text{comp}_u\,\mathbf{v} = \dfrac{8}{\sqrt{13}}$

**171.** a. $\mathbf{w} = \left\langle \dfrac{24}{25}, -\dfrac{18}{25} \right\rangle$; b. $\mathbf{q} = \left\langle \dfrac{51}{25}, \dfrac{68}{25} \right\rangle$, $\mathbf{v} = \mathbf{w} + \mathbf{q} = \left\langle \dfrac{24}{25}, -\dfrac{18}{25} \right\rangle + \left\langle \dfrac{51}{25}, \dfrac{68}{25} \right\rangle$

**173.** a. $2\sqrt{2}$; b. $109.47°$

**175.** $17\,\text{N}\cdot\text{m}$

**177.** $1175\ \text{ft}\cdot\text{lb}$

**179.** $4330.13$ ft-lb

**181.** a. $\|\,\mathbf{F}_1 + \mathbf{F}_2\,\| = 52.9$ lb; b. The direction angles are $\alpha = 74.5°$, $\beta = 36.7°$, and $\gamma = 57.7°$.

**183.** a. $\mathbf{u} \times \mathbf{v} = \langle 0, 0, 4 \rangle$;

b.

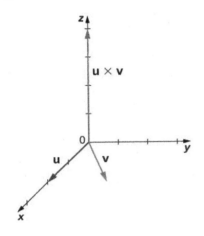

**185.** a. $\mathbf{u} \times \mathbf{v} = \langle 6, -4, 2 \rangle$;

b.

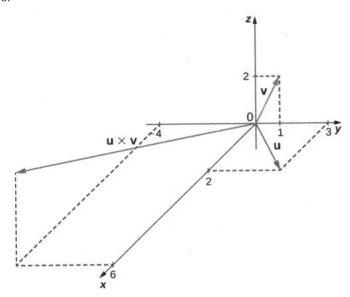

**187.** $-2\mathbf{j} - 4\mathbf{k}$

**189.** $\mathbf{w} = -\frac{1}{3\sqrt{6}}\mathbf{i} - \frac{7}{3\sqrt{6}}\mathbf{j} - \frac{2}{3\sqrt{6}}\mathbf{k}$

**191.** $\mathbf{w} = -\frac{4}{\sqrt{21}}\mathbf{i} - \frac{2}{\sqrt{21}}\mathbf{j} - \frac{1}{\sqrt{21}}\mathbf{k}$

**193.** $\alpha = 10$

**197.** $-3\mathbf{i} + 11\mathbf{j} + 2\mathbf{k}$

**199.** $\mathbf{w} = \langle -1, e^t, -e^{-t} \rangle$

**201.** $-26\mathbf{i} + 17\mathbf{j} + 9\mathbf{k}$

**203.** $72°$

**209.** 7

**211.** a. $5\sqrt{6}$; b. $\frac{5\sqrt{6}}{2}$; c. $\frac{5\sqrt{6}}{\sqrt{59}}$

**213.** a. 2; b. 2

**215.** $\mathbf{v} \cdot (\mathbf{u} \times \mathbf{w}) = -1$, $\quad \mathbf{w} \cdot (\mathbf{u} \times \mathbf{v}) = 1$

**217.** $\mathbf{a} = \langle 1, 2, 3 \rangle$, $\quad \mathbf{b} = \langle 0, 2, 5 \rangle$, $\quad \mathbf{c} = \langle 8, 9, 2 \rangle$; $\mathbf{a} \cdot (\mathbf{b} \times \mathbf{c}) = -9$

**219.** a. $\alpha = 1$; b. $h = 1$,

**225.** Yes, $\overrightarrow{AD} = \alpha \overrightarrow{AB} + \beta \overrightarrow{AC}$, where $\alpha = -1$ and $\beta = 1$.

**227.** $-\mathbf{k}$

**229.** $\langle 0, \pm 4\sqrt{5}, 2\sqrt{5} \rangle$

**233.** $\mathbf{w} = \langle w_3 - 1, w_3 + 1, w_3 \rangle$, where $w_3$ is any real number

**235.** 8.66 ft-lb

**237.** 250 N

**239.** $\mathbf{F} = 4.8 \times 10^{-15} \mathbf{k}$ N

**241.** a. $\mathbf{B}(t) = \langle \frac{2\sin t}{\sqrt{5}}, -\frac{2\cos t}{\sqrt{5}}, \frac{1}{\sqrt{5}} \rangle$;

b.

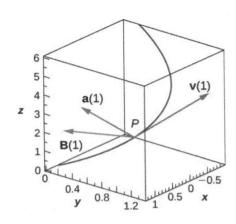

**243.** a. $\mathbf{r} = \langle -3, 5, 9 \rangle + t \langle 7, -12, -7 \rangle$, $t \in \mathbb{R}$; b. $x = -3 + 7t, y = 5 - 12t, z = 9 - 7t$, $t \in \mathbb{R}$; c.

$\frac{x+3}{7} = \frac{y-5}{-12} = \frac{z-9}{-7}$; d. $x = -3 + 7t, y = 5 - 12t, z = 9 - 7t$, $t \in [0, 1]$

**245.** a. $\mathbf{r} = \langle -1, 0, 5 \rangle + t \langle 5, 0, -2 \rangle$, $t \in \mathbb{R}$; b. $x = -1 + 5t, y = 0, z = 5 - 2t$, $t \in \mathbb{R}$; c.

$\frac{x+1}{5} = \frac{z-5}{-2}, y = 0$; d. $x = -1 + 5t, y = 0, z = 5 - 2t$, $t \in [0, 1]$

**247.** a. $x = 1 + t, y = -2 + 2t, z = 3 + 3t$, $t \in \mathbb{R}$; b. $\frac{x-1}{1} = \frac{y+2}{2} = \frac{z-3}{3}$; c. $(0, -4, 0)$

**249.** a. $x = 3 + t, y = 1, z = 5$, $t \in \mathbb{R}$; b. $y = 1, z = 5$; c. The line does not intersect the $xy$-plane.

**251.** a. $P(1, 3, 5)$, $v = \langle 1, 1, 4 \rangle$; b. $\sqrt{3}$

**253.** $\frac{2\sqrt{2}}{\sqrt{3}}$

**255.** a. Parallel; b. $\frac{\sqrt{2}}{\sqrt{3}}$

**259.** $(-12, 6, -4)$

**261.** The lines are skew.

**263.** The lines are equal.

**265.** a. $x = 1 + t, y = 1 - t, z = 1 + 2t$, $t \in \mathbb{R}$; b. For instance, the line passing through $A$ with direction vector

$\mathbf{j} : x = 1, z = 1$; c. For instance, the line passing through $A$ and point $(2, 0, 0)$ that belongs to $L$ is a line that intersects;

$L : \frac{x-1}{-1} = y - 1 = z - 1$

**267.** a. $3x - 2y + 4z = 0$; b. $3x - 2y + 4z = 0$

**269.** a. $(x - 1) + 2(y - 2) + 3(z - 3) = 0$; b. $x + 2y + 3z - 14 = 0$

**271.** a. $\mathbf{n} = 4\mathbf{i} + 5\mathbf{j} + 10\mathbf{k}$; b. $(5, 0, 0)$, $(0, 4, 0)$, and $(0, 0, 2)$;

c.

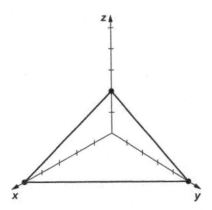

**273**. a. $\mathbf{n} = 3\mathbf{i} - 2\mathbf{j} + 4\mathbf{k}$; b. $(0, 0, 0)$;

c.

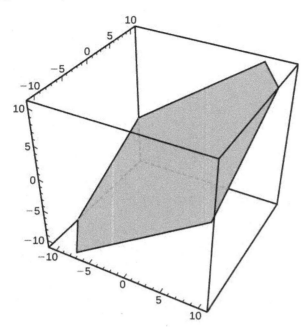

**275**. $(3, 0, 0)$

**277**. $x = -2 + 2t,\ y = 1 - 3t,\ z = 3 + t,\quad t \in \mathbb{R}$

**281**. a. $-2y + 3z - 1 = 0$; b. $\langle\, 0, -2, 3\, \rangle \cdot \langle\, x - 1, y - 1, z - 1\, \rangle = 0$; c. $x = 0,\ y = -2t,\ z = 3t,\quad t \in \mathbb{R}$

**283**. a. Answers may vary; b. $\dfrac{x-1}{1} = \dfrac{z-6}{-1},\ y = 4$

**285**. $2x - 5y - 3z + 15 = 0$

**287**. The line intersects the plane at point $P(-3, 4, 0)$.

**289**. $\dfrac{16}{\sqrt{14}}$

**291**. a. The planes are neither parallel nor orthogonal; b. $62°$

**293**. a. The planes are parallel.

**295**. $\dfrac{1}{\sqrt{6}}$

**297**. a. $\dfrac{18}{\sqrt{29}}$; b. $P\left(-\dfrac{51}{29}, \dfrac{130}{29}, \dfrac{62}{29}\right)$

**299**. $4x - 3y = 0$

**301**. a. $\mathbf{v}(1) = \langle\, \cos 1, -\sin 1, 2\, \rangle$; b. $(\cos 1)(x - \sin 1) - (\sin 1)(y - \cos 1) + 2(z - 2) = 0$;

c.

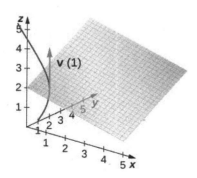

**303**. The surface is a cylinder with the rulings parallel to the $y$-axis.

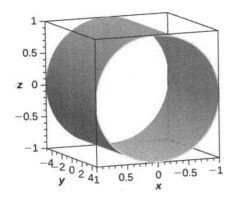

**305.** The surface is a cylinder with rulings parallel to the $y$-axis.

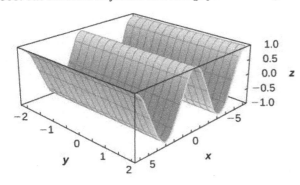

**307.** The surface is a cylinder with rulings parallel to the $x$-axis.

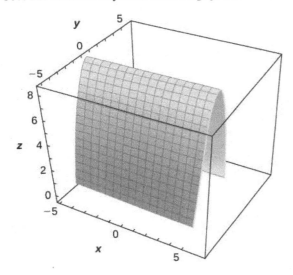

**309.** a. Cylinder; b. The $x$-axis
**311.** a. Hyperboloid of two sheets; b. The $x$-axis
**313.** b.
**315.** d.
**317.** a.

**319.** $-\dfrac{x^2}{9} + \dfrac{y^2}{\frac{1}{4}} + \dfrac{z^2}{\frac{1}{4}} = 1$,   hyperboloid of one sheet with the $x$-axis as its axis of symmetry

**321.** $-\dfrac{x^2}{\frac{10}{3}} + \dfrac{y^2}{2} - \dfrac{z^2}{10} = 1$,   hyperboloid of two sheets with the $y$-axis as its axis of symmetry

**323.** $y = -\dfrac{z^2}{5} + \dfrac{x^2}{5}$, hyperbolic paraboloid with the y-axis as its axis of symmetry

**325.** $\dfrac{x^2}{15} + \dfrac{y^2}{3} + \dfrac{z^2}{5} = 1$, ellipsoid

**327.** $\dfrac{x^2}{40} + \dfrac{y^2}{8} - \dfrac{z^2}{5} = 0$, elliptic cone with the z-axis as its axis of symmetry

**329.** $x = \dfrac{y^2}{2} + \dfrac{z^2}{3}$, elliptic paraboloid with the x-axis as its axis of symmetry

**331.** Parabola $y = -\dfrac{x^2}{4}$,

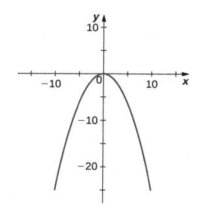

**333.** Ellipse $\dfrac{y^2}{4} + \dfrac{z^2}{100} = 1$,

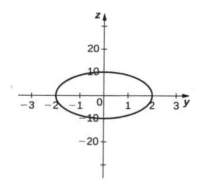

**335.** Ellipse $\dfrac{y^2}{4} + \dfrac{z^2}{100} = 1$,

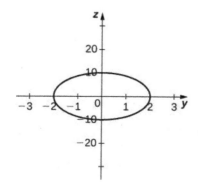

**337.** a. Ellipsoid; b. The third equation; c. $\dfrac{x^2}{100} + \dfrac{y^2}{400} + \dfrac{z^2}{225} = 1$

**339.** a. $\dfrac{(x+3)^2}{16} + \dfrac{(z-2)^2}{8} = 1$; b. Cylinder centered at $(-3, 2)$ with rulings parallel to the $y$-axis

**341.** a. $\dfrac{(x-3)^2}{4} + (y-2)^2 - (z+2)^2 = 1$; b. Hyperboloid of one sheet centered at $(3, 2, -2)$, with the $z$-axis as its axis of

symmetry

**343.** a. $(x+3)^2 + \dfrac{y^2}{4} - \dfrac{z^2}{3} = 0$; b. Elliptic cone centered at $(-3, 0, 0)$, with the $z$-axis as its axis of symmetry

**345.** $\dfrac{x^2}{4} + \dfrac{y^2}{16} + z^2 = 1$

**347.** $(1, -1, 0)$ and $\left(\dfrac{13}{3}, 4, \dfrac{5}{3}\right)$

**349.** $x^2 + z^2 + 4y = 0$, elliptic paraboloid

**351.** $(0, 0, 100)$

**355.** a. $x = 2 - \dfrac{z^2}{2}$, $y = \pm\dfrac{z}{2}\sqrt{4 - z^2}$, where $z \in [-2, 2]$;

b.

**357.**

two ellipses of equations $\dfrac{x^2}{2} + \dfrac{y^2}{\frac{9}{2}} = 1$ in planes $z = \pm 2\sqrt{2}$

**359.** a. $\dfrac{x^2}{3963^2} + \dfrac{y^2}{3963^2} + \dfrac{z^2}{3950^2} = 1;$

b.

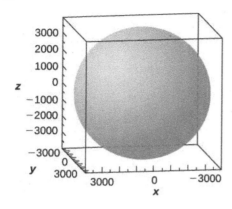

;

c. The intersection curve is the ellipse of equation $\dfrac{x^2}{3963^2} + \dfrac{y^2}{3963^2} = \dfrac{(2950)(4950)}{3950^2},$ and the intersection is an ellipse.; d. The

intersection curve is the ellipse of equation $\dfrac{2y^2}{3963^2} + \dfrac{z^2}{3950^2} = 1.$

**361.** a.

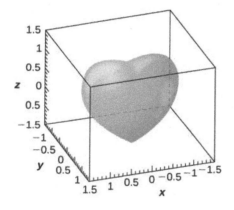

b. The intersection curve is $\left(x^2 + z^2 - 1\right)^3 - x^2 z^3 = 0.$

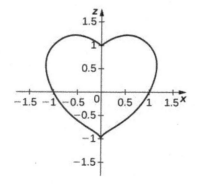

**363.** $\left(2\sqrt{3}, \ 2, \ 3\right)$

**365.** $\left(-2\sqrt{3},\ -2,\ 3\right)$

**367.** $\left(2,\ \frac{\pi}{3},\ 2\right)$

**369.** $\left(3\sqrt{2},\ -\frac{\pi}{4},\ 7\right)$

**371.** A cylinder of equation $x^2 + y^2 = 16,$  with its center at the origin and rulings parallel to the $z$-axis,

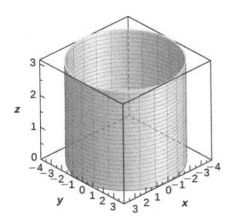

**373.** Hyperboloid of two sheets of equation $-x^2 + y^2 - z^2 = 1,$  with the $y$-axis as the axis of symmetry,

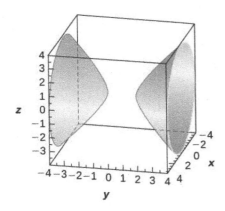

**375.** Cylinder of equation $x^2 - 2x + y^2 = 0,$  with a center at $(1,\ 0,\ 0)$ and radius $1,$  with rulings parallel to the $z$-axis,

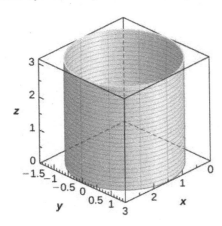

**377.** Plane of equation $x = 2,$

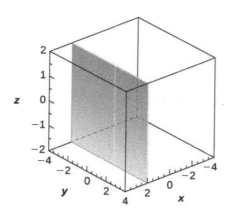

**379.** $z = 3$

**381.** $r^2 + z^2 = 9$

**383.** $r = 16 \cos \theta, \, r = 0$

**385.** $(0, 0, -3)$

**387.** $\left(6, -6, \sqrt{2}\right)$

**389.** $(4, 0, 90°)$

**391.** $(3, 90°, 90°)$

**393.** Sphere of equation $x^2 + y^2 + z^2 = 9$ centered at the origin with radius $3$,

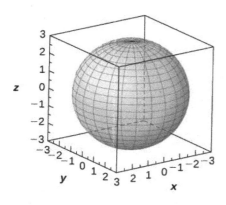

**395.** Sphere of equation $x^2 + y^2 + (z - 1)^2 = 1$ centered at $(0, 0, 1)$ with radius $1$,

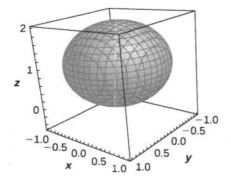

**397.** The $xy$-plane of equation $z = 0$,

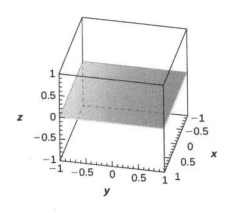

**399.** $\varphi = \frac{\pi}{3}$ or $\varphi = \frac{2\pi}{3}$; Elliptic cone

**401.** $\rho \cos \varphi = 6$; Plane at $z = 6$

**403.** $\left(\sqrt{10}, \frac{\pi}{4}, 0.3218\right)$

**405.** $\left(3\sqrt{2}, \frac{\pi}{2}, \frac{\pi}{4}\right)$

**407.** $\left(2, -\frac{\pi}{4}, 0\right)$

**409.** $\left(8, \frac{\pi}{3}, 0\right)$

**411.** Cartesian system, $\{(x, y, z) | 0 \le x \le a, 0 \le y \le a, 0 \le z \le a\}$

**413.** Cylindrical system, $\{(r, \theta, z) | r^2 + z^2 \le 9, r \ge 3 \cos \theta, 0 \le \theta \le 2\pi\}$

**415.** The region is described by the set of points $\{(r, \theta, z) | 0 \le r \le 1, 0 \le \theta \le 2\pi, r^2 \le z \le r\}$.

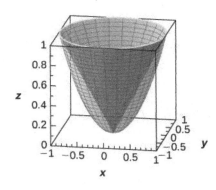

**417.** $(4000, -77°, 51°)$

**419.** $43.17°W$, $22.91°S$

**421.** a. $\rho = 0$, $\rho + R^2 - r^2 - 2R \sin \varphi = 0$;

c.

## Review Exercises

**423**. True

**425**. False

**427**. a. $\langle 24, -5 \rangle$ ; b. $\sqrt{85}$; c. Can't dot a vector with a scalar; d. $-29$

**429**. $a = \pm 2$

**431**. $\langle \frac{1}{\sqrt{14}}, -\frac{2}{\sqrt{14}}, -\frac{3}{\sqrt{14}} \rangle$

**433**. 27

**435**. $x = 1 - 3t$, $y = 3 + 3t$, $z = 5 - 8t$, $\mathbf{r}(t) = (1 - 3t)\mathbf{i} + 3(1 + t)\mathbf{j} + (5 - 8t)\mathbf{k}$

**437**. $-x + 3y + 8z = 43$

**439**. $x = k$ trace: $k^2 = y^2 + z^2$ is a circle, $y = k$ trace: $x^2 - z^2 = k^2$ is a hyperbola (or a pair of lines if $k = 0$), $z = k$ trace: $x^2 - y^2 = k^2$ is a hyperbola (or a pair of lines if $k = 0$). The surface is a cone.

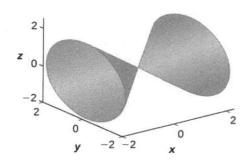

**441**. Cylindrical: $z = r^2 - 1$, spherical: $\cos \varphi = \rho \sin^2 \varphi - \frac{1}{\rho}$

**443**. $x^2 - 2x + y^2 + z^2 = 1$, sphere

**445**. 331 N, and 244 N

**447**. 15 J

**449**. More, 59.09 J

# Chapter 3

## Checkpoint

**3.1**. $\mathbf{r}(0) = \mathbf{j}$, $\mathbf{r}(1) = -2\mathbf{i} + 5\mathbf{j}$, $\mathbf{r}(-4) = 28\mathbf{i} - 15\mathbf{j}$ The domain of $\mathbf{r}(t) = \left(t^2 - 3t\right)\mathbf{i} + (4t + 1)\mathbf{j}$ is all real numbers.

**3.2**.

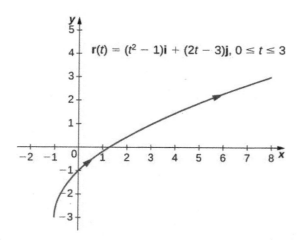

**3.3**. $\lim\limits_{t \to -2} \mathbf{r}(t) = 3\mathbf{i} - 5\mathbf{j} - \mathbf{k}$

**3.4**. $\mathbf{r}'(t) = 4t\mathbf{i} + 5\mathbf{j}$

**3.5.** $\mathbf{r}'(t) = (1 + \ln t)\mathbf{i} + 5e^t\mathbf{j} - (\sin t + \cos t)\mathbf{k}$

**3.6.** $\frac{d}{dt}[\mathbf{r}(t) \cdot \mathbf{r}'(t)] = 8e^{4t}$ $\frac{d}{dt}[\mathbf{u}(t) \times \mathbf{r}(t)]$ $= -\left(e^{2t}(\cos t + 2\sin t) + \cos 2t\right)\mathbf{i} + \left(e^{2t}(2t + 1) - \sin 2t\right)\mathbf{j} + (t\cos t + \sin t - \cos 2t)\mathbf{k}$

**3.7.** $\mathbf{T}(t) = \frac{2t}{\sqrt{4t^2 + 5}}\mathbf{i} + \frac{2}{\sqrt{4t^2 + 5}}\mathbf{j} + \frac{1}{\sqrt{4t^2 + 5}}\mathbf{k}$

**3.8.** $\int_1^3 \left[(2t + 4)\mathbf{i} + \left(3t^2 - 4t\right)\mathbf{j}\right]dt = 16\mathbf{i} + 10\mathbf{j}$

**3.9.** $\mathbf{r}'(t) = \langle 4t, 4t, 3t^2 \rangle$, so $s = \frac{1}{27}\left(113^{3/2} - 32^{3/2}\right) \approx 37.785$

**3.10.** $s = 5t$, or $t = s/5$. Substituting this into $\mathbf{r}(t) = \langle 3\cos t, 3\sin t, 4t \rangle$ gives $\mathbf{r}(s) = \langle 3\cos\left(\frac{s}{5}\right), 3\sin\left(\frac{s}{5}\right), \frac{4s}{5} \rangle$, $s \geq 0$.

**3.11.** $\kappa = \frac{6}{101^{3/2}} \approx 0.0059$

**3.12.** $\mathbf{N}(2) = \frac{\sqrt{2}}{2}(\mathbf{i} - \mathbf{j})$

**3.13.** $\kappa = \frac{4}{\left[1 + (4x - 4)^2\right]^{3/2}}$ At the point $x = 1$, the curvature is equal to 4. Therefore, the radius of the osculating circle is $\frac{1}{4}$. A graph of this function appears next:

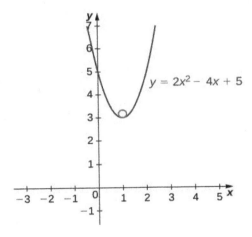

$y = 2x^2 - 4x + 5$

The vertex of this parabola is located at the point $(1, 3)$. Furthermore, the center of the osculating circle is directly above the vertex. Therefore, the coordinates of the center are $\left(1, \frac{13}{4}\right)$. The equation of the osculating circle is $(x - 1)^2 + \left(y - \frac{13}{4}\right)^2 = \frac{1}{16}$.

**3.14.**
$\mathbf{v}(t) = \mathbf{r}'(t) = (2t - 3)\mathbf{i} + 2\mathbf{j} + \mathbf{k}$
$\mathbf{a}(t) = \mathbf{v}'(t) = 2\mathbf{i}$
$v(t) = \|\mathbf{r}'(t)\| = \sqrt{(2t - 3)^2 + 2^2 + 1^2} = \sqrt{4t^2 - 12t + 14}$ The units for velocity and speed are feet per second, and

the units for acceleration are feet per second squared.

**3.15.**

a.
$\mathbf{v}(t) = \mathbf{r}'(t) = 4\mathbf{i} + 2t\mathbf{j}$
$\mathbf{a}(t) = \mathbf{v}'(t) = 2\mathbf{j}$
$a_{\mathbf{T}} = \frac{2t}{\sqrt{t^2 + 4}}, a_{\mathbf{N}} = \frac{2}{\sqrt{t^2 + 4}}$

b. $a_{\mathbf{T}}(-3) = -\dfrac{6\sqrt{13}}{13}$, $a_{\mathbf{N}}(-3) = \dfrac{2\sqrt{13}}{13}$

**3.16.** 967.15 m

**3.17.** $a = 1.224 \times 10^9 \, \text{m} \approx 1{,}224{,}000 \, \text{km}$

## Section Exercises

**1.** $f(t) = 3 \sec t$, $g(t) = 2 \tan t$

**3.**

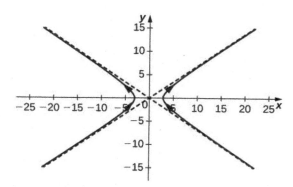

**5.** a. $\langle \dfrac{\sqrt{2}}{2}, \dfrac{\sqrt{2}}{2} \rangle$,  b. $\langle \dfrac{1}{2}, \dfrac{\sqrt{3}}{2} \rangle$,  c. Yes, the limit as $t$ approaches $\pi/3$ is equal to $\mathbf{r}(\pi/3)$,  d.

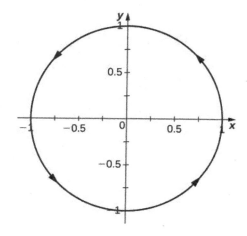

**7.** a. $\langle e^{\pi/4}, \dfrac{\sqrt{2}}{2}, \ln\left(\dfrac{\pi}{4}\right) \rangle$ ; b. $\langle e^{\pi/4}, \dfrac{\sqrt{2}}{2}, \ln\left(\dfrac{\pi}{4}\right) \rangle$ ; c. Yes

**9.** $\langle e^{\pi/2}, 1, \ln\left(\dfrac{\pi}{2}\right) \rangle$

**11.** $2e^2 \mathbf{i} + \dfrac{2}{e^4} \mathbf{j} + 2\mathbf{k}$

**13.** The limit does not exist because the limit of $\ln(t-1)$ as $t$ approaches infinity does not exist.

**15.** $t > 0$, $t \neq (2k+1)\dfrac{\pi}{2}$,  where k is an integer

**17.** $t > 3$, $t \neq n\pi$,  where $n$ is an integer

**19.**

Cross Section

(a)

Side View

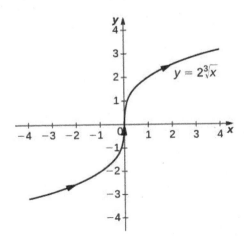

(b)

**21.** All $t$ such that $t \in (1, \infty)$

**23.** $y = 2\sqrt[3]{x},$   a variation of the cube-root function

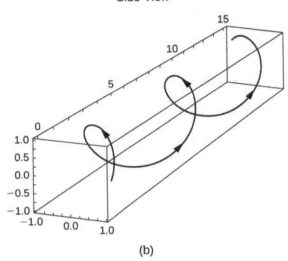

**25.** $x^2 + y^2 = 9$, a circle centered at $(0, 0)$ with radius 3, and a counterclockwise orientation

**27.**

**29.**

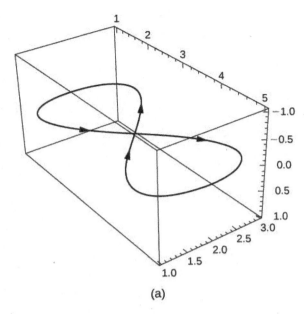

(a)

View in the *yt*-plane

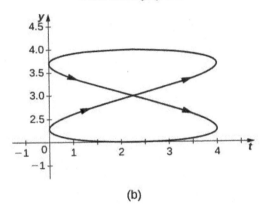

(b)

Find a vector-valued function that traces out the given curve in the indicated direction.

**31.** For left to right, $y = x^2$, where t increases

**33.** $(50, 0, 0)$

**35.**

**37**.

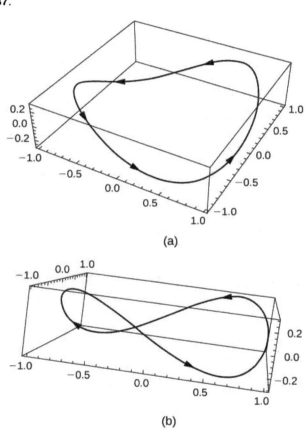

(a)

(b)

**39**. One possibility is $r(t) = \cos t \mathbf{i} + \sin t \mathbf{j} + \sin(4t) \mathbf{k}$. By increasing the coefficient of $t$ in the third component, the number of turning points will increase.

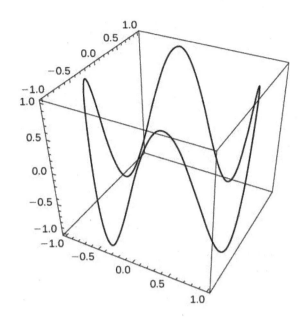

**41.** $\langle 3t^2, 6t, \frac{1}{2}t^2 \rangle$

**43.** $\langle -e^{-t}, 3\cos(3t), \frac{5}{\sqrt{t}} \rangle$

**45.** $\langle 0, 0, 0 \rangle$

**47.** $\langle \frac{-1}{(t+1)^2}, \frac{1}{1+t^2}, \frac{3}{t} \rangle$

**49.** $\langle 0, 12\cos(3t), \cos t - t\sin t \rangle$

**51.** $\frac{1}{\sqrt{2}} \langle 1, -1, 0 \rangle$

**53.** $\frac{1}{\sqrt{1060.5625}} \langle 6, -\frac{3}{4}, 32 \rangle$

**55.** $\frac{1}{\sqrt{9\sin^2(3t) + 144\cos^2(4t)}} \langle 0, -3\sin(3t), 12\cos(4t) \rangle$

**57.** $\mathbf{T}(t) = \frac{-12}{13}\sin(4t)\mathbf{i} + \frac{12}{13}\cos(4t)\mathbf{j} + \frac{5}{13}\mathbf{k}$

**59.** $\langle 2t, 4t^3, -8t^7 \rangle$

**61.** $\sin(t) + 2te^t - 4t^3\cos(t) + t\cos(t) + t^2e^t + t^4\sin(t)$

**63.** $900t^7 + 16t$

**65.**

    a.

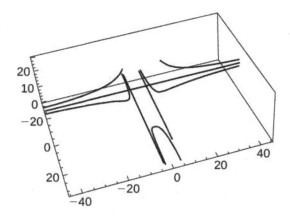

b. Undefined or infinite

**67.** $\mathbf{r}'(t) = -b\omega\sin(\omega t)\mathbf{i} + b\omega\cos(\omega t)\mathbf{j}$. To show orthogonality, note that $\mathbf{r}'(t) \cdot \mathbf{r}(t) = 0$.

**69.** $0\mathbf{i} + 2\mathbf{j} + 4t\mathbf{j}$

**71.** $\frac{1}{3}\left(10^{3/2} - 1\right)$

**73.**

$$
\begin{aligned}
\|\mathbf{v}(t)\| &= k \\
\mathbf{v}(t) \cdot \mathbf{v}(t) &= k \\
\frac{d}{dt}(\mathbf{v}(t) \cdot \mathbf{v}(t)) &= \frac{d}{dt}k = 0 \\
\mathbf{v}(t) \cdot \mathbf{v}'(t) + \mathbf{v}'(t) \cdot \mathbf{v}(t) &= 0 \\
2\mathbf{v}(t) \cdot \mathbf{v}'(t) &= 0 \\
\mathbf{v}(t) \cdot \mathbf{v}'(t) &= 0.
\end{aligned}
$$

The last statement implies that the velocity and acceleration are perpendicular or orthogonal.

**75.** $\mathbf{v}(t) = \langle\, 1 - \sin t,\ 1 - \cos t \,\rangle, \quad \text{speed} = -\mathbf{v}(t)\| = \sqrt{4 - 2(\sin t + \cos t)}$

**77.** $x - 1 = t,\ y - 1 = -t,\ z - 0 = 0$

**79.** $\mathbf{r}(t) = \langle\, 18,\, 9 \,\rangle$ at $t = 3$

**81.** $\sqrt{593}$

**83.** $\mathbf{v}(t) = \langle\, -\sin t,\ \cos t,\ 1 \,\rangle$

**85.** $\mathbf{a}(t) = -\cos t\mathbf{i} - \sin t\mathbf{j} + 0\mathbf{j}$

**87.** $\mathbf{v}(t) = \langle\, -\sin t,\ 2\cos t,\ 0 \,\rangle$

**89.** $\mathbf{a}(t) = \langle\, -\frac{\sqrt{2}}{2},\ -\sqrt{2},\ 0 \,\rangle$

**91.** $\|\mathbf{v}(t)\| = \sqrt{\sec^4 t + \sec^2 t \tan^2 t} = \sqrt{\sec^2 t(\sec^2 t + \tan^2 t)}$

**93.** 2

**95.** $\langle\, 0,\ 2\sin t\left(t - \frac{1}{t}\right) - 2\cos t\left(1 + \frac{1}{t^2}\right),\ 2\sin t\left(1 + \frac{1}{t^2}\right) + 2\cos t\left(t - \frac{2}{t}\right) \,\rangle$

**97.** $\mathbf{T}(t) = \langle\, \dfrac{t^2}{\sqrt{t^4 + 1}},\ \dfrac{-1}{\sqrt{t^4 + 1}} \,\rangle$

**99.** $\mathbf{T}(t) = \frac{1}{3}\langle\, 1,\ 2,\ 2 \,\rangle$

**101.** $\frac{3}{4}\mathbf{i} + \ln(2)\mathbf{j} + \left(1 - \frac{1}{e}\right)\mathbf{j}$

**103.** $8\sqrt{5}$

**105.** $\frac{1}{54}\left(37^{3/2} - 1\right)$

**107.** Length $= 2\pi$

**109.** $6\pi$

**111.** $e - \frac{1}{e}$

**113.** $\mathbf{T}(0) = \mathbf{j}, \quad \mathbf{N}(0) = -\mathbf{i}$

**115.** $\mathbf{T}(t) = \langle\, 2e^t, \, e^t \cos t - e^t \sin t, \, e^t \cos t + e^t \sin t \,\rangle$

**117.** $\mathbf{N}(0) = \langle\, \frac{\sqrt{2}}{2}, 0, \frac{\sqrt{2}}{2} \,\rangle$

**119.** $\mathbf{T}(t) = \dfrac{1}{\sqrt{4t^2 + 2}} < 1, \, 2t, \, 1 >$

**121.** $\mathbf{T}(t) = \dfrac{1}{\sqrt{100t^2 + 13}}(3\mathbf{i} + 10t\mathbf{j} + 2\mathbf{k})$

**123.** $\mathbf{T}(t) = \dfrac{1}{\sqrt{9t^4 + 76t^2 + 16}}\left(\left[3t^2 - 4\right]\mathbf{i} + 10t\mathbf{j}\right)$

**125.** $\mathbf{N}(t) = \langle\, -\sin t, 0, -\cos t \,\rangle$

**127.** Arc-length function: $s(t) = 5t$; r as a parameter of $s$: $\mathbf{r}(s) = \left(3 - \frac{3s}{5}\right)\mathbf{i} + \frac{4s}{5}\mathbf{j}$

**129.** $\mathbf{r}(s) = \left(1 + \frac{s}{\sqrt{2}}\right)\sin\left(\ln(1 + \frac{s}{\sqrt{2}})\right)\mathbf{i} + \left(1 + \frac{s}{\sqrt{2}}\right)\cos\left[\ln\left(1 + \frac{s}{\sqrt{2}}\right)\right]\mathbf{j}$

**131.** The maximum value of the curvature occurs at $x = \sqrt[4]{5}$.

**133.** $\frac{1}{2}$

**135.** $\kappa \approx \dfrac{49.477}{\left(17 + 144t^2\right)^{3/2}}$

**137.** $\frac{1}{2\sqrt{2}}$

**139.** The curvature approaches zero.

**141.** $y = 6x + \pi$ and $x + 6 = 6\pi$

**143.** $x + 2z = \frac{\pi}{2}$

**145.** $\dfrac{a^4 b^4}{\left(b^4 x^2 + a^4 y^2\right)^{3/2}}$

**147.** $\frac{10\sqrt{10}}{3}$

**149.** $\frac{38}{3}$

**151.** The curvature is decreasing over this interval.

**153.** $\kappa = \dfrac{6}{x^{2/5}\left(25 + 4x^{6/5}\right)}$

**155.** $\mathbf{v}(t) = (6t)\mathbf{i} + (2 - \cos(t))\mathbf{j}$

**157.** $\mathbf{v}(t) = \langle\, -3\sin t, \, 3\cos t, \, 2t \,\rangle, \quad \mathbf{a}(t) = \langle\, -3\cos t, \, -3\sin t, \, 2 \,\rangle, \quad \text{speed} = \sqrt{9 + 4t^2}$

**159.** $\mathbf{v}(t) = -2\sin t\,\mathbf{j} + 3\cos t\,\mathbf{k}, \quad \mathbf{a}(t) = -2\cos t\,\mathbf{j} - 3\sin t\,\mathbf{k}, \quad \text{speed} = \sqrt{4\sin^2(t) + 9^{\cos(t)}}$

**161.** $\mathbf{v}(t) = e^t\mathbf{i} - e^{-t}\mathbf{j}, \quad \mathbf{a}(t) = e^t\mathbf{i} + e^{-t}\mathbf{j}, \quad \|\mathbf{v}(t)\| \, \sqrt{e^{2t} + e^{-2t}}$

**163.** $t = 4$

**165.** $\mathbf{v}(t) = (\omega - \omega\cos(\omega t))\mathbf{i} + (\omega\sin(\omega t))\mathbf{j},$

$\mathbf{a}(t) = \left(\omega^2 \sin(\omega t)\right)\mathbf{i} + \left(\omega^2 \cos(\omega t)\right)\mathbf{j},$

$\text{speed} = \sqrt{\omega^2 - 2\omega^2 \cos(\omega t) + \omega^2 \cos^2(\omega t) + \omega^2 \sin^2(\omega t)} = \sqrt{2\omega^2(1 - \cos(\omega t))}$

**167.** $\|\mathbf{v}(t)\| = \sqrt{9 + 4t^2}$

**169.** $\mathbf{v}(t) = \langle\, e^{-5t}(\cos t - 5\sin t),\ -e^{-5t}(\sin t + 5\cos t),\ -20e^{-5t}\,\rangle$

**171.**
$$\mathbf{a}(t) = \langle\, e^{-5t}(-\sin t - 5\cos t) - 5e^{-5t}(\cos t - 5\sin t),$$
$$-e^{-5t}(\cos t - 5\sin t) + 5e^{-5t}(\sin t + 5\cos t),\ 100e^{-5t}\,\rangle$$

**173.** 44.185 sec

**175.** $t = 88.37$ sec

**177.** 88.37 sec

**179.** The range is approximately 886.29 m.

**181.** $\mathbf{v} = 42.16$ m/sec

**183.** $\mathbf{r}(t) = 0\mathbf{i} + \left(\frac{1}{6}t^3 + 4.5t - \frac{14}{3}\right)\mathbf{j} + \left(\frac{t^3}{6} - \frac{1}{2}t + \frac{1}{3}\right)\mathbf{k}$

**185.** $a_T = 0,\quad a_N = a\omega^2$

**187.** $a_T = \sqrt{3}e^t,\quad a_N = \sqrt{2}e^t$

**189.** $a_T = 2t,\quad a_N = 4 + 2t^2$

**191.** $a_T\dfrac{6t + 12t^3}{\sqrt{1 + t^4 + t^2}},\quad a_N = 6\sqrt{\dfrac{1 + 4t^2 + t^4}{1 + t^2 + t^4}}$

**193.** $a_T = 0,\quad a_N = 2\sqrt{3}\pi$

**195.** $\mathbf{r}(t) = \left(\frac{-1}{m}\cos t + c + \frac{1}{m}\right)\mathbf{i} + \left(\frac{-\sin t}{m} + \left(v_0 + \frac{1}{m}\right)t\right)\mathbf{j}$

**197.** 10.94 km/sec

**201.** $a_T = 0.43$ m/sec$^2$,

$a_N = 2.46$ m/sec$^2$

## Review Exercises

**203.** False, $\dfrac{d}{dt}[\mathbf{u}(t) \times \mathbf{u}(t)] = 0$

**205.** False, it is $|\mathbf{r}'(t)|$

**207.** $t < 4,\quad t \neq \dfrac{n\pi}{2}$

**209.**

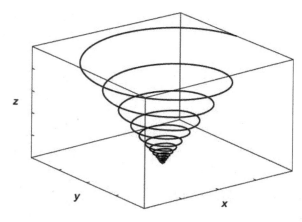

**211.** $\mathbf{r}(t) = \langle\, t,\ 2 - \frac{t^2}{8},\ -2 - \frac{t^2}{8}\,\rangle$

**213.** $\mathbf{u}'(t) = \langle\, 2t,\ 2,\ 20t^4\,\rangle,\quad \mathbf{u}''(t) = \langle\, 2,\ 0,\ 80t^3\,\rangle,\quad \dfrac{d}{dt}[\mathbf{u}'(t) \times \mathbf{u}(t)] = \langle\, -480t^3 - 160t^4,\ 24 + 75t^2,\ 12 + 4t\,\rangle,$

$\dfrac{d}{dt}[\mathbf{u}(t) \times \mathbf{u}'(t)] = \langle\, 480t^3 + 160t^4,\ -24 - 75t^2,\ -12 - 4t\,\rangle,\qquad \dfrac{d}{dt}[\mathbf{u}(t) \cdot \mathbf{u}'(t)] = 720t^8 - 9600t^3 + 6t^2 + 4,\qquad$ unit tangent vector: $\mathbf{T}(t) = \dfrac{2t}{\sqrt{400t^8 + 4t^2 + 4}}\mathbf{i} + \dfrac{2}{\sqrt{400t^8 + 4t^2 + 4}}\mathbf{j} + \dfrac{20t^4}{\sqrt{400t^8 + 4t^2 + 4}}\mathbf{k}$

**215.** $\dfrac{\ln(4)^2}{2}\mathbf{i} + 2\mathbf{j} + \dfrac{2(2 + \sqrt{2})}{\pi}\mathbf{k}$

**217.** $\dfrac{\sqrt{37}}{2} + \dfrac{1}{12}\sinh^{-1}(6)$

**219.** $\mathbf{r}(t(s)) = \cos\left(\dfrac{2s}{\sqrt{65}}\right)\mathbf{i} + \dfrac{8s}{\sqrt{65}}\mathbf{j} - \sin\left(\dfrac{2s}{\sqrt{65}}\right)\mathbf{k}$

**221.** $\dfrac{e^{2t}}{\left(e^{2t} + 1\right)^2}$

**223.** $a_T = \dfrac{e^{2t}}{\sqrt{1 + e^{2t}}},\quad a_N = \dfrac{\sqrt{2e^{2t} + 4e^{2t}\sin t \cos t + 1}}{\sqrt{1 + e^{2t}}}$

**225.** $\mathbf{v}(t) = \left\langle 2t, \frac{1}{t}, \cos(\pi t) \right\rangle$ m/sec, $\mathbf{a}(t) = \left\langle 2, -\frac{1}{t^2}, -\sin(\pi t) \right\rangle$ m/sec$^2$, speed $= \sqrt{4t^2 + \frac{1}{t^2} + \cos^2(\pi t)}$ m/sec; at

$t = 1$, $\mathbf{r}(1) = \langle 1, 0, 0 \rangle$ m, $\mathbf{v}(1) = \langle 2, -1, 1 \rangle$ m/sec, $\mathbf{a}(1) = \langle 2, -1, 0 \rangle$ m/sec$^2$, and speed $= \sqrt{6}$ m/sec

**227.** $\mathbf{r}(t) = \mathbf{v}_0 t - \frac{g}{2}t^2\,\mathbf{j}$, $\mathbf{r}(t) = \left\langle v_0(\cos\theta)t, v_0(\sin\theta)t, -\frac{g}{2}t^2 \right\rangle$

# Chapter 4

## Checkpoint

**4.1.** The domain is the shaded circle defined by the inequality $9x^2 + 9y^2 \le 36$, which has a circle of radius $2$ as its boundary. The range is $[0, 6]$.

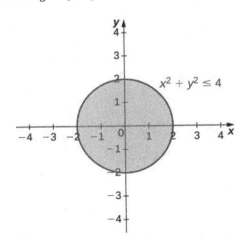

**4.2.** The equation of the level curve can be written as $(x - 3)^2 + (y + 1)^2 = 25$, which is a circle with radius $5$ centered at $(3, -1)$.

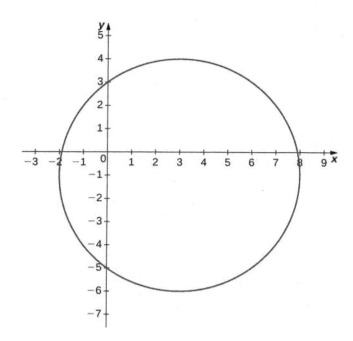

**4.3**. $z = 3 - (x - 1)^2$. This function describes a parabola opening downward in the plane $y = 3$.

**4.4**. domain$(h) = \{(x, y, t) \in \mathbb{R}^3 | y \geq 4x^2 - 4\}$

**4.5**. $(x - 1)^2 + (y + 2)^2 + (z - 3)^2 = 16$ describes a sphere of radius 4 centered at the point $(1, -2, 3)$.

**4.6**. $\displaystyle\lim_{(x, y) \to (5, -2)} \sqrt[3]{\dfrac{x^2 - y}{y^2 + x - 1}} = \dfrac{3}{2}$

**4.7**. If $y = k(x - 2) + 1$, then $\displaystyle\lim_{(x, y) \to (2, 1)} \dfrac{(x - 2)(y - 1)}{(x - 2)^2 + (y - 1)^2} = \dfrac{k}{1 + k^2}$. Since the answer depends on $k$, the limit fails to exist.

**4.8**. $\displaystyle\lim_{(x, y) \to (5, -2)} \sqrt{29 - x^2 - y^2}$

**4.9**.

1. The domain of $f$ contains the ordered pair $(2, -3)$ because $f(a, b) = f(2, -3) = \sqrt{16 - 2(2)^2 - (-3)^2} = 3$

2. $\displaystyle\lim_{(x, y) \to (a, b)} f(x, y) = 3$

3. $\displaystyle\lim_{(x, y) \to (a, b)} f(x, y) = f(a, b) = 3$

**4.10**. The polynomials $g(x) = 2x^2$ and $h(y) = y^3$ are continuous at every real number; therefore, by the product of continuous functions theorem, $f(x, y) = 2x^2 y^3$ is continuous at every point $(x, y)$ in the $xy$-plane. Furthermore, any constant function is continuous everywhere, so $g(x, y) = 3$ is continuous at every point $(x, y)$ in the $xy$-plane. Therefore, $f(x, y) = 2x^2 y^3 + 3$ is continuous at every point $(x, y)$ in the $xy$-plane. Last, $h(x) = x^4$ is continuous at every real number $x$, so by the continuity of composite functions theorem $g(x, y) = \left(2x^2 y^3 + 3\right)^4$ is continuous at every point $(x, y)$ in the $xy$-plane.

**4.11**. $\displaystyle\lim_{(x, y, z) \to (4, -1, 3)} \sqrt{13 - x^2 - 2y^2 + z^2} = 2$

**4.12**. $\dfrac{\partial f}{\partial x} = 8x + 2y + 3, \quad \dfrac{\partial f}{\partial y} = 2x - 2y - 2$

$$\frac{\partial f}{\partial x} = \left(3x^2 - 6xy^2\right)\sec^2\left(x^3 - 3x^2 y^2 + 2y^4\right)$$

**4.13.**
$$\frac{\partial f}{\partial y} = \left(-6x^2 y + 8y^3\right)\sec^2\left(x^3 - 3x^2 y^2 + 2y^4\right)$$

**4.14.** Using the curves corresponding to $c = -2$ and $c = -3$, we obtain

$$\frac{\partial f}{\partial y}\Big|_{(x,\,y)\,=\,(0,\,\sqrt2)} \approx \frac{f(0,\,\sqrt3) - f(0,\,\sqrt2)}{\sqrt3 - \sqrt2} = \frac{-3 - (-2)}{\sqrt3 - \sqrt2}\cdot\frac{\sqrt3 + \sqrt2}{\sqrt3 + \sqrt2} = -\sqrt3 - \sqrt2 \approx -3.146.$$ The exact answer is

$$\frac{\partial f}{\partial y}\Big|_{(x,\,y)\,=\,(0,\,\sqrt2)} = (-2y|_{(x,\,y)\,=\,(0,\,\sqrt2)} = -2\sqrt2 \approx -2.828.$$

**4.15.** $\dfrac{\partial f}{\partial x} = 4x - 8xy + 5z^2 - 6, \qquad \dfrac{\partial f}{\partial y} = -4x^2 + 4y, \qquad \dfrac{\partial f}{\partial z} = 10xz + 3$

$$\frac{\partial f}{\partial x} = 2xy\,\sec\!\left(x^2 y\right)\tan\!\left(x^2 y\right) - 3x^2 yz^2\sec^2\!\left(x^3 yz^2\right)$$

**4.16.** $\dfrac{\partial f}{\partial y} = x^2\sec\!\left(x^2 y\right)\tan\!\left(x^2 y\right) - x^3 z^2\sec^2\!\left(x^3 yz^2\right)$

$$\frac{\partial f}{\partial z} = -2x^3 yz\,\sec^2\!\left(x^3 yz^2\right)$$

$$\frac{\partial^2 f}{\partial x^2} = -9\sin(3x - 2y) - \cos(x + 4y)$$

$$\frac{\partial^2 f}{\partial x \partial y} = 6\sin(3x - 2y) - 4\cos(x + 4y)$$

**4.17.**
$$\frac{\partial^2 f}{\partial y \partial x} = 6\sin(3x - 2y) - 4\cos(x + 4y)$$

$$\frac{\partial^2 f}{\partial y^2} = -4\sin(3x - 2y) - 16\cos(x + 4y)$$

**4.19.** $z = 7x + 8y - 3$

**4.20.** $\qquad\qquad L(x,\,y) = 6 - 2x + 3y, \qquad\qquad$ so $\qquad\qquad L(4.1,\,0.9) = 6 - 2(4.1) + 3(0.9) = 0.5$

$f(4.1,\,0.9) = e^{5 - 2(4.1) + 3(0.9)} = e^{-0.5} \approx 0.6065.$

**4.21.** $\qquad\qquad\qquad\qquad f(-1,\,2) = -19, \quad f_x(-1,\,2) = 3,\ f_y(-1,\,2) = -16,\ E(x,\,y) = -4(y - 2)^2.$

$$\lim_{(x,\,y)\,\to\,(x_0,\,y_0)} \frac{E(x,\,y)}{\sqrt{(x - x_0)^2 + (y - y_0)^2}} = \lim_{(x,\,y)\,\to\,(-1,\,2)} \frac{-4(y - 2)^2}{\sqrt{(x + 1)^2 + (y - 2)^2}}$$

$$\le \lim_{(x,\,y)\,\to\,(-1,\,2)} \frac{-4\left((x + 1)^2 + (y - 2)^2\right)}{\sqrt{(x + 1)^2 + (y - 2)^2}}$$

$$= \lim_{(x,\,y)\,\to\,(2,\,-3)} -4\sqrt{(x + 1)^2 + (y - 2)^2}$$

$$= 0.$$

**4.22.** $\begin{aligned} dz &= 0.18 \\ \Delta z &= f(1.03,\,-1.02) - f(1,\,-1) = 0.180682 \end{aligned}$

**4.23.**
$$\begin{aligned}
\frac{dz}{dt} &= \frac{\partial f}{\partial x}\frac{dx}{dt} + \frac{\partial f}{\partial y}\frac{dy}{dt} \\
&= (2x - 3y)(6\cos 2t) + (-3x + 4y)(-8\sin 2t) \\
&= -92\sin 2t\cos 2t - 72\left(\cos^2 2t - \sin^2 2t\right) \\
&= -46\sin 4t - 72\cos 4t.
\end{aligned}$$

**4.24.** $\dfrac{\partial z}{\partial u} = 0, \qquad \dfrac{\partial z}{\partial v} = \dfrac{-21}{(3\sin 3v + \cos 3v)^2}$

$$\frac{\partial w}{\partial u} = 0$$

**4.25.** $\dfrac{\partial w}{\partial v} = \dfrac{15 - 33\sin 3v + 6\cos 3v}{(3 + 2\cos 3v - \sin 3v)^2}$

$$\frac{\partial w}{\partial t} = \frac{\partial w}{\partial x}\frac{\partial x}{\partial t} + \frac{\partial w}{\partial y}\frac{\partial y}{\partial t}$$

**4.26.** $\dfrac{\partial w}{\partial u} = \dfrac{\partial w}{\partial x}\dfrac{\partial x}{\partial u} + \dfrac{\partial w}{\partial y}\dfrac{\partial y}{\partial u}$

$$\frac{\partial w}{\partial v} = \frac{\partial w}{\partial x}\frac{\partial x}{\partial v} + \frac{\partial w}{\partial y}\frac{\partial y}{\partial v}$$

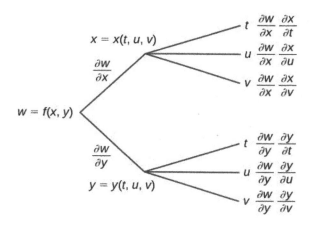

**4.27.** $\dfrac{dy}{dx} = \dfrac{2x + y + 7}{2y - x + 3}\Big|_{(3,\,-2)} = \dfrac{2(3) + (-2) + 7}{2(-2) - (3) + 3} = -\dfrac{11}{4}$

Equation of the tangent line: $y = -\dfrac{11}{4}x + \dfrac{25}{4}$

**4.28.**
$$D_{\mathbf{u}} f(x,\, y) = \frac{(6xy - 4y^3 - 4)(1)}{2} + \frac{\left(3x^2 - 12xy^2 + 6y\right)\sqrt{3}}{2}$$

$$D_{\mathbf{u}} f(3,\, 4) = \frac{72 - 256 - 4}{2} + \frac{(27 - 576 + 24)\sqrt{3}}{2} = -94 - \frac{525\sqrt{3}}{2}$$

**4.29.** $\nabla f(x,\, y) = \dfrac{2x^2 + 2xy + 6y^2}{(2x + y)^2}\mathbf{i} - \dfrac{x^2 + 12xy + 3y^2}{(2x + y)^2}\mathbf{j}$

**4.30.** The gradient of $g$ at $(-2, 3)$ is $\nabla g(-2, 3) = \mathbf{i} + 14\mathbf{j}$. The unit vector that points in the same direction as $\nabla g(-2, 3)$

is $\qquad \dfrac{\nabla g(-2,\, 3)}{\|\nabla g(-2,\, 3)\|} = \dfrac{1}{\sqrt{197}}\mathbf{i} + \dfrac{14}{\sqrt{197}}\mathbf{j} = \dfrac{\sqrt{197}}{197}\mathbf{i} + \dfrac{14\sqrt{197}}{197}\mathbf{j},$ which gives an angle of

$\theta = \arcsin\left((14\sqrt{197})/197\right) \approx 1.499$ rad. The maximum value of the directional derivative is $\|\nabla g(-2,\, 3)\| = \sqrt{197}$.

**4.31.** $\nabla f(x,\, y) = (2x - 2y + 3)\mathbf{i} + (-2x + 10y - 2)\mathbf{j}$

$\nabla f(1,\, 1) = 3\mathbf{i} + 6\mathbf{j}$

Tangent vector: $6\mathbf{i} - 3\mathbf{j}$ or $-6\mathbf{i} + 3\mathbf{j}$

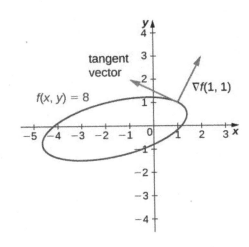

**4.32.** $\nabla f(x, y, z) = \dfrac{2x^2 + 2xy + 6y^2 - 8xz - 2z^2}{(2x + y - 4z)^2}\mathbf{i} - \dfrac{x^2 + 12xy + 3y^2 - 24yz + z^2}{(2x + y - 4z)^2}\mathbf{j}$

$\qquad\qquad\qquad + \dfrac{4x^2 - 12y^2 - 4z^2 + 4xz + 2yz}{(2x + y - 4z)^2}\mathbf{k}.$

**4.33.** $D_{\mathbf{u}}f(x, y, z) = -\dfrac{3}{13}(6x + y + 2z) + \dfrac{12}{13}(x - 4y + 4z) - \dfrac{4}{13}(2x + 4y - 2z)$

$\qquad D_{\mathbf{u}}f(0, -2, 5) = \dfrac{384}{13}$

**4.34.** $(2, -5)$

**4.35.** $\left(\dfrac{4}{3}, \dfrac{1}{3}\right)$ is a saddle point, $\left(-\dfrac{3}{2}, -\dfrac{3}{8}\right)$ is a local maximum.

**4.36.** The absolute minimum occurs at $(1, 0)$: $f(1, 0) = -1$. The absolute maximum occurs at $(0, 3)$: $f(0, 3) = 63$.

**4.37.** $f$ has a maximum value of $976$ at the point $(8, 2)$.

**4.38.** A maximum production level of $13890$ occurs with $5625$ labor hours and $\$5500$ of total capital input.

**4.39.** $f\left(\dfrac{\sqrt{3}}{3}, \dfrac{\sqrt{3}}{3}, \dfrac{\sqrt{3}}{3}\right) = \dfrac{\sqrt{3}}{3} + \dfrac{\sqrt{3}}{3} + \dfrac{\sqrt{3}}{3} = \sqrt{3}$

$\qquad f\left(-\dfrac{\sqrt{3}}{3}, -\dfrac{\sqrt{3}}{3}, -\dfrac{\sqrt{3}}{3}\right) = -\dfrac{\sqrt{3}}{3} - \dfrac{\sqrt{3}}{3} - \dfrac{\sqrt{3}}{3} = -\sqrt{3}.$

**4.40.** $f(2, 1, 2) = 9$ is a minimum.

## Section Exercises

**1.** $17, 72$

**3.** $20\pi$. This is the volume when the radius is $2$ and the height is $5$.

**5.** All points in the $xy$-plane

**7.** $x < y^2$

**9.** All real ordered pairs in the $xy$-plane of the form $(a, b)$

**11.** $\{z | 0 \le z \le 4\}$

**13.** The set $\mathbb{R}$

**15.** $y^2 - x^2 = 4$, a hyperbola

**17.** $4 = x + y$, a line; $x + y = 0$, line through the origin

**19.** $2x - y = 0$, $2x - y = -2$, $2x - y = 2$; three lines

**21.** $\dfrac{x}{x + y} = -1$, $\dfrac{x}{x + y} = 0$, $\dfrac{x}{x + y} = 2$

**23.** $e^{xy} = \dfrac{1}{2}$, $e^{xy} = 3$

**25**. $xy - x = -2$, $xy - x = 0$, $xy - x = 2$

**27**. $e^{-2}x^2 = y$, $y = x^2$, $y = e^2 x^2$

**29**. The level curves are parabolas of the form $y = cx^2 - 2$.

**31**. $z = 3 + y^3$, a curve in the $zy$-plane with rulings parallel to the $x$-axis

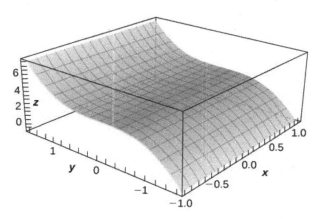

**33**. $\dfrac{x^2}{25} + \dfrac{y^2}{4} \leq 1$

**35**. $\dfrac{x^2}{9} + \dfrac{y^2}{4} + \dfrac{z^2}{36} < 1$

**37**. All points in $xyz$-space

**39**.

**41**.

**43**.

**45.**

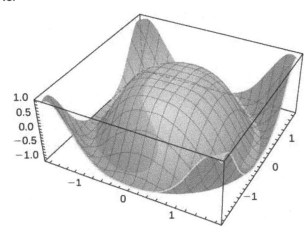

**47.** The contour lines are circles.

**49.** $x^2 + y^2 + z^2 = 9$, a sphere of radius 3

**51.** $x^2 + y^2 - z^2 = 4$, a hyperboloid of one sheet

**53.** $4x^2 + y^2 = 1$,

**55.** $1 = e^{xy}(x^2 + y^2)$

**57.** $T(x, y) = \dfrac{k}{x^2 + y^2}$

**59.** $x^2 + y^2 = \dfrac{k}{40}$, $x^2 + y^2 = \dfrac{k}{100}$. The level curves represent circles of radii $\sqrt{10k}/20$ and $\sqrt{k}/10$.

**61.** 2.0

**63.** $\dfrac{2}{3}$

**65.** 1

**67.** $\dfrac{1}{2}$

**69.** $-\dfrac{1}{2}$

**71.** $e^{-32}$

**73.** 11.0

**75.** 1.0

**77.** The limit does not exist because when $x$ and $y$ both approach zero, the function approaches $\ln 0$, which is undefined (approaches negative infinity).

**79.** every open disk centered at $(x_0, y_0)$ contains points inside $R$ and outside $R$

**81**. 0.0

**83**. 0.00

**85**. The limit does not exist.

**87**. The limit does not exist. The function approaches two different values along different paths.

**89**. The limit does not exist because the function approaches two different values along the paths.

**91**. The function $f$ is continuous in the region $y > -x$.

**93**. The function $f$ is continuous at all points in the $xy$-plane except at $(0, 0)$.

**95**. The function is continuous at $(0, 0)$ since the limit of the function at $(0, 0)$ is $0$, the same value of $f(0, 0)$.

**97**. The function is discontinuous at $(0, 0)$. The limit at $(0, 0)$ fails to exist and $g(0, 0)$ does not exist.

**99**. Since the function $\arctan x$ is continuous over $(-\infty, \infty)$, $g(x, y) = \arctan\left(\frac{xy^2}{x+y}\right)$ is continuous where $z = \frac{xy^2}{x+y}$ is continuous. The inner function $z$ is continuous on all points of the $xy$-plane except where $y = -x$. Thus, $g(x, y) = \arctan\left(\frac{xy^2}{x+y}\right)$ is continuous on all points of the coordinate plane *except* at points at which $y = -x$.

**101**. All points $P(x, y, z)$ in space

**103**. The graph increases without bound as $x$ and $y$ both approach zero.

**105**. a.

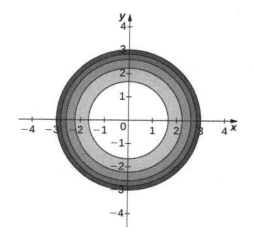

b. The level curves are circles centered at $(0, 0)$ with radius $9 - c$. c. $x^2 + y^2 = 9 - c$ d. $z = 3$ e. $\{(x, y) \in \mathbb{R}^2 \,|\, x^2 + y^2 \le 9\}$ f. $\{z | 0 \le z \le 3\}$

**107**. 1.0

**109**. $f(g(x, y))$ is continuous at all points $(x, y)$ that are not on the line $2x - 5y = 0$.

**111**. 2.0

**113**. $\frac{\partial z}{\partial y} = -3x + 2y$

**115**. The sign is negative.

**117**. The partial derivative is zero at the origin.

**119**. $\frac{\partial z}{\partial y} = -3\sin(3x)\sin(3y)$

**121**. $\frac{\partial z}{\partial x} = \frac{6x^5}{x^6 + y^4}; \frac{\partial z}{\partial y} = \frac{4y^3}{x^6 + y^4}$

**123**. $\frac{\partial z}{\partial x} = ye^{xy}; \frac{\partial z}{\partial y} = xe^{xy}$

**125**. $\frac{\partial z}{\partial x} = 2\sec^2(2x - y), \frac{\partial z}{\partial y} = -\sec^2(2x - y)$

**127**. $f_x(2, -2) = \frac{1}{4} = f_y(2, -2)$

**129**. $\frac{\partial z}{\partial x} = -\cos(1)$

**131**. $f_x = 0, \quad f_y = 0, \quad f_z = 0$

**133**. a. $V(r, h) = \pi r^2 h$ b. $\frac{\partial V}{\partial r} = 2\pi r h$ c. $\frac{\partial V}{\partial h} = \pi r^2$

**135**. $f_{xy} = \frac{1}{(x - y)^2}$

**137**. $\frac{\partial^2 z}{\partial x^2} = 2, \frac{\partial^2 z}{\partial y^2} = 4$

**139**. $f_{xyy} = f_{yxy} = f_{yyx} = 0$

**141**.
$$\frac{d^2 z}{dx^2} = -\frac{1}{2}(e^y - e^{-y})\sin x$$
$$\frac{d^2 z}{dy^2} = \frac{1}{2}(e^y - e^{-y})\sin x$$
$$\frac{d^2 z}{dx^2} + \frac{d^2 z}{dy^2} = 0$$

**143**. $f_{xyz} = 6y^2 x - 18yz^2$

**145**. $\left(\frac{1}{4}, \frac{1}{2}\right), (1, 1)$

**147**. $(0, 0), (0, 2), (\sqrt{3}, -1), (-\sqrt{3}, -1)$

**149**. $\frac{\partial^2 z}{\partial x^2} + \frac{\partial^2 z}{\partial y^2} = e^x \sin(y) - e^x \sin y = 0$

**151**. $c^2 \frac{\partial^2 z}{\partial x^2} = e^{-t}\cos\left(\frac{x}{c}\right)$

**153**. $\frac{\partial f}{\partial y} = -2x + 7$

**155**. $\frac{\partial f}{\partial x} = y\cos xy$

**159**. $\frac{\partial F}{\partial \theta} = 6, \frac{\partial F}{\partial x} = 4 - 3\sqrt{3}$

**161**. $\frac{\delta f}{\delta x}$ at $(500, 1000) = 172.36, \quad \frac{\delta f}{\delta y}$ at $(500, 1000) = 36.93$

**163**. $\left(\frac{\sqrt{145}}{145}\right)(12\mathbf{i} - \mathbf{k})$

**165**. Normal vector: $\mathbf{i} + \mathbf{j}$,   tangent vector: $\mathbf{i} - \mathbf{j}$

**167**. Normal vector: $7\mathbf{i} - 17\mathbf{j}$,   tangent vector: $17\mathbf{i} + 7\mathbf{j}$

**169**. $-1.094\mathbf{i} - 0.18238\mathbf{j}$

**171**. $-36x - 6y - z = -39$

**173**. $z = 0$

**175**. $5x + 4y + 3z - 22 = 0$

**177**. $4x - 5y + 4z = 0$

**179**. $2x + 2y - z = 0$

**181**. $-2(x - 1) + 2(y - 2) - (z - 1) = 0$

**183**. $x = 20t + 2, \; y = -4t + 1, \; z = -t + 18$

**185**. $x = 0, \; y = 0, \; z = t$

**187**. $x - 1 = 2t; \; y - 2 = -2t; \; z - 1 = t$

**189**. The differential of the function $z(x, y) = dz = f_x dx + f_y dy$

**191**. Using the definition of differentiability, we have $e^{xy} x \approx x + y$.

**193**. $\Delta z = 2x\Delta x + 3\Delta y + (\Delta x)^2$.   $(\Delta x)^2 \to 0$ for small $\Delta x$ and $z$ satisfies the definition of differentiability.

**195**. $\Delta z \approx 1.185422$ and $dz \approx 1.108$. They are relatively close.

**197**. $16 \; \text{cm}^3$

**199**. $\Delta z = $ exact change $= 0.6449$,   approximate change is $dz = 0.65$. The two values are close.

**201**. 13% or 0.13

**203**. 0.025

**205**. 0.3%

**207**. $2x + \frac{1}{4}y - 1$

**209**. $\frac{1}{2}x + y + \frac{1}{4}\pi - \frac{1}{2}$

**211**. $\frac{3}{7}x + \frac{2}{7}y + \frac{6}{7}z$

**213**. $z = 0$

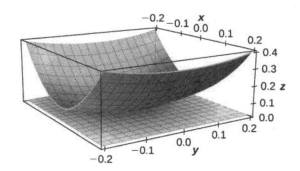

**215**. $\dfrac{dw}{dt} = y\cos z + x\cos z(2t) - \dfrac{xy\sin z}{\sqrt{1 - t^2}}$

**217**. $\dfrac{\partial w}{\partial s} = -30x + 4y, \quad \dfrac{\partial w}{\partial t} = 10x - 16y$

**219**. $\dfrac{\partial f}{\partial r} = r\sin(2\theta)$

**221**. $\dfrac{df}{dt} = 2t + 4t^3$

**223**. $\dfrac{df}{dt} = -1$

**225.** $\dfrac{df}{dt} = 1$

**227.** $\dfrac{dw}{dt} = 2e^{2t}$ in both cases

**229.** $2\sqrt{2}t + \sqrt{2}\pi = \dfrac{du}{dt}$

**231.** $\dfrac{dy}{dx} = -\dfrac{3x^2 + y^2}{2xy}$

**233.** $\dfrac{dy}{dx} = \dfrac{y - x}{-x + 2y^3}$

**235.** $\dfrac{dy}{dx} = -\sqrt[3]{\dfrac{y}{x}}$

**237.** $\dfrac{dy}{dx} = -\dfrac{ye^{xy}}{xe^{xy} + e^y(1 + y)}$

**239.** $\dfrac{dz}{dt} = 42t^{13}$

**241.** $\dfrac{dz}{dt} = -\dfrac{10}{3}t^{7/3} \times e^{1 - t^{10/3}}$

**243.** $\dfrac{\partial z}{\partial u} = \dfrac{-2\sin u}{3\sin v}$ and $\dfrac{\partial z}{\partial v} = \dfrac{-2\cos u \cos v}{3\sin^2 v}$

**245.** $\dfrac{\partial z}{\partial r} = \sqrt{3}e^{\sqrt{3}}, \quad \dfrac{\partial z}{\partial \theta} = (2 - 4\sqrt{3})e^{\sqrt{3}}$

**247.** $\dfrac{\partial w}{\partial t} = \cos(xyz) \times yz \times (-3) - \cos(xyz)xze^{1 - t} + \cos(xyz)xy \times 4$

**249.** $f(tx, ty) = \sqrt{t^2 x^2 + t^2 y^2} = t^1 f(x, y), \quad \dfrac{\partial f}{\partial y} = x\dfrac{1}{2}(x^2 + y^2)^{-1/2} \times 2x + y\dfrac{1}{2}(x^2 + y^2)^{-1/2} \times 2y = 1f(x, y)$

**251.** $\dfrac{34\pi}{3}$

**253.** $\dfrac{dV}{dt} = \dfrac{1066\pi}{3}\text{cm}^3/\text{min}$

**255.** $\dfrac{dA}{dt} = 12 \text{ in.}^2/\text{min}$

**257.** $2°\text{C/sec}$

**259.** $\dfrac{\partial u}{\partial r} = \dfrac{\partial u}{\partial x}\left(\dfrac{\partial x}{\partial w}\dfrac{\partial w}{\partial r} + \dfrac{\partial x}{\partial t}\dfrac{\partial t}{\partial r}\right) + \dfrac{\partial u}{\partial y}\left(\dfrac{\partial y}{\partial w}\dfrac{\partial w}{\partial r} + \dfrac{\partial y}{\partial t}\dfrac{\partial t}{\partial r}\right)$
$\qquad + \dfrac{\partial u}{\partial z}\left(\dfrac{\partial z}{\partial w}\dfrac{\partial w}{\partial r} + \dfrac{\partial z}{\partial t}\dfrac{\partial t}{\partial r}\right)$

**261.** $-3\sqrt{3}$

**263.** $-1$

**265.** $\dfrac{2}{\sqrt{6}}$

**267.** $\sqrt{3}$

**269.** $-1.0$

**271.** $\dfrac{22}{25}$

**273.** $\dfrac{2}{3}$

**275.** $\dfrac{-\sqrt{2}(x + y)}{2(x + 2y)^2}$

**277.** $\dfrac{e^x(y + \sqrt{3})}{2}$

**279.** $\dfrac{1 + 2\sqrt{3}}{2(x + 2y)}$

**281.** $\langle\, 5, 4, 3\, \rangle$

**283.** $-320$

**285.** $\dfrac{3}{\sqrt{11}}$

**287.** $\dfrac{31}{255}$

**289.**

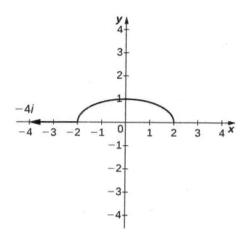

**291.** $\dfrac{4}{3}\mathbf{i} - 3\mathbf{j}$

**293.** $\sqrt{2}\mathbf{i} + \sqrt{2}\mathbf{j} + \sqrt{2}\mathbf{k}$

**295.** $1.6(10^{19})$

**297.** $\dfrac{5\sqrt{2}}{99}$

**299.** $\sqrt{5},\ \langle\, 1, 2\, \rangle$

**301.** $\sqrt{\dfrac{13}{2}},\ \langle\, -3, -2\, \rangle$

**303.** a. $x + y + z = 3$, b. $x - 1 = y - 1 = z - 1$

**305.** a. $x + y - z = 1$, b. $x - 1 = y = -z$

**307.** a. $\dfrac{32}{\sqrt{3}}$, b. $\langle\, 38, 6, 12\, \rangle$, c. $2\sqrt{406}$

**309.** $\langle\, u, v\, \rangle = \langle\, \pi\cos(\pi x)\sin(2\pi y),\, 2\pi\sin(\pi x)\cos(2\pi y)\, \rangle$

**311.** $\left(\dfrac{2}{3}, 4\right)$

**313.** $(0, 0)\ \left(\dfrac{1}{15}, \dfrac{1}{15}\right)$

**315.** Maximum at $(4, -1, 8)$

**317.** Relative minimum at $(0, 0, 1)$

**319.** The second derivative test fails. Since $x^2 y^2 > 0$ for all $x$ and $y$ different from zero, and $x^2 y^2 = 0$ when either $x$ or $y$ equals zero (or both), then the absolute minimum occurs at $(0, 0)$.

**321.** $f\left(-2, -\dfrac{3}{2}\right) = -6$ is a saddle point.

**323.** $f(0, 0) = 0;\ (0, 0, 0)$ is a saddle point.

**325.** $f(0, 0) = 9$ is a local maximum.

**327.** Relative minimum located at $(2, 6)$.

**329.** $(1, -2)$ is a saddle point.

**331.** $(2, 1)$ and $(-2, 1)$ are saddle points; $(0, 0)$ is a relative minimum.

**333.** $(-1, 0)$ is a relative maximum.

**335.** $(0, 0)$ is a saddle point.

**337.** The relative maximum is at $(40, 40)$.

**339.** $\left(\frac{1}{4}, \frac{1}{2}\right)$ is a saddle point and $(1, 1)$ is the relative minimum.

**341.** A saddle point is located at $(0, 0)$.

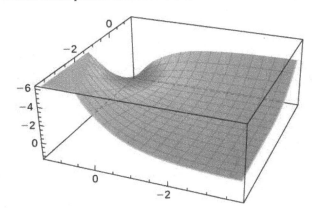

**343.** There is a saddle point at $(\pi, \pi)$, local maxima at $\left(\frac{\pi}{2}, \frac{\pi}{2}\right)$ and $\left(\frac{3\pi}{2}, \frac{3\pi}{2}\right)$, and local minima at $\left(\frac{\pi}{2}, \frac{3\pi}{2}\right)$ and $\left(\frac{3\pi}{2}, \frac{\pi}{2}\right)$.

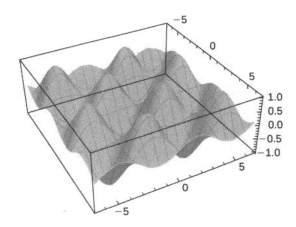

**345.** $(0, 1, 0)$ is the absolute minimum and $(0, -2, 9)$ is the absolute maximum.

**347.** There is an absolute minimum at $(0, 1, -1)$ and an absolute maximum at $(0, -1, 1)$.

**349.** $\left(\sqrt{5}, 0, 0\right), \left(-\sqrt{5}, 0, 0\right)$

**351.** 18 by 36 by 18 in.

**353.** $\left(\frac{47}{24}, \frac{47}{12}, \frac{235}{24}\right)$

**355.** $x = 3$ and $y = 6$

**357.** $V = \dfrac{64,000}{\pi} \approx 20,372 \text{ cm}^3$

**359.** maximum: $2\frac{\sqrt{3}}{3}$, minimum: $\frac{-2\sqrt{3}}{3}$

**361.** maximum: $\left(\frac{\sqrt{2}}{2}, 0, \sqrt{2}\right)$, minimum: $\left(\frac{-\sqrt{2}}{2}, 0, -\sqrt{2}\right)$

**363.** maximum: $\frac{3}{2}$, minimum $= 1$

**365**. maxima: $f\left(\frac{3\sqrt{2}}{2}, 2\sqrt{2}\right) = 24$, $f\left(-\frac{3\sqrt{2}}{2}, -2\sqrt{2}\right) = 24$; minima: $f\left(-\frac{3\sqrt{2}}{2}, 2\sqrt{2}\right) = -24$, $f\left(\frac{3\sqrt{2}}{2}, -2\sqrt{2}\right) = -24$

**367**. maximum: $2\sqrt{11}$ at $f\left(\frac{2}{\sqrt{11}}, \frac{6}{\sqrt{11}}, \frac{-2}{\sqrt{11}}\right)$; minimum: $-2\sqrt{11}$ at $f\left(\frac{-2}{\sqrt{11}}, \frac{-6}{\sqrt{11}}, \frac{2}{\sqrt{11}}\right)$

**369**. 2.0

**371**. $19\sqrt{2}$

**373**. $\left(\frac{1}{\sqrt[3]{2}}, \frac{-1}{\sqrt[3]{2}}\right)$

**375**. $f(1, 2) = 5$

**377**. $f\left(\frac{1}{3}, \frac{1}{3}, \frac{1}{3}\right) = \frac{1}{3}$

**379**. minimum: $f(2, 3, 4) = 29$

**381**. The maximum volume is $4$ ft$^3$. The dimensions are $1 \times 2 \times 2$ ft.

**383**. $\left(1, \frac{1}{2}, -3\right)$

**385**. 1.0

**387**. $\sqrt{3}$

**389**. $\left(\frac{2}{5}, \frac{19}{5}\right)$

**391**. $\frac{1}{2}$

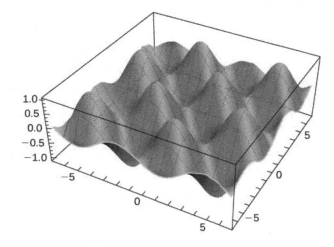

**393**. Roughly 3365 watches at the critical point $(80, 60)$

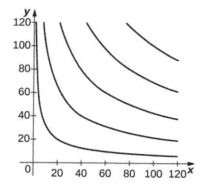

## Review Exercises

**395**. True, by Clairaut's theorem

**397**. False

**399**. Answers may vary

**401**. Does not exist

**403**. Continuous at all points on the $x$, $y$-plane, except where $x^2 + y^2 > 4$.

**405**. $\dfrac{\partial u}{\partial x} = 4x^3 - 3y$, $\quad \dfrac{\partial u}{\partial y} = -3x$, $\quad \dfrac{\partial u}{\partial t} = 2$, $\quad \dfrac{\partial u}{\partial t} = 3t^2$, $\quad \dfrac{\partial u}{\partial t} = 8x^3 - 6y - 9xt^2$

**407**. $\quad h_{xx}(x, y, z) = \dfrac{6xe^{2y}}{z}$, $\qquad h_{xy}(x, y, z) = \dfrac{6x^2 e^{2y}}{z}$, $\qquad h_{xz}(x, y, z) = -\dfrac{3x^2 e^{2y}}{z^2}$, $\qquad h_{yx}(x, y, z) = \dfrac{6x^2 e^{2y}}{z}$,

$h_{yy}(x, y, z) = \dfrac{4x^3 e^{2y}}{z}$, $\qquad h_{yz}(x, y, z) = -\dfrac{2x^3 e^{2y}}{z^2}$, $\qquad h_{zx}(x, y, z) = -\dfrac{3x^2 e^{2y}}{z^2}$, $\qquad h_{zy}(x, y, z) = -\dfrac{2x^3 e^{2y}}{z^2}$,

$h_{zz}(x, y, z) = \dfrac{2x^3 e^{2y}}{z^3}$

**409**. $z = \dfrac{1}{9}x - \dfrac{2}{9}y + \dfrac{29}{9}$

**411**. $dz = 4dx - dy$, $\quad dz(0.1, 0.01) = 0.39$, $\quad \Delta z = 0.432$

**413**. $3\sqrt{85}$, $\langle 27, 6 \rangle$

**415**. $\nabla f(x, y) = -\dfrac{\sqrt{x} + 2y^2}{2x^2 y}\mathbf{i} + \left(\dfrac{1}{x} - \dfrac{1}{\sqrt{x}y^2}\right)\mathbf{j}$

**417**. maximum: $\dfrac{16}{3\sqrt{3}}$, minimum: $-\dfrac{16}{3\sqrt{3}}$

**419**. $2.3228 \text{ cm}^3$

# INDEX